# SELLING YOUR COINS & BANKNOTES?

Warwick and Warwick have an expanding requirement for coin and banknote collections, British and worldwide and for coins and notes of individual value. Our customer base is increasing dramatically and we need an ever larger supply of quality material to keep pace with demand. The market has never been stronger and if you are considering the sale of your collection, now is the time to act.

## FREE VALUATIONS

We will provide a free, professional and without obligation valuation of your collection. Either we will make you a fair, binding private treaty offer, or we will recommend inclusion of your property in our next specialist public auction.

## FREE TRANSPORTATION

We can arrange insured transportation of your collection to our Warwick offices completely free of charge. If you decline our offer, we ask you to cover the return carriage costs only.

## FREE VISITS

Visits by our valuers are possible anywhere in the country or abroad, usually within 48 hours, in order to value larger collections. Please telephone for details.

## ADVISORY DAYS

We are staging a series of advisory days and will be visiting all areas of England, Scotland, Wales and Ireland during the coming months. Please visit our website or telephone for further details.

## EXCELLENT PRICES

Because of the strength of our customer base we are in a position to offer prices that we feel sure will exceed your expectations.

## ACT NOW

Telephone or email Richard Beale today with details of your property.

# BRITISH NUMISMATIC TRADE ASSOCIATION

**LONDON AREA**
*A.H. Baldwin & Sons Ltd -
www.baldwin.co.uk
*ArtAncient Ltd - www.artancient.com
*ATS Bullion - www.atsbullion.com
*Baldwin's of St. James's -
info@bsjauctions.com
*Classical Numismatic Group LLC -
www.cngcoins.com
*Heritage Auctions UK - www.ha.com
*Knightsbridge Coins -
info@knightsbridgecoins.com
*Morton & Eden Ltd-
www.mortonandeden.com
*Numismatica Ars Classica -
www.arsclassicacoins.com
*Pax Romana - www.paxromana.auction
*Philip Cohen Numismatics -
www.coinheritage.co.uk
*Sovereign Rarities Ltd - www.sovr.co.uk
*Spink & Son Ltd - www.spink.com
* The Coin Cabinet Ltd -
www.thecoincabinet.co.uk
André de Clermont - www.declermont.
com
Arthur Bryant Coins Ltd -
www.bryantcoins.com
Beaver Coin Room
Bonhams incorporating Glendining's -
www.bonhams.com
C.J. Martin (Coins) Ltd –
www.antiquities.co.uk
Christopher Eimer -
www.christophereimer.co.uk
Dix Noonan Webb - www.dnw.co.uk
Jon Blyth - www.jonblyth.com
Physical Gold Ltd - www.physicalgold.
co.uk
Simmons Gallery - www.simmonsgallery.
co.uk
The London Coin Company Ltd -
www.thelondoncoincompany.com

**AVON**
Saltford Coins - www.saltfordcoins.com

**BERKSHIRE**
*Douglas Saville Numismatic Books -
www.douglassaville.com

**BUCKINGHAMSHIRE**
Charles Riley - www.charlesriley.co.uk

**CAMBRIDGESHIRE**
Den Of Antiquity International Ltd -
www.denofantiquity.co.uk

**CHESHIRE**
Colin Cooke - www.colincooke.com

**CORNWALL**
Richard W. Jeffery

**DEVON**
Glenn S. Ogden - www.glennogdencoins.com

**DORSET**
*Dorset Coin Co Ltd -
www.dorsetcoincompany.co.uk
Timothy Medhurst Coins & Antiquities -
www.timothymedhurst.co.uk

**ESSEX**
*Time Line - www.time-lines.co.uk

**GLOUCESTERSHIRE**
Silbury Coins Ltd - www.silburycoins.com

**HAMPSHIRE**
Studio Coins - www.studiocoins.net
Victory Coins
Wessex Coins - www.wessexcoins.co.uk
West Essex Coin Investment

**HERTFORDSHIRE**
DRG Coins and Antiquities -
www.drgcoinsandantiquities.com
KB Coins - www.kbcoins.com
Whitmore Coins, Tokens and Medallions -
john@whitmorectm.com

**KENT**
*London Coins Ltd - www.londoncoins.co.uk
*Peter Morris - www.petermorris.co.uk

**LEICESTERSHIRE**
Hall's Hammered Coins -
www.hallshammeredcoins.com

**MERSEYSIDE**
*Merseyside Collectors Centre -
www.mccentre.co.uk

**MONMOUTHSHIRE**
Anthony M. Halse - www.coinsandtokens.
com

**NORFOLK**
*BucksCoins – www. buckscoins.com
Roderick Richardson -
www.roderickrichardson.com
Chris Rudd - www.celticcoins.com

**NOTTINGHAMSHIRE**
History in Coins - www.historyincoins.com

**OXFORDSHIRE**
Richard Gladdle - Gladdle@plumpudding.org

**SHROPSHIRE**
M. Veissid - m.veissid@btinternet.com

**SUFFOLK**
* Lockdale Coins Ltd - www.lockdales.
com
Simon Monks - www.simonmonks.co.uk

**SURREY**
*M.J. Hughes - www.gbgoldcoins.co.uk
Mark Rasmussen Numismatist -
www.rascoins.com

**SUSSEX**
John Newman Coins -
www.johnnewmancoins.com

**TYNE AND WEAR**
*Corbitts Ltd - www.corbitts.com

**WARWICKSHIRE**
* Peter Viola
* Warwick & Warwick Ltd -
www.warwickandwarwick.com

**WEST MIDLANDS**
*Atkinsons Coins and Bullion -
www.atkinsonsbullion.com
*Birmingham Coins
David Craddock
Paul Davis Birmingham Ltd

**WILTSHIRE**
Hammered British Coins -
www.hammeredbritishcoins.com
*Gold-Traders (UK) Ltd -
https://britanniacoincompany.com

**YORKSHIRE**
AMR Coins - www.amrcoins.com
Keith Chapman - www.anglosaxoncoins.
com
Paul Clayton
Paul Davies Ltd
*Paul Dawson York Ltd

**SCOTLAND**
Paul Menzies Ltd - www.paulmenziesltd.
com
*Scotmint Ltd - www.scotmint.com

**WALES**
Colin Rumney
Lloyd Bennett - www.coinsofbritain.com

*Retail premises

# WWW.BNTA.NET

# Get to know and understand your

Financial Instruments

Collecting the financial instruments of the past – gold, silver or copper coins – is a pursuit many of us turn to as an escape from the tribulations of everyday life in our hectic world.

But acquisition is only part of the picture. To really know and understand the coins of a particular period or ruler, take the opportunity to look at some of the masterly works of scholarship that have appeared in the pages of the *British Numismatic Journal* since before the First World War. Scholarship that is now available to you, online, at **www.britnumsoc.org**.

We're not just about coins, though. Among our 600-plus membership are collectors and students of tokens, medals and paper money of the British Isles, the Commonwealth and other territories that have been subject to British rule. Our monthly meetings in London feature talks on all aspects of numismatics, from the Iron Age and Roman periods right up to the present, so there's something for everyone, and we also have an annual meeting in New York in January.

There has never been a better time to join the Society as we are currently running a special reduced rate of £15 per annum for the first two years of membership (normally £32). Under 25 or in full-time study? Then enjoy a further reduction to only £10 per annum. To apply, visit **www.britnumsoc.org/membership** today.

## The British Numismatic Society

**Promoting the study of British numismatics since 1903**

# COINS OF ENGLAND

## & THE UNITED KINGDOM
### Pre-Decimal Issues

**55th Edition**

LONDON

A Catalogue of the Coins of Great Britain
and Ireland
first published 1929

Standard Catalogue of British Coins
Coins of England and the United Kingdom
56th edition, 2021

© Spink & Son Ltd, 2020
69 Southampton Row, Bloomsbury
London WC1B 4ET
www.spinkbooks.com

www.spink.com

Typeset by Design to Print UK Ltd,
9 & 10 Riverview Business Park, Forest Row, East Sussex RH18 5DW
www.designtoprintuk.com
Printed and bound in Malta
by Gutenberg Press Ltd.

Cover design: Russell Whittle
Email: uk47@me.com

ISBN 978-1-912667-51-2

# CONTENTS

# ACKNOWLEDGEMENTS

We wish to acknowledge the valuable contributions of the following.

Richard Abdy *(The British Museum)*
Tony Abramson
Dr Martin Allen *(Fitzwilliam Museum)*
Keith Bayford
Joe Bispham
Jon Blyth
James Booth
Ron Churchill
Nigel Clark
Chris Comber
Barrie Cook *(The British Museum)*
Simon Cope
Jonathan Cope
Dave Craddock
Joe Cribb *(The British Museum)*
Mike Cuddeford
Paul Davies
Charles Davis
Tim Everson
David Fletcher
Glen Gittoes
Eric Green
Dave Greenhalgh
David Guest
Peter Hendra

Heritage Auctions UK
Steve Hill
Peter Jackson
Richard Kelleher *(The Fizwilliam Museum)*
Geoff Kitchen
Stewart Lyon
William MacKay
Nigel Mills
Graeme Monk
Neil Paisley
Rob Pearce
Gary Poole
Nigel Prevost
Mark Rasmussen
Martin Roberts
The Schneider Family
Dr Irving Schneider
Peter D Spencer
Bob Thomas
Andrew Wayne
Tim Webb Ware
Walter Wilkinson
Gareth Williams *(The British Museum)*
Paul & Bente R. Withers

**Museums/Institutions**
The Trustees of the British Museum, London
The Fitzwilliam Museum, Cambridge

**Photography**
Richard Hodges
Paul & Bente R. Withers
Wioletta Madaj

# ABBREVIATIONS

| | | | |
|---|---|---|---|
| Archb. | Archbishop | laur. | laureate |
| Æ | bronze | mm. | mintmark |
| R | silver | mon. | monogram |
| N | gold | O., obv. | obverse |
| Bp. | Bishop | p. | new penny, pence |
| BV | bullion value | pl | plume |
| cuir. | cuirassed | quat. | quatrefoil |
| d. | penny, pence | qtr. | quarter |
| diad. | diademed | rad. | radiate |
| dr. | draped | R., rev. | reverse |
| ex. | exergue | r. | right |
| grs. | grains | s. | shillings |
| hd. | headstg. | stg. | standing |
| i.c. | inner circle | trun. | truncation |
| illus. | illustration | var. | variety |
| l. | left | wt. | weight |

# FOREWORD

Welcome to the 56th Edition of *Coins of England and the United Kingdom*, providing you with up-to-date valuations for the British numismatic marketplace in 2021.

And what a difference twelve months makes! We recall sitting here excitedly pondering the fulfilment of 'visions' in this eponymous year. How quickly that morphed into an '*Annus Horribilis*' for Planet Earth. Or perhaps that is how 2020 could be recorded, were it not for the unmistakeable ray of light that has resulted from endless months of quarantine – the rediscovery and cultivation of our shared passion for coin collecting. Therefore it is this theme of positivity rather than diversity that we have chosen to reflect in or symbolic cover coin – a silver Penny from the reign of King Alfred for whom 2021 also marks the 1,150th Anniversary of his Coronation.

Just like us, Alfred endured hardship. His accession to the throne would soon be eclipsed by fear of the 'Great Heathen Army'. An unstoppable Viking force under whom his 'Heptarchic' contemporaries had been put to the sword, their territories overrun, and Christianity all but extinguished. For Alfred there could be no retreat, Wessex now stood alone. The very fate of his kingdom, and indeed England, would be decided on the battlefield of Ethadun in May 878. With history seldom recorded by anyone but the victor, this gutsy 'last stand' and triumph against the odds earned Alfred his own epithet 'the Great'. Within a decade, he would have resettled *Lundenwic*, then an important trading town on the banks of the River Thames. Its recapture was not lost on Alfred, who in perhaps the most forward-thinking piece of British coin design chose to emblazon his Penny with a symbolic tribute to the town, forever immortalising his reign and the city of LONDONIA to the world. So much so that its iconic monogram was reused a millennium later by Messrs Spink and Son in their trial designs for a Crown of Edward VII, and indeed again for mementos at the British Empire Exhibition of 1924.

While our ability to visit such cities as London seems lost in the maze of evolving global travel restrictions, it is fair to say that this has been a year of renewal at Spink. Not only through the renovations at our established Bloomsbury premises, but equally through the review of our auction programme and private treaty offerings too. As a result, it gives us great pleasure to record the birth of the 'Numismatic e-Circular' - a reimagination of our world-famous fixed-price listing that ran in paper format until 2014 - now converted into a slick and exhilarating e-Auction format. Although managed by 21st Century technology, its themes and style are very much in the essence of the very first listing back in December 1892. By the close of the year we will have held a dozen of these bi-monthly sales, with over a million pounds crossing the virtual auctioneer's block and practically every type of coin from £20 to £20,000!

At the same time our printed catalogue sales have been reconsidered also to ensure that their appearance on your doorstep can mean only that a truly unmissable spectacle awaits. For those in tune with our programme already, you will know exactly this feeling when you joined us for the Stratos Sale of Spectacular English Gold Coins on 15th September 2020. Five hours of heightened saleroom drama resulted in a white glove auction and over £2.23million pounds spent in fierce head-to-head battles! That was then followed by the magnificent Ennismore Collection of Anglo-Saxon and Viking Coins, offering many of the plate coins you see gracing the pages to follow.

However, success was by no means guaranteed at the time of the historic announcement on 23rd March 2020. We recall that Monday clearly. How could we forget when lockdown is announced on the eve of a public coin auction? Having established that we could proceed behind closed doors and through the assistance of our online platform

SpinkLive and a skeleton staff, Spink led the numismatic industry that day as it so often has done before, paving the way for the buoyant and confident marketplace we see in 2021. While prevailing collector trends are increasingly difficult to track in this internet-paced world, we are confident that this indispensable guide will stand you in very good stead, whether you are just starting out, or already have your treasured nest eggs to enjoy.

Wherever you read this, and whatever circumstances you may find yourself in, we hope this book brings joy, and finds you and your family happy and healthy.

Gregory Edmund

A note from Emma Howard, Editor, Coins of England: our thanks to everyone who has submitted suggestions for new inclusions or corrections to existing entries. As ever, all submissions are subject to the scrutiny and approval of our editorial committee, who have approved any corrections and provided a complete overhaul of price changes to reflect the activity in the market over the past year.

*A note on bullion value in this edition: we have listed the 2021 spot price for gold quoted on page 493 onwards at £1,400 an ounce, but obviously this is subject to fluctuation because the price of gold has been and continues to be so volatile.*

# INTRODUCTION

## Arrangement

The arrangement of this catalogue is not completely uniform, but generally it is divided into metals (gold, silver, copper, etc) under each reign, then into coinages, denominations and varieties. In the Celtic section the uninscribed coins are listed before the dynastic coins; under Charles II all the hammered coins precede the milled coinage; the reign of George III is divided into coins issued up to 1816 and the new coinage from 1816 to the end of the reign; and under Elizabeth II the decimal issues are separated from the pre-decimal *(£.s.d.)* coinages and listed in a separate volume of the SCBC since 2015. For the first time in 2020 the two volumes have been made available for purchase independently of one another.

Every major coin type is listed though not every variety. We have endeavoured to give rather more coverage to the varieties of relatively common coins, such as the pennies of Edward I, II and III, than to the very much rarer coins of, for instance, King Offa of Mercia.

## Values

The values given represent the range of retail prices at which coins are being offered for sale at the time of going to press and **not** the price which a dealer will pay for those coins. These prices are based on our knowledge of the numismatic market, the current demand for particular coins, recent auction sale prices and, in those cases where certain coins have not appeared for sale for some years, our estimation of what they would be likely to sell at today, bearing in mind their rarity and appeal in relation to somewhat similar coins where a current value is known. Values are given for two grades of preservation from the Celtic period onwards and three to four grades of preservation for coins of the 17th to the 20th century.

Collectors normally require coins in the best condition they can afford and, except in the case of a really rare coin, a piece that is considerably worn is not wanted and has little value. The values given in the catalogue are for the exact state of preservation stated at the head of each column and bearing in mind that a score of identical coins in varying states of wear could be lined up in descending order from mint condition (FDC, *fleur de coin*), through very fine (VF) to *poor* state. It will be realized that only in certain instances will the values given apply to particular coins. A 'fine' (F) coin may be worth anything between one quarter and a half of the price quoted for a 'very fine' (VF); on the other hand, a piece in really mint condition will be valued substantially higher than the price quoted for 'extremely fine' (EF). The designation BV has been adopted for coins whose value on the market has yet to exceed its bullion value. Purchasing sovereigns, catalogued as BV, will attract a dealers' premium.

We emphasise again that the purpose of this catalogue is to give a general value for a particular class of coin in a specified state of preservation, and also to give the collector an idea of the range and value of coins in the English series. The value of any particular piece depends on three things:

Its exact design, legend, mintmark or date.

Its exact state of preservation; this is of prime importance.

The demand for it in the market at any given time.

Some minor varieties are much scarcer than others and, as the number of coins issued varies considerably from year to year, coins of certain dates and mintmarks are rarer and of more value than other pieces of similar type. The prices given for any type are for the commonest variety, mintmark or date of that type.

## The Scope

Coin collecting, numismatics, is a fascinating hobby. It requires very little physical exertion and only as much mental effort as one wishes or is able to put into it at any time. There is vast scope and boundless ramifications and byways encompassing not only things historical and geographical, but also touching on economics, metallurgy, heraldry, literature, the fine arts, politics, military history and many other disciplines. This catalogue is solely concerned with British coinage from its earliest times right up to date. From the start the beginner should appreciate that the coinage of our own nation may be seen as a small but very important part of the whole story of world currency.

The first coins, made of electrum, a natural alloy of gold and silver, were issued in western Asia Minor (Lydia) in the later seventh century BC. Over the next century or so coinage of gold and silver spread across the Aegean to mainland Greece, southwards to the eastern Mediterranean lands and eventually westward to the Greek colonies in southern Italy, Sicily (Magna Graecia) and beyond. The coins of the Greeks are noted for their beautiful, sometimes exquisite craftsmanship, with many of the coin types depicting the patron deities of their cities. Coins of Philip II of Macedon (359-336 BC), father of Alexander the Great, circulated amongst the Celtic peoples of the Danubian Basin and were widely copied through central Europe and by the Gauls in France. Gold Gaulish staters were reaching Britain around the beginning of the first century BC and the earliest gold to be struck in the island must have been produced shortly afterwards. Although their types and designs copy the Apollo head and racing charioteer of Philip II's gold coins, they are stylistically much removed from the original representation and very individually Celtic in concept.

The coins of the Romans cover some seven centuries and include an enormous number of different types that were current throughout a major part of the civilised world from Spain to Syria and from the Rhine in the north to the Sudan in the south. The Roman province of Britain was part of this vast empire for four hundred years from AD 43 until the early fifth century. Innumerable Roman coins have been recovered from sites in this country, most being made of brass or bronze. Many of these are quite inexpensive and very collectable. In recent years many hoards of gold and silver coins have been found, usually by use of metal detectors.

Following the revival of commerce after the Dark Ages, coinage in Western Europe was virtually restricted to silver until the thirteenth century, though gold was still being minted in Byzantium and in the Islamic world. In the Middle Ages many European cities had their own distinctive coinage and money was issued not only by the kings but also by nobles, bishops and abbots. From the time of the later Crusades gold returned to the West, and the artistic developments of the Renaissance in the fifteenth century brought improved portraiture and new minting techniques.

Large silver crown-size thalers were first minted at Joachimsthal in Bohemia early in the sixteenth century. The substantial shipments of silver coming to Europe from the mines of Spanish America over the next couple of centuries led to a fine series of larger coins being issued by the European states and cities. The larger size allowed greater artistic freedom in the designs and the portraits on the coins.

Both Germany and Italy became unified nation states during the later nineteenth century, thereby substantially reducing the number of mints and coin types. Balancing the reduction in European minting authorities were the new coins that were issued by the independent states of South and Central America. Since the 1950s many new nations have established their independence and their coinage provides a large field for the collector of modern coins.

It can be seen that the scope for the collector is truly vast, but besides the general run of official coinage there is also the large series of token coins—small change unofficially produced to supplement the inadequate supply of authorised currency. These tokens were issued by merchants, innkeepers and manufacturers in many towns and villages in the seventeenth, eighteenth and nineteenth centuries and many collectors specialise in their local issues.

Some coins have designs of a commemorative nature; an example being the Royal Wedding crown of 1981, but there are also large numbers of commemorative medals which, though never intended for use as coinage, are sometimes confused with coins because they are metal objects of a similar shape and sometimes a similar size to coins. This is another interesting field for collectors as these medals often have excellent portraits of famous men or women, or they may commemorate important events or scientific discoveries. Other metallic objects of coin-like appearance that can be confusing for the beginner are reckoning counters, advertising tickets, various other tickets and passes, and items such as brass coin weights.

## Minting processes

From the time of the earliest Greek coins in the late seventh century BC to about the middle of the sixteenth century AD, coins were made by hand. The method of manufacture was simple. The obverse and reverse designs were engraved or punched into the prepared ends of two bars of bronze or iron, shaped or tapered to the diameter of the required coin. The obverse die, known as the *pile*, was usually spiked so that it could be anchored firmly into a block of wood or metal. The reverse die, the *trussel*, was held by hand or grasped by tongs.

The coin was struck by placing a metal blank between the two dies and striking the trussel with a hammer. Thus, all coinage struck by this method is known as 'hammered'. Some dies are known to have been hinged so there would be an exact register between the upper and lower die. Usually a 'pair of dies' consisted of one obverse die (normally the more difficult to make because it had the finer detail, such as the ruler's portrait) and two reverse dies. This was because the shaft of iron bearing the reverse design eventually split under the constant hammering; two reverse dies were usually needed to last out the life of the obverse die.

Some time toward the middle of the sixteenth century, experiments, first in Germany and later in France, resulted in the manufacture of coins by machinery.

The term 'milled', which is applied to all machine-made coins, comes from the type of machinery used – the mill and screw press. With this machinery the obverse die was fixed as the lower die and the reverse die brought down into contact with the blank by heavy vertical pressure applied by a screw or worm-drive connected to a cross bar with heavy weights at each end. These weights usually had long leather thongs attached which allowed a more powerful force to be applied by the operators who revolved the arms of the press. New blanks were placed on the lower die and the struck coins were removed by hand. The screw press brought more pressure to bear on the blanks and this pressure was evenly applied, producing a far better and sharper coin.

Various attempts were made during the reigns of Elizabeth I and Charles I to introduce this type of machinery with its vastly superior products. Unfortunately problems associated with the manufacture of blanks to a uniform weight greatly reduced the rate of striking and the hand manufacture of coins continued until the Restoration in 1660, when Charles II brought to London from Holland the Roettiers brothers and their improved screw press.

The first English coins made for circulation by this new method were the silver crowns of 1662, which bore an inscription on the edge, DECVS ET TVTAMEN, 'an ornament and a safeguard', a reference to the fact that the new coins could not be clipped, a crime made easy by the thin and often badly struck hammered coins.

The mill and screw press was used until new steam-powered machinery made by Boulton and Watt was installed in the new mint on Tower Hill in London. This machinery had been used most successfully by Boulton to strike the large 'cartwheel' two- and one- penny pieces of 1797 and other coins, including 'overstriking' Spanish *eight-reale* pieces into Bank of England 'dollars' since the old Mint presses were not able to exert sufficient power to do this. This new machinery was first used at the Mint to strike the 'new coinage' halfcrowns of 1816, and it operated at a far greater speed than the old type of mill and screw presses and achieved a greater sharpness of design.

The very latest coining presses now operating at the Royal Mint at Llantrisant in South Wales, are capable of striking at a rate of up to 800 coins a minute.

## Condition

One of the more difficult problems for the beginner is to assess accurately the condition of a coin. A common fault among collectors is to overgrade and, consequently, to overvalue their coins.

Most dealers will gladly spare a few minutes to help new collectors. Many dealers issue price lists with illustrations, enabling collectors to see exactly what the coins look like and how they have been graded.

Coins cannot always be graded according to precise rules. Hammered coins often look weak or worn on the high parts of the portrait and the tops of the letters; this can be due to weak striking or worn dies and is not always attributable to wear through long use in circulation. Milled coins usually leave the Mint sharply struck so that genuine wear is easier to detect. However a x5 or x10 magnifying glass is essential, especially when grading coins of Edward VII and George V where the relief is very low on the portraits and some skill is required to distinguish between an uncirculated coin and one in EF condition.

The condition or grade of preservation of a coin is usually of greater importance than its rarity. By this we mean that a common coin in superb condition is often more desirable and more highly priced than a rarity in poor condition. Coins that have been pierced or mounted as a piece of jewellery generally have little interest to collectors.

One must also be on the lookout for coins that have been 'plugged', i.e. that have been pierced at some time and have had the hole filled in, sometimes with the missing design or letters re-engraved.

Badly cleaned coins will often display a complexity of fine interlaced lines and such coins have a greatly reduced value. It is also known for coins to be tooled or re-engraved on the high parts of the hair, in order to 'increase' the grade of coin and its value. In general it is better to have a slightly more worn coin than a better example with such damage.

Professional grading services have come to exert considerable influence over the grading of coins and the subsequent prices they can command. Whilst such services can provide an accurate way to grade coins, and are well-suited to milled and machine made issues, the resulting grading remains an opinion with grading of hammered and ancient requiring different considerations to milled and machine-made coins. Associated with professional grading is the practise of sealing the coin within a clear plastic container, colloquially referred to as slabbing. Whilst now a well-established practice in the US market it has had less impact in the UK where collectors prefer to handle a coin which allows for closer examination of the surfaces and the edges, a necessity for a milled coin with an inscribed edge which once enscapulated cannot be examined.

## Cleaning coins

Speaking generally, *do not* clean coins. More coins are ruined by injudicious cleaning than through any other cause, and a badly cleaned coin loses much of its value. A nicely toned piece is usually considered desirable. Really dirty gold and silver can, however, be carefully washed in soap and water. Copper coins should never be cleaned or washed, they may be lightly brushed with a brush that is not too harsh.

## Buying and selling coins

Exchanging coins with other collectors, searching around the antique shops, telling your relatives and friends that you are interested in coins, or even trying to find your own with a metal detector, are all ways of adding to your collection. However, the time will come when the serious collector needs to acquire specific coins or requires advice on the authenticity or value of a coin.

At this point an expert is needed, and the services of a reputable coin dealer or independent numismatic consultant are necessary. There are now a large number of coin dealers in the UK, many of whom belong to the B.N.T.A. (The British Numismatic Trade Association). Many dealers publish their own lists of coins. Studying these lists is a good way for a collector to learn about coins and to classify and catalogue their own collections.

The internet has made it very much easier to locate, view and acquire coins online not just in the United Kingdom but worldwide. Many dealers now offer lists of stock online. It has also revolutionised the availability of coins at auction with printed catalogues supplemented by online catalogues and the increasing use of online bidding making the need to attend an auction on the day less critical than it once was. As a result buying and selling at auction has grown as a way to add to and dispose of collections. In buying at auction it is always advisable to examine the coin before deciding to bid and it should be borne in mind that the description given will only be as good as the expertise of the person describing the coin. It is still possible to find and acquire bargains at auction, but the chance of doing so is perhaps less these days than it once was. It should also be pointed out that auction houses charge the buyer a premium on the hammer price, generally at 20%, on which, in the United Kingdom , VAT is applicable with the total price paid generally  hammer price plus 24%. Coins disposed of at auction will be subject to a vendor's commission charge made by the auction house which can be up to 15% of the price realised. An active market for buying and selling coins exists also on e-bay, however in general items offered here should be treated with caution with the onus on checking the veracity of the coin very much with the bidder.

*The Standard Catalogue of British Coins* has been published since 1929. It serves as a price guide for all coin collectors. Spink also publish books on many aspects of English, Greek, Roman and Byzantine coins and on British tokens which serve as a valuable source of information for coin collectors. Our books are available directly from Spink at www.spinkbooks.com selected high street booksellers and online outlets such as Amazon.

## Numismatic Clubs and Societies

There are over thirty numismatic societies and clubs in the British Isles. Joining one is the best way to meet fellow enthusiasts, learn about your coins and other series in a friendly and informative way. For details and contacts for a club or society near you see Appendix III, page 596 or online, www.coinclubs.org.uk. The British Association of Numismatic Societies (BANS), which acts as the national body for all Societies, holds two weekend meetings each year with a range of speakers in convivial surroundings.

## Useful suggestions

*Security and insurance.* The careful collector should not keep valuable coins at home unless they are insured and have adequate protection. Local police and insurance companies will give advice on what precautions may be necessary.

Most insurance companies will accept a valuation based on *The Standard Catalogue.* It is usually possible to have the amount added to a householder's contents policy but particularly valuable individual coins may have to be separately listed. A 'Fire, Burglary and Theft' policy will cover loss only from the insured's address, but an 'All Risks' policy will usually cover accidental damage and loss anywhere within the U.K.

Until fairly recently most high street banks offered safe-deposit boxes which formed a useful way for holding a collection in a secure environment. However in recent years many high street banks have stopped providing such services. The alternative is to acquire and install a safe at your home where coins can be stored. There are many options available here and most insurance companies will offer reduced premiums for coins securely stored at the home.

*Keeping a record.* All collectors are advised to have an up-to-date record of their collection and, if possible, photographs of the more important and more easily identifiable coins. This should be kept in a separate place from the collection so that a list and photographs can be given to the police should loss occur. Note the price paid, from whom purchased, the date of acquisition and the condition of the coin.

*Storage and handling.* New collectors should get into the habit of handling coins by the edge. This is especially important as far as highly polished proof coins are concerned.

Collectors may initially keep their coins in paper or plastic envelopes housed in boxes, albums or special containers. Many collectors will eventually wish to own a hardwood coin cabinet in which the collection can be properly arranged and displayed. If a home-made cabinet is being constructed avoid using oak and cedar wood; mahogany, walnut and rosewood are ideal. It is important that coins are not kept in a humid atmosphere; especial care must be taken with copper and bronze coins which are very susceptible to damp or condensation which may result in a green verdigris forming on them.

# SUSSEX SOVEREIGN

## U.K. based Japanese coin dealer
## イギリス拠点の日系コイン商

## From beginner to numismatist

The new collector can best advance to becoming an experienced numismatist by examining as many coins as possible, noting their distinctive features and by learning to use the many books of reference that are available. It will be an advantage to join a local numismatic society, as this will provide an opportunity for meeting other enthusiasts and obtaining advice from more experienced collectors. Most societies have a varied programme of lectures, exhibitions and occasional auctions of members' duplicates.

Those who become members of one or both of the national societies, the Royal Numismatic Society and the British Numismatic Society, receive an annual journal containing authoritative papers and have access to the societies' library and programme of lectures.

Many museums have coin collections available for study, although they may not always be displayed, and a number of museum curators are qualified numismatists. Many collectors enjoy deepening their knowledge of the coins they collect by referring to books and articles which provide detailed study of specific coins and coinages. These provide more detail on varieties than can be included here in the Standard Catalogue. References to relevant studies and books are given within this catalogue to allow for more detailed study. Appendix 1 gives details of a selection of key works useful to the specialist collector.

# SOME NUMISMATIC TERMS EXPLAINED

| | |
|---|---|
| Obverse | That side of the coin which normally shows the monarch's head or name. |
| Reverse | The side opposite to the obverse, the 'Tails'. |
| Blank | The coin as a blank piece of metal, i.e. before it is struck. |
| Flan | The whole piece of metal after striking. |
| Type | The main, central design. |
| Legend | The inscription. Coins lacking a legend are called 'mute' or anepigraphic. |
| Field | That flat part of the coin between the main design and the inscription or edge. |
| Exergue | That part of the coin below the main design, usually separated by a horizontal line, and normally occupied by the date. |
| Die | The block of metal, with design cut into it, which actually impresses the coin blank with the design. |
| Die variety | Coin showing slight variation of design. |
| Mule | A coin with the current type on one side and the previous (and usually obsolete) type on the other side, or a piece struck from two dies that are not normally used together. |
| Graining or reeding | The crenellations around the edge of the coin, commonly known as 'milling'. |
| Proof | Carefully struck coin from special dies with a mirror-like or matt surface. (In this country 'Proof' is not a term used to describe the state of preservation, but the method of striking.) |
| Hammered | Refers to the old craft method of striking a coin between dies hammered by hand. |
| Milled | Coins struck by dies worked in a coining press. The presses were hand powered from 1560-1800, powered by steam from 1790 and by electricity from 1895. |

# CELTIC COINAGE EXPLAINED

The Celtic or Ancient British issues are amongst the most interesting and varied of all British coins. They are our earliest coins and are the product of a society that left no historical sources of its own. It is therefore often difficult to be specific about for whom, when or where they were produced. Despite only being used for approximately a hundred and fifty years they do provide a rich variety of designs and types in gold, silver and bronze. Collectors looking for a theme to concentrate on may find the coins of one tribe, an individual ruler or a particular phase in the coinage interesting.

## Grading Celtic Coins

The majority of Celtic coins were struck by hand, sometimes resulting in a loss of definition through weak striking. In addition, the design on the dies was often bigger than the blank flan employed, resulting in the loss of some of the design. Coins with full legends are generally more valuable than examples with incomplete legends. Bronze coins in good condition (VF or better) and especially toned examples attract a premium. Factors that detract from a coin's value are chips, scratches and verdigris on bronze coins. It is important to take into account these factors as well as the amount of wear on a coin when assessing its grade.

| | Cunobelin Bronze Unit | Epaticcus Silver Unit | Cunobelin Gold Stater |
|---|---|---|---|
| Fine | | | |
| Very Fine | | | |

## Plated Coins

Plated gold staters, quarter staters and silver units are recorded for many known types. They vary considerably in the quality of their production and are usually priced at around a quarter of the substantive type's value. Their exact purpose or relation to the type they copy is not fully understood.

## References and Select Bibliography.

*ABC*    Rudd, C. (2010), Ancient British Coinage.
*V*       Van Arsdell, R.D. (1989), Celtic Coinage of Britain.
*BMC*   Hobbs, R. (1996), British Iron Age Coins in the British Museum.

de Jersey, P. (1996), Celtic Coinage in Britain. *A good general introduction to the series.*
Nash, D. (1987), Coinage in the Celtic World. *Sets the coinage in its social context.*

The layout of the following list is derived from the standard works by Van Arsdell and the British Museum Catalogue by Richard Hobbs. References are made to these works where possible, in the case of the last work it should be noted that the British Museum collection is not exhaustive, and therefore should not be used to assess the rarity of a coin with, for example Rudd ABC listing many more varieties than can be listed here.

## IMPORTED COINAGE

The earliest coinage in the British isles originated as continental imports around the middle of the 2nd Century BC, and primarily from the various tribes inhabiting northern Gaul (modern-day France and Belgium). It is not clear how the coins first came to be used, but surviving historical records suggest a period in which British and Gallic tribes shared close socio-economic and political ties. The development of Royal hierarchies within these tribal communities, as well as the hiring and sharing of mercenaries during times of conflict, further aided circulation, as in the case of Caesar's 'Gallic Wars' at the end of this period.

These gold staters are principally subdivided into the 'Gallo-Belgic' series A-F. The earliest (A), is attributed to the Ambiani tribe (sited around the Somme Valley and Amiens), and is most notable for its supreme artistry and close imitation of Philip II of Macedon's prototype (359-336 BC) which would serve as a canon for this entire series. As the coinage developed, the quality of *Ambiani* workmanship rapidly deteriorated to the extent that the once-recognisable laureate head of Apollo and the depiction of a charioteer became merely an assortment of disarticulated crescents, pellets or other abstract motifs (C and E). Recent studies have suggested the 'defaced' issues (B) could relate to the *Nervii* (Brussels and Hainault) or the *Caletes* (NE Normandy), whilst the triple-tailed horse issues of series F can be confidently associated with the *Suessiones* (Soissons). Quarter-Staters can be subdivided along similar lines, the only exception being found in series D, where the distinctive 'Boat-Tree' design is attributed to the sea-faring *Morini* tribe (Pas-de-Calais).

### GALLO-BELGIC ISSUES

|  | 2 | 5 | 7 | 9 |
|---|---|---|---|---|

|  | | F | VF |
|---|---|---|---|
|  | | £ | £ |

**From 150 B.C.**

| 1 | **Gold Stater**. *Large flan*. Series A, head r., ℞. horse and charioteer l., rosette below. *VA 10; ABC 1* | 1500 | 8500 |
|---|---|---|---|
| 2 | — — —, head l., ℞. horse r. *VA 12; ABC 4 ['Bellovaci']* | 900 | 5250 |
| 3 | — *Small flan*. B, defaced obverse die, ℞. as last *VA 30; ABC 7* | 425 | 2000 |
| 4 | — — —, similar, ℞. horse and rider l., lyre motif below *VA 33; ABC 10* | 525 | 2500 |
| 5 | — — C, devolved head r., ℞. horse r. *VA 44; ABC 13* | 250 | 900 |
| 6 | **Gold Quarter Stater**. *Large flan*. Series A, as S.1. *VA 15; ABC 28* | 250 | 900 |
| 7 | — — —, as S.2. *VA 20; ABC 31 ['Bellovaci']* | 225 | 850 |
| 8 | — *Small flan*. B, as S.3 *VA 35; ABC 34* | 275 | 950 |
| 9 | — — —, as S.4. *VA 37; ABC 37* | 175 | 575 |
| 10 | — — D, various abstract symbols or uniface, ℞. tree-motif surrounded by geometric lines, rings or pellets, cf. S.46 *VA 67-69; ABC 40-49* | 75 | 185 |

## c.60-50 B.C. (Gallic War issues)

|        | 11 | 11 (Var.) | 14 |        |        |
|--------|----|-----------|----|--------|--------|

|    |                                                                                                                                      | F £ | VF £ |
|----|--------------------------------------------------------------------------------------------------------------------------------------|-----|------|
| 11 | **Gold Stater**. Series E, uniface or with detail to periphery [rare], R. dis-jointed horse r., various patterns around and in exergue. *VA 50-56; ABC 16* | 150 | 425  |
| 12 | — F, devolved head r., R. triple-tailed horse r. *VA 85; ABC 22*                                                                      | 575 | 2000 |
| 13 | — Xc, digamma monogram in blank field, R. sinuous horse r., normal or reversed 'S' below *VA 87; ABC 19*                              | 250 | 900  |

### Armorica (Channel Islands and North-west Gaul): c.75-50 B.C.

|    |                                                                                                                      | F  | VF  |
|----|----------------------------------------------------------------------------------------------------------------------|----|-----|
| 14 | **Billon Stater**. Type I, head r. with corded hair, R. stylised horse r., with rider and Victory, lash ends in loop, boar below | 45 | 225 |
| 15 | — II, similar, R. Victory only, lash ends in small cross of pellets                                                   | 40 | 200 |
| 16 | — III, similar, anchor-shaped nose, R. similar to S.14                                                                | 40 | 200 |
| 17 | — IV, similar, rev. horse and rider with reins, lash ends in three prongs, lyre-motif below                          | 45 | 225 |
| 18 | — V, similar, R. lash ends in long cross of pellets                                                                   | 55 | 275 |
| 19 | — VI, similar, R. lash ends in 'ladder' motif                                                                         | 55 | 275 |
| 20 | **Billon Quarter Stater**, various types, as above                                                                    | 65 | 325 |

# CELTIC COINS STRUCK IN BRITAIN

Coin production in Britain began at the very end of the second century B.C. with the cast potin coinage of Kent (Nos 62-64). Inspired by Gaulish issues and ultimately derived from the potin coins of Massalia (Marseilles) in southern Gaul, the precise function and period of use of this coinage is not fully understood. The domestic production of gold coins started around 70 B.C., these issues are traditionally known as British A-P and are derived from imported Gallo-Belgic issues. Broadly contemporary with these issues are quarter staters, silver units, and bronze units. Work by John Sills has further enhanced our understanding of this crucial early period with the identification of two new British staters (Insular Belgic C or Kentish A and the Ingoldisthorpe type) and their related quarters and a Westerham quarter stater. The Insular Belgic C or Kentish A type derived from Gallo-Belgic C now becomes the first British stater.

## EARLY UNINSCRIBED COINAGE FROM c.65 B.C.

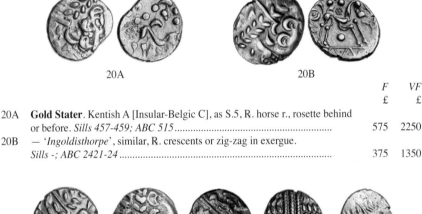

20A                                 20B

|  |  | F £ | VF £ |
|---|---|---|---|
| 20A | **Gold Stater**. Kentish A [Insular-Belgic C], as S.5, R. horse r., rosette behind or before. *Sills 457-459; ABC 515* | 575 | 2250 |
| 20B | — '*Ingoldisthorpe*', similar, R. crescents or zig-zag in exergue. *Sills -; ABC 2421-24* | 375 | 1350 |

21            22            23            24            25

| 21 | — British A, '*Westerham*', devolved head r., R. abstract horse formed of pellets, crescents and lines. *BMC 1-32; VA 200-202; ABC 482, 2430* | 225 | 650 |
|---|---|---|---|
| 22 | — B, '*Chute*', similar, R. 'crab' motif below. *BMC 35-76; VA 1205; ABC 746* | 175 | 525 |
| 23 | — C, '*Yarmouth*', similar, three-pronged 'eye', rev. linear horse right, 'bird-headed' star before. *BMC 78-85; VA 1220; ABC 518* | 750 | 3000 |
| 24 | — D, '*Cheriton*', as B, with large crescent face. *BMC 86-128; VA 1215; ABC 755* | 225 | 625 |
| 25 | — E, '*Waldingfield*', similar to A, R. annulets below *VA 1462; ABC 2335* | 400 | 1350 |

27              28

|  | F £ | VF £ |
|---|---|---|
| 26   — F, 'Clacton', type I, similar to A, R. rosette below. *BMC 137-144; VA 1458; ABC 2332 ['Late']* ..................... | 450 | 1500 |
| 27   — G, — type II, as last, R. sinuous horse r., pellet and lines below. *BMC 145-179; VA 30, 1455; ABC 2326-29 ['Early']* ..................... | 275 | 1000 |
| 28   — H, North-East Coast, type I, similar to F and G, R. horse r., rosette below. *BMC 181-191; VA 800; ABC 1716-19* ..................... | 175 | 500 |

29            30           31

| 29   — I, —, type II, as last, R. horse l., pellet, rosette or star below. *BMC 193-211; VA 804-807; ABC 1722, 1728-1734, 1740* ..................... | 175 | 500 |
|---|---|---|
| 30   — J, Norfolk Wolf, type I, as S.5 and 20A, R. wolf r., pellets above. *BMC 212-216; VA 610; ABC 1393* ..................... | 350 | 1250 |
| 31   — — —, type II [base gold issue], as last, R. wolf l. *BMC 217-278; VA 610; ABC 1396-99* ..................... | 175 | 575 |

32 (Middle)           32 (Early)

| 32   — L, 'Whaddon Chase', Early-Middle types, as F and G, R. horse r., rosette below. *BMC 279-343; VA 1470, 1485; ABC 2240; 2347; 2433-45* ......... | 225 | 800 |
|---|---|---|

33           33A

| 33   — —, Late types, uniface, R. similar to last, annulet below. *BMC 344-346; VA 1498-1505; ABC 2338-44* ..................... | 250 | 925 |
|---|---|---|
| 33A   — 'Climping', similar to S.32, R. horse l., bird motif above, pellets-in-annulets around. *BMC —; VA —; ABC —* ..................... | 575 | 2000 |

34

35

|  | | F £ | VF £ |
|---|---|---|---|

34   — Lx, North-Thames, blank except reversed 'SS' motif, R. as S.33. *BMC 350; VA 1509; ABC 2237* ..............................................................................    650    2250

35   — Lz, Weald, uniface, R. horse r., 'thumbs-up' motif above, large wheel below. *BMC 347-349; VA 1507; ABC 186* .........................................................    750    3000

36

36   — Ma, '*Wonersh*', crossed wreath, crescents back-to-back at centre, R. horse r., rosette below. *BMC 351-356; VA 1520; ABC 527* ....................................    450    1500

37             38

37   — Mb, '*Savernake Forest*', uniface, R. as last. *BMC 361-364; VA 1526; ABC 2091* ...............................................................................................    150    475

38   — Qa, British 'Remic' types, devolved head right, R. triple-tailed horse r., wheel below. *BMC 445-458; VA 210-214; ABC 485, 494-497* ...............    225    800

39             39B

39   — Qb, —, uniface, R. similar. *BMC 461-476; VA 216; ABC 488* ............    200    625

39A   **Gold Quarter Stater**. Kentish A [Insular-Belgic C], similar to S.10, but rosette in obverse field. *Sills 431; ABC 530* .......................................................    275    975

39B   — '*Ingoldisthorpe*', similar to last, spermatozoids in fields. *ABC 2448* ..    325    1100

39C   — British A, '*Westerham*', similar to last, L-shapes in fields. (ABC 2448)    225    850

40   — D, '*Cheriton*', as S.24, R. cross motif with pellets. *BMC 129-136; cf. VA 143; cf. ABC 770* ...........................................................................................    250    900

41                                     43

|      |                                                                                                                                   | F<br>£ | VF<br>£ |
|------|-----------------------------------------------------------------------------------------------------------------------------------|-------|---------|
| 41   | — F/G, '*Clacton*', blank or with faint patterns, R. ornamental cross with pellets. *BMC 180; VA 1460; ABC 2356* ............... | 125   | 425     |
| 42   | — H, -, de Jersey type, blank or with faint patterns, R. ornamental cross with pellets. *BMC 192; ABC 2350*.......... | 125   | 425     |
| 43   | — Lx, North Thames, stylised wreath on corded line, 'faces' in two angles, R. horse r., various motifs. *BMC 365-367; VA 234; ABC 2463-66* .......... | 150   | 600     |

44                                     45

|      |                                                                                                                                   | F<br>£ | VF<br>£ |
|------|-----------------------------------------------------------------------------------------------------------------------------------|-------|---------|
| 44   | — Ly, North Kent, uniface, R. horse r., U-shaped motif above. *BMC 371-374; VA 158; ABC 201* ....................... | 120   | 400     |
| 45   | — Lz, Weald, straight wreath with crescents or annulets in fields, R. horse r., floral sun above or below. *BMC 375, 548-50; VA 250; ABC 623-626* ..... | 150   | 475     |
| 45A  | — — —, similar to last, R. triple-tailed horse l., floral sun above, cog-wheel below. *BMC 552; ABC 629 [48]* ............... | 250   | 800     |
| 45B  | — Mc, '*Wonersh*', as S.36, R. horse l. or r., floral sun or wheel below. *VA 1688; ABC 617-620*................... | 350   | 1000    |

46                                     47

|      |                                                                                                                                   | F<br>£ | VF<br>£ |
|------|-----------------------------------------------------------------------------------------------------------------------------------|-------|---------|
| 46   | — O, Geometric types, unintelligible patterns, some blank on obv. *BMC 410-432; VA 143, 1225-29; ABC 533-536, 767* ........................... | 90    | 275     |
| 47   | — P, Trophy types, blank on obv., R. 'trophy' surrounded by various motifs. *BMC 437-444; VA 145, 147; ABC 192-195, 2243*.............. | 110   | 325     |
| 47A  | — — —, Eastern variants, four-petalled flower or reversed S, R. similar to last. *BMC 436; VA 146; ABC 2246-49*............... | 135   | 450     |

48

|      |                                                                                                                                   | F<br>£ | VF<br>£ |
|------|-----------------------------------------------------------------------------------------------------------------------------------|-------|---------|
| 48   | — Qc, British 'Remic' types, devolved head r., R. [usually] triple-tailed horse l. or r., various motifs surround. *BMC 478-538; VA 220-232; ABC 500-512, 554-584, 2093-99, 2225-2234, 2359-62, 2368-71* ......................... | 150   | 475     |
| 48A  | — — —, Ornamental variants, R. triple-tailed horse l., various motifs around. *BMC 539-544; VA 236, 256; ABC 779-791*............ | 350   | 1000    |
| 48B  | — — —, Wreath variants, ringed annulet or flower at centre, R. horse l. or r., various motifs surround. (*BMC 545-546; VA 242-244; ABC 602-605, 611-614, 2365-71, 2469* ............... | 200   | 700     |

49

|  | | F £ | VF £ |
|---|---|---|---|

49 — Xd, diademed head of good style l., reversed S before, R. sinuous horse l., wheel below. *BMC 571-575; VA 78; ABC 551* ........................................... 325 1000

50                  50 (Var.)

50 **Silver Unit**. head left or right, R. horse l. or r. *BMC 376-382; VA 80, 1546, 1549, 1555; ABC 1507, 2472-75, 2481-84 [53]*...................................... 100 350

51                    53

51 — head l., R. stag or goat with horns r. *BMC 383; VA 1552; ABC 2487 [54]* 100 350
52 **Silver Half Unit**. Zoomorphic types, annulate horses and beasts. *BMC 391-400; VA 474, 1626, 1643; ABC 719, 935-941, 2283-2309, 2401, 2496-2502, 2535 [55]* 80 325
53 **Silver Unit**. British Lz, Danebury group, head r., with corded hair, R. annulate horse l, flower above. *BMC 580-582; VA 262; ABC 1013* ...................... 125 475

54                    54A

54 — helmeted head r., R. annulate horse r., wheel below. *BMC 583-592; VA 264; ABC 662 [58]*........................................................................................ 90 400
54A **Silver Half Unit**. Cruciform pattern with ornaments in angles, R. horse l., motifs surround. *ABC 2505* ....................................................... 125 525
55 **Silver Minim**. helmeted head r., R. horse r., pellet mane. *BMC 642-643; VA 268-270; ABC 728 [59]*....................................................... 50 185

56

56 **Silver Unit**. horned head r., R. as S.54. *BMC 595-601; VA 280; ABC 866* 75 275
57 — head l., pellet-in-ring before, R. as S.54. *BMC 610-612; VA 284; ABC 857* 50 185

58

| | | F £ | VF £ |
|---|---|---|---|
| 58 | —, serpentine dragon l., head back-turned, ℞. similar to S.54. *BMC 631-633; VA 286; ABC 896* ............................................................................... | 125 | 475 |

59

61

| 59 | **Silver Minim**. Concave square, ℞. two-tailed annulate horse l., wheel above. *BMC 654-656; VA 482; ABC 1046* ............................................................. | 40 | 145 |
|---|---|---|---|
| 60 | **Bronze Unit.** Lx. Winged horse l. ℞. Winged horse l. *ABC 273; V. 1629; BMC 401* ...................................................................................................... | 60 | 250 |
| 61 | Chichester Cock type. Head r. ℞. Head r. surmounted by cock. *ABC 737; V. — BMC 657-59* ................................................................................. | 70 | 275 |

## POTIN, c.120-100 B.C.
### (Cast copper/tin alloy, mainly Kent)

62

| | | F £ | VF £ |
|---|---|---|---|
| 62 | **Unit.** Thurrock type. Head l. R. Bull butting l. or r. *ABC 120, 123, 126, 129, 132; V. 1402-42; BMC 660-666.* .................................................................. | 20 | 65 |

63 64

| | | F £ | VF £ |
|---|---|---|---|
| 63 | Class I type. Crude head. R. Lines representing bull *(Allen types A-L.) ABC 147, 150, 153, 156, 162, 165, 168, 171; V. 104, 106, 108, 112, 114, 115, 117, 119, 120, 122, 123, 125, 127, 129, 131, 133; BMC 667-714.* .................. | 25 | 80 |
| 64 | Class II type. Smaller flan, large central pellet. *(Allen types M-P.) ABC 174; V. 135-39; BMC 715-23.* ......................................................... | 20 | 70 |

# CELTIC DYNASTIC AND LATER UNINSCRIBED COINAGE

From Julius Caesar's expeditions to Britain in 55/54 B.C. and his conquest of Gaul in 52 B.C. to the Claudian invasion in A.D. 43, southern Britain was increasingly drawn into the orbit of the Roman world. This process is reflected not only in the coins but also in what we know about their issuers and the tribes they ruled. Latin legends begin to appear for the first time and increasingly accompany objects and designs drawn from the classical world. A lot of what we know about the Celtic tribes and their rulers, beyond just their names on coins, is drawn from contemporary and slightly later Roman historical sources. A great deal however is still uncertain and almost all attributions to either tribes or historically attested individuals have to be seen as tentative.

The coin-producing tribes of Britain can be divided into two groups, those of the core and those of the periphery. The tribes of the core, the Atrebates/Regni, Trinovantes/Catuvellauni and Cantii, by virtue of their geographical location controlled contact with the Roman world. Unlike the tribes of the periphery they widely employed Latin legends, classical designs and used bronze coinage in addition to gold and silver.

Following the Roman invasion of A.D. 43 it is likely that some coinage continued to be produced for a short time. However in A.D. 61 with the death of King Prasutagus and the suppression of the Boudiccan revolt that followed, it is likely that Celtic coinage came to an end.

## TRIBAL MAP

# ATREBATES AND REGNI

The joint tribal area of these two groups corresponds roughly with Berkshire and Sussex and parts of northern and eastern Hampshire. The Atrebatic portion being in the north of this region with its main centre at Calleva (Silchester). The Regni occupying the southern part of the region centred around Chichester.

## COMMIUS

(Mid to Late 1st Century B.C.)

The first inscribed staters to appear in Britain, closely resemble British Q staters (no.38) and are inscribed 'COMMIOS'. Staters and silver units with an inscribed 'E' are also thought to be related. Traditionally this Commius was thought to be the Gaulish chieftain who Caesar refers to in De Bello Gallico, as firstly serving him in his expeditions to Britain and finally fleeing to Britain c. 50 B.C. This attribution does however present chronological problems, and the appearance of a few early staters reading 'COM COMMIOS' suggests that the Commius who issued coins is more likely to have been the son of Caesar's Commius.

![coin images]

65

|    |                                                                                                                      | F<br>£ | VF<br>£ |
|----|----------------------------------------------------------------------------------------------------------------------|--------|---------|
| 65 | **Gold Stater**. Devolved head r, R. triple-tailed horse r., COM-MIOS below. *BMC 724-729; VA 350; ABC 1022* ....... | 275    | 850     |

66                           67

|    |                                                                                                                                                            | F<br>£ | VF<br>£ |
|----|------------------------------------------------------------------------------------------------------------------------------------------------------------|--------|---------|
| 66 | —, similar to last, R. E above horse. *BMC 730; VA 352; ABC 1025* ....... | 350 | 1050 |
| 67 | **Gold Quarter Stater**. Blank except for digamma, R. annulate horse l., E above, annulet and corded line below. *BMC 724-729; VA 353-1; ABC 1028*...... | 200 | 550 |
| 68 | —, similar to last, R. cogwheel above horse. *VA 353-5; ABC 1031 [67]*. | 150 | 400 |

![coin images]

69

|    |                                                                                                                      | F<br>£ | VF<br>£ |
|----|----------------------------------------------------------------------------------------------------------------------|--------|---------|
| 69 | **Silver Unit**. Head l., concentric rings before, R. horse l., wheel or E above. *BMC 731-758; VA 355; ABC 1034-40*.................................................... | 50 | 200 |

![coin images]

70

|    |                                                                                                                      | F<br>£ | VF<br>£ |
|----|----------------------------------------------------------------------------------------------------------------------|--------|---------|
| 70 | **Silver Minim**. Similar to last. *BMC 759-760; VA 358; ABC 1043*......... | 35 | 150 |

## TINCOMARUS or TINCOMMIUS
### (Late 1st Century B.C. – Early 1st Century A.D.)

Successor to Commius and on his coins styled as 'COM.F' (son of Commius). Early coins of the reign like his predecessors are very obviously Celtic in their style. However later coins exhibit an increasing tendency towards Roman designs. Indeed Tincommius is recorded as a suppliant king of the Roman emperor Augustus (Res Gestae, xxxii), finally fleeing to Rome in the early 1st century A.D. The discovery of the Alton Hoard in 1996 brought to light gold staters with the new legend TINCOMARVS.

72                                   73

|    |                                                                                                                                 | F £ | VF £ |
|----|---------------------------------------------------------------------------------------------------------------------------------|-----|------|
| 71 | **Gold Stater.** *Celtic style.* Devolved Apollo head r. ℞. TINC COMM. F. around horse. *ABC —; V. 362; BMC —.* | 750 | 2500 |
| 72 | Similar but legend reads TINCOMARVS. *ABC 1049; V. 363; BMC 761-765.* | 450 | 1650 |
| 73 | **Gold Quarter Stater.** Spiral with pellet centre. ℞. Horse r. T above. *ABC 1094; V. 366; BMC 781-797.* | 125 | 375 |

74                                   75

|    |                                                                                                                               |     |      |
|----|-------------------------------------------------------------------------------------------------------------------------------|-----|------|
| 74 | TINCOM, zig-zag ornament below. ℞. Horse l. *ABC 1073; V. 365; BMC 798-810.* | 150 | 450 |
| 75 | **Gold Stater.** *Classical style.* TINC(O) on a sunk tablet. ℞. Horseman with javelin r. often with CF in field. *ABC 1055, 1058, 1061; V. 375-76; BMC 765-769.* | 400 | 1350 |

76                                   77

|    |                                                                                                                               |     |      |
|----|-------------------------------------------------------------------------------------------------------------------------------|-----|------|
| 76 | COM.(F). on a sunk tablet. ℞. Horseman with javelin r. TIN in field *ABC 1067; V. 385; BMC 770-774.* | 325 | 1100 |
| 77 | **Gold Quarter Stater.** TINC on a tablet, C above, A or B below. ℞. Winged head (Medusa?) facing. *ABC 1076; V. 378; BMC 811-826.* | 450 | 1650 |
| 78 | TIN on tablet. ℞. Boar l. *ABC 1079; V. 379; BMC 827-837.* | 125 | 375 |

79      83      85

| | | F £ | VF £ |
|---|---|---|---|
| 79 | COMF on tablet. Ŗ. Horse r. TIN around. *ABC 1082; V. 387; BMC 838-841.* | 135 | 450 |
| 80 | — Ŗ. Horse l. TIC around. *ABC 1088; V. 388; BMC 842-851.* | 135 | 450 |
| 81 | COM on tablet. Ŗ. Horse l. T above. *ABC 1091; V. 389; BMC 852-3.* | 150 | 525 |
| 82 | COMF on tablet. Ŗ. Horse r. TINC around. *ABC 1085; V. 390; BMC 854-879.* | 135 | 450 |
| 83 | **Silver Unit.** Laureate head r. TINCOM in front, V behind. Ŗ. Eagle stg. on snake. *ABC 1106; V. 397; BMC 880-905.* | 45 | 225 |
| 84 | Laureate head l. Ŗ. Bull l. TINC around. *ABC 1112; V. 396; BMC 906-910.* | 45 | 225 |
| 85 | Laureate head r. Ŗ. Bull r. TIN(C) around. *ABC 1115, 1118; V. 381; BMC 911-925.* | 45 | 225 |

86      88      90

| | | | |
|---|---|---|---|
| 86 | Facing head. Ŗ. Bull l. TINC around. *ABC 1109; V. 370; BMC 926-29* | 50 | 250 |
| 87 | TINC in angles of cross, Ŗ. Lion l. *ABC 1124; V. 372; BMC 930-45.* | 45 | 225 |
| 88 | Star. Ŗ. Boy riding dolphin r. TINC in field. *ABC 1127; V. 371; BMC 946-977.* | 35 | 185 |
| 89 | TINC around pellet. Ŗ. Lion l. *ABC 1121; V. 382; BMC 978-80.* | 45 | 225 |
| 90 | Head l. TINCOMMIVS in front. Ŗ. Horse l. lyre above. *ABC 1100; V. 473; BMC —-. (Formerly attributed to Verica)* | 45 | 225 |
| 91 | **Silver Minim.** CF within two interlinked squares. Ŗ. Boar? r. TINC. *ABC 1136; V. 383-1; BMC 981-82.* | 35 | 135 |
| 92 | As above but CO. Ŗ. Bull r. TI. *ABC 1139; V. 383-5; BMC —-* | 40 | 145 |
| 93 | C inside box, box above and below. Ŗ. Bull r. TIN. *ABC 1274; V. 383-7; BMC 983* | 40 | 145 |

91      94

| | | | |
|---|---|---|---|
| 94 | Cross, T? in angles. Ŗ. uncertain object. *ABC 1142; V. 483; BMC 984-85. (Formerly attributed to Verica)* | 35 | 135 |

## EPPILLUS
### (Later 1st Century B.C. – Early 1st Century A.D.)

His reign is likely to have coincided with that of Tincommius's. Eppillus also claimed to be a son of Commius. Two coinages appear in his name, one for Kent and one minted at Calleva (Silchester, Hants.) in the northern part of the territory of the Atrebates and Regni. The coins of Calleva conform to the southern denominational structure of gold and silver with fractions of each, whilst the Kentish series is distinctly tri-metallic, replacing the silver minim with bronze. A joint coinage was issued by Eppillus and Verica. It is not understood if Eppillus held both territories simultaneously.

## COINAGE STRUCK AT CALLEVA

|  |  | F<br>£ | VF<br>£ |
|---|---|---|---|
| 95 | **Gold Stater.** Devolved Apollo head r. R. EPPI COMMI F around horse. *ABC 1145; V. 405; BMC —* | 2250 | 8500 |
| 96 | **Gold Quarter Stater.** CALLEV, star above and below. R. Hound r. EPPI. *ABC 1148, 1151; V. 407-08; BMC 986-1005.* | 140 | 450 |
| 97 | COMM F EPPILV, around crescent. R. Horse r. *ABC 1157; V. 409; BMC 1006-1009.* | 150 | 525 |
| 98 | EPPI COMF in two lines. R. Winged horse r. *ABC 1154; V. 435; BMC 1010-15.* | 140 | 475 |
| 99 | **Silver Unit.** Crescent REX CALLE above and below. R. Eagle r. EPP. *ABC 1160; V .415. BMC 1016-1060.* | 45 | 225 |
| 100 | Bearded hd. r. in wreath. R. Boar r. EPPI(L) F CO(M). *ABC 1163; V. 416; BMC 1061-87.* | 50 | 250 |
| 101 | Bearded hd. in pellet border. R. Lion r. EPP COMF. *ABC 1166; V. 417; BMC 1088-1115.* | 50 | 250 |
| 102 | **Silver Minim.** Floral cross. R. Eagle r. EPPI. *ABC 1169; V. 420; BMC 1116-17* | 45 | 200 |
| 103 | Spiral and pellets. R. Ram r. EPP. *ABC 1172; V. 421; BMC 1118-20.* | 45 | 200 |
| 104 | Bulls head facing. R. Ram r. EPP. *ABC 1175; V. 422; BMC 1121-24.* | 50 | 210 |
| 105 | Wreath pattern. R. Boar r. EPP. *ABC 1280; V. 423; BMC —-* | 60 | 250 |
| 106 | Crescent cross. R. Hand holding trident. *ABC 1298; V. 487; BMC —.* | 50 | 210 |

## KENTISH TYPES

107

| | | F £ | VF £ |
|---|---|---|---|
| 107 | **Gold Stater.** COMF within wreath. ℞. Horseman l. EPPILLVS above. *ABC 384; V. 430; BMC 1125-26.* | 2250 | 8500 |
| 108 | Victory holding wreath l., within wreath. ℞. Horseman r. holding carnyx, F EPPI COM below. *ABC 387; V. 431; BMC 1127-28.* | 3250 | 12500 |
| 109 | **Gold Quarter Stater.** Crossed wreaths, EPPI in angles. ℞. Horse l. *ABC 390; V. 436; BMC 1129.* | 475 | 1500 |
| 110 | COMF in pellet border. ℞. Horse r. EPPI. *ABC 393; V. 437; BMC 1130-31.* | 425 | 1350 |
| 111 | **Silver Unit.** Head l. EPPIL in field. ℞. Horseman holding carnyx, EPPILL. *ABC 399; V. 441; BMC 1132.* | 325 | 1100 |
| 112 | **Bronze Unit.** Bow cross, EPPI COMF around. ℞. Eagle facing. *ABC 408; V. 450; BMC 1137-38.* | 45 | 250 |
| 113 | Bull r., EPPI COF around. ℞. eagle facing. *ABC 411; V. 451; BMC 1139-41.* | 45 | 250 |
| 114 | Head l., EPPI in front. ℞. Victory l. holding wreath and standard. *ABC 414; V. 452; BMC 1142.* | 50 | 275 |
| 115 | Bearded hd. r., EPPI CF. ℞. Biga r. CF. *ABC 417; V. 453; BMC —* | 60 | 325 |

## JOINT TYPES OF EPPILUS AND VERICA

116 117

| | | | |
|---|---|---|---|
| 116 | **Silver Unit.** Diademed head l., TOVTO before. ℞. Victory walking r., E-P in field. *BMC 1133-34; VA 442; ABC 432* | 650 | 2250 |
| 117 | Head r. VIR CO in front. ℞. Capricorn l. EPPI COMF. *ABC 435; V. 443; BMC 1135-36.* | 175 | 575 |

## VERICA
### (c. 10.-c. A.D. 40)

The exact details of Verica's succession and relationship to Eppillus and Tincommius are not fully understood. However by c. A.D. 10 it seems likely that Verica was the sole ruler of the southern region. His close contact with Rome, both political and economic, seen in the increasing use of classical designs on his coins, culminated in his flight to Rome in c. A.D. 42 to seek assistance from Claudius.

|     |                                                                                                                              | F £ | VF £ |
|-----|------------------------------------------------------------------------------------------------------------------------------|-----|------|
| 118 | **Gold Stater.** COM:F on tablet. R. Horseman r. holding spear, VIR below. *ABC 1187; V. 460; BMC 1143-44.* | 350 | 1250 |
| 119 | COM.F. on tablet, pellet in ring ornament above and below. R. Similar to last. *ABC 1184; 461; BMC 1146-53.* | 350 | 1250 |

120                                             121

| 120 | COM.F on tablet. R. Horseman r. holding spear, VIR above, REX below. *ABC 1190; V. 500; BMC 1155-58.* | 300 | 950 |
| 121 | Vine-leaf dividing VI RI. R. Horseman r. with shield and spear. COF in field. *ABC 1193; V. 520-1; BMC 1159-73.* | 325 | 1100 |
| 122 | Similar, reads VE RI. *ABC 1193; V. 520-5/7; BMC 1174-76.* | 350 | 1200 |

123                              124

| 123 | **Gold Quarter Stater.** COMF on tablet. R. Horse l. VIR. *ABC 1196; V. 465; BMC 1177-78.* | 150 | 475 |
| 124 | COMF on tablet, pellet in ring ornament above and below R. Horse r. VI. *ABC 1199; V. 466; BMC 1179-1206.* | 135 | 375 |
| 125 | COMF on tablet, pellet border. R. Horse r. VI above. *ABC 1202; V. 467; BMC 1207-16.* | 165 | 575 |

126                    127                    128

| 126 | COM FILI. in two lines, scroll in between. R. Horse r. VIR(I) above. *ABC 1205; V. 468; BMC 1217-22.* | 150 | 550 |
| 127 | VERI COMF, crescent above, star below. R. Horse r. REX below. *ABC 1208; V. 501; BMC 1223-36.* | 150 | 525 |
| 128 | VERI beneath vine-leaf. R. Horseman r. with sword and shield, FRX in field. *ABC 1211; V. 525; BMC 1237-38.* | 375 | 1350 |
| 129 | COM, horseman r. R. Seated figure, VERICA around. *ABC 1214; V. 526; BMC 1239.* | 550 | 2000 |
| 130 | Similar to last. R. Laureate bust r., VIRI in front. *ABC 1217; V. 527; BMC 1240.* | 525 | 1850 |

|  | F £ | VF £ |
|---|---|---|

131     132     133

|  | F £ | VF £ |
|---|---|---|
| 131 **Silver Unit.** COMF, crescent and or pellet in ring above and below. R. Boar r. VI(RI) below. *ABC 1220, 1223; V. 470/72; BMC 1241-1331.* | 65 | 275 |
| 132 VERICA COMMI F around pellet in ring. R. Lion r. REX below. *ABC 1229; V. 505; BMC 1332-1359.* | 65 | 275 |
| 133 COMMI F, horseman with shield r. R. VERI CA, mounted warrior with spear r. *ABC 1238; V. 530; BMC 1360-92.* | 65 | 275 |

134     135     136

| 134 Two cornucopiae, COMMI F. R. Figure seated r. VERICA. *ABC 1241; V. 531; BMC 1393-1419.* | 50 | 200 |
|---|---|---|
| 135 Bust r. VIRI. R. Figure seated l. *ABC 1244; V. 532; BMC 1420.* | 110 | 575 |
| 136 Naked figure l. R. Laureate bust r., COMMI F. *ABC 1250; V. 533; BMC 1421-49.* | 50 | 200 |

137     138

| 137 VERICA REX, bull r. R. Figure stg. l., COMMI F. *ABC 1235; V. 506; BMC 1450-84.* | 50 | 200 |
|---|---|---|
| 138 COMF, in tablet and scroll. R. Eagle facing, VI RI. *ABC 1226; V. 471; BMC 1485-1505.* | 50 | 200 |
| 139 VIRIC across field, ornaments above and below. R. Pegasus r., star design below. *ABC 1256; V. —; BMC —.* | 90 | 375 |
| 140 Head r. Verica. R. COMMI F., eagle l. *ABC 1253; V. 534; BMC —.* | 100 | 450 |

141     143     146

| 141 **Silver Minim.** COF in tablet, R. Facing head (Medusa?), VE below. *ABC 1271; V. 384; BMC 1506.. (Formerly attributed to Tincommius)* | 50 | 200 |
|---|---|---|
| 142 Head r. R. Horse r., VIRICO. *ABC 1289; V. 480; BMC —.* | 50 | 200 |
| 143 Pellet and ring pattern. R. Lion r. VIR. *ABC 1292; V. 484; BMC 1514-17.* | 45 | 175 |
| 144 VIRIC reversed. R. Boar r. *ABC 1283; V. 485; BMC 1518* | 45 | 175 |
| 145 Cross. R. Trident. *ABC 1295; V. 486-1; BMC —-* | 50 | 200 |
| 146 Uncertain. R. Boar r. *ABC 1280; V. 510-1; BMC —.* | 40 | 160 |
| 147 Crescent cross. R. Boar r. *ABC 1301; V. 510-5; BMC 1521-23.* | 45 | 175 |

148            149            150            152

|       |                                                                                      | F | VF |
|-------|--------------------------------------------------------------------------------------|------|------|
|       |                                                                                      | £ | £ |
| 148   | VIR VAR in tablets. Ɍ. Winged horse r. CO. *ABC 1262; V. 511;* |      |      |
|       | *BMC 1507-12.* .................................................................. | 45 | 175 |
| 149   | Vine-leaf, CFO. Ɍ. Horse r. VERI CA. *ABC 1307; V. 550; BMC 1524-25* | 45 | 175 |
| 150   | CF in torc. Ɍ. Head r. VERIC. *ABC 1310; V. 551; BMC 1526-33.* ......... | 40 | 170 |
| 151   | Altar, CF, Ɍ. Bull's head facing, VERICA. *ABC 1313; V. 552;* |      |      |
|       | *BMC 1534-37.* ................................................................. | 75 | 275 |
| 152   | Temple, CF. Ɍ. Bull r, VER REX. *ABC 1316; V. 553; BMC 1538-41* ..... | 40 | 170 |

153            157            162

| 153   | Cornucopia, VER COM. R. Lion r. *ABC 1319; V. 554; BMC 1542*........ | 45 | 185 |
|-------|--------------------------------------------------------------------------------------|------|------|
| 154   | Two cornucopiae. Ɍ. Eagle l. *ABC 1322; V. 555; BMC 1543-58*............ | 40 | 160 |
| 155   | Floral pattern, CF. Ɍ. Lion r. *ABC 1325; V. 556; BMC 1559-63.* ............ | 45 | 175 |
| 156   | Sphinx r., CF, Ɍ. dog curled up, VERI. *ABC 1328; V. 557;* |      |      |
|       | *BMC 1564-68.* ................................................................. | 40 | 170 |
| 157   | VERI. Ɍ. Urn, COMMI F. *ABC 1286; V. 559; BMC —*........................ | 50 | 200 |
| 158   | A in star. Ɍ. Bird r. *ABC 1133; V. 561; BMC 1569-71* ......................... | 100 | 400 |
| 159   | Urn, Rex. Ɍ. Eagle r., VERRICA COMMI F. *ABC 1331; V. 563;* |      |      |
|       | *BMC 1572-78.* ................................................................. | 30 | 160 |
| 160   | VIR inside tablet. Ɍ. Boars head r. *ABC 1268; V. 564; BMC 1579-81.* .. | 40 | 165 |
| 161   | Cross. Ɍ. bull l. *ABC 1334; V. —; BMC 1582* ....................................... | 45 | 185 |
| 162   | Boars head r., CF, Ɍ. Eagle, VE. *ABC 1337; V. —; BMC 1583-86* ......... | 40 | 160 |
| 163   | Head r, COMM IF., Ɍ. Sphinx, R VE. *ABC 1340; V. —; BMC 1587-89* . | 45 | 185 |
| 164   | A in tablet. Ɍ. Boar r. VI CO. *ABC 1277; V. —; BMC 1590* .................... | 60 | 300 |
|       | *The two following coins are possibly issues of Epatticus.* |      |      |
| 165   | Bull r. Ɍ. Eagle with snake l. *ABC 1358; V. 512; BMC 2366-70* ............. | 45 | 185 |
| 166   | Bust r. Ɍ. dog r. *ABC 1361; V. 558; BMC 2371-74* ................................. | 50 | 200 |

# CANTII

The Cantii, who gave their name to Kent, occupied a similar area to that of the modern county. Caesar considered this the most civilised part of Britain and the early production of potin units in Kent can be seen as indicative of this. A number of Kentish rulers for whom we have coins, appear to be dynasts from the two neighbouring kingdoms, who were involved in struggles to acquire territory. Eppillus (see Atrebates and Regni) produced coins specifically for circulation in Kent and like those of Cunobelin they circulated widely.

## EARLY UNINSCRIBED

| 167   | **Gold Stater.** Ly. Blank. Ɍ. Horse l. numerous ring ornaments in field. |      |      |
|-------|--------------------------------------------------------------------------------------|------|------|
|       | *ABC 183; V. 142; BMC 2472.* ................................................. | 800 | 3250 |
| 168   | Blank. Ɍ. Horse r. numerous ornaments in field. *ABC 294; V. 157;* |      |      |
|       | *BMC—* .................................................................. | 800 | 3250 |

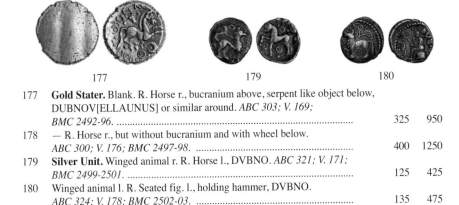

|  |  | F £ | VF £ |
|---|---|---|---|
| 169 | Lz. Blank. R. Horse l., box with cross hatching below. *ABC 177, 180; V. 150, 144; BMC 2466-68.* | 900 | 3500 |
| 170 | **Gold Quarter Stater.** Ly. Blank. R. Horse r., pentagram below. *ABC 309; V. 163; BMC 2473-74.* | 150 | 500 |
| 171 | Blank. R. Horse r., 'V' shape above. *ABC 312; V. 170; BMC 2475-77.* | 145 | 475 |
| 172 | Lz. Blank. R. Horse l., 'V' shape above. *ABC 198; V. 151; BMC 2469-70.* | 135 | 400 |

| 173 | **Silver Unit.** Curved star. R. Horse l. Pentagram below. *ABC 2258; V. 164; BMC —.* | 135 | 400 |
|---|---|---|---|
| 174 | Serpent torc. R. Horse r., box with cross hatching below. *cf Mossop 8; ABC 243; BMC 2478* | 175 | 600 |
| 175 | **Silver Half Unit.** Spiral of three arms. R. Horse l. *ABC 2261; V. —; BMC 2479* | 85 | 325 |
| 176 | **Bronze Unit.** Various animal types, R. Various animal types. *ABC 258, 267, 270, 285, 288, 291; V. 154/167; BMC 2480-91. (80/141-44)* | 50 | 300 |

## INSCRIBED

### DUBNOVELLAUNUS

(Late 1st Century B.C.)

Likely to be the same Dubnovellaunus recorded on coins in Essex (see Trinovantes / Catuvellauni). The two coinages share the same denominational structure and have some stylistic similarities. It has been suggested that Dubnovellaunus is the British king of that name mentioned along with Tincommius as a client king in the Res Gestae of the Roman emperor Augustus.

| 177 | **Gold Stater.** Blank. R. Horse r., bucranium above, serpent like object below, DUBNOV[ELLAUNUS] or similar around. *ABC 303; V. 169; BMC 2492-96.* | 325 | 950 |
|---|---|---|---|
| 178 | — R. Horse r., but without bucranium and with wheel below. *ABC 300; V. 176; BMC 2497-98.* | 400 | 1250 |
| 179 | **Silver Unit.** Winged animal r. R. Horse l., DVBNO. *ABC 321; V. 171; BMC 2499-2501.* | 125 | 425 |
| 180 | Winged animal l. R. Seated fig. l., holding hammer, DVBNO. *ABC 324; V. 178; BMC 2502-03.* | 135 | 475 |

181

| | | F £ | VF £ |
|---|---|---|---|
| 181 | **Bronze Unit.** Horse r. R. Lion l., DVBN. *ABC 342; V. 166; BMC 2504-06.* . | 60 | 250 |
| 182 | Boar l., DVBNO. R. Horseman r. *ABC 348; V. 181; BMC 2507-08.* .......... | 60 | 250 |
| 183 | Boar r., DVBNO. R. Eagle facing. *ABC 345; V. 180; BMC 2509-10.* ..... | 55 | 225 |

## VOSENOS

( Late 1st Century B.C./ Early 1st Century A.D.)

Little is known of this ruler who issued coins in a characteristically Kentish style similar to those of Dubnovellaunus.

184                                                185

| | | | |
|---|---|---|---|
| 184 | **Gold Stater.** Blank. R. Horse l., bucranium above, serpent like object below., [VOSE]NOS. *ABC 357; V. 184; BMC 2511-12.* ..................................... | 2250 | 7000 |
| 185 | **Gold Quarter Stater.** Blank. R. Horse r., VOSI below. *ABC 360; V. 185; BMC 2514-15.* ....................................................................................... | 475 | 1650 |
| 186 | **Silver Unit.** Horse and griffin. R. Horse r., retrograde legend. *ABC 363; V. 186; BMC —.* ....................................................................................... | 200 | 750 |

## "SA" or "SAM"

(Late 1st Century B.C./ Early 1st Century A.D.)

An historically unattested individual whose coins are stylistically associated with those of Dubnovellaunus and Vosenos. His coins have been predominantly found in north Kent

187                                                187B

| | | | |
|---|---|---|---|
| 187 | **Silver Unit.** Head l., R. Horse l., SA below. *ABC 369; V. —; BMC —* .... | 200 | 750 |
| 187A | **Bronze Unit.** Boar l., R. Horse l., SA below. *ABC 375; V. 187; BMC 2516-19.* | 70 | 250 |
| 187B | Horse l., SAM below. R. Horse l., SAM below. *ABC 281; V. —; BMC —* | 75 | 300 |

# AMMINUS
(Early 1st Century A.D.)

Issued a coinage stylistically distinct from other Kentish types and with strong affinities to those of Cunobelin. Indeed it has been suggested that he is the Adminius recorded by Suetonius, as a son of Cunobelin. The enigmatic legend DVN or DVNO may be an unknown mint site.

189

| | | F | VF |
| | | £ | £ |
|---|---|---|---|
| 188 | **Silver Unit.** Plant, AMMINUS around. R. Winged horse r., DVN. *ABC 456; V. 192; BMC 2522-23.* | 125 | 475 |
| 189 | (Last year 190). A in wreath. R. Capricorn r., S AM (I). *ABC 468; V. 194; BMC 2520-21.* | 110 | 425 |
| 190 | **Bronze Unit.** (Last year 189). AM in wreath. R. Horse r., DVNO. *ABC 462; V. 193; BMC — —* | 60 | 250 |
| 191 | Head r. R. Hippocamp r., AM. *ABC 471; V. 195; BMC 2524.* | 70 | 300 |

# TRINOVANTES AND CATUVELLAUNI

Occupying the broad area of Essex, southern Suffolk, Bedfordshire, Buckinghamshire, Hertfordshire, parts of Oxfordshire, Cambridgeshire and Northamptonshire, they are likely to have been two separate tribes for most of their history. The Trinovantes were originally located in the eastern half of this area, with their main centre at Camulodunum (Colchester). The original Catuvellauni heartland was further west, with their main centre at Verulamium (St.Albans). The whole area eventually came under the control of Cunobelin at the end of the period.

## TRINOVANTES

### ADDEDOMAROS
(Late 1st Century B.C.)

Unknown to history, he appears to have been a contemporary of Tasciovanus. The design of his staters is based on the Whaddon Chase type (No.32) which circulated widely in this region.

| 200 | 201 | 202 |

| 200 | **Gold Stater.** Crossed wreath. R. Horse r., wheel below, AθθIIDOM above. *ABC 2514; V. 1605; BMC 2390-94.* | 275 | 900 |
|---|---|---|---|
| 201 | Six armed spiral. R. Horse r., cornucopia below, AθθIIDOM above. *ABC 2517; V. 1620; BMC 2396-2404.* | 250 | 800 |
| 202 | Two opposed crescents. R. Horse r., branch below, spiral or wheel above, AθθDIIDOM. *ABC 2511; V. 1635; BMC 2405-2415.* | 325 | 1100 |

203                                204

| 203 | **Gold Quarter Stater.** Circular flower pattern. R. Horse r. *ABC 2526; V. 1608;* *BMC 2416.* .................. | 165 | 475 |
|-----|------|------|------|
| 204 | Cross shaped flower pattern. R. Horse r. *ABC 2529; V. 1623;* *BMC 2417-21.* .................. | 150 | 400 |
| 205 | Two opposed crescents. R. Horse r., AθθDIIDOM around. *ABC 2520, 2541;* *V. 1638; BMC 2422-24.* .................. | 200 | 650 |
| 206 | **Bronze Unit.** Head l. R. Horse l. *ABC 2544; V. 1615/46 BMC 2450-60.* | 35 | 125 |

## DUBNOVELLAUNUS
(Late 1st Century B.C./ Early 1st Century A.D.)

Dubnovellaunus is likely to have been the successor to Addedomaros, with whom his coins are stylistically related. It is not clear if he was the same Dubnovellaunus who also issued coins in Kent (see Cantii) or if he is the same Dumnobeallaunos mentioned in the Res Gestae of the emperor Augustus c. A.D. 14.

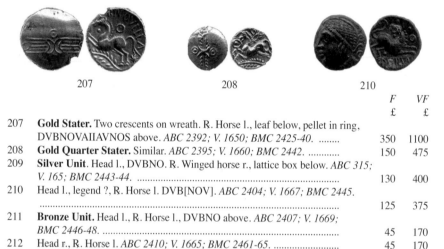

207                          208                          210

|     |      | F £ | VF £ |
|-----|------|------|------|
| 207 | **Gold Stater.** Two crescents on wreath. R. Horse l., leaf below, pellet in ring, DVBNOVAIIAVNOS above. *ABC 2392; V. 1650; BMC 2425-40.* ........ | 350 | 1100 |
| 208 | **Gold Quarter Stater.** Similar. *ABC 2395; V. 1660; BMC 2442.* ............ | 150 | 475 |
| 209 | **Silver Unit.** Head l., DVBNO. R. Winged horse r., lattice box below. *ABC 315;* *V. 165; BMC 2443-44.* .................. | 130 | 400 |
| 210 | Head l., legend ?, R. Horse l. DVB[NOV]. *ABC 2404; V. 1667; BMC 2445.* .................. | 125 | 375 |
| 211 | **Bronze Unit.** Head l., R. Horse l., DVBNO above. *ABC 2407; V. 1669;* *BMC 2446-48.* .................. | 45 | 170 |
| 212 | Head r., R. Horse l. *ABC 2410; V. 1665; BMC 2461-65.* .................. | 45 | 170 |

## DIRAS
(Late 1st Century B.C./ Early 1st Century A.D.)
An historically unattested ruler, responsible for a gold stater related stylistically to Dubnovellaunus's.

213    **Gold Stater.** Blank. R. Horse r., DIRAS? above, yoke like object above.
*ABC 297; V. 162; BMC 2449.* .................................................................. 2250   8500

## CATUVELLAUNI

### TASCIOVANUS
(Late 1st Century B.C./ Early 1st Century A.D.)
The early gold coins of Tasciovanus, like those of his contemporary Addedomaros, are based on the Whaddon Chase stater. Verulamium (St. Albans) appears to have been his principal mint, appearing as VER or VERL on the coinage. Staters and quarter staters inscribed CAM (Camulodunum/ Colchester) are known and perhaps suggest brief or weak control of the territory to the east. The later coins of Tasciovanus use increasingly Romanised designs. The adoption of the title RICON, perhaps a Celtic equivalent to the Latin REX (King), can be seen as a parallel move to that of his contemporary Tincommius to the south.

214               217               219

|  |  | F £ | VF £ |
|---|---|---|---|
| 214 | **Gold Stater.** Crescents in wreath. R. TASCIAV and bucranium over horse r. *ABC 2553; V. 1680; BMC 1591-1603.* ................................... | 425 | 1350 |
| 215 | — R. Similar reads TAXCIAV. *ABC 2550; V. 1682; BMC 1604-05.* ...... | 525 | 1750 |
| 216 | — R. Similar reads TASCIOVAN above, CAM below. *ABC 2559; V. 1684; BMC 1606-07.* ................................................................ | 900 | 3500 |
| 217 | — R. Horseman r. helmeted and with carnyx, TASC in field. *ABC 2562, 2565; V. 1730-32; BMC 1608-1613.* ................................... | 375 | 1250 |
| 218 | Crescents in wreath, with V or VER in design. R. Similar to last. *ABC 2568, 2571; V. 1734-35; BMC 1623-24.* ....................................... | 450 | 1500 |

221               224               226

| 219 | TASCIO(V) RICON in panel. R. Horseman l., wearing armour and holding sword and shield. *ABC 2577, 2580; V. 1780; BMC 1628-36.* .... | 475 | 1750 |
|---|---|---|---|
| 220 | **Gold Quarter Stater.** Floral design. R. Horse r. *ABC 2583; V. —; BMC 1638-39* | 200 | 700 |
| 221 | Crossed Wreath. R. Horse l. *ABC 2586; V. 1688; BMC 1651-53.* ........... | 125 | 350 |
| 222 | — R. Horse r., CAM. *ABC 2589; V. 1694; BMC 1640.* ......................... | 185 | 650 |
| 223 | Similar, TASCI in wreath. R. Horse r., TASC. *ABC 2595; V. 1692; BMC 1641.* ...................................................................................... | 125 | 350 |
| 224 | Similar, VERO in wreath. R. Horse l., TAS. *ABC 2598; V. 1690; BMC 1642-43.* .................................................................................. | 135 | 400 |
| 225 | TASCIO on tablet. R. Horse l. *ABC 444; V. 1848; BMC 1646.* ............. | 375 | 1250 |
| 226 | TASC on tablet. R. Horse l. *ABC 2601; V. 1786; BMC 1647-50.* .......... | 135 | 400 |

| | | F | VF |
|---|---|---:|---:|
| | | £ | £ |
| 227 | **Silver Unit.** Head l. R. Horse r. *ABC 2604; V. 1698; BMC 1654* ........... | 80 | 275 |
| 228 | Cross and box. R. Horse r., VER in front. *ABC 2631; V. —; BMC 1655* . | 80 | 300 |
| 229 | Cross and crescent. R. Horse l., TASCI. *ABC 2607; V. —; BMC 1665-57* | 80 | 275 |
| 230 | Bearded head l. R. Horseman r., TASCIO. *ABC 2610; V. 1745; BMC 1667-68.* ........... | 95 | 375 |
| 231 | Winged horse l., TAS. R. Griffin r., within circle of pellets. *ABC 2649; V. 1790; BMC 1660.* ........... | 85 | 325 |
| 232 | Eagle stg. l., TASCIA. R. Griffin r. *ABC 2646; V. 1792; BMC 1658-59.* | 90 | 350 |
| 233 | VER in beaded circle. R. Horse r., TASCIA. *ABC 2622; V. 1699; BMC 1670-73.* ........... | 90 | 350 |
| 234 | — R. Naked horseman. *ABC 2625; V. 1747; BMC 1674-76.* ........... | 90 | 350 |

235                   238

| 235 | Laureate hd. r., TASCIA. R. Bull l. *ABC 2643; V. 1794; BMC 1681-82.* | 90 | 350 |
|---|---|---:|---:|
| 236 | Cross and box, VERL. R. Boar r. TAS. *ABC 2628; V. 1796; BMC 1661-62.* ........... | 85 | 325 |
| 237 | TASC in panel. R. Winged horse l. *ABC 2637; V. 1798; BMC 1664-65.* | 80 | 300 |
| 238 | — R. Horseman l., carrying long shield. *ABC 2640; V. 1800; BMC 1677-79.* ........... | 90 | 350 |
| 239 | Two crescents. R. Winged griffin, VIR. *ABC 2619; V. —; BMC 1666* .... | 95 | 375 |
| 240 | Head r., TAS?. R. Horseman r. *ABC —; V. —; BMC 1669* ........... | 95 | 375 |

241

| 241 | **Bronze Double Unit.** Head r., TASCIA, VA. R. Horseman r. *ABC 2652; V. 1818; BMC 1685-87.* ........... | 85 | 275 |
|---|---|---:|---:|

242

| 242 | **Bronze Unit.** Two heads in profile, one bearded. R. Ram l., TASC. *ABC 2655; V. 1705; BMC 1711-13.* ........... | 30 | 175 |
|---|---|---:|---:|
| 243 | Bearded head r. VER(L). R. Horse l., VIIR or VER. *ABC 2658; V. 1707; BMC 1714-21.* ........... | 25 | 160 |
| 244 | Bearded head r. R. Horse l., TAS. *ABC 2661; V. 1709; BMC 1722-23.* .. | 30 | 175 |
| 245 | Head r., TASC. R. Winged horse l., VER. *ABC 2664; V. 1711; BMC 1688-89.* ........... | 25 | 160 |
| 246 | — R. Horseman r., holding carnyx, VIR. *ABC 2676; V. 1750; BMC 1724-27.* ........... | 25 | 160 |

247

| | | F £ | VF £ |
|---|---|---|---|
| 247 | VERLAMIO between rays of star. R. Bull l. *ABC 2679; V. 1808; BMC 1745-51.* ...................... | 25 | 150 |
| 248 | Similar without legend. R. Bull r. *ABC 2685; V. 1810; BMC 1752-55.* .. | 30 | 175 |
| 249 | Similar. R. Horse l., TASCI. *ABC 2688; V. 1812; BMC 1709-10.* .......... | 30 | 175 |
| 250 | Head r., TASCIO. R. Lion r., TA SCI. *ABC 2691; V. 1814; BMC 1736-38.* | 25 | 160 |
| 251 | Head r. R. Figure std. l., VER below. *ABC 2751; V. 1816; BMC 1739-44.* | 30 | 175 |
| 252 | Cross and Crescents. R. Boar r., VER. *ABC 2667; V. 1713; BMC 1702-05.* ...................... | 25 | 160 |
| 253 | Laureate head r. R. Horse l., VIR. *ABC 2694; V. 1820; BMC 1706-08.* .. | 25 | 160 |
| 254 | Raised band across centre, VER or VERL below. R. Horse grazing r. *ABC 2673; V. 1717; BMC* —. ...................... | 35 | 185 |
| 255 | **Bronze Fractional Unit.** Animal r. R. Sphinx l. *ABC 2700; V. 1824; BMC 1760-61.* ...................... | 30 | 160 |
| 256 | Head l., VER. R. Goat r. *ABC 2709; V. 1715; BMC 1765-68.* ............... | 25 | 150 |
| 257 | Head r. R. Boar r. *ABC 2712; V. 1826; BMC 1762-64.* ......................... | 25 | 160 |
| 258 | Head l. R. Animal with curved tail. *ABC 2697; V. 1822; BMC 1759.* ..... | 30 | 160 |

## ASSOCIATES OF TASCIOVANUS
### (Early 1st Century A.D.)

Towards the end of his reign, a number of joint issues bearing his name and the name of either Sego or Dias appear. In addition coins similar in style to those of Tasciovanus appear with either the name Andoco or Rues. It has been suggested that these issues belong to a period of struggle following the death of Tasciovanus and are all rival contestants for the throne. Another theory is that they are associates or sub-kings of Tasciovanus responsible for areas within the wider territory.

## SEGO

259

| 259 | **Gold Stater.** TASCIO in tablet, annulets above. R. Horseman with carnyx r., SEGO. *ABC 441; V. 1845; BMC 1625-27.* ............................................. | 1750 | 6500 |
|---|---|---|---|

260

| | | F £ | VF £ |
|---|---|---|---|
| 260 | **Silver Unit.** SEGO on panel. ℞. Horseman r. *ABC 447; V. 1851; BMC 1684.* .............................................................................................. | 375 | 1350 |
| 261 | **Bronze Unit.** Star shaped pattern. ℞. Winged sphinx l., SEGO. *ABC 453; V. 1855; BMC 1690.* ............................................................................................. | 110 | 450 |

## ANDOCO

262

| 262 | **Gold Stater.** Crescents in wreath. ℞. Bucranium over horse r., AND below. *ABC 2715; V. 1860; BMC 2011-14.* ........................................................ | 725 | 2250 |
|---|---|---|---|
| 263 | **Gold Quarter Stater.** Crossed wreaths, ANDO in angles. ℞. Horse l. *ABC 2718; V. 1863; BMC 2015-17.* .............................................................. | 225 | 750 |

264

| 264 | **Silver Unit.** Bearded head l. ℞. Winged horse l., ANDOC. *ABC 2721; V. 1868; BMC 2018.* .............................................................................................. | 110 | 400 |
|---|---|---|---|

265

| 265 | **Bronze Unit.** Head r., ANDOCO. ℞. Horse r., ANDOCO. *ABC 2727; V. 1871; BMC 2019-20.* .......................................................................................... | 40 | 225 |
|---|---|---|---|
| 266 | Head r., TAS ANDO. ℞. Horse r. *ABC 2730; V. 1873; BMC —.* ............. | 50 | 275 |

## DIAS

267                                     268

| 267 | **Silver Unit.** Saltire over cross within square. ℞. Boar r., TASC DIAS. *ABC 2742; V. —; BMC 1663.* ................................................................. | 90 | 300 |
|---|---|---|---|
| 268 | DIAS CO, in star. ℞. Horse l., VIR. *ABC 2739; V. 1877; BMC 1683.* .... | 95 | 325 |

269

| | | F | VF |
| | | £ | £ |

269 **Bronze Unit.** Bearded head r., DIAS TASC. R. Centaur r., playing pan pipes.
*ABC 2748; V. 1882; BMC 1728-35.* ........................................................ 40 250

## RUES

270 **Bronze Unit.** Lion r., RVII. R. Eagle. *ABC 2760; V. 1890; BMC 1691.* . 35 200
271 — R. Similar reads RVE. *ABC 2760; V. 1890-3; BMC 1692.* ................. 30 185

272 273

272 Bearded head r., RVIIS. R. Horseman r., VIR. *ABC 2754; V. 1892;*
*BMC 1698-1701.* ....................................................................... 30 185
273 RVIIS on tablet. R. Winged sphinx l. *ABC 2757; V. 1895;*
*BMC 1693-97.* .......................................................................... 30 185
274 **Bronze Fractional Unit.** Annulet within square with curved sides. R.
Eagle l.,RVII. *ABC 2763; V. 1903; BMC 1756-58.* ................................ 35 200

## CUNOBELIN
### (Early 1st Century A.D. to *c.* A.D. 40)

Styled as son of Tasciovanus on some of his coins, Cunobelin appears to have ruled over the unified territories of the Trinovantes and Catuvellauni, with additional territory in Kent. His aggressive policy of expansion that involved members of his family eventually led to Roman concern over the extent of his power. Following his death just prior to A.D. 43, the emperor Claudius took the decision to invade Britain.

During his long reign an extensive issue of gold, silver and bronze coins used ever increasingly Romanised designs. It has been estimated from a study of known dies that around one million of his gold corn ear staters were produced. His main centre and mint was at Camulodunum (Colchester) appearing as the mint signature CAMV. The names SOLIDV and AGR appear on a few coins associated with Cunobelin and are likely to represent personal names.

280 281

280 **Gold Stater.** Biga type. CAMVL on panel. R. Two horses l., wheel below,
CVNOBELIN. *ABC 2771; V. 1910; BMC 1769-71.* .............................. 725 2250
281 Linear type. Corn ear dividing CA MV. R. Horse r., branch above., CVN.
*ABC 2774; V. 1925; BMC 1772-76.* ........................................................ 325 850

|     |                                                                                                                                                  |  F £ |  VF £ |
|-----|--------------------------------------------------------------------------------------------------------------------------------------------------|------|-------|
| 282 | — Similar, privy mark 'x' above a letter in *obv*. legend. *ABC 2774; VA 1925-3/5; BMC 1777-81.* ................................................. | 450  | 1350  |

283                                   285

| 283 | Wild type. Corn ear dividing CA MV. R̶. Horse r., branch above., CVN(O). *ABC 2783; V. 1931/33; BMC 1784-92/1804-08.* ..................... | 325 | 850  |
|-----|------------------------------------------------------------------------------------------------------------------------------------------------|-----|------|
| 284 | — Similar, heart shaped object between horses forelegs. *ABC 2780; V. 1931-3; BMC 1793.* ............................................... | 575 | 2000 |
| 285 | — Similar, privy mark pellet or pellet triangle above a letter(s) in *obv*. legend. *ABC 2777; V. 1931-5/7/9; BMC 1797-1803.* ............... | 325 | 900  |

286                                   288

| 286 | Plastic type. Corn ear dividing CA MV. R̶. Horse r., branch above., CVNO. *ABC 2786, 2792; V. 2010-1/3/5; BMC 1809-11/15-23.* ............ | 300 | 800  |
|-----|------------------------------------------------------------------------------------------------------------------------------------------------|-----|------|
| 287 | — Similar, 'B' in front of horse. *ABC 2789; V. 2010-7; BMC 1813.* ...... | 525 | 1850 |

289                                   290

| 288 | Classic type. Corn ear dividing CA MV. R̶. Horse r., branch above., CVNO. *ABC 2795, 2798; V. 2025/27; BMC 1827-31/33.* ................... | 450 | 1350 |
|-----|------------------------------------------------------------------------------------------------------------------------------------------------|-----|------|
| 289 | — Similar, horse l., lis like object above. *ABC 2804; V. 2029; BMC 1834-35.* ............................................................... | 575 | 2000 |
| 290 | **Gold Quarter Stater.** Biga type. Similar to 280. *ABC 2807; V. 1913; BMC 1836/A.* ............................................................. | 300 | 975  |

292                                   296

| 292 | Linear type. Similar to 281. *ABC 2810; V. 1927; BMC 1837-42.* .......... | 150 | 450 |
|-----|---------------------------------------------------------------------------|-----|-----|
| 293 | Wild type. Similar to 283. *ABC 2813; V. 1935; BMC 1843-44.* .............. | 150 | 450 |
| 294 | Plastic type. Similar to 286. *ABC 2816; V. 2015; BMC 1846-48.* .......... | 135 | 425 |
| 295 | — Similar but corn ear dividing CAM CVN. *ABC 2819; V. 2017; BMC 1845.* ................................................................. | 175 | 575 |
| 296 | Classic type. Similar to 288. *ABC 2822; V. 2038; BMC —.* .................. | 200 | 650 |

299

| | | F | VF |
| | | £ | £ |

299 **Silver Unit.** Two bull headed serpents, inter twined. R. Horse l., CVNO.
*ABC 2831; V. 1947; BMC 1856.* ................................................................ 90 450

300 Curled serpent inside wheel. R. Winged horse l., CVN. *ABC 2834; V. —;*
*BMC 1857* ......................................................................................... 90 450

301 CVN on panel R. Dog l., (C)M. *ABC 2846; V. 1949; BMC 1858-59.* ..... 80 350

302 CVNO BELI on two panels. R. CVN below horseman r. *ABC 2858, 2861;*
*V. 1951/53; BMC 1862.* ......................................................................... 75 300

303 Head l., CAMVL. R. CVNO beneath Victory std. r. *ABC 2855; V. 2045;*
*BMV 1863-65.* ...................................................................................... 80 325

304                 305

304 Two leaves dividing CVN. R. Horseman r., CAM. *ABC 2888; V. 2047;*
*BMC 1866-67.* ....................................................................................... 75 300

305 Flower dividing CAMV. R. CVNO below horse r. *ABC 2885; V. 2049;*
*BMC1867A.* ........................................................................................... 85 400

306 CVNO on panel. R. CAMV on panel below griffin. *ABC 2897; V. 2051;*
*BMC 1868-69.* ....................................................................................... 80 350

307 CAMVL on panel. R. CVNO below centaur l. carrying palm. *ABC 2828;*
*V. 1918; BMC —.* ................................................................................. 80 350

308 CAMVL on panel. R. Figure seated l. holding wine amphora, CVNOBE.
*ABC 2849; V. —; BMC —.* ................................................................. 75 300

309 Plant, CVNOBELINVS. R. Figure stg. r. holding club and thunderbolt
dividing CA MV. *ABC 2906; V .—; BMC 1897.* ................................... 85 400

310 Laur. hd. r., CVNOBELINVS. R. Winged horse springing l., CAMV
below. *ABC 2909; V. —; BMC —.* ....................................................... 85 400

311 CVNO on panel, wreath around. R. Winged horse r., TASC F. *ABC 2876;*
*V. 2053; BMC 1870.* .............................................................................. 85 375

312                 313

312 Head r., CVNOBELINI. R. Horse r., TASCIO. *M. ABC 2873; V. 2055;*
*BMC 1871-73.* ....................................................................................... 75 300

313 Winged bust r., CVNO. R. Sphinx std. l., TASCIO. *ABC 2870; V. 2057;*
*BMC 1874-78.* ....................................................................................... 60 240

314                                    316                                    318

|     |                                                                                                                      | F £ | VF £ |
|-----|----------------------------------------------------------------------------------------------------------------------|-----|------|
| 314 | Draped female fig. r., TASCIIOVAN. R. Figure std. r. playing lyre, tree behind. *ABC 2867; V. 2059; BMC 1879-82.* | 70  | 275  |
| 315 | Figure stg. l., holding club and lionskin., CVNO. R. Female rider r., TASCIOVA. *ABC 2864; V. 2061; BMC 1884-85.* | 70  | 275  |
| 316 | Female head r., CVNOBELINVS. R. Victory r., TASCIO(VAN). *ABC 2882; V. —; BMC 1883.* | 70  | 275  |
| 317 | Fig. r. carrying dead animal, CVNOBELINVS. R. Fig. stg. holding bow, dog at side, TASCIIOVANI. *ABC 2879; V. 2063; BMC 1886-88.* | 75  | 300  |
| 318 | CVNO on panel, horn above, dolphin below. R. Fig. stg. r. altar behind. *ABC 2900; V. 2065; BMC 1889-90.* | 85  | 400  |
| 319 | CVN on panel. R. Fig. holding club walking r., CVN. *ABC 2840; V. 2067; BMC 1891-92.* | 85  | 400  |
| 320 | CVN in wreath. R. CAM, dog? trampling on serpent r. *ABC 2891; V. 2069; BMC 1893.* | 90  | 450  |
| 321 | Winged horse l., CVN. R. Std. fig. r. *ABC 2903; V. 2071; BMC 1896.* | 85  | 425  |
| 322 | CVNO in angles of cross. R. Capricorn r., CVNO. *ABC 2843; V. —; BMC 1898* | 85  | 400  |
| 323 | **Bronze Unit.** Head l., CVNO. R. Boar l., branch above. *ABC 2993; V. 1969; BMC—.* | 40  | 175  |
| 324 | CVNOB ELINI in two panels. R. Victory std. l., TASC. *ABC 2918; V. 1971; BMC 1921-27.* | 30  | 150  |
| 325 | Winged horse l., CAM. R. Winged Victory stg l., CVN. *ABC 2921; V. 1973; BMC 1938-43.* | 35  | 175  |

326

|     |                                                                                                                      | F £ | VF £ |
|-----|----------------------------------------------------------------------------------------------------------------------|-----|------|
| 326 | Bearded head facing R. Boar l., CVN. *ABC 2912; V.1963; BMC 1904-05.* | 40  | 175  |
| 327 | Ram-headed animal coiled up in double ornamental circle. R. Animal l., CAM. *ABC 2915; V. 1965; BMC —.* | 40  | 175  |
| 328 | Griffin r., CAMV. R. Horse r., CVN. *ABC 2945; V. 2081; BMC 1909-12.* | 35  | 160  |
| 329 | Bearded head l., CAMV. R. CVN or CVNO below horse l. *ABC 2951; V. 2085/2131; BMC 1900-01.* | 35  | 160  |
| 330 | Laureate head r., CVNO. R. CVN below bull butting l. *ABC 2948; V. 2083; BMC 1902-03.* | 40  | 175  |
| 331 | Crude head r., CVN. R. Figure stg. l., CVN. *ABC —; V. 2135; BMC —.* | 40  | 200  |

332

|  | | F | VF |
|---|---|---|---|
|  | | £ | £ |
| 332 | CAMVL / ODVNO in two panels. ℞. CVNO beneath sphinx crouching l. ABC 2924; V. 1977; BMC 1928-30. ............. | 35 | 160 |
| 333 | Winged horse l., CAMV. ℞. Victory stg. r. divides CV NO. ABC 2927; V. 1979; BMC 1931-34. ............. | 35 | 160 |
| 334 | Victory walking r. ℞. CVN below, horseman r. ABC 2930; V. 1981; BMC 1935. ............. | 40 | 175 |
| 335 | Head l., CAM. ℞. CVNO below eagle. ABC 2954; V. 2087; BMC −. ... | 40 | 175 |

336         337

| 336 | Head l., CVNOBELINI. ℞. Centaur r., TASCIOVANI.F. ABC 2957; V. 2089; BMC 1968-71. ............. | 30 | 150 |
|---|---|---|---|
| 337 | Helmeted bust r. ℞. TASCIIOVANII above, sow stg. r., F below. ABC 2960; V. 2091; BMC 1956-60. ............. | 30 | 150 |
| 338 | Horseman galloping r. holding dart and shield, CVNOB. ℞. Warrior stg. l., TASCIIOVANTIS. ABC 2963; V. 2093; BMC 1961-67. ............. | 30 | 150 |

339         340

| 339 | Helmeted bust l., CVOBELINVS REX. ℞. TASC FIL below boar l., std. on haunches. ABC 2933; V. 1983; BMC 1952-55. ............. | 35 | 160 |
|---|---|---|---|
| 340 | Bare head r., CVNOBELINVS REX. ℞. TASC below bull butting r. ABC 2966; V. 2095; BMC 1944-51. ............. | 30 | 150 |
| 341 | Bare head l., CVNO. ℞. TASC below bull stg. r. ABC 2996; V. 1985; BMC −. ............. | 40 | 175 |

342         343

| 342 | Head l., CVNOBELIN. ℞. Metal worker std. r. holding hammer, working on a vase, TASCIO. ABC 2969; V. 2097; BMC 1972-83. ............. | 35 | 160 |
|---|---|---|---|
| 343 | Winged horse r., CVNO. ℞. Victory r. sacrificing bull, TASCI. ABC 2972; V. 2099; BMC 1913-19. ............. | 30 | 135 |
| 344 | CVNO on panel within wreath. ℞. CAMV below horse, prancing r. ABC 2975; V. 2101; BMC 1987-90. ............. | 35 | 160 |

345                                              346

|     |                                                                                                    | F | VF |
|-----|----------------------------------------------------------------------------------------------------|---|----|
|     |                                                                                                    | £ | £  |
| 345 | Bearded head of Jupiter Ammon l., CVNOBELIN. ℞. CAM below horseman galloping r. *ABC 2978; V. 2103; BMC 1984-86.* ...... | 40 | 175 |
| 346 | Janus head, CVNO below. ℞. CAMV on panel below, sow std. r. beneath a tree. *ABC 2981; V. 2105; BMC 1998-2003.* ......... | 35 | 175 |

347

| 347 | Bearded head of Jupiter Ammon r., CVNOB. ℞. CAM on panel below lion crouched r. *ABC 2984; V. 2107; BMC 1991-97.* ......... | 35 | 175 |
|-----|----------------------------------------------------------------------------------------------------|-----|-----|
| 348 | Sphinx r., CVNO. ℞. Fig stg. l. divides CA M. *ABC 2987; V. 2109; BMC 2004-09.* ......... | 35 | 175 |
| 349 | Horse r. ℞. CVN below horseman r. *ABC 2936; V. 1987; BMC 1936-47.* ... | 40 | 185 |
| 350 | Animal l. looking back. ℞. CVN below horse l. *ABC 2990; V. 1967; BMC—.* ......... | 40 | 175 |
| 350A | Ship, CVN below. ℞. Fig. r. dividing S E. *ABC 2939; V. 1989; BMC 2010.* | 150 | 800 |

## "SOLIDV"

351

| 351 | **Silver Unit.** SOLIDV in centre of looped circle. ℞, Stg. fig. l., CVNO. *ABC 474; V. 2073; BMC 1894-95.* ......... | 275 | 850 |
|-----|----------------------------------------------------------------------------------------------------|-----|-----|

## "AGR"

352                                   353

| 352 | **Gold Quarter Stater**. Corn ear dividing CAM CVN. ℞. Horse r., branch above., AGR below. *ABC 3002; V. —; BMC 1854* ......... | 325 | 1100 |
|-----|----------------------------------------------------------------------------------------------------|-----|------|
| 353 | — ℞. Horse r., branch above., cross and A below. *ABC 2999; V. —; BMC 1855* ......... | 350 | 1250 |

354

| | | F | VF |
|---|---|---|---|
| | | £ | £ |
| 354 | **Silver Unit.** AGR inside wreath. ℞. Female dog r., AGR below. *ABC 3005; V. —;* | | |
| | *BMC 1899* ........................................................................................... | 250 | 900 |

## EPATICCUS
### (1st Half 1st Century A.D.)

Epaticcus, styled as a son of Tasciovanus on his coins, was most probably a brother of Cunobelin. The corn ear employed on his staters is similar to those his brother produced at Colchester. His coins appear in northern Atrebatic territory and conform to the area's denominational structure. It seems likely that Epaticcus's coinage reflects an incursion into Atrebatic territory by the Trinovantian/ Catuvellaunian dynasty.

355

| 355 | **Gold Stater.** Corn ear dividing TAS CIF. ℞. Horseman r., with spear and shield. EPATI. *ABC 1343; V. 575; BMC 2021-23.* ................................... | 1000 | 3750 |

356                                          357

| 356 | **Silver Unit.** Head of Hercules r., EPAT(I). ℞. Eagle stg. on snake. *ABC 1346; V. 580; BMC 2024-2268/2270-76.* ......................................... | 30 | 125 |
| 357 | Victory seated r. TASCIOV. ℞. Boar r., EPAT. *ABC 1349; V. 581; BMC 2294-2328.* ................................................................................... | 35 | 150 |

358

| 358 | Bearded head l., TASCIO. ℞. EPATI below lion r. *ABC 1352; V. 582; BMC 2329* | 95 | 425 |
| 359 | EPATI inside panel. ℞. Lion r. *ABC 1355; V. 583; BMC 2330.* ............... | 90 | 400 |

360 (x1.5)                     361 (x1.5)

| 360 | **Silver Minim.** EPATI. ℞. Boars head r., TA. *ABC 1370; V. 585; BMC 2331-46.* | 30 | 140 |
| 361 | TA inside star. ℞. Winged horse r., EPA below. *ABC 1367; V. 560; BMC 2351-57.* ................................................................................ | 30 | 150 |
| 362 | Helmeted head r. ℞. Horse r., E below. *ABC 1364; V. —; BMC 2358-63* | 30 | 150 |
| 363 | EPATI. ℞. Winged horse r., cross below. *ABC 1373; V .—; BMC 2365...* | 35 | 175 |

# CARATACUS
## (1st Half 1st Century A.D.)

Coins inscribed CARA have been traditionally associated with the historically attested son of Cunobelin, Caratacus the leader of British resistance against Rome. His coins appear in the same area as those of Epaticcus and he may have been his successor.

|            | 364 |            |  364A (x1.5) |         |
|------------|-----|------------|--------------|---------|

|       |                                                                                      | F<br>£ | VF<br>£ |
|-------|--------------------------------------------------------------------------------------|--------|---------|
| 364   | **Silver Unit.** Head of Hercules r., CARA. R. Eagle stg. on snake. *ABC 1376; V. 593; BMC 2376-84.* ............ | 125    | 525     |
| 364A  | **Silver Minim.** CARA around pellet in ring. R. Winged horse r. *ABC 1379; V. 595; BMC 2385-89.* ............ | 85     | 350     |

# DUROTRIGES
## (Mid 1st Century B.C. to Mid 1st Century A.D.)

The Durotriges inhabited West Hampshire, Dorset and adjoining parts of Somerset and Wiltshire. Their coinage is one of the most distinctive in Britain due to its rapid debasement. The disappearance of precious metals from the coinage should perhaps be linked to the declining trade between the south-west and western Gaul, following the Roman conquest of the Gaul. Hengistbury Head is the probable mint site of the cast bronzes. Coins inscribed CRAB have been traditionally associated with the tribe.

## UNINSCRIBED

|     |                                                                 |     |     |
|-----|-----------------------------------------------------------------|-----|-----|
| 365 | **Silver Stater.** White Gold type. Derived from Westerham stater (no. 21). *ABC 2157; V. 1235, 52, 54, 55; BMC 2525-2731.* ............ | 110 | 425 |

|            | 366 |            |  368 |         |
|------------|-----|------------|------|---------|

|     |                                                                 | F   | VF  |
|-----|-----------------------------------------------------------------|-----|-----|
| 366 | Silver type. Similar. *ABC 2169; V. 1235, 52, 54, 55; BMC 2525-2731.* . | 60  | 200 |
| 367 | Billon type. Similar. *ABC 2166; V. 1235, 52, 54, 55; BMC 2525-2731,* , | 20  | 75  |
| 368 | **Silver Quarter Stater.** Geometric type. Crescent design. R. Zig-zag pattern. *ABC 2205, 2208, 2211, 2214, 2217; V. 1242/29; BMC 2734-79.* . *Quality of metal varies, obv.almost blank on later issues* ............ | 25  | 90  |

369                              371

|     |                                                                                                                    | F | VF |
|-----|--------------------------------------------------------------------------------------------------------------------|------|------|
|     |                                                                                                                    | £ | £ |
| 369 | Starfish type. Spiral. R. Zig-zag pattern. *ABC 2220; V. 1270; BMC 2780-81* | 50 | 225 |
| 370 | Hampshire Thin Flan type. Crude head of lines and pellets. R. Stylised horse l. *ABC 911; V. 1280; BMC 2782-87.* ................................ | 75 | 350 |
| 371 | **Bronze Stater.** Struck Bronze type. Similar to No.365-67. *ABC 2175; V. 1290; BMC 2790-2859.* ........................................................................ | 20 | 50 |

372

| 372 | Cast Bronze type. Many varities, as illustration. *ABC 2178, 2181, 2184, 2187, 2190, 2193, 2196, 2199; V. 1322-70; BMC 2860-2936.* ................ | 25 | 125 |

## INSCRIBED

### "CRAB"

373

| 373 | **Silver Unit.** CRAB in angles of cross. R. Eagle. *ABC 1385; V. 1285; BMC 2788.* ........................................................................................ | 225 | 750 |
| 373A | **Silver Minim.** CRAB on tablet. R. Star shape. *ABC 1388; V. 1286; BMC 2789.* ........................................................................................ | 125 | 375 |

# DOBUNNI

(Mid 1st Century B.C. to Mid 1st Century A.D.)

Dobunnic territory stretched over Gloucestershire, Hereford and Worcester and into parts of Somerset, Wiltshire and Gwent. The earliest Dobunnic coins are developed from the British Q stater, and have the distinctive tree-like motif of the tribe on the obverse. The inscribed coinage is difficult to arrange chronologically and it may be that some of the rulers named held different parts of the territory simultaneously.

## UNINSCRIBED

374
374 (variant)

375

|  | | F £ | VF £ |
|---|---|---|---|
| 374 | **Gold Stater.** Plain except for tree-like object. R. Triple tailed horse r., wheel below. *ABC 2003; V. 1005; BMC 2937-40.* | 650 | 2750 |
| 375 | **Gold Quarter Stater.** Plain with traces of wreath pattern. R. Horse r. *ABC 2009; V. 1010-3; BMC 2942-46.* | 175 | 475 |
| 376 | Wreath pattern. R. Horse l., pellet in ring motifs in field. *ABC 2105; V. 1015; BMC 2949.* | 175 | 500 |

377

378

| | | | |
|---|---|---|---|
| 377 | **Silver Unit.** Allen types A-F/I-J. Regular series. Head r. R. Triple tailed horse l. or r. *ABC 2012, 2015, 2018, 2021, 2024, 2027, 2036; V. 1020/45/49/74/78/95/ 1135/1137; BMC 2950-3011. (63-64). Style becomes progressively more abstract, from-* | 45 | 200 |
| 378 | Allen types L-O. Irregular series. Similar to last. *ABC 2030, 2122, 2125, 2137, 2140; V. 1170-85; BMC 3012-22. (63-64)* | 50 | 225 |

## INSCRIBED

The following types are not arranged chronologically.

### ANTED

379

| | | | |
|---|---|---|---|
| 379 | **Gold Stater.** Dobunnic emblem. R. ANTED or ANTEDRIG over triple tailed horse r., wheel below. *ABC 2066, 2069; V. 1062-69; BMC 3023-3031.* | 450 | 1650 |

| | F | VF |
|---|---|---|
| | £ | £ |

380  **Silver Unit.** Crude head r. R. ANTED over horse. *ABC 2072; V. 1082; BMC 3032-38.* ...................................................................................   35   160

## EISV

381                              382

381  **Gold Stater.** Dobunnic emblem. R. EISV or EISVRIG over triple tailed horse r., wheel below. *ABC 2078; V. 1105; BMC 3039-42.* ..............................   525  1850

382  **Silver Unit.** Crude head r. R. Horse l., EISV. *ABC 2081, 2084; V. 1110; BMC 3043-55.* ......................................................................................   35   150

## INAM or INARA

383  **Gold Stater.** Dobunnic emblem. R. INAM or INARA over triple tailed horse r., wheel below. *ABC 2060; V. 1140; BMC 3056.* ..........................  1250  5000

## CATTI

384

384  **Gold Stater.** Dobunnic emblem. R. CATTI over triple tailed horse r., wheel below. *ABC 2057; V. 1130; BMC 3057-60.* ...........................................   400  1500

## COMUX

385

385  **Gold Stater.** Dobunnic emblem. R. COMVX retrograde, over triple tailed horse r., wheel below. *ABC 2054; V. 1092; BMC 3061-63.* .....................  1100  4250

## CORIO

386                                              387

|     |                                                                                                                                                               | F £ | VF £ |
| --- | --- | --- | --- |
| 386 | **Gold Stater.** Dobunnic emblem. ℞. CORIO over triple tailed horse r., wheel below. *ABC 2048; V. 1035; BMC 3064-3133.* ......................................... | 375 | 1350 |
| 387 | **Gold Quarter Stater.** COR in centre. ℞. Horse r., without legend. *ABC 2051; V. 1039; BMC 3134.* ................................................................. | 350 | 1250 |

## BODVOC

388                                              389

|     |                                                                                                                         | F £ | VF £ |
| --- | --- | --- | --- |
| 388 | **Gold Stater.** BODVOC across field. ℞. Horse r., without legend. *ABC 2039; V. 1052; BMC 3135-42.* .......................................................... | 750 | 3250 |
| 389 | **Silver Unit.** Head l., BODVOC. ℞. Horse r., without legend. *ABC 2042; V. 1057; BMC 3143-45.* ...................................................................... | 125 | 400 |

# CORIELTAUVI

The Corieltauvi, formerly known as the Coritani, occupied Lincolnshire and adjoining parts of Yorkshire, Northamptonshire, Leicestershire and Nottinghamshire. The earliest staters, the South Ferriby type, are developed from Gallo-Belgic C staters, and are associated with the silver Boar/ Horse types. The distinctive dish shaped scyphate coinages have no parallels in Britain and stand apart from the main series. The later inscribed issues present a complex system of inscriptions. It has been suggested that some of the later inscriptions refer to pairs of names, possibly joint rulers or moneyers and rulers.

### EARLY UNINSCRIBED
(Mid to Late 1st Century B.C.)

390

|     |                                                                                                                                                                                                               |     |     |
| --- | --- | --- | --- |
| 390 | **Gold Stater.** South Ferriby type. Crude laureate head. ℞. Disjointed horse l., rosette or star below, anchor shape and pellets above. *ABC 1737, 1743, 1746, 1752; V. 809-815/19; BMC 3146-3179.* ......................................... | 175 | 450 |

393      394      395

| | F £ | VF £ |
|---|---|---|
| 391   Wheel type. Similar, but wheel below horse. *ABC 1749; V. 817; BMC 3180* | 425 | 1350 |
| 392   Kite type. Similar to 390, but diamond shape containing pellets above, spiral below horse. *ABC 1761; V. 825; BMC 3181-84.* .......................... | 225 | 650 |
| 393   Domino type. Similar to last, but with rectangle containing pellets. *ABC 1758; V. 829; BMC 3185-86.* ........................................................ | 185 | 500 |
| 394   Trefoil type. Trefoil with central rosette of seven pellets. ℞. Similar to 390. *ABC 1755; V. 821; BMC —.* | 1250 | 5250 |
| 395   North Lincolnshire Scyphate type. Stylised boar r. or l. ℞. Large S symbol with pellets and rings in field. *ABC 1764, 1770, 1773; V. —; BMC 3187-93* ............................................................................... | 185 | 500 |

*\* chipped or cracked specimens are often encountered and are worth less*

396      398      399

| | F £ | VF £ |
|---|---|---|
| 396   **Silver Unit.** Boar/Horse type I. Boar r., large pellet and ring motif above, reversed S below. ℞. Horse l. or r., pellet in ring above. *ABC 869, 1779, 1782, 1785, 1791, 1797; V. 855-60, 864, 867; BMC 3194-3214.* ............ | 50 | 250 |
| 397   Boar Horse type II. Vestiges of boar on obv. ℞. Horse l. or r. *ABC 1800; V. 875-877; BMC 3214-27.* ........................................................ | 30 | 120 |
| 398   Boar Horse type III. Blank. ℞. Horse l.or r. *ABC 1803, 1806, 1812, 1815; BMC 3228-35.* ............................................................................... | 20 | 75 |
| 399   **Silver Fractional Unit.** Similar to 396-97. *ABC 1827, 1836; V. 862/66; BMC 3236-3250.* ........................................................................ | 25 | 80 |
| 400   Similar to 398. *ABC 1833; V. 877-81; BMC 3251-55. (70/71)* ............... | 20 | 70 |
| 401   Pattern/Horse. Flower pattern. ℞. Horse l. *ABC 1606; V. —; BMC 3256-57.* | 65 | 300 |

# INSCRIBED
(Early to Mid 1st Century A.D.)
The following types are not arranged chronologically.

## AVN COST

402                              403

|  |  | F | VF |
|---|---|---|---|
|  |  | £ | £ |
| 402 | **Gold Stater.** Crude wreath design. R. Disjointed horse l., AVN COST. *ABC 1929;V. 910; BMC 3258.* ..................... | 325 | 1350 |
| 403 | **Silver Unit.** Remains of wreath or blank. R. AVN COST, horse l. *ABC 1935, 1938; V. 914; BMC 3261-66.* ................. | 25 | 100 |
| 403A | **Silver Unit.** Inscription between three lines. R. Horse l. AVN. *ABC —; V-; BMC —.* | 75 | 225 |
| 404 | **Silver Fractional Unit.** Similar. *ABC 1953; l V. 918; BMC 3267-68.* ... | 30 | 90 |

## ESVP RASV

405

| 405 | **Gold Stater.** Crude wreath design. R. Disjointed horse l., IISVP RASV. *ABC 1917; V. 920; BMC 3269.* ................ | 275 | 1000 |
|---|---|---|---|
| 406 | **Silver Unit.** Similar. *ABC 1920; V. 924; BMC 3272-73.* ........ | 40 | 150 |

## VEP

407

| 407 | **Gold Stater.** Blank or with traces of wreath. R. Disjointed horse l., VEP. *ABC 1851; V. 905; BMC 3274-75.* ......... | 375 | 1500 |
|---|---|---|---|
| 408 | **Silver Unit.** Blank or with traces of wreath. R. VEP, horse r. *ABC 1866; V. 963; BMC 3277-82.* .............. | 30 | 125 |
| 409 | **Silver Half Unit.** Similar. *ABC 1887; V. 967; BMC 3283-3295.* ........... | 25 | 100 |

## VEP CORF

410                                  412

|   |   | F £ | VF £ |
|---|---|---|---|

410 **Gold Stater.** Crude wreath design. R. Disjointed horse l., VEP CORF.
*ABC 1854, 1857, 1860, 1863; V. 930/40/60; BMC 3296-3304.* .............. 225 800

411 **Silver Unit.** Similar. *ABC 1869, 1878, 1881; V. 934/50;*
*BMC 3305-14.* ...................................................................................... 30 125

412 Similar but VEPOC (M)ES, pellet in ring below horse. *ABC 1869; V. 955;*
*BMC —.* ................................................................................................... 35 145

413 **Silver Half Unit.** Similar. *ABC 1890, 1893, 1896, 1899, 1902, 1908;*
*V. 938/58; BMC 3316-24. (293/95)* ........................................................ 30 100

## DVMNO TIGIR SENO

414                                  415

414 **Gold Stater.** DVMN(OC) across wreath. R. Horse l., TIGIR SENO. *ABC 1971;*
*V. 972; BMC 3325-27.* ........................................................................... 475 1850

415 **Silver Unit.** DVMNOC in two lines. R. Horse r., TIGIR SENO. *ABC 1974;*
*V. 974; BMC 3328-29.* ........................................................................... 110 450

## VOLISIOS DVMNOCOVEROS

416

416 **Gold Stater.** VOLISIOS between three lines in wreath. R. Horse r. or l.,
DVMNOCOVEROS. *ABC 1980; V. 978-80; BMC 3330-3336.* ............. 300 1100

417 **Silver Unit.** Similar. R. Horse r., DVMNOCO. *ABC 1983; V. 980;*
*BMC 3339.* .............................................................................................. 125 500

418 **Silver Half Unit.** Similar. *ABC 1986; V. 984; BMC 3340-41.* ................ 65 225

## VOLISIOS DVMNOVELLAUNOS

419

|  |  | F £ | VF £ |
|---|---|---|---|
| 419 | **Gold Stater.** VOLISIOS between three lines in wreath. R. Horse r. or l., DVMNOVELAVNOS. *ABC 1995; V .988; BMC 3342-43.* ..................... | 325 | 1350 |
| 420 | **Silver Half Unit.** As last but DVMNOVE. *ABC 1998; V. 992; BMC 3344-46.* | 90 | 350 |

## VOLISIOS CARTIVEL

| 420A | **Gold Stater.** VOLISIOS between three lines in wreath. R. Horse l. CARTILLAVNOS. *ABC —; VA 933; BMC —..* ....................................... | 950 | 4000 |
|---|---|---|---|
| 421 | **Silver Half Unit.** VOLISIOS between three lines in wreath. R. Horse r., CARTILEV. *ABC 1992; V. 994; BMC 3347-48.* .................................... | 185 | 700 |

## IAT ISO E

| 422 | **Silver Unit.** IAT ISO (retrograde) on tablet, rosettes above and below. R. Horse r., E above. *ABC 1959; V. 998; BMC 3349-51.* ............................ | 95 | 400 |
|---|---|---|---|

## CAT

| 422A | **Silver Unit.** Boar r., pellet ring above, CAT above. R. Horse r. *ABC 1845; V. —; BMC 3352* ...................................................................................... | 200 | 750 |
|---|---|---|---|

## LAT ISON

423

| 423 | **Gold Stater.** LAT ISO(N) in two lines retrograde. R. Horse r., ISO in box above, N below. *ABC 1956; V. —; BMC —. Only recorded as an AE/AV plated core, as illustrated.* ....................................................................... | *Extremely rare* |
|---|---|---|

# ICENI

The Iceni, centred on Norfolk but also occupying neighbouring parts of Suffolk and Cambridgeshire, are well attested in the post conquest period as the tribe who under Boudicca revolted against Roman rule. Their earliest coins are likely to have been the British J staters, Norfolk Wolf type (no.30/31), replaced around the mid first century B.C. by the Snettisham, Freckenham and Irstead type gold staters and quarter staters. Contemporary with these are silver Boar/Horse and Face/Horse units and fractions. The introduction of legends around the beginning of the millennia led to the adoption of a new obverse design of back to back crescents. The continuation of the coinage after the Roman invasion is attested by the coins of King Prasutagus. Some of the Face/Horse units (no.434) have been attributed to Queen Boudicca but this attribution is uncertain.

## EARLY UNINSCRIBED
(Mid to Late 1st Century B.C.)

424

|  | | F £ | VF £ |
|---|---|---|---|
| 424 | **Gold Stater.** Snettisham type. Blank or with traces of pellet cross. R. Horse r., serpent like pellet in ring motif above. *ABC 1402, 1405; V.—; BMC 3353-59* | 525 | 1750 |
| 425 | Similar. Blank or with three short curved lines. R. Horse r., symbol above more degraded. *ABC 1408, 1411; V. —; BMC 3360-83* | 325 | 1000 |

426

427

| 426 | Freckenham type. Two opposed crescents with stars or pellets in field. R. Horse r., various symbols in field. *ABC 1441, 1444, 1447, 1450; V. 620; BMC 3384-89.* | 300 | 950 |
|---|---|---|---|
| 427 | Similar. Blank or with traces of pellet cross. R. Horse r., wheel or arch containing pellets above. *ABC 1414, 1417, 1420; V. 624; BMC 3390-95.* | 325 | 1100 |

428

| 428 | Similar. Trefoil on cross design. R. Similar. *ABC 1423, 1426, 1432, 1435; V. 626; BMC 3396-3419.* | 300 | 950 |
|---|---|---|---|

<table>
<tr><td></td><td></td><td>F<br>£</td><td>VF<br>£</td></tr>
</table>

|  |  | F<br>£ | VF<br>£ |
|---|---|---|---|
| 429 | **Gold Quarter Stater.** Snettisham type. Wreath cross. R. Horse r. *ABC 1462;* *V. —; BMC 3420-35*.................. | 125 | 375 |
| 430 | Irstead type. Hatched box, wreaths at sides. R. Horse r. *ABC 1474, 1480;* *V. 628; BMC 3436-39.* ................ | 120 | 350 |
| 431 | **Silver Unit.** Boar / Horse type. Boar r. R. Horse r. *ABC 1576, 1579, 1582;* *V. 655-59; BMC 3440-3512.* ................. | 30 | 135 |
| 432 | Bury type. Head l. or r. R. Horse l. or r. *ABC 1495, 1498, 1501; V. —;* *BMC 3524-35*........ | 70 | 300 |
| 433 | Early Face / Horse type. Celticised head l. or r. R. Horse l. or r. *ABC 1522, 1525, 1531, 1537, 1540, 1546, 1549, 1552, 1555, 1558; BMC 3536-3555.* ..... | 75 | 325 |
| 434 | Face / Horse Regular type. Head r. R. Horse r. *ABC 1564, 1567; V. 790-94; BMC 3556-3759. Attributed to Queen Boudicca by R.D. van Arsdell* ..... | 45 | 200 |
| 435 | Early Pattern / Horse type. Cross of two opposed crescents. R. Horse l. or r. *ABC 1588, 1591; V. 675-79; BMC 3763-74.* ................... | 30 | 120 |

|  |  | | |
|---|---|---|---|
| 436 | ECEN symbol type. Two opposed crescents. R. Horse r. *ABC 1678, 1681;* *V. 752; BMC 4297-4325* ........................ | 25 | 85 |

|     |                                                                 | F £ | VF £ |
|-----|-----------------------------------------------------------------|-----|------|

437 **Silver Half Unit.** Boar / Horse type. Similar to 431. *ABC 1621, 1624; V. 661; BMC 3513-20.* ........................................................................    25    85

438 **Silver Fractional Unit.** Early Pattern / Horse type. Similar to 435. *ABC 1612, 1693; V. 681-83; BMC 3775-89. (76/A)* .................................    30   120

## INSCRIBED
(Early to Mid 1st Century A.D.)
The following types are not arranged chronologically.

### CAN DVRO

439

439 **Silver Unit.** Boar. R. Horse r., CAN(S) above, DVRO below. *ABC 1630; V. 663; BMC 3521-23.* .............................................................................    75   325

### ANTED

440

440 **Gold Stater.** Triple crescent design. R. Horse r., ANTED monogram below. *ABC 1639; V. 705; BMC 3790.* ...............................................................   575  2250

441

441 **Silver Unit.** Two opposed crescents. R. Horse r., ANTED. *ABC 1642, 1645; V. 710-11/15; BMC 3791-4025.* ..............................................................    25    90

442 **Silver Fractional Unit.** Similar to last. *ABC 1648; V. 720; BMC 4028-31.*    30   110

## ECEN

443

|  | | F £ | VF £ |
|---|---|---|---|
| 443 | **Gold Stater.** Triple crescent design. Ŗ. Horse r., ECEN below. *ABC 1651; V. 725; BMC 4032.* | 725 | 2500 |
| 443A | **Silver Unit.** Two opposed crescents. Ŗ, Horse r., ECEN. *ABC 1657; V. 730; BMC 4033-4215.* | 35 | 125 |
| 443B | **Silver Half Unit.** Similar to last. *ABC 1684; V. 736; BMC 4216-17.* | 25 | 100 |

## EDN

| 444 | **Silver Unit.** Two opposed crescents. Ŗ, Horse r., ED, E, EI or EDN. *ABC 1672, 1675; V. 734/40; BMC 4219-81.* | 30 | 120 |
|---|---|---|---|

## ECE

| 444A | **Gold Stater** Triple crescent design R. Horse r., ECE. *ABC − ; V. − ; ..* | 850 | 3250 |
|---|---|---|---|

445

| 445 | **Silver Unit.** Two opposed crescents. Ŗ, Horse r., ECE. *ABC 1660, 1663, 1666, 1669; V. 761-66; BMC 4348-4538. (278-80)* | 25 | 100 |
|---|---|---|---|

## SAENU

| 446 | **Silver Unit.** Two opposed crescents. R. Horse r., SAENV. *ABC 1699; V. 770; BMC 4540-57.* | 35 | 135 |
|---|---|---|---|

## AESU

447

| 447 | **Silver Unit.** Two opposed crescents. Ŗ. Horse r., AESV. *ABC 1702; V. 775; BMC 4558-72.* | 35 | 135 |
|---|---|---|---|

## ALE SCA

| 448 | **Silver Unit.** Boar r., ALE. Ŗ. Horse r., SCA. *ABC 1708; V. 996; BMC 4576* | 175 | 750 |
|---|---|---|---|

## AEDIC SIA

| | F £ | VF £ |
|---|---|---|

449 **Silver Unit.** AEDIC in two lines. ℞. Horse r., SIA? below. *ABC 1633; V.—;* *BMC 4581* ......................................................................................... 250 950

## PRASUTAGUS

450

450 **Silver Unit.** Romanised head l., SUB RII PRASTO. ℞. Rearing horse r., ESICO FECIT. *ABC 1711; V. 780; BMC 4577-80.* ................................. 575 2500
*This legend translates as "Under King Prasto, Esico made me", giving the name of both King and moneyer.*

The systematic conquest of Britain by the Romans began in A.D. 43 when the Emperor Claudius (41-54), anxious to enhance his military reputation, authorised an invasion in which he personally participated, albeit in a purely symbolic role. The initial military contact between the two cultures had taken place almost a century before when Julius Caesar, during the course of his conquest of Celtic Gaul, led expeditions to the island in 55 and 54 B.C. Although no actual Roman occupation of Britain resulted from Caesar's reconnoitring campaigns, commercial intercourse was certainly accelerated, as evidenced by the 'Romanisation' of the British Celtic coinage in the final decades of its production.

The Claudian conquest, commencing in A.D. 43, brought about a complete change in the nature of the currency circulating in Britain and ushered in a period lasting more than three and a half centuries during which Roman coinage was the only official medium of exchange. Local copies of the money brought with them by the four legions of the invading army began to appear at a very early stage, the most popular type for imitation being the well-known Claudian copper as with reverse type fighting Minerva. Some of these copies are well-executed and of a style not much inferior to the prototype, suggesting that their local minting may have been officially sanctioned by the Roman government in order to make good a shortage of currency in the newly-conquered territory. Other examples are of much poorer style and execution and are frequently well below the normal weight of a Claudian as (usually between 10 and 11 grams). These copies must have been issued unofficially and provide evidence of the huge demand for this type of currency in a population which had never before experienced the benefits of having base metal coins available for small everyday transactions.

In the decades that followed, the boundaries of the Roman province of Britannia were continually pushed further north and west until, under the celebrated Flavian governor Gnaeus Julius Agricola, the Roman army even penetrated to northern Scotland (A.D. 83/4). A few years later, under Trajan, the northern frontier was established along the Tyne-Solway line, a barrier made permanent by the construction of Hadrian's Wall following the emperor's visit to the province in 122. For a brief period in the mid-2nd century the frontier was temporarily advanced to the Forth-Clyde line with the building of the Antonine Wall, though this seems to have been abandoned early in the reign of Marcus Aurelius (ca. 163) when the Hadrianic barrier was re-commissioned and became the permanent frontier. The security thus provided to the now-peaceful province in the south facilitated urban expansion and the development of commerce. The new prosperity brought a flood of Roman coinage into the island-province and it was no longer necessary for shortages to be made good by large scale local imitation.

Until the mid-3rd century the production of Roman coinage remained the prerogative of the mint in the capital, with only occasional issues from provincial centres to serve short-term local needs. But with the deepening political and economic crisis in the third quarter of the century there was a dramatic decentralisation of minting operations, with permanent establishments being set up in many important cities in the western as well as the eastern provinces. Britain, however, still remained without an official mint at this time and in the dark days of the 270s, when the separatist Gallic Empire to which Britain belonged was close to collapse, large scale production of imitative antoniniani (commonly called 'barbarous radiates') occurred in the province. The integrity and prestige of the Empire was, to some extent, restored by a rapid succession of Illyrian 'soldier emperors', until the situation was finally stabilised by Diocletian (A.D. 284-305) who established the tetrarchy system under which governmental responsibility was shared by four rulers. By the end of the 3rd century Britain had been reorganised into a civil diocese of four provinces: it had already been subdivided into Britannia Superior and Britannia Inferior almost a hundred years before, under Septimius Severus or Caracalla.

It was left to the colourful and enigmatic usurper Carausius (A.D. 287-293) to establish mints in Britain. It was, of course, vital for him to do so as his dominion was mostly confined to the island-province. Londinium (London) was his principal mint, with a secondary establishment at a place usually signing itself 'C' (probably Camulodunum, modern Colchester). After the downfall of Carausius' murderer and successor Allectus (293-296) Britain was restored to the central government, an event commemorated by the celebrated gold medallion of Constantius I showing the Caesar riding alongside the Thames approaching the gateway of the city of Londinium. At this point the mysterious 'C' mint disappears from the picture. Londinium, on the other hand, retained its status as an official mint under Diocletian's tetrarchy and its successors down to A.D. 325, when it was closed by Constantine the Great who regarded it as superfluous to his needs. In nearly four decades of existence as a Roman mint Londinium had produced a varied and extensive coinage in the names of almost all the emperors, empresses and Caesars of the period. It was destined never again to be active during Roman times, unless the extremely rare gold and silver issues of the late 4th century usurper Magnus Maximus, signed AVG, AVGOB and AVGPS, are correctly attributed to Londinium under its late Roman name of Augusta.

The termination of Roman rule in the British provinces is traditionally dated to A.D. 410 when the emperor Honorius, in response to an appeal for aid from his British subjects, told them to arrange for their own defence as best they might ('Rescript of Honorius'). In reality, the end probably came quite gradually. As the machinery of government ground to a halt and the soldiers stopped receiving their pay there would have been a steady drift of population away from the semi-ruinous cities and military installations to the countryside, where they could better provide for themselves through farming. Under these conditions the need for coinage would have been drastically reduced, as a primitive economy based on barter would largely have replaced the complex monetary economy of the late Roman period. In any case the supply of coinage from the Continent would now have dried up. The few monetary transactions which still took place were made with worn-out coins from earlier periods augmented by local imitations, production of which in Britain had resumed in the mid-4th century. Such was the pitiful end of the long tradition of Roman coinage in the remote island-province of Britannia. More than two centuries of 'Dark Ages' were to elapse before England's new rulers, the Anglo-Saxons, commenced the issue of gold thrymsas, the designs of many of which were based on late Roman types.

As Rome's Imperial coinage provided the currency needs of this country over a period of almost four centuries no representative collection of British coins is complete without some examples of these important issues. The following listing is divided into four categories: 1. Regular Roman issues, all of which would have been legal tender in Britain after A.D. 43; 2. Issues with types referring specifically to the province of Britannia, usually in commemoration of military campaigns in the north; 3. Official Roman coinage struck in Britain; 4. Imitations of Roman coins produced in Britain, all but possibly some of the earliest being of unofficial origin. The reference 'R.R.C.' is to the listing of the type in Michael Crawford's *Roman Republican Coinage* (Cambridge, 1974); and 'R.I.C.' to *Roman Imperial Coinage* (Spink, London, 1923-2019, in ten volumes).

For more detailed collectors' information on Roman coinage, including a more comprehensive listing of types, the reader is referred to *Roman Coins and their Values Volumes I to V* by David R. Sear. A complete catalogue of silver issues may be found in the 5 volumes of *Roman Silver Coins* (H.A. Seaby and C.E. King) which provides a quick and convenient reference and is especially aimed at the collector. Gilbert Askew's *The Coinage of Roman Britain* (2nd edition) concentrates on those issues which are particularly associated with the Roman province of Britannia, but does not provide valuations. Other works on this subject include R. Reece's *Coinage in Roman Britain* and *The Coinage of Roman Britain,* and also David R. Sear's *The History and Coinage of the Roman Imperators, 49—27 BC* which is devoted to the vital two decades of transition from Republic to Empire. Some of these titles are now out of print, but many can be bought via Spink Books, www.spinkbooks.com, or by emailing books@spink.com.

The standard works on the coinages of the Roman Republic and the Roman Empire have already been mentioned *(Roman Republican Coinage and Roman Imperial Coinage).* These monumental publications are essential to the advanced collector and student and their importance cannot be overstated. The British Museum Catalogues are also vital. They contain superb interpretive material in their introductions and are very fully illustrated. A similar work is Anne S. Robertson's *Roman Imperial Coins in the Hunter Coin Cabinet,* in 5 volumes (volume 4 is especially important for the later 3rd century coinage). For more general reading we may recommend J.P.C. Kent and M. & A. Hirmer's *Roman Coins,* undoubtedly the most lavishly illustrated book on the subject; C.H.V. Sutherland's *Roman Coins;* and R.A.G. Carson's *Coins of the Roman Empire.* Finally, for a most useful single-volume work on interpretation and background information, we would suggest *A Dictionary of Ancient Roman Coins* by John Melville Jones.

# 1. REGULAR ROMAN ISSUES

A token selection of the types of Roman coins which might be found on Romano-British archaeological sites. Many of the rarer emperors and empresses have been omitted and the types listed often represent only one of hundreds of variant forms which might be encountered.

|  |  | *F* £ | *VF* £ |
|---|---|---|---|
| 451 | **THE REPUBLIC: P. Aelius Paetus** (moneyer), 138 B.C. Æ *denarius*. Helmeted hd. of Roma r. Rev. The Dioscuri galloping r. R.R.C. 233/1 ... *Although dating from long before the Roman conquest many Republican coins circulated well into the Imperial period and found their way to Britain where they are often represented in early hoards.* | 40 | 120 |
| 452 | **L. Thorius Balbus** (moneyer), 105 B.C. Æ denarius. Hd. of Juno Sospita r., clad in goat's skin. Rev. Bull charging r. *R.R.C. 316/1.* ....................... | 45 | 130 |
| 453 | **Q. Antonius Balbus** (moneyer), 83-82 B.C. Æ *denarius*. Laur. hd. of Jupiter r. Rev. Victory in quadriga r. *R.R.C. 364/1.* .................................. | 45 | 130 |

454                                        455B

| 454 | **C. Calpurnius Piso** (moneyer), 67 B.C. Æ *denarius*. Laur. hd. of Apollo r. Rev. Horseman galloping r., holding palm-branch. *R.R.C. 408/1a.* ...... | 45 | 130 |
|---|---|---|---|
| 455 | **Mn. Acilius Glabrio** (moneyer), 49 B.C. Æ *denarius*. Laur. hd. of Salus r. Rev. Valetudo stg. l., holding snake and resting on column. *R.R.C. 442/1.* | 40 | 120 |
| 455A | **Pompey the Great** (imperator) 49-48 BC. Æ *denarius*. Diademed head of Numa r. Rev. MAGN PRO COS. Prow of galley r. *R.R.C. 446/1.* ........... | 220 | 550 |
| 455B | **Scipio** (imperator) 47-46 BC, Æ *denarius*. Laureate head of Jupiter r. Rev. SCIPIO IMP. Elephant r. *R.R.C. 459/1.* ............................................ | 125 | 300 |
| 455C | **Pompey Junior** (imperator) 46-45 BC. Æ *denarius*. Helmeted head of Roma r. Rev. CN MAGNVS IMP. Hispania stg r presenting palm branch to Pompeian soldier. *RRC 469/1a.* ................................................................ | 160 | 380 |
| 455D | **Sextus Pompey** (imperator) 45-36 BC. Æ *denarius*. Bare head of Pompey. Rev. Neptune stg l between brothers Anapias and Amphinomus. *R.R.C. 511/3a.* | 360 | 925 |
| 455E | **Julius Caesar** (dictator), visited Britain 55 and 54 B.C., died 44 B.C. *N aureus.* Veiled head of Vesta r. Rev. A. HIRTIVS PR. Jug between lituus and axe. *R.R.C. 466/1.* ................................................................................................ | 1500 | 3600 |

456                                        456B

| 456 | Æ *denarius*. CAESAR. Elephant r. Rev. Priestly emblems. *R.R.C. 443/1.* | 230 | 575 |
|---|---|---|---|
| 456A | — Wreathed hd. of Caesar r. Rev. P. SEPVLLIVS MACER. Venus stg. l., holding Victory and sceptre. *R.R.C. 480/9.* .............................................. | 700 | 1750 |
| 456B | Head of Venus. Rev CAESAR. Aeneas l bearing his father Anchises on shoulder. *R.R.C. 458/1.* ........................................................................ | 160 | 375 |

456F

|  | | F £ | VF £ |
|---|---|---|---|

456C Head of Venus r. Rev. CAESAR. Trophy of Gallic arms between seated
captives. *R.R.C. 468/1* ............................................................................. 175 400

456D **Brutus** (imperator) 42 BC. Æ *denarius*. Head of Apollo r. Rev. BRVTVS IMP.
Trophy. *R.R.C. 506/2.* .................................................................... 260 625

456E **Cassius** (imperator) 42 BC. Æ *denarius*. Head of Libertas. Rev. LENTVLVS
SPINT. Jug and lituus. *R.R.C. 500/3* .............................................. 180 450

456F **Ahenobarbus** (imperator) 41-40 BC. Æ *denarius*. Bare head r. Rev. CN
DOMITIVS IMP. Prow of galley r, surmounted by trophy. *R.R.C. 519/2.* 360 900

457 **Mark Antony** (triumvir), died 30 B.C. Æ *denarius*. Galley r. Rev. LEG. II.
Legionary eagle between two standards. *R.R.C. 544/14.* ....................... 140 350

457A Head of Antony r. Rev. CAESAR DIC. Head of Caesar r. *R.R.C. 488/2.* 360 950

457B Bare head of Antony. Rev. CAESAR IMP PONT III VIR RPC. Bare head
of Octavian. *R.R.C. 517/2* .................................................................... 260 625

457C **Cleopatra VII** 34 BC Æ *denarius*. Bust of Cleopatra r. Rev. ANTONI
ARMENIA DEVICTA. Head of Antony r. *R.R.C. 543/1.* ....................... 2900 6750

458 459

458 **Octavian** (triumvir), named Augustus 27 B.C. Æ *denarius*. Bare hd. of
Octavian r. Rev. IMP. CAESAR. Trophy set on prow. *R.I.C. 265a.* .......... 180 450

458A **THE EMPIRE: Augustus,** 27 B.C.-A.D. 14. *N aureus*. Rev. IMP XII ACT.
Apollo stg r, holding lyre. *R.I.C. 192a.* .................................................... 2000 4800

459 Æ *denarius*. Rev. C. L. CAESARES AVGVSTI F COS DESIG PRINC IVVENT.
The emperor's grandsons, Gaius and Lucius, stg. facing, with spears and shields.
*R.I.C. 207.* ................................................................................................ 140 325

*Almost all the coins in the Roman Imperial series have a head or bust of the
emperor, empress or prince as their obverse type. Therefore, in most instances
only the reverses will be described in the following listings.*

459A — Rev IMP X. Bull butting r. *R.I.C. 167a.* ............................................. 175 450

460 Æ *as.* ROM. ET AVG. The altar of Lugdunum. *R.I.C. 230.* .................... 85 220

460A Æ *quadrans.* Obv. Anvil. Rev. Moneyers' inscription around large S. C.
*R.I.C. 443.* ................................................................................................ 25 60

461 **Augustus and Agrippa,** general and designated heir of Augustus, died
12 B.C. Æ *dupondius.* Obv. Their hds. back to back. Rev. COL. NEM.
Crocodile r., chained to palm-branch. *R.I.C. 159.* .................................... 120 280

*See also no. 468.*

461A **Gaius Caesar,** 17 BC, grandson of Augustus. Æ *denarius*. Rev. AVGVST.
Candelabrum within floral wreath. *R.I.C. 539* ........................................ 425 1200

464

|      |                                                                                 | F £  | VF £ |
|------|---------------------------------------------------------------------------------|------|------|

462    **Divus Augustus,** deified A.D. 14. Æ as. PROVIDENT S. C. Large altar.
       *R.I.C. 81.* .................................................................................    85    220
463    **Tiberius,** A.D. 14-37. *N aureus.* PONTIF MAXIM. Livia (?) seated r.,
       holding sceptre and branch. *R.I.C. 29.* .................................................    1300    3000
464    *R denarius.* Similar. *R.I.C. 30.* .................................................    160    400
       *This type is commonly referred to as the 'Tribute Penny' of the Bible (Matthew
       22, 17-21).*
464A   *Æ sestertius.* Tiberius seated l. Rev Inscription around large S. C. *R.I.C. 48.*    300    875
464B   *Æ as.* Inscription around large S. C. *R.I.C. 44.* ...............................    80    200
465    **Livia,** wife of Augustus, mother of Tiberius. *Æ dupondius.* Obv. Veiled bust of
       Livia as Pietas r. Rev. Inscription of Drusus Caesar around large S. C. *R.I.C. 43.*    170    450
466    **Drusus,** son of Tiberius. *Æ as.* Inscription around large S. C. *R.I.C. 45.*    85    230
466A   **Caligula,** A.D. 37-41. *N aureus.* Rev. SPQR/PP/OBCS in three lines within
       oak wreath. R.I.C. 27. ...............................................................    4000    10000
466B   *R denarius,* SPQR/PP/OBCS in three lines within oak wreath, *R.I.C. 28.*    750    2200
466C   *Æ sestertius.* Rev. ADLOCVT COH. Caligula stg l on platform, haranguing
       soldiers. *R.I.C. 40.* .................................................................    425    1300

467

467    *Æ as.* VESTA S. C. Vesta seated l. *R.I.C. 38.* .................................    110    350

468

468    **Agrippa,** grandfather of Caligula, died 12 B.C. *Æ as.* S. C. Neptune stg.
       l., holding dolphin and trident. *R.I.C. 58.* .................................    95    250
       *See also no. 461 and under Category 4.*

|  | F | VF |
|---|---|---|
|  | £ | £ |

469 **Germanicus,** father of Caligula, brother of Claudius, died A.D. 19. Æ *as.*
Inscription of Caligula around large S. C. *R.I.C. 35.* ............................... 90 230

470 **Agrippina Senior,** mother of Caligula, died A.D. 33. Æ *sestertius.* S.P.Q.R.
MEMORIAE AGRIPPINAE. Carpentum drawn l. by two mules. *R.I.C. 55.* 500 1800

470A **Claudius,** A.D. 41-54, initiated the conquest of Britain by his invasion in
A.D. 43. $A$ *aureus* Rev. EX SC/OBCIVES/SERVATOS in three lines within
oak wreath. *R.I.C. 15.* ............. 2100 5400

470B $R$ *denarius.* PACI AVGVSTAE, winged Nemesis advancing r, snake at feet.
*R.I.C. 52.* ................ 475 1350

470C Æ *sestertius.* Rev. SPES AVGVSTA SC. Spes walking l, holding flower.
*R.I.C. 115. (see also no 744)* ................. 270 780

471

474

471 Æ *as.* LIBERTAS AVGVSTA S. C. Libertas stg. r., holding pileus.
*R.I.C. 113.* ................ 80 220

471A Æ *quadrans.* Obv. Hand holding scales. Rev. Inscription around large
S. C. *R.I.C. 85.* ................. 30 60
*See also under Categories 2 and 4.*

472 **Nero Claudius Drusus,** father of Claudius, died 9 B.C. Æ *sestertius.*
TI. CLAVDIVS CAESAR AVG. P. M. TR .P. IMP. P. P. S. C. Claudius seated
l. on curule chair amidst arms. *R.I.C. 109.* ............................ 300 1100
*See also under Category 4.*

473 **Antonia,** mother of Claudius, died A.D. 37. Æ *dupondius.* TI. CLAVDIVS
CAESAR AVG P.M. TR. P. IMP. S. C. Claudius stg. l., holding simpulum.
*R.I.C. 92.* ................ 130 380
*See also under Category 4.*

474 **Nero,** 54-68, emperor at the time of Queen Boudicca's rebellion in Britain.
$A$ *aureus.* SALVS. Salus seated l. *R.I.C. 66.* ........................ 1350 3400

475 $R$ *denarius.* IVPPITER CVSTOS. Jupiter seated l. *R.I.C. 53.* ............... 150 440

476 Æ *sestertius.* ROMA S. C. Roma seated l., holding Victory and parazonium.
*R.I.C. 274.* ................ 325 1200

476A Æ *as.* S. C. Victory hovering l., holding shield inscribed S. P. Q. R. *R.I.C. 312.* 90 260

476B **Civil Wars** (Gaul). $R$ *denarius.* Clasped hands. Rev. FIDES PRAETOR
IANORUM. Clasped r hands. R.I.C. 121. ............................... 325 900

476C **Galba,** 68-69. $A$ *aureus.* Rev. SPQR/OB CS in two lines within oak
wreath. *R.I.C. 164* ................ 2800 7000

477 $R$ *denarius.* S.P.Q.R. / OB / C.S. within oak-wreath. *R.I.C. 167.* ............... 200 550

477A **Otho,** 69. $A$ *aureus.* Rev. SECVRITAS PR. Securitas stg l, holding wreath
and sceptre. *R.I.C. 7.* ................ 4600 11500

478 $R$ *denarius.* SECVRITAS P. R. Securitas stg. l. *R.I.C. 10.* ..................... 375 1000

478A **Vitellius,** 69. $A$ *aureus.* Rev. CONCORDIA PR. Concordia seated l, holding
patera and cornucopiae. *R.I.C. 72* ................ 3000 7500

|     |                                                                                                                                                                                                                                              |  F<br>£ |  VF<br>£ |
|-----|------|------|------|
| 479 | Æ denarius. CONCORDIA P. R. Concordia seated l. *R.I.C. 90*. ............. | 200 | 500 |
| 480 | **Vespasian,** 69-79, commanded Legio II in the Claudian invasion of Britain (43) and appointed Agricola to governorship of the province in 77/8. *N aureus.* ANNONA AVG. Annona seated l. *R.I.C. 131a*. ........................................ | 1100 | 2900 |

481

| 481  | Æ *denarius.* VICTORIA AVGVSTI. Victory advancing r., crowning standard. *R.I.C. 52.* ............. | 50 | 120 |
|------|------|------|------|
| 481A | Æ *sestertius*. Rev. JVDAEA CAPTA SC. Palm tree with standing Jewish captive r and female captive seated r. *R.I.C. 424* ..................................... | 550 | 1600 |
| 481B | Æ *dupondius.* FELICITAS PVBLICA S. C. Felicitas stg. l. *R.I.C. 554*... | 60 | 175 |
| 481C | **Titus,** 79-81 (Caesar 69-79). *N aureus.* Rev. TRP VIIII IMP XIIII COS VII PP. Venus stg r resting on column. *R.I.C. 9.* ..................... | 1600 | 3800 |
| 482  | Æ *denarius.* TR. P. IX. IMP. XV. COS. VIII. P. P. Thunderbolt on throne. *R.I.C. 23a.* ................................ | 100 | 275 |
| 482A | **Julia Titi,** daughter of Titus and mistress of Domitian. Æ *denarius.* Rev. VENVS AVGVST. Venus stg r resting on column. *R.I.C. 56* .................. | 350 | 950 |
| 482B | **Domitian,** 81-96 (Caesar 69-81), recalled Agricola in 83/4 and abandoned the conquest of northern Scotland (ca. 87). *N aureus.* Rev. GERMANICVS COS XV. Minerva stg l holding spear. *R.I.C. 163.* ........................................... | 1500 | 3600 |

483                                                485

| 483  | Æ *denarius.* IMP. XIX. COS. XIIII. CENS. P. P. P. Minerva stg. l., resting on spear. *R.I.C. 140.* .......................................... | 60 | 175 |
|------|------|------|------|
| 483A | Æ *sestertius.* Rev. IOVI VICTORI SC. Jupiter seated l, holding Victory and sceptre. *R.I.C. 358.* ................................ | 180 | 475 |
| 484  | Æ *dupondius.* VIRTVTI AVGVSTI S. C. Virtus stg. r. *R.I.C. 393.* ......... | 55 | 150 |
| 484A | Æ *as.* MONETA AVGVSTI S. C. Moneta stg. l. *R.I.C. 354b.* ................. | 55 | 150 |
| 484B | **Domitia,** wife of Domitian. Æ *denarius.* Rev CONCORDIA AVGVST. Peacock stg r. *R.I.C. 212* ..................................... | 575 | 1600 |
| 484C | **Nerva,** 96-98. *N aureus.* Rev. CONCORDIA EXERCITVVM. Clasped r hands. *R.I.C. 14.* ................................ | 2500 | 5600 |
| 485  | Æ denarius. AEQVITAS AVGVST. Aequitas stg. l. *R.I.C. 13.* ................. | 95 | 260 |
| 485A | Æ *as.* LIBERTAS PVBLICA S. C. Libertas stg. l. *R.I.C. 86* .................. | 80 | 250 |
| 486  | **Trajan,** 98-117, established the northern frontier in Britain along the Tyne-Solway line (ca. 100). *N aureus.* P. M. TR. P. COS. VI. P. P. S. P. Q. R. Genius stg. l., holding patera and corn-ears. *R.I.C. 347.* ........................ | 1400 | 3500 |

487        489

|  | F £ | VF £ |
|---|---|---|

487   Æ *denarius.* COS. V. P. P. S. P. Q. R. OPTIMO PRINC. Military trophy.
*R.I.C. 147.* .............................................................................................   50   130

488   Æ *sestertius.* S. P. Q. R. OPTIMO PRINCIPI S. C. Spes walking l.,
holding flower. *R.I.C. 519.* ......................................................................   95   400

488A   Æ *dupondius.* SENATVS POPVLVSQVE ROMANVS S. C. Emperor
advancing between two trophies. *R.I.C. 676.* .........................................   65   150

489   **Hadrian,** 117-138, visited Britain in 122 and initiated the construction of
a fortified frontier line (Hadrian's Wall). Ν *aureus.* HISPANIA. Hispania
reclining l. *R.I.C. 305.* ...............................................................................   1600   4000

490   Æ *denarius.* P. M. TR. P. COS. III. Roma stg. l., holding Victory and spear.
*R.I.C. 76.* ...................................................................................................   60   175

491   Æ *sestertius.* COS. III. S. C. Neptune stg. r., holding dolphin and trident,
foot on prow. *R.I.C. 632.* .........................................................................   100   400

491A   Æ *as.* FELICITATI AVG COS. III. P. P. S. C. Galley travelling l. over waves.
*R.I.C. 719.* .................................................................................................   65   170
     *See also under Category 2.*

492   **Sabina,** wife of Hadrian. Æ *denarius.* IVNONI REGINAE. Juno stg. l.
*R.I.C. 395a.* ...............................................................................................   75   190

493   **Aelius Caesar,** heir of Hadrian, 136-138. Æ *denarius.* CONCORD. TR.
POT. COS. II. Concordia seated l. *R.I.C. 436.* .......................................   125   320

493A   Æ *as.* TR. POT. COS. II. S. C. Spes walking l., holding flower. *R.I.C. 1067.*   80   220

494   **Antoninus Pius,** 138-161, ordered the expansion of the Roman province to
include southern Scotland and constructed the Antonine Wall on the Forth-Clyde
line (beginning ca. 143). An uprising in northern Britain in the 150s resulting in a
permanent withdrawal to the Hadrianic frontier early in the next reign.
Ν *aureus.* COS. IIII. Togate emperor stg. l., holding globe. *R.I.C. 233b.*   1300   3000

495   Æ *denarius.* PIETATI AVG. COS. IIII. Pietas stg. l. between two children,
holding two more in her arms. *R.I.C. 313c.* .............................................   40   100

496

496   Æ *sestertius.* SALVS AVG. S. C. Salus stg. l. at altar, feeding snake.
*R.I.C. 635.* .................................................................................................   80   275

496A   Æ *dupondius.* TR. POT. XX. COS. IIII. S. C. Providentia stg. l., pointing
at globe at her feet and holding sceptre. *R.I.C. 2025.* ...............................   45   110
     *See also under Categories 2 and 3.*

|     |     | F  | VF |
|-----|-----|----|----|
|     |     | £  | £  |

497  **Antoninus Pius and Marcus Aurelius Caesar**. Æ *denarius*. Obv. Laur.
hd. of Antoninus Pius r. Rev. AVRELIVS CAESAR AVG PII F. COS. Bare
hd. of young Marcus Aurelius r. *R.I.C. 417a*. ......................................... 140  320

498                                                                      501

498  **Divus Antoninus Pius,** deified 161. Æ *denarius*. CONSECRATIO.
Four-storeyed crematorium of Antoninus Pius. *R.I.C. 436*. ................... 45  110
499  **Diva Faustina Senior,** wife of Antoninus Pius, deified 141. Æ *denarius*.
AETERNITAS. Aeternitas stg. l., holding globe and billowing veil. *R.I.C. 351*. 40  100
499A  Æ *sestertius*. AVGVSTA S. C. Ceres stg. l., holding two torches. *R.I.C. 1120*. 65  190
500  **Marcus Aurelius,** 161-180 (Caesar 139-161), re-established Hadrian's Wall
as the permanent northern frontier of the province, ca. 163. *N aureus*.
PROV. DEOR. TR. P. XV. COS. III. Providentia stg. l., holding globe and
cornucopiae. *R.I.C. 19*. ............................................................... 1500  3400
501  Æ *denarius*. PIETAS AVG. Priestly emblems. *R.I.C. 424a*. .................. 45  120
501A  — SALVTI AVG. COS. III. Salus stg. l. at altar, feeding snake. *R.I.C. 222*. 45  120
502  Æ *sestertius*. CONCORD. AVGVSTOR. TR. P. XVI. COS. III. S. C. Marcus
Aurelius and Lucius Verus stg. face to face, clasping hands. *R.I.C. 826*.. 100  450
502A  Æ *as*. HONOS TR. POT. II. COS. II. S. C. Honos stg. r. *R.I.C. 1271a*. .. 45  150
503  **Divus Marcus Aurelius,** deified 180. Æ *denarius*. CONSECRATIO.
Eagle stg. r. on altar. *R.I.C. 272*. ................................................ 45  110

504                                                     506A

504  **Faustina Junior,** daughter of Antoninus Pius, wife of Marcus Aurelius.
Æ *denarius*. FECVNDITAS. Fecunditas stg. r., holding sceptre and child.
*R.I.C. 677*. .................................................................................. 40  100
504A  Æ *sestertius*. HILARITAS S. C. Hilaritas stg. l. *R.I.C. 1642*. .................. 65  250
505  **Diva Faustina Junior,** deified 175. Æ *as*. S. C. Crescent and seven stars.
*R.I.C. 1714*. ............................................................................... 45  150
506  **Lucius Verus,** 161-169. Æ denarius. PAX TR. P. VI. IMP. IIII. COS. II.
Pax stg. l. *R.I.C. 561*. ................................................................ 65  160
506A  Æ *dupondius*. TR. P. IIII. IMP. II. COS. II. S. C. Mars stg. r., resting on
spear and shield. *R.I.C. 1387*. ..................................................... 55  190
507  **Lucilla,** daughter of Marcus Aurelius, wife of Lucius Verus. Æ *denarius*.
IVNONI LVCINAE. Juno stg. l., holding child in swaddling clothes.
*R.I.C. 771*. ................................................................................. 50  130
507A  Æ *sestertius*. PIETAS S. C. Pietas stg. l., altar at feet. *R.I.C. 1756*. ......... 70  280

|  | F | VF |
|---|---|---|
|  | £ | £ |

508 **Commodus,** 177-192 (Caesar 175-177), major warfare on the British frontier early in the reign; situation restored by Ulpius Marcellus in 184/5, followed by unrest in the British legions. *R denarius*. LIB. AVG. IIII. TR. P. VI. IMP. IIII. COS. III. P. P. Liberalitas stg. l. *R.I.C. 22.* ...................... 55 140

509                                                              511

509 *Æ sestertius*. IOVI VICTORI IMP. III. COS. II. P. P. S. C. Jupiter seated l. *R.I.C. 1612.* .................... 85 360
509A *Æ as*. ANN. AVG. TR. P. VII. IMP. IIII. COS. III. P. P. S. C. Annona stg. l., modius at feet. *R.I.C. 339 (See also under Category 2.)* ........................ 40 110
510 **Crispina,** wife of Commodus. *R denarius*. CONCORDIA. Clasped hands. *R.I.C. 279.* .................... 55 140
511 **Pertinax,** January-March 193, formerly governor of Britain, ca. 185-7. *R denarius*. PROVID. DEOR. COS. II. Providentia stg l., reaching up to star. *R.I.C. 11a.* .................... 360 950

512                        513                        514A

512 **Didius Julianus,** March-June 193. *R denarius*. CONCORD MILIT. Concordia Militum stg. l., holding standards. *R.I.C. 1.* ...................... 725 1650
513 **Clodius Albinus,** 195-197 (Caesar 193-195), governor of Britain (from 191/2) at the time of his imperial proclamation by his troops. *R denarius*. MINER. PACIF. COS. II. Minerva stg. l. *R.I.C. 7.* .................... 95 240
513A — FIDES LEGION. COS. II. Clasped hands holding legionary eagle. *R.I.C. 20b.* 110 260
514 **Septimius Severus,** 193-211, restored the frontier forts in northern Britain following the downfall of Clodius Albinus; later repaired Hadrian's Wall, and spent the years 208-11 in Britain campaigning in Scotland; divided Britannia into two provinces, Superior and Inferior; died at York, February 211. *R denarius*. VIRT AVGG. Roma stg. l., holding Victory, spear and shield. *R.I.C. 171a.* 30 70
514A — P.M. TR. P. XVIII. COS. III. P. P. Jupiter stg. l. between two children. *R.I.C. 240 (See also under Category 2.)* .................... 30 70
515 **Julia Domna,** wife of Septimius Severus, mother of Caracalla and Geta, accompanied her husband and sons on the British expedition, 208-211, and probably resided in London during the northern campaigns. *R denarius*. VENERI VICTR. Venus stg. r., resting on column. *R.I.C. 536.* ............... 30 65
515A — VESTA. Vesta stg. l., holding palladium and sceptre. *R.I.C. 390.* ........ 30 65

516                                              519

|     |                                                                                                                                                                                                                                                                                                                                                                                              | F £ | VF £ |
| --- | --- | --- | --- |
| 516 | **Caracalla,** 198-217 (Caesar 196-198), accompanied his father and brother on the British expedition, 208-211, and led the final campaign in Scotland in 210 during Severus' illness; made frontier dispositions before returning to Rome and finalized his father's arrangements for the division of Britain into two provinces. Æ *antoninianus* (*double denarius,* introduced in 215). VENVS VICTRIX. Venus stg. l., holding Victory and resting on shield. *R.I.C. 311c.* | 70 | 180 |
| 517 | Æ *denarius.* PART. MAX. PONT. TR. P. IIII. Trophy with two captives at base. *R.I.C. 54b.* | 30 | 70 |
| 517A | — P. M. TR. P. XV. COS. III. P. P. Hercules stg. l., holding olive-branch and club. *R.I.C. 192.* *See also under Category 2.* | 30 | 70 |
| 518 | **Plautilla,** wife of Caracalla. Æ *denarius.* PROPAGO IMPERI. Caracalla and Plautilla clasping hands. *R.I.C. 362.* | 40 | 100 |
| 519 | **Geta,** 209-212 (Caesar 198-209), accompanied his father and brother on the British expedition, 208-211, and took charge of the civil administration in London during the northern campaigns. Æ *denarius.* PRINC. IVVENTVTIS. Prince stg. l. beside trophy, holding branch and spear. *R.I.C. 18.* | 40 | 100 |
| 519A | — FORT RED TR. P. III. COS. II. Fortuna seated l. *R.I.C. 75.* *See also under Category 2.* | 35 | 85 |
| 520 | **Macrinus,** 217-218. Æ *denarius.* PROVIDENTIA DEORVM. Providentia stg. l., globe at feet. *R.I.C. 80.* | 65 | 175 |
| 521 | **Diadumenian,** 218 (Caesar 217-218). Æ *denarius.* PRINC. IVVENTVTIS. Prince stg. l., two standards behind. *R.I.C. 109.* | 150 | 375 |

522

| 522 | **Elagabalus,** 218-222. Æ *antoninianus.* MARS VICTOR. Mars advancing r. *R.I.C. 122.* | 70 | 180 |
| --- | --- | --- | --- |
| 522A | Æ *denarius.* P. M. TR. P. III. COS. III. P. P. Jupiter seated l., eagle at feet *R.I.C. 27.* | 35 | 85 |
| 523 | **Julia Paula,** first wife of Elagabalus. Æ *denarius.* CONCORDIA. Concordia seated l. *R.I.C. 211.* | 60 | 140 |
| 524 | **Aquilia Severa,** second wife of Elagabalus. Æ *denarius.* CONCORDIA. Concordia stg. l., altar at feet. *R.I.C. 226.* | 70 | 180 |
| 525 | **Julia Soaemias,** mother of Elagabalus. Æ *denarius.* VENVS CAELESTIS. Venus seated l., child at feet. *R.I.C. 243.* | 45 | 100 |

|     |     | F | VF |
|-----|-----|---|----|
|     |     | £ | £ |

526 **Julia Maesa,** grandmother of Elagabalus and Severus Alexander. Æ
denarius. SAECVLI FELICITAS. Felicitas stg. l., altar at feet. *R.I.C. 271.*   35   90
527 **Severus Alexander,** 222-235 (Caesar 221-222). Æ denarius.
PAX AETERNA AVG. Pax stg. l. *R.I.C. 165.* ..................................   35   75
527A — P. M. TR. P. XIII. COS. III. P. P. Sol advancing l., holding whip. *R.I.C. 123.*   35   75

528

528 Æ sestertius. MARS VLTOR S. C. Mars advancing r., with spear and shield.
*R.I.C. 635.* ...................................................................................   50   140
529 **Orbiana,** wife of Severus Alexander. Æ denarius. CONCORDIA AVGG.
Concordia seated l. *R.I.C. 319.* .....................................................   100   240

530                          531A

530 **Julia Mamaea,** mother of Severus Alexander. Æ denarius. VESTA.
Vesta stg. l. *R.I.C. 362.* ...............................................................   30   70
530A Æ sestertius. FELICITAS PVBLICA S. C. Felicitas stg. facing, hd. l.,
resting on column. *R.I.C. 676.* ......................................................   45   120
531 **Maximinus I,** 235-238. Æ denarius. PAX AVGVSTI. Pax stg. l. *R.I.C. 12.*   35   80
531A Æ sestertius. SALVS AVGVSTI S. C. Salus seated l., feeding snake arising
from altar. *R.I.C. 85.* ....................................................................   50   140
532 **Maximus Caesar,** son of Maximinus I. Æ denarius. PRINC IVVENTVTIS.
Prince stg. l., two standards behind. *R.I.C. 3.* ...........................   70   200
533 **Gordian I Africanus,** March-April 238, governor of Britannia Inferior
late in the reign of Caracalla. Æ denarius. P. M. TR. P. COS. P. P. Togate
emperor stg. l. *R.I.C. 1.* ................................................................   550   1400
534 **Gordian II Africanus,** March-April 238. Æ denarius. VIRTVS AVGG.
Virtus stg. l., with shield and spear. *R.I.C. 3.* ...........................   550   1400
535 **Balbinus,** April-July 238. Æ antoninianus. FIDES MVTVA AVGG.
Clasped hands. *R.I.C. 11.* ..............................................................   120   275
535A Æ denarius. PROVIDENTIA DEORVM. Providentia stg. l., globe at feet. *R.I.C. 7.*   100   250
536 **Pupienus,** April-July 238. Æ antoninianus. AMOR MVTVVS AVGG.
Clasped hands. *R.I.C. 9a.* ...............................................................   120   275
536A Æ denarius. PAX PVBLICA. Pax seated l. *R.I.C. 4.* ...............................   90   240

537                                   539

|     |     | F<br>£ | VF<br>£ |
|-----|-----|--------|---------|

537    **Gordian III,** 238-244 (Caesar 238). Æ *antoninianus*. LAETITIA AVG. N.
       Laetitia stg. l. *R.I.C. 86.* .............................................................   25   50
538    Æ *denarius*. DIANA LVCIFERA. Diana stg. r., holding torch. *R.I.C. 127.*   25   50
538A   Æ *sestertius*. AETERNITATI AVG. S.C. Sol stg. l., holding globe. *R.I.C. 297a.*   40   100
539    **Philip I,** 244-249. Æ *antoninianus*. ROMAE AETERNAE. Roma seated l.
       *R.I.C. 65.* ....................................................................................   25   55
539A   Æ *sestertius*. SECVRIT. ORBIS S. C. Securitas seated l. *R.I.C. 190.* .....   45   120
540    **Otacilia Severa,** wife of Philip I. Æ *antoninianus*. PIETAS AVGVSTAE.
       Pietas stg. l. *R.I.C. 125c.* ............................................................   25   55
540A   Æ *sestertius*. CONCORDIA AVGG. S. C. Concordia seated l. *R.I.C. 203a.*   45   120
541    **Philip II,** 247-249 (Caesar 244-247). Æ *antoninianus*. PRINCIPI IVVENT.
       Prince stg. l., holding globe and spear. *R.I.C. 218d.* ...............................   25   60
541A   Æ *sestertius*. PAX AETERNA S. C. Pax stg. l. *R.I.C. 268c.* ....................   45   120

542                                   543

542    **Trajan Decius,** 249-251. Æ *antoninianus*. DACIA. Dacia stg. l., holding
       staff with ass's hd. *R.I.C. 12b.* ....................................................   25   60
542A   Æ *sestertius*. PANNONIAE S. C. The two Pannoniae stg., each holding
       standard. *R.I.C. 124a.* ...................................................................   50   140
543    **Herennia Etruscilla,** wife of Trajan Decius. Æ *antoninianus*. PVDICITIA
       AVG. Pudicitia stg. l. *R.I.C. 58b.* ...................................................   30   65
544    **Herennius Etruscus,** 251 (Caesar 250-251). Æ *antoninianus*. PIETAS
       AVGG. Mercury stg. l., holding purse and caduceus. *R.I.C. 142b.* ..........   35   90
545    **Hostilian,** 251 (Caesar 251). Æ *antoninianus*. PRINCIPI IVVENTVTIS.
       Apollo seated l., holding branch. *R.I.C. 180.* ...........................................   55   140
546    **Trebonianus Gallus,** 251-253. Æ *antoninianus*. FELICITAS PVBLICA.
       Felicitas stg. l., resting on column. *R.I.C. 34A.* .......................................   25   55
546A   Æ *sestertius*. SALVS AVGG S. C. Salus stg. r., feeding snake held in her
       arms. *R.I.C. 121a.* ..........................................................................   60   150
547    **Volusian,** 251-253 (Caesar 251). Æ *antoninianus*. VIRTVS AVGG.
       Virtus stg. l. *R.I.C. 186.* ...............................................................   25   60
548    **Aemilian,** 253. Æ *antoninianus*. PACI AVG. Pax stg. l., resting on column.
       *R.I.C. 8.* ...........................................................................................   100   240
549    **Valerian,** 253-260. Billon antoninianus. FIDES MILITVM. Fides stg. r.,
       holding two standards. *R.I.C. 241* ......................................................   25   55

|  | | F £ | VF £ |
|---|---|---|---|
| 550 | **Diva Mariniana,** wife of Valerian, deified 253. Billon *antoninianus.* CONSECRATIO. Empress seated on peacock flying r. *R.I.C. 6.* ............ | 60 | 150 |
| 551 | **Gallienus,** 253-268, during whose reign Rome temporarily lost control over Britain when Postumus rebelled and established the independent Gallic Empire in 260. Billon *antoninianus.* VIRT GALLIENI AVG. Emperor advancing r., captive at feet. *R.I.C. 54.* ...................... | 15 | 35 |

552

| 552 | — DIANAE CONS. AVG. Doe l. *R.I.C. 176.* ......................... | 15 | 30 |
|---|---|---|---|
| 552A | — SOLI INVICTO. Sol stg. l., holding globe. *R.I.C. 658.* ..................... | 15 | 25 |
| 553 | **Salonina,** wife of Gallienus. Billon *antoninianus.* VENVS FELIX. Venus seated l., child at feet. *R.I.C. 7.* ................................. | 15 | 30 |
| 553A | — IVNONI CONS. AVG. Doe l. *R.I.C. 16.* ......................... | 15 | 30 |
| 554 | **Valerian Junior,** son of Gallienus, Caesar 256-258. Billon *antoninianus.* IOVI CRESCENTI. Infant Jupiter seated on goat r. *R.I.C. 13.* ............... | 30 | 65 |
| 555 | **Divus Valerian Junior,** deified 258. Billon *antoninianus.* CONSECRATIO. Large altar. *R.I.C. 24.* ............................. | 30 | 65 |
| 556 | **Saloninus,** 260 (Caesar 258-260). Billon *antoninianus.* PIETAS AVG. Priestly emblems. *R.I.C. 9.* ............................. | 30 | 65 |
| 557 | **Macrianus,** usurper in the East, 260-261. Billon *antoninianus.* SOL. INVICTO. Sol stg. l., holding globe. *R.I.C. 12.* ...................... | 60 | 140 |
| 558 | **Quietus,** usurper in the East, 260-261. Billon *antoninianus.* INDVLGENTIAE AVG. Indulgentia seated l. *R.I.C. 5.* ......................... | 60 | 140 |

559

| 559 | **Postumus,** usurper in the West, 260-268, founder of the 'Gallic Empire' which temporarily detached Britain from the rule of the central government, a state of affairs which continued until Aurelian's defeat of Tetricus in 273. Billon *antoninianus.* HERC. DEVSONIENSI. Hercules stg. r. *R.I.C. 64.* | 15 | 40 |
|---|---|---|---|
| 560 | — MONETA AVG. Moneta stg. l. *R.I.C. 75.* ......................... | 15 | 35 |
| 560A | Æ *sestertius.* FIDES MILITVM. Fides stg. l., holding two standards. *R.I.C. 128.* ............................. | 75 | 220 |
| 561 | **Laelianus,** usurper in the West, 268. Billon *antoninianus.* VICTORIA AVG. Victory advancing r. *R.I.C. 9.* ............................. | 340 | 825 |
| 562 | **Marius,** usurper in the West, 268. Billon *antoninianus.* CONCORDIA MILITVM. Clasped hands. *R.I.C. 7.* ......................... | 95 | 250 |

|   | | F £ | VF £ |
|---|---|---|---|

563 **Victorinus**, usurper in the West, 268-270. Billon *antoninianus*. INVICTVS. Sol advancing l. *R.I.C. 114.* ... | 15 | 30

564 **Tetricus,** usurper in the West, 270-273, defeated by Aurelian, thus ending the 'Gallic Empire' and the isolation of Britain from the authority of Rome. Billon *antoninianus*. LAETITIA AVGG. Laetitia stg. l. *R.I.C. 87.* ... | 15 | 30
*See also under Category 4.*

565 **Tetricus Junior,** son of Tetricus, Caesar 270-273. Billon *antoninianus*. SPES PVBLICA. Spes walking l., holding flower *R.I.C. 272.* ... | 15 | 30
*See also under Category 4.*

566 **Claudius II Gothicus,** 268-270. Billon *antoninianus*. IOVI STATORI. Jupiter stg. r. *R.I.C. 52.* ... | 15 | 30

567 **Divus Claudius II,** deified 270. Billon *antoninianus*. CONSECRATIO. Large altar. *R.I.C. 261.* ... | 15 | 30
*See also under Category 4.*

568 **Quintillus,** 270. Billon *antoninianus*. DIANA LVCIF. Diana stg. r., holding torch. *R.I.C. 49.* ... | 30 | 80

569 **Aurelian,** 270-275, restored Britain to the rule of the central government through his defeat of Tetricus in 273; possibly began construction of the chain of 'Saxon Shore' forts on the eastern and southern coastlines. Billon *antoninianus*. ORIENS AVG. Sol stg. l. between two captives. *R.I.C. 63.* | 20 | 40

569A — RESTITVT. ORBIS. Female stg. r., presenting wreath to emperor stg. l. *R.I.C. 399.* | 20 | 40

570 **Aurelian and Vabalathus,** ruler of Palmyra 267-272 and usurper in the East from 271. Billon *antoninianus*. Obv. Laur. bust of Vabalathus r. Rev. Rad. bust of Aurelian r. *R.I.C. 381* | 45 | 120

571                                    574A

571 **Severina,** wife of Aurelian. Billon *antoninianus*. PROVIDEN. DEOR. Concordia (or Fides) Militum stg. r., facing Sol stg. l. *R.I.C. 9.* | 25 | 60

572 **Tacitus,** 275-276. Billon *antoninianus*. SECVRIT. PERP. Securitas stg. l., leaning on column. *R.I.C. 163.* | 25 | 60

573 **Florian,** 276. Billon *antoninianus*. LAETITIA FVND. Laetitia stg. l. *R.I.C. 34.* | 45 | 120

574 **Probus,** 276-282, suppressed governor's revolt in Britain and lifted restrictions on viticulture in Britain and Gaul. Billon *antoninianus*. ADVENTVS PROBI AVG. Emperor on horseback l., captive seated before. *R.I.C. 160.* | 20 | 40

574A — VICTORIA GERM. Trophy between two captives. *R.I.C. 222.* | 20 | 50

574B **Proculus** (usurper 280-281) Billon *antoninianus*. VICTORIA AUG. Female figure stg l. | 13000 | 38000

575 **Carus,** 282-283. Billon *antoninianus*. PAX EXERCITI. Pax stg. l., holding olive-branch and standard. *R.I.C. 75.* | 30 | 70

|     |     | F<br>£ | VF<br>£ |
|-----|-----|--------|---------|

576   **Divus Carus,** deified 283. Billon *antoninianus*. CONSECRATIO. Eagle
      facing, hd. l. *R.I.C. 28.* ............................................................................ 30   70
577   **Carinus,** 283-285 (Caesar 282-283). Billon *antoninianus*. SAECVLI
      FELICITAS. Emperor stg. r. *R.I.C. 214.* ................................................. 25   60
578   **Magnia Urbica,** wife of Carinus. Billon *antoninianus*. VENVS VICTRIX.
      Venus stg. l., holding helmet, shield at feet. *R.I.C. 343.* ........................... 75   180
579   **Numerian,** 283-284 (Caesar 282-283). Billon *antoninianus*. CLEMENTIA
      TEMP. Emperor stg. r., receiving globe from Jupiter stg. l. *R.I.C. 463.*.... 30   70
580   **Diocletian,** 284-305. Æ *argenteus*. VIRTVS MILITVM. The four tetrarchs
      sacrificing before gateway of military camp. *R.I.C. 27a (Rome).* ............. 150   300
581   Billon *antoninianus*. IOVI CONSERVAT AVGG. Jupiter stg. l. *R.I.C. 162.* 20   40
582   Æ *follis*. GENIO POPVLI ROMANI. Genius stg. l. R.I.C. 14a *(Alexandria).* 20   40
582A  — (post-abdication coinage, after 305). PROVIDENTIA DEORVM QVIES
      AVGG. Quies and Providentia stg. facing each other. *R.I.C. 676a (Treveri).* 35   85
      *See also under Category 3.*
583   **Maximian,** 286-305 and 306-308, failed in his attempts to suppress the
      usurpation of Carausius in Britain. Æ *argenteus*. VICTORIA SARMAT. The
      four tetrarchs sacrificing before gateway of military camp. *R.I.C. 37b (Rome).* 140   280

584

584   Billon *antoninianus*. SALVS AVGG. Salus stg. r., feeding snake held in
      her arms. *R.I.C. 417.* ............................................................................ 20   35
585   Æ *follis*. SAC. MON. VRB. AVGG. ET CAESS. NN. Moneta stg. l.
      *R.I.C. 105b (Rome).* ............................................................................ 20   40
585A  — (second reign). CONSERVATORES VRB SVAE. Roma seated in
      hexastyle temple. *R.I.C. 84b (Ticinum).* ................................................. 20   40
      *See also under Category 3.*
      *[For coins of the usurpers **Carausius** and **Allectus** see under Category 3]*
586   **Constantius I,** 305-306 (Caesar 293-305), invaded Britain 296 and defeated
      the usurper Allectus, thus restoring the island to the rule of the central government;
      Britain now divided into four provinces and the northern frontier defences
      reconstructed; died at York, July 306. Æ *argenteus*. PROVIDENTIA AVGG.
      The four tetrarchs sacrificing before gateway of military camp. *R.I.C. 11a (Rome).* 160   320

587

587   Æ *follis*. GENIO POPVLI ROMANI. Genius stg. l. *R.I.C. 26a (Aquileia).* 20   40

|  | F £ | VF £ |
|---|---|---|

587A — SALVIS AVGG. ET CAESS. FEL. KART. Carthage stg. l., holding fruits. *R.I.C. 30a (Carthage).* ........... 20 | 45
*See also under Category 3.*

588                                          593

588 **Galerius,** 305-311 (Caesar 293-305). Æ argenteus. VIRTVS MILITVM. The four tetrarchs sacrificing before gateway of military camp. *R.I.C. 15b (Ticinum).* ........... 150 | 300
588A — XC / VI in wreath. *R.I.C. 16b (Carthage).* ........... 200 | 450
589 *Æ follis.* GENIO AVGG ET CAESARVM NN. Genius stg. l. *R.I.C. 11b (Cyzicus).* ........... 20 | 40
589A — GENIO IMPERATORIS. Genius stg. l. *R.I.C. 101a (Alexandria).* ...... 20 | 35
*See also under Category 3.*
590 **Galeria Valeria,** wife of Galerius. *Æ follis.* VENERI VICTRICI. Venus stg. l. *R.I.C. 110 (Alexandria).* ........... 40 | 100
591 **Severus II,** 306-307 (Caesar 305-306). *Æ follis.* FIDES MILITVM. Fides seated l. *R.I.C. 73 (Ticinum).* ........... 40 | 100
*See also under Category 3.*
592 **Maximinus II,** 310-313 (Caesar 305-310). *Æ follis.* GENIO CAESARIS. Genius stg. l. *R.I.C. 64 (Alexandria).* ........... 20 | 35
592A — GENIO POP. ROM. Genius stg. l. *R.I.C. 845a (Treveri).* ........... 15 | 30
*See also under Category 3.*
593 **Maxentius,** 306-312 (Caesar 306). *Æ follis.* CONSERV. VRB. SVAE. Roma seated in hexastyle temple. *R.I.C. 210 (Rome).* ........... 20 | 40
594 **Romulus,** son of Maxentius, deified 309. *Æ quarter follis.* AETERNAE MEMORIAE. Temple with domed roof. *R.I.C. 58 (Ostia).* ........... 70 | 180
595 **Licinius,** 308-324. *Æ follis.* GENIO AVGVSTI. Genius stg. l. *R.I.C. 198b (Siscia).* ........... 15 | 30
595A Æ 3. IOVI CONSERVATORI AVGG. Jupiter stg. l. *R.I.C. 24 (Nicomedia).* ........... 15 | 30
*See also under Category 3.*
596 **Licinius Junior,** son of Licinius, Caesar 317-324. Æ 3. CAESARVM NOSTRORVM around wreath containing VOT. / V. *R.I.C. 92 (Thessalonica).* ........... 15 | 30
597 **Constantine I, the Great,** 307-337 (Caesar 306-307), campaigned with his father Constantius I against the Picts in northern Britain, summer 306, and proclaimed emperor by the legions at York on Constantius' death in July; closed the London mint early in 325 ending almost four decades of operation. *Æ follis.* GENIO POP ROM. Genius stg. l. *R.I.C. 719b (Treveri).* ........... 20 | 40
598 — SOLI INVICTO COMITI. Sol stg. l. *R.I.C. 307 (Lugdunum).* ........... 15 | 30
598A Æ 3. PROVIDENTIAE AVGG. Gateway of military camp. *R.I.C. 153 (Thessalonica)* ........... 15 | 25

599                         599B                         600

|  | | F | VF |
|---|---|---|---|
|  | | £ | £ |

599    — VIRTVS EXERCIT. Trophy between two captives. *R.I.C. 280 (Treveri).*    20    40
599A   Æ 3/4. GLORIA EXERCITVS. Two soldiers stg. either side of two standards.
       *R.I.C. 518 (Treveri).* ...............................................................    10    20
       *See also under Category 3.*
599B   Silver third siliqua, after 330. Obv Female bust r. Rev. K within border of
       pellets. *(Constantinopolis).* ...........................................    120    300
600    **'Urbs Roma',** after 330. Æ 3/4. Obv. Helmeted bust of Roma l. Rev.
       She-wolf l., suckling twins. *R.I.C. 195 (Nicomedia).* ...............    10    25

601                         604

601    **'Constantinopolis',** after 330. Æ 3/4. Obv. Helmeted bust of
       Constantinopolis l. Rev. Victory stg. l., foot on prow. *R.I.C. 339 (Rome).*    10    25
602    **Fausta,** wife of Constantine I. Æ 3. SALVS REIPVBLICAE. Empress
       stg. l., holding two children. *R.I.C. 459 (Treveri)* ....................    20    50
       *See also under Category 3.*
603    **Helena,** mother of Constantine I. Æ 3. SECVRITAS REIPVBLICAE.
       Empress stg. l., holding branch. *R.I.C. 38 (Alexandria).* ..........................    20    50
603A   Æ 4 (posthumous issue, 337-340). PAX PVBLICA. Pax stg. l. *R.I.C. 78*
       *(Treveri).* ...............................................................    15    30
       *See also under Category 3.*
604    **Theodora,** second wife of Constantius I. Æ 4 (posthumous issue, 337-340).
       PIETAS ROMANA. Pietas stg. r., holding child. R.I.C. 43 *(Treveri).* ......    15    35
605    **Crispus,** eldest son of Constantine I, Caesar 317-326. Æ 3. CAESARVM
       NOSTRORVM around wreath containing VOT. / V. *R.I.C. 68 (Aquileia).*    15    30
       *See also under Category 3.*
606    **Delmatius,** nephew of Constantine I, Caesar 335-337. Æ 3/4. GLORIA
       EXERCITVS. Two soldiers stg. either side of two standards. *R.I.C. 90*
       *(Antioch).* ...............................................................    35    85
607    **Hanniballianus,** nephew of Constantine I, Rex 335-337. Æ 4. SECVRITAS
       PVBLICA. River-god Euphrates reclining r. *R.I.C. 147 (Constantinople).*    150    325
608    **Constantine II,** 337-340 (Caesar 317-337). Æ 3. BEATA
       TRANQVILLITAS. Altar inscribed VOT / IS / XX. *R.I.C. 312 (Treveri).*    15    30
608A   Æ 3/4. GLORIA EXERCITVS. Two soldiers stg. either side of standard.
       *R.I.C. 392 (Rome) (See also under Category 3.)* ....................................    10    20
609    **Constans,** 337-350 (Caesar 333-337), visited Britain in 343, the last
       reigning emperor to do so. Æ 2. FEL. TEMP. REPARATIO. Soldier r.,
       dragging barbarian from hut beneath tree. *R.I.C. 103 (Aquileia).* ............    25    50

609A

611B

| | | F<br>£ | VF<br>£ |
|---|---|---|---|
| 609A | — FEL. TEMP. REPARATIO. Emperor stg. l. on galley steered by Victory. *R.I.C. 219 (Treveri).* | 25 | 50 |
| 609B | Æ 4. VICTORIAE DD. AVGG. Q. NN. Two Victories stg. face to face. *R.I.C. 195 (Treveri).* | 10 | 20 |
| 610 | **Constantius II,** 337-361 (Caesar 324-337). Æ 3/4. GLORIA EXERCITVS. Two soldiers stg. either side of two standards. *R.I.C. 85 (Cyzicus).* | 10 | 20 |
| 611 | Æ *siliqua.* VOTIS / XXX. / MVLTIS / XXXX. in wreath. *R.I.C. 207 (Arelate).* | 65 | 170 |
| 611A | Æ 2. FEL. TEMP. REPARATIO. Emperor stg. l. on galley. *R.I.C. 218 (Treveri).* | 25 | 50 |
| 611B | Æ 3. FEL. TEMP. REPARATIO. Soldier advancing l., spearing fallen horseman. *R.I.C. 189 (Lugdunum).* | 10 | 20 |

*See also under Categories 3 and 4.*

612

616

| | | | |
|---|---|---|---|
| 612 | **Magnentius,** usurper in the West, 350-353, temporarily detached Britain from the rule of the legitimate Constantinian dynasty. Æ 1. SALVS DD. NN. AVG. ET CAES. *Chi-Rho* Christian monogram between Alpha and Omega. *R.I.C. 34 (Ambianum).* | 130 | 300 |
| 612A | Æ 2. FELICITAS REIPVBLICAE. Emperor stg. l., holding Victory and labarum. *R.I.C. 264 (Treveri).* | 30 | 65 |
| | *See also under Category 4.* | | |
| 613 | **Decentius,** brother of Magnentius, Caesar 351-353. Æ 2. VICTORIAE DD. NN. AVG. ET CAE. Two Victories supporting between them shield inscribed VOT. / V. / MVLT. / X. *R.I.C. 146 (Lugdunum).* | 40 | 90 |
| | *See also under Category 4.* | | |
| 614 | **Vetranio,** 'usurper' in the Balkans, 350. Æ 2. CONCORDIA MILITVM. Emperor stg. l., holding two labara. *R.I.C. 281 (Siscia).* | 50 | 120 |
| 615 | **Constantius Gallus,** Caesar under Constantius II, 351-354. Æ 2. FEL. TEMP. REPARATIO. Soldier advancing l., spearing fallen horseman. *R.I.C. 94 (Cyzicus).* | 25 | 50 |
| 615A | **Julian II,** 360-363 (Caesar 355-360). Æ *miliarense.* Rev. VIRTVS EXERCITVM. Soldier stg l, holding spear and resting on shield. *R.I.C. 290. (Arelate)* | 450 | 1100 |
| 616 | Æ *siliqua.* VOT. / X. / MVLT. / XX. in wreath. *R.I.C. 309 (Arelate).* | 65 | 170 |

|        |                                                                 | F | VF |
|--------|-----------------------------------------------------------------|---|----|
|        |                                                                 | £ | £  |
| 617    | Æ 1. SECVRITAS REIPVB. Bull stg. r. *R.I.C. 411 (Siscia)*................... | 50 | 150 |
|        | *Beware of recent forgeries.*                                   |   |    |
| 617A   | Æ 3. VOT. / X. / MVLT. / XX. in wreath. *R.I.C. 108 (Sirmium)*............. | 15 | 30 |
| 618    | **Jovian,** 363-364. Æ 3. VOT. / V. / MVLT. / X. in wreath. *R.I.C. 426 (Siscia)*. | 25 | 50 |

619                       620

| 619  | **Valentinian I,** 364-375 (in the West), during whose reign the Roman province of Britannia was devastated by the simultaneous attack of hordes of invaders on several fronts (the 'Barbarian Conspiracy'); order eventually restored by Count Theodosius, father of the future emperor . *N solidus.* RESTITVTOR REIPVBLICAE. Emperor stg. r., holding standard and Victory. *R.I.C. 2b (Antioch)*. ............... | 340 | 800 |
|------|-----------------------------------------------------------------------------------|-----|------|
| 619A | Æ *miliarense.* Rev. VICTORIA AVGVSTORVM. Victory stg r, inscribing shield. *R.I.C. 24a. (Trier)*............... | 400 | 1050 |
| 619B | Æ *siliqua.* Rev. VRBS ROMA. Roma seated l. *R.I.C. 27a (Trier)*.......... | 70 | 180 |
| 619C | Æ 3. GLORIA ROMANORVM. Emperor advancing r., dragging barbarian and holding labarum. *R.I.C. 14a (Siscia)*. ................ | 15 | 25 |
| 619D | — SECVRITAS REIPVBLICAE. Victory advancing l. *R.I.C. 32a (Treveri)*. | 15 | 25 |
| 619E | **Valens,** 364-378 (in the East). *N solidus.* Rev. RESTITVTOR REIPVBLICAE. Valens stg , holding labarum and Victory. *R.I.C. 2d (Antioch)* ............... | 340 | 800 |
| 619F | Æ *miliarense.* Rev. VIRTVS EXERCITVS. Valens stg, holding standard. *R.I.C. 26c (Trier)* ..................... | 380 | 1000 |
| 620  | Æ *siliqua.* VRBS ROMA. Roma seated l. *R.I.C. 27e (Treveri)*. ............. | 70 | 180 |
| 620A | Æ 3. SECVRITAS REIPVBLICAE. Victory advancing l. *R.I.C. 42b (Constantinople)*. ..................... | 15 | 25 |
| 621  | **Procopius,** usurper in the East, 365-366. Æ 3. REPARATIO FEL. TEMP. Emperor stg. r., holding standard and shield. *R.I.C. 17a (Constantinople)*. | 50 | 130 |
| 621A | **Gratian,** 367-383 (in the West), overthrown by Magnus Maximus who had been proclaimed emperor by the army in Britain. *N solidus.* Rev. VICTORIA AVGG. Two Emperors enthroned holding globe, Victory behind. *R.I.C. 17g (Trier)* ..................... | 360 | 850 |
| 621B | Æ *miliarense.* Rev. VIRTVS EXERCITVS. Gratian stg, holding standard. *R.I.C. 40 .(Lugdunum)* ..................... | 400 | 1050 |
| 622  | Æ *siliqua.* VRBS ROMA. Roma seated l. *R.I.C. 27f (Treveri)*. ............. | 70 | 180 |
| 622A | **Valentinian II,** 375-392 (in the West). *N solidus.* Rev. VICTORIA AVGG. Two Emperors enthroned holding globe, Victory behind. *R.I.C. 34b (Thessalonica)* ..................... | 380 | 1000 |
| 622B | Æ *miliarense.* Rev. GLORIA ROMANORVM. Valentinian stg , holding standard. *R.I.C. 40 (lugdunum)* ..................... | 400 | 1050 |
| 622C | Æ *siliqua.* Rev. VIRTVS ROMANORVM. Roma seated l. *R.I.C. 43a. (Lugdunum)*..................... | 75 | 190 |
| 623  | Æ 2. REPARATIO REIPVB. Emperor stg. l., raising kneeling female figure. *R.I.C. 20c (Arelate)*. ..................... | 20 | 40 |
| 623A | Æ 4. SALVS REIPVBLICAE. Victory advancing l., dragging barbarian. *R.I.C. 20a (Alexandria)*. ..................... | 15 | 25 |

| | | F | VF |
|---|---|---|---|
| | | £ | £ |

623B **Theodosius I,** the Great, 379-395 (in the East), son of the Count Theodosius who had cleared Britain of barbarian invaders in the reign of Valentinian I; the Emperor Theodosiua twice restored Britain to the rule of the central government, by his defeat of the usurpers Magnus Maximus (in 388) and Eugenius (in 394).
*N solidus.* Rev. CONCORDIA AUGGG. Constantinopolis seated, holding sceptre and shield. *R.I.C. 71a (Constantinople)* .................................... 360 950

623C *R miliarense.* Rev. VIRTUS EXERCITUS. Theodosius stg , holding standard. *R.I.C. 53c (Trier)* ................................... 400 1050

624 *R siliqua.* CONCORDIA AVGGG. Constantinopolis enthroned facing, foot on prow. *R.I.C. 55a (Treveri).* ................................... 70 180

624A

624A — VIRTVS ROMANORVM. Roma enthroned facing. *R.I.C (Aquileia) 28d.* 70 180

624B Æ 2. VIRTVS EXERCIT. Emperor stg. r., foot on captive, holding labarum and globe. *R.I.C. 24b (Heraclea).* ................................... 25 50

625 **Aelia Flaccilla,** wife of Theodosius I. Æ 2. SALVS REIPVBLICAE. Victory seated r., inscribing Christian monogram on shield set on cippus. *R.I.C. 81 (Constantinople).* ................................... 30 75

625A **Magnus Maximus,** usurper in the West, 383-388, proclaimed emperor by the army in Britain, invaded Gaul, and overthrew the legitimate western emperor Gratian; possibly reopened the London mint for a brief issue of precious metal coinage (Rudyard Kipling presented a rather fanciful version of his career in "Puck of Pook's Hill"). *N solidus.* Rev. RESTITVTOR REPVBLICAE. Maximus stg, holding labarum and Victory. *R.I.C. 76 (Trier)* ................ 1400 3250

625B *R miliarense.* Rev. VIRTVS EXERCITVS. Maximus stg, holding labarum. *R.I.C. 82 (Trier)* ................................... 780 1950

626                                    627

626 *R siliqua.* VIRTVS ROMANORVM. Roma enthroned facing. *R.I.C. 84b (Treveri)* *(See also under Category 3.)* ................................... 85 240

626A **Flavius Victor,** son of Magnus Maximus, co-emperor 387-388. *R siliqua.* VIRTVS ROMANORVM. Roma seated facing on throne. *R.I.C. 84d (Treveri)* 325 750

627 Æ 4. SPES ROMANORVM. Gateway of military camp. *RIC 55b (Aquileia).* 50 125

627A **Eugenius,** usurper in the West, 392-394, recognized in Britain until his defeat by Theodosius the Great. *N solidus.* VICTORIA AUGG. Two emperors enthroned facing holding globe. *R.I.C. 28 (Treveri)* ................................... 3300 8750

627B *R miliarense.* Rev. VIRTVS EXERCITVS. Eugenius stg, holding standard. *R.I.C. 105 (Trier)* ................................... 1750 4300

628                                     629

|     |                                                                  | F | VF |
|-----|------------------------------------------------------------------|---|----|
|     |                                                                  | £ | £  |

628  ΛR *siliqua*. VIRTVS ROMANORVM. Roma seated l. on cuirass.
     *R.I.C. 32c (Milan).* ............................................................... 340    850

629  **Arcadius,** 395-408 (in the East, co-emperor with his father Theodosius I
     from 383). ΛV *solidus.* VICTORIA AVGGG. Emperor stg. r., foot on
     captive, holding standard and Victory. *R.I.C. 1205 (Milan).* .................. 350    900

629A ΛR *miliarense*. Rev. GLORIA ROMANORVM. Arcadius stg, raising r hand
     and holding globe in l. *R.I.C. 25b (Milan)* .............................................. 420   1050

629B ΛR *siliqua*. Rev. VOT V MVLT X in wreath. *R.I.C. 13 (Milan)* ............... 75    180

629C Æ 2. GLORIA ROMANORVM. Emperor stg. l., holding standard and
     shield, captive at feet. *R.I.C. 41 (Antioch).* ....................................... 25     60

630  **Honorius,** 395-423 (in the West, co-emperor with his father Theodosius I and
     brother Arcadius from 393), this reign saw the end of Roman rule in Britain
     following a succession of usurpations in the province, culminating in that of
     Constantine III against whom the Britons rebelled in 409; Honorius' celebrated '
     Rescript' of the following year instructed the provincials to look to their own
     defence as he was no longer able to assist them. ΛV *solidus.* VICTORIA
     AVGGG. Emperor stg. r., foot on captive, holding standard and Victory.
     *R.I.C. 1287 (Ravenna).* ........................................................... 340    800

630A ΛR *miliarense*. Rev. VIRTVS EXERCITVS *(Rome)*.............................. 450   1100

630B ΛR *siliqua*. VIRTVS ROMANORVM. Roma seated l. on cuirass.
     *R.I.C. 1228 (Milan).* .............................................................. 70    180

631

631  **Constantine III,** usurper in the West, 407-411, proclaimed emperor by the
     army in Britain, but his authority rejected by the Romano-Britons two years
     later, thus effectively ending 366 years of Roman rule in Britain. ΛR *siliqua.*
     VICTORIA AVGGG. Roma enthroned l. *R.I.C. 1532 (Treveri)*.............. 210    475

632  **Valentinian III,** 425-455 (in the West), during whose reign the Saxon
     conquest of the former Roman province commenced, following the final
     unsuccessful appeal of the Romano-Britons for help addressed to the general
     Aetius in 446. ΛV *solidus.* VICTORIA AVGGG. Emperor stg. facing, foot
     on human-headed serpent. *R.I.C. 2010 (Ravenna).* ................................. 350    850

632A Æ 4. VOT. PVB. Gateway of military camp. *R.I.C. 2123 (Rome).* .......... 35     90

## 2. ISSUES WITH TYPES REFERRING SPECIFICALLY
## TO THE PROVINCE OF BRITANNIA

Struck in Rome, unless otherwise indicated. These usually commemorate military operations in the northern frontier region of the province or beyond.

633                                             635

|  | | F | VF |
|---|---|---|---|
|  | | £ | £ |
| 633 | **Claudius,** A.D. 41-54. AV aureus, celebrating the early stages of the Roman conquest of Britain which commenced in A.D. 43. DE BRITANN on architrave of triumphal arch. *R.I.C. 33.* | 2900 | 6400 |
| 634 | Æ *denarius.* Similar. *R.I.C. 34.* | 725 | 1800 |
| 634A | Æ *didrachm* of Caesarea in Cappadocia. DE BRITANNIS. Emperor in triumphal quadriga r. *R.I.C. 122.* | 625 | 1650 |
| 635 | **Hadrian,** 117-138. Æ as, commemorating the restoration of order in the province following a serious uprising (or invasion) in the north, probably early in the governorship of Q. Pompeius Falco (118-122). BRITANNIA PONT. MAX. TR. POT. COS. III. S. C. Britannia seated facing on rock. *R.I.C. 577a.* | 340 | 850 |
| 636 | Æ *sestertius,* commemorating Hadrian's visit to the province in 122, when he planned and initiated the construction of the northern frontier system which bears his name. ADVENTVI AVG. BRITANNIAE S.C. Emperor and Britannia stg. either side of altar. *R.I.C. 882.* | 6400 | 21000 |

638A

| 637 | — BRITANNIA S. C. Britannia seated facing, foot resting on rock. *R.I.C. 845.* | 6700 | 22000 |
|---|---|---|---|
| 637A | Æ *dupondius* or as. *Similar. R.I.C. 846.* | 625 | 1750 |
| 638 | Æ *sestertius,* commemorating Hadrian's attention to the legionary garrison strength of the province, principally his transfer of *VI Victrix* from Germany in 122. EXERC. BRITANNICVS S. C. Emperor on horseback r., addressing gathering of troops. *R.I.C. 912.* | 6400 | 21000 |
| 638A | — EXERC. BRITANNICVS S.C. Emperor stg. r. on tribunal, addressing gathering of troops. *R.I.C. 913.* | 6400 | 21000 |

|     |    | F    | VF    |
| --- | -- | ---  | ---   |
|     |    | £    | £     |

639   **Antoninus Pius,** 138-161. *N aureus,* commemorating the conquests in
Scotland by the governor Q. Lollius Urbicus (138/9-142/3) at which time
construction of the Antonine Wall was begun. BRITAN. IMPERATOR II.
Victory stg. l. on globe. *R.I.C. 113*..................................................................      2200    5000

640

| No. | Description | F | VF |
| --- | --- | --- | --- |
| 640 | *Æ sestertius.* BRITANNIA S. C. Britannia seated l. on rock, holding standard. *R.I.C. 742.* | 875 | 2250 |
| 641 | — BRITAN. IMPERATOR II. S. C. Helmeted Britannia seated l., foot on rock. *R.I.C. 743.* | 875 | 2250 |
| 642 | — BRITAN. IMPERATOR II. S. C. Britannia seated l. on globe above waves, holding standard. *R.I.C. 744.* | 975 | 2650 |
| 643 | — BRITAN. IMPERATOR II. S. C. Victory stg. l. on globe. *R.I.C. 719.* | 325 | 800 |
| 643A | — BRITANNIA IMPERATOR II. S. C. Britannia seated l. on rock, holding standard. *R.I.C. 745.* | 875 | 2250 |
| 644 | *Æ as.* IMPERATOR II. S. C. Victory hovering l., holding shield inscribed BRI / TAN. *R.I.C. 732.* | 160 | 375 |
| 645 | *Æ dupondius,* commemorating the quelling of a serious uprising in the north, ca. 154/5, necessitating the evacuation of the recently constructed Antonine Wall in Scotland. BRITANNIA COS. IIII. S. C. Britannia seated l. on rock, shield and vexillum in background. *R.I.C. 930.* | 325 | 750 |
| 646 | *Æ as.* Similar. *R.I.C. 934.* | 140 | 375 |

*Many specimens of this type are carelessly struck on inadequate flans.
Moreover, they have been found in significant quantities on Romano-British
sites, notably in Coventina's Well at Carrawburgh fort on Hadrian's Wall,
raising the interesting possibility that they may have been issued from a
temporary mint in Britain. The style of the engraving is quite regular,
indicating that even if locally produced these coins would have been struck
from normal Roman dies brought to Britain especially for this purpose.
See under Category 3.*

647   **Commodus,** 177-192. *Æ sestertius,* commemorating the victories in
Scotland of the governor Ulpius Marcellus in 184/5. These were in
retribution for a major barbarian invasion several years earlier resulting
in serious damage to Hadrian's Wall, which had been temporarily overrun,
and the defeat and death of an unknown governor. BRITT. P. M. TR. P.
VIIII. IMP. VII. COS. IIII. P. P. S. C. Britannia stg. l., holding curved
sword and helmet. *R.I.C. 437.* ..................................................................    5750   18500

648

|            |     | F   | VF  |
|------------|-----|-----|-----|
|            |     | £   | £   |

648 — VICT. BRIT. P. M. TR. P. VIIII. (or X.) IMP. VII. COS. IIII. P. P. S. C.
Victory seated r., about to inscribe shield. *R.I.C. 440, 452*...................... | 230 | 650

649

649 **Septimius Severus,** 193-211. *N aureus,* commemorating the success of
the punitive Roman campaigns in Scotland during 209 and 210 culminating
in the illness and death of Severus at York in Feb. 211. VICTORIAE BRIT.
Victory advancing l. *R.I.C. 334.* .............................................................. | 2850 | 7250

650 — VICTORIAE BRIT. Victory advancing r., leading child by hand.
*R.I.C. 302.*.................................................................................................. | 3100 | 7400

651 *AR denarius.* VICTORIAE BRIT. Victory advancing r. *R.I.C. 332.* ......... | 70 | 150

651A — VICTORIAE BRIT. Victory stg. facing beside palm-tree with shield
attached. *R.I.C. 336.*.................................................................................. | 75 | 160

651B — VICTORIAE BRIT. Victory stg. l. *R.I.C. 333.*.................................... | 80 | 170

651C — VICTORIAE BRIT. Victory seated l., holding shield. *R.I.C. 335.*....... | 75 | 160

652

652 *Æ sestertius.* VICTORIAE BRITTANNICAE S. C. Two Victories placing
shield on palm-tree with captives at base. *R.I.C. 818.*.............................. | 480 | 1500

653 — P. M. TR. P. XVIII. COS. III. P. P. S. C. Similar. *R.I.C. 796.* ............. | 290 | 700

654 *Æ dupondius.* VICT. BRIT. P. M. TR. P. XIX. COS. III. P. P. S. C. Victory
stg. r. between two captives, holding vexillum. *R.I.C. 809.* .................... | 170 | 450

655 *Æ as.* VICTORIAE BRITTANNICAE S. C. Similar. *R.I.C. 837a.*........... | 190 | 475

|                                                                      | F | VF |
|                                                                      | £ | £ |

656   Billon *tetradrachm* of Alexandria in Egypt. NEIKH KATA BRET. Nike
        flying l. *Milne 2726*. ...................................................................   925   2250
657   **Caracalla,** 198-217. *N aureus,* commemorating the victories achieved
        by the Romans in Scotland during the campaigns led jointly by Severus
        and Caracalla in 209, and by Caracalla alone the following year during
        his father's illness. VICTORIAE BRIT. Victory seated l., holding shield.
        *R.I.C. 174.* ...................................................................................   3100   7400

658                                            659A

658   *R denarius*. VICTORIAE BRIT. Victory advancing l. *R.I.C. 231*. .........   75   160
658A  — VICTORIAE BRIT. Victory advancing r., holding trophy. *R.I.C. 231A*.   75   160
659   Æ *sestertius*. VICTORIAE BRITTANNICAE S. C. Victory stg. r., erecting
        trophy to r. of which Britannia stands facing, captive at feet. *R.I.C. 464*.   400   1100
659A  — VICT. BRIT. TR. P. XIIII. COS. III. S.C. Similar. *Cf. R.I.C. 483c*. ....   350   925
660   Æ *dupondius*. VICTORIAE BRITTANNICAE S. C. Victory stg. r.,
        inscribing shield set on palm-tree. *R.I.C. 467*...........................................   170   425
661   Æ *as*. VICT. BRIT. TR. P. XIIII. COS. III. S. C. Similar. *R.I.C. 490*.......   150   380
662   **Geta,** 209-212. *R denarius,* commemorating the victories achieved by
        his father and brother in Scotland in 209-10 while he and his mother were
        resident in London. VICTORIAE BRIT. Victory stg. l. *R.I.C. 92*............   80   170
662A  — VICTORIAE BRIT. Victory advancing r. *R.I.C. 91*. ..........................   80   170

663

663   Æ *sestertius*. VICTORIAE BRITTANNICAE S. C. Victory seated r.,
        inscribing shield set on knee. *R.I.C. 166*. ....................................................   475   1450
663A  — VICT. BRIT. TR. P. III. COS. II. S. C. Similar. *R.I.C. 172b*. ..............   400   1050
664   Æ *as*. VICTORIAE BRITTANNICAE S. C. Victory seated l., balancing
        shield on knee. *R.I.C. 191a*. ...................................................................   170   480
665   Billon *tetradrachm* of Alexandria in Egypt. NEIKH KATA BRETAN.
        Nike advancing l. *B.M.C. (Alexandria) 1481*. .........................................   1000   2500

## 3. OFFICIAL ROMAN COINAGE STRUCK IN BRITAIN

The London mint, and the associated 'C' mint (new research indicates that this was a secondary mint that operated initially in North London and subsequently moved around the country with Carausius), were created by the usurper Carausius soon after his seizure of Britain in 287. Prior to this, in the mid-2nd century, there may have been minting of 'Britannia' asses of Antoninus Pius in the province using dies brought from Rome, though this has not been firmly established. After the downfall of the rebel British regime in 296 the minting establishment in London (though not the subsidiary mint) was retained by the tetrarchal government and the succeeding Constantinian administration. Early in 325, however, Constantine the Great closed the London mint after almost four decades of operation. A possible brief revival under the usurper Magnus Maximus has been postulated for gold and silver coins marked 'AVG', 'AVGOB' and 'AVGPS', though the attribution has not received universal acceptance.

For more on the bronze coinage struck at London Mint c.296-97 to c.325 see Cloke, H.J. and Toone, L., *The London Mint of Constantius and Constantine* (Spink 2015).

|  |  | F | VF |
|---|---|---|---|
|  |  | £ | £ |
| 666 | **Antoninus Pius,** 138-161. Æ *as,* struck in northern Britain (?) in 155. BRITANNIA COS. IIII. S. C. Britannia seated l. on rock, shield and vexillum in background. *R.I.C. 930.* | 175 | 480 |

*Many poorly struck examples of this type have been found on Romano-British sites, notably at Brocolitia (Carrawburgh) fort on Hadrian's Wall in Northumberland, where no fewer than 327 specimens were discovered in the great votive deposit in the well which formed part of the shrine of the water-nymph Coventina. There appears to be a very real possibility that many of these 'Britannia' asses had been issued from a temporary mint in Britain, most likely situated in the north. The dies, however, are quite regular, and would thus have been brought from Rome to the island province for the express purpose of supplementing the money supply at a time of crisis.*

| 667 | **Carausius,** usurper in Britain and northwestern Gaul, A.D. 286-293. ₳ *aureus,* London. CONSERVAT. AVG. Jupiter stg. l., eagle at feet, ML in ex. *R.I.C. 1.* | 34000 | 95000 |
| 667A | Æ *denarius* ADVENTVS AUG. Emperor riding l., captive before horse. *R.I.C. 1068* | 1700 | 3800 |
| 667B | — CONCORDIA AVG. Clasped hands. RSR. *R.I.C. 545* | 1300 | 3000 |
| 668 | — EXPECTATE VENI. Britannia stg. r. and emperor l., clasping hands, RSR in ex. *R.I.C. 555.* | 1600 | 3600 |

669                                    672A

| 669 | — RENOVAT. ROMANO. She-wolf r., suckling twins, RSR in ex. *R.I.C. 571.* | 1400 | 3200 |
| 669A | — Rev. VIRTVS AVG. Lion walking l. RSR in exergue. *R.I.C. 591.* | 1900 | 4200 |
| 669B | — Rev. VOTO PVBLICO, MVLTIS XX IMP in altar. RSR below. *R.I.C. 595.* | 1500 | 3400 |
| 670 | Billon *antoninianus,* London. COMES AVG. Victory stg. l., S—P in field, ML in ex. *R.I.C. 14.* | 110 | 300 |
| 670A | — HILARITAS AVG. Hilaritas stg. l., B—E in field, MLXXI in ex. *R.I.C. 41.* | 85 | 210 |

|   |   | F | VF |
|---|---|---|---|
|   |   | £ | £ |
| 671 | — LAETITIA AVG. Laetitia stg. l., F—O in field, ML in ex. *R.I.C. 50.*. | 70 | 175 |
| 671A | — LEG. II. AVG. Capricorn l., ML in ex. *R.I.C. 58.* | 160 | 400 |
|   | *Legio II Augusta was stationed at Isca (Caerleon in South Wales).* |   |   |
| 672 | — LEG. XX. V. V. Boar stg. r. *R.I.C. 82.* | 175 | 450 |
|   | *Legio XX Valeria Victrix was stationed at Deva (Chester in the northwest Midlands).* |   |   |
| 672A | — PAX AVG. Pax stg. l., F—O in field, ML in ex. *R.I.C. 101.* | 55 | 140 |
| 673 | — Similar, but without mint mark. *R.I.C. 880.* | 50 | 130 |
| 673A | — PROVIDENT. AVG. Providentia stg. l., B—E in field, MLXXI in ex. *R.I.C. 149.* | 65 | 170 |
| 674 | — SALVS AVGGG. Salus stg. r., feeding snake held in her arms, S—P in field, ML in ex. *R.I.C. 164.* | 90 | 220 |
|   | *The reverse legends with triple-ending (AVGGG.) presumably are subsequent to Carausius' recognition by Diocletian and Maximian in 289 following the failure of the latter's attempt to dislodge the usurper from his island stronghold.* |   |   |
| 674A | — TEMPORVM FELICITAS. Felicitas stg. l., B—E in field, ML in ex. *R.I.C. 172.* | 65 | 170 |
| 675 | — VIRTVS AVGGG. Mars (or Virtus) stg. r., holding spear and shield, S—P in field, MLXXI in ex. *R.I.C. 183.* | 90 | 220 |
| 676 | Billon *antoninianus*, Colchester (?). CONCORDIA MILIT. Emperor stg. r. and Concordia l., clasping hands, C in ex. *R.I.C. 205.* | 140 | 375 |
| 676A | — EXPECTATE VENI. Britannia stg. r. and emperor l., clasping hands, MSC in ex. *R.I.C. 216.* | 200 | 550 |
| 677 | — FELICITAS AVG. Galley with mast and rowers, CXXI in ex. *R.I.C. 221.* | 185 | 500 |
| 677A | — FORTVNA RAEDVX. Fortuna seated l., SPC in ex. *R.I.C. 237.* | 110 | 280 |
| 678 | — LAETITIA AVG. Laetitia stg. l., globe at feet, S—P in field, C in ex. *R.I.C. 255.* | 65 | 170 |
| 678A | —-MONETA AVG. Moneta stg. l., CXXI in ex. *R.I.C. 287.* | 80 | 200 |
| 679 | — ORIENS AVG. Sol stg. l., C in ex. *R.I.C. 293.* | 90 | 220 |
| 679A | — PAX AVGGG. Pax stg. l., S—P in field, MC in ex. *R.I.C. 335.* | 60 | 140 |

680

| 680 | — PROVID. AVG. Providentia stg. l., S—P in field, C in ex. *R.I.C. 353.* | 65 | 170 |
|---|---|---|---|
| 680A | — SALVS AVG. Salus stg. l. at altar, feeding snake, S—C in field, C in ex. *R.I.C. 396.* | 85 | 220 |
| 681 | — SPES PVBLICA. Spes walking l., holding flower, S—P in field, C in ex. *R.I.C. 413.* | 95 | 240 |
| 681A | — VICTORIA AVG. Victory advancing l., captive at feet, MC in ex. *R.I.C. 429.* | 100 | 275 |
| 682 | **Carausius, Diocletian and Maximian,** after 289. Billon *antoninianus*, Colchester (?). Obv. CARAVSIVS ET FRATRES SVI. Conjoined busts of the three emperors l. Rev. PAX AVGGG. Pax stg. l., S—P in field, C in ex. *R.I.C. 1.* | 1900 | 5000 |

682A                                           683

|  | F | VF |
|---|---|---|
|  | £ | £ |

682A — MONETA AVGGG. Moneta stg. l., S—P in field, C in ex. *R.I.C.* —..    2100   5250
*See also nos. 693-4 and 698-700 as well as regular Carausian types with*
*the triple-ending 'AVGGG.' on reverse.*
683 **Allectus,** usurper in Britain, 293-296. *N aureus,* London. ORIENS AVG.
Sol stg. l. between two captives, ML in ex. *R.I.C. 4.*............................ 38000 110000
684 Æ *antoninianus,* London. LAETITIA AVG. Laetitia stg. l., S—A in field,
35000MSL in ex. *R.I.C. 22.*..................................................... 80   200

684A

684A — PAX AVG. Pax stg. l., S—A in field, ML in ex. *R.I.C. 28.* ................. 65   170
685 — PROVID. AVG. Providentia stg. l., holding globe and cornucopiae,
S—P in field, ML in ex. *R.I.C. 36.* .......................................... 80   200
685A — SALVS AVG. Salus stg. r., feeding snake held in her arms, S—A in
field, MSL in ex. *R.I.C. 42.*................................................. 90   240
686 — TEMPOR. FELICITAS. Felicitas stg. l., S—A in field, ML in ex. *R.I.C. 47.* 80   200
686A — VICTORIA AVG. Victory advancing l., S—P in field, ML in ex. *R.I.C. 48.* 100   260
687 Æ *antoninianus,* Colchester (?). AEQVITAS AVG. Aequitas stg. l., S—P
in field, C in ex. *R.I.C. 63.* ................................................ 80   200
687A — FIDES MILITVM. Fides stg. l., holding two standards, S—P in field,
C in ex. *R.I.C. 69.* .......................................................... 100   240

688A

688 — LAETITIA AVG. Laetitia stg. l., S—P in field, CL in ex. *R.I.C. 79.* .. 85   220
*This form of mint mark has given rise to the alternative identification of*
*this mint as Clausentum (Bitterne, Hants.)*
688A — MONETA AVG. Moneta stg. l., S—P in field, C in ex. *R.I.C. 82.* ...... 80   200

|     |     |     |     | F | VF |
| --- | --- | --- | --- | --- | --- |
|     |     |     |     | £ | £ |
| 689 | — PAX AVG. Pax stg. l., S—P in field, C in ex. *R.I.C. 86.* ................. | | | 65 | 170 |
| 689A | — PROVIDENTIA AVG. Providentia stg. l., globe at feet, S—P in field, C in ex. *R.I.C. 111.* ................ | | | 70 | 180 |
| 690 | — TEMPORVM FELIC. Felicitas stg. l., S—P in field, CL in ex. *R.I.C. 117.* | | | 80 | 200 |
| 690A | — VIRTVS AVG. Mars stg. r., holding spear and shield, S—P in field, C in ex. *R.I.C. 121.* ................ | | | 90 | 240 |
| 691 | Æ *'quinarius'*, London. VIRTVS AVG. Galley l., QL in ex. *R.I.C. 55.* .... | | | 65 | 180 |

*An experimental denomination issued only during this reign, the types of the so-called 'quinarius' would seem to indicate that it was in some way associated with the operations of the fleet upon which the survival of the rebel regime in Britain was totally dependent.*

692                                        693

| 692 | Æ *'quinarius'*, Colchester (?). LAETITIA AVG. Galley r., QC in ex. *R.I.C. 124.* ............. | | | 65 | 180 |
| --- | --- | --- | --- | --- | --- |
| 692A | — VIRTVS AVG. Galley l., QC in ex. *R.I.C. 128.* ................ | | | 65 | 180 |
| 693 | **Diocletian,** 284-305. Billon *antoninianus* of London, struck by Carausius between 289 and 293. PAX AVGGG. Pax stg. l., S—P in field, MLXXI in ex. *R.I.C. 9.* ............. | | | 75 | 200 |
| 694 | Billon *antoninianus* of Colchester (?), same date. PROVID AVGGG. Providentia stg. l., globe at feet, S—P in field, C in ex. *R.I.C. 22* ............ | | | 80 | 220 |

695

| 695 | Æ *follis*, London. GENIO POPVLI ROMANI. Genius stg. l., LON in ex. *R.I.C. 1a.* ............. | | | 220 | 550 |
| --- | --- | --- | --- | --- | --- |

*By the time the central government had recovered control of Britain in 296 the antoninianus had been replaced by the larger follis under Diocletian's sweeping currency reform. London was retained as an official imperial mint, but the secondary British establishment (at Colchester?) was now abandoned. Except for its initial issue in 297 (marked 'LON') the London mint under the tetrarchic government produced only unsigned folles throughout its first decade of operation. Perhaps Constantius did not wish to draw attention to his employment of a mint which had been the creation of a rebel regime.*

| 696 | — Similar, but without mint mark. *R.I.C. 6a.* ................ | | | 30 | 65 |
| --- | --- | --- | --- | --- | --- |

|                                                                                                      | F    | VF   |
|                                                                                                      | £    | £    |
| 697 — (post-abdication coinage, after 305). PROVIDENTIA DEORVM QVIES AVGG. Quies and Providentia stg. facing each other (no mint mark). *R.I.C. 77a.* | 45   | 100  |

697A                                    704

| 697A — QVIES AVGG. Quies stg. l., holding branch and sceptre, PLN in ex. *R.I.C. 98.* | 40 | 100 |
| 698 **Maximian,** 286-305 and 306-308. Æ *aureus* of London, struck by Carausius between 289 and 293. SALVS AVGGG. Salus stg. r., feeding snake held in her arms, ML in ex. *R.I.C. 32.* | 30000 | 80000 |
| 699 Billon *antoninianus* of London, same date. PROVIDENTIA AVGGG. Providentia stg. l., S—P in field, MLXXI in ex. *R.I.C. 37.* | 65 | 160 |
| 700 Billon *antoninianus* of Colchester (?), same date. PAX AVGGG. Pax stg. l., S—P in field, C in ex. *R.I.C. 42.* | 65 | 160 |
| 701 Æ *follis,* London. GENIO POPVLI ROMANI. Genius stg. l., LON in ex. *R.I.C. 2.* | 190 | 450 |
| 702 — Similar, but without mint mark. *R.I.C. 23b.* | 30 | 65 |
| 703 — (post-abdication coinage, after 305). PROVIDENTIA DEORVM QVIES AVGG. Quies and Providentia stg. facing each other (no mint mark). *R.I.C. 77b.* | 45 | 100 |

706

| 704 — (second reign). GENIO POP. ROM. Genius stg. l., PLN in ex. *R.I.C. 90.* | 35 | 80 |
| 704A — HERCVLI CONSERVATORI. Hercules stg. l., resting on club, PLN in ex. *R.I.C. 91.* | 45 | 110 |
| 705 **Constantius I,** 305-306 (Caesar 293-305). Æ *follis,* London (as Caesar). GENIO POPVLI ROMANI. Genius stg. l., LON in ex. *R.I.C. 4a.* | 220 | 550 |
| 706 — Similar, but without mint mark. *R.I.C. 30.* | 25 | 55 |
| 707 — (as Augustus). Similar. *R.I.C. 52a.* | 30 | 65 |
| 708 **Divus Constantius I,** deified 306. Æ *follis,* London. MEMORIA FELIX. Altar flanked by eagles, PLN in ex. *R.I.C. 110.* | 35 | 90 |
| 709 **Galerius,** 305-311 (Caesar 293-305). Æ *follis,* London (as Caesar). GENIO POPVLI ROMANI. Genius stg. l., LON in ex. *R.I.C. 4b.* | 190 | 450 |

|     |                                                                                                      | F  | VF |
|-----|------------------------------------------------------------------------------------------------------|----|----|
|     |                                                                                                      | £  | £  |
| 710 | — Similar, but without mint mark. *R.I.C. 15.* ...........................................            | 25 | 50 |
| 711 | — (as Augustus). Similar. *R.I.C. 42.* ...........................................                    | 25 | 50 |
| 711A| — GENIO POP. ROM. Genius stg. l., PLN in ex. *R.I.C. 86.* ...................                          | 30 | 65 |
| 712 | **Severus II,** 306-307 (Caesar 305-306). Æ *follis,* London (as Caesar).                              |    |    |
|     | GENIO POPVLI ROMANI. Genius stg. l. (no mint mark). *R.I.C. 58a* ...                                   | 50 | 120|
| 713 | — (as Augustus). Similar. *R.I.C. 52c.* ...........................................                   | 50 | 120|
| 714 | **Maximinus II,** 310-313 (Caesar 305-310). Æ *follis,* London (as Caesar).                            |    |    |
|     | GENIO POPVLI ROMANI. Genius stg. l. (no mint mark). *R.I.C. 57.* .....                                 | 25 | 55 |
| 715 | —-GENIO POP. ROM. Genius stg. l., PLN in ex. *R.I.C. 89a* ...............                              | 25 | 60 |
| 716 | — (as Augustus). Similar, but with star in r. field. *R.I.C. 209b.* ...............                    | 25 | 55 |
| 717 | **Licinius,** 308-324. Æ *follis,* London. GENIO POP. ROM. Genius stg. l.,                             |    |    |
|     | star in r. field, PLN in ex. *R.I.C. 209c.* .....................................                     | 25 | 55 |
| 717A| — Similar, but with S—F in field. *R.I.C. 3.* ...........................................             | 25 | 50 |
| 718 | — SOLI INVICTO COMITI. Sol stg. l., holding globe, S—P in field,                                       |    |    |
|     | MSL in ex. *R.I.C. 79.* ...........................................                                   | 25 | 50 |
| 719 | **Constantine I, the Great,** 307-337 (Caesar 306-307). Æ *follis,* London                             |    |    |
|     | (as Caesar). GENIO POPVLI ROMANI. Genius stg. l. (no mint mark).                                       |    |    |
|     | *R.I.C. 72.* ...........................................                                              | 35 | 80 |
| 719A| — GENIO POP. ROM. Genius stg. l., PLN in ex. *R.I.C. 88b* .................                            | 25 | 55 |
| 720 | — PRINCIPI IVVENTVTIS. Prince stg. l., holding standards, PLN in ex.                                   |    |    |
|     | *R.I.C. 97.* ...........................................                                              | 35 | 85 |
| 721 | — (as Augustus). ADVENTVS AVG. Emperor on horseback l., captive                                        |    |    |
|     | on ground before, star in r. field, PLN in ex. *R.I.C. 133.* .........................                | 40 | 90 |
| 722 | — COMITI AVGG. NN. Sol stg. l., holding globe and whip, same mint                                      |    |    |
|     | mark. *R.I.C. 155.* ...........................................                                       | 30 | 65 |
| 723 | — CONCORD. MILIT. Concordia stg. l., holding standards, same mint                                      |    |    |
|     | mark. *R.I.C. 195.* ...........................................                                       | 25 | 60 |
| 724 | — MARTI CONSERVATORI. Mars. stg. r., holding spear and shield,                                         |    |    |
|     | star in l. field, PLN in ex. *R.I.C. 254.* .....................................                      | 25 | 60 |
| 724A| — SOLI INVICTO COMITI. Sol stg. l., holding globe, S—F in field,                                       |    |    |
|     | MLL in ex. *R.I.C. 27.* ...........................................                                   | 20 | 45 |
| 725 | Æ 3, London. VICTORIAE LAETAE PRINC. PERP. Two Victories                                               |    |    |
|     | supporting shield, inscribed VOT. / P. R., over altar, PLN in ex. *R.I.C. 159.*                        | 20 | 40 |

726

| 726 | — VIRTVS EXERCIT. Vexillum, inscribed VOT. / XX., between two                                          |    |    |
|-----|------------------------------------------------------------------------------------------------------|----|----|
|     | captives, PLN in ex. R.I.C. 191. ...........................................                          | 20 | 40 |
| 727 | — BEAT. TRANQLITAS. Altar, inscribed VOT / IS / XX., surmounted                                        |    |    |
|     | by globe and three stars, PLON in ex. *R.I.C. 267* ...............................                    | 20 | 40 |
| 727A| — SARMATIA DEVICTA. Victory advancing r., trampling captive,                                           |    |    |
|     | PLON and crescent in ex. *R.I.C. 289.* ...........................................                   | 30 | 60 |
| 728 | — PROVIDENTIAE AVGG. Gateway of military camp, PLON in ex.                                             |    |    |
|     | *R.I.C. 293.* ...........................................                                             | 20 | 40 |

|     |                                                                                 | F    | VF  |
|-----|---------------------------------------------------------------------------------|------|-----|
|     |                                                                                 | £    | £   |
| 729 | **Fausta,** wife of Constantine I. Æ 3, London. SALVS REIPVBLICAE. Empress stg. l., holding two children, PLON in ex. *R.I.C. 300.* ............... | 130 | 350 |
| 730 | **Helena,** mother of Constantine I. Æ 3, London. SECVRITAS REIPVBLICE. Empress stg. l., holding branch, PLON in ex. *R.I.C. 299.* ........................ | 130 | 350 |
| 731 | **Crispus,** eldest son of Constantine I, Caesar 317-326. Æ 3, London. SOLI INVICTO COMITI. Sol stg. l., holding globe, crescent in l. field, PLN in ex. *R.I.C. 144.* ............ | 25 | 50 |
| 731A | — VIRTVS EXERCIT. Vexillum, inscribed VOT. / XX., between two captives, PLN in ex. *R.I.C. 194.* ............ | 25 | 50 |
| 732 | — BEATA TRANQVILLITAS. Altar, inscribed VOT / IS / XX., surmounted by globe and three stars, P—A in field, PLON in ex. *R.I.C. 211.* | 20 | 40 |
| 733 | — CAESARVM NOSTRORVM around wreath containing VOT. / X., PLON and crescent in ex. *R.I.C. 291.* ..................................................... | 20 | 40 |

734

| 734 | — PROVIDENTIAE CAESS. Gateway of military camp, PLON in ex. *R.I.C. 295.* ................................................................................... | 20 | 40 |
|-----|---------------------------------------------------------------------------------|------|-----|
| 735 | **Constantine II,** 337-340 (Caesar 317-337). Æ 3, London (as Caesar). CLARITAS REIPVBLICAE. Sol stg. l., holding globe, crescent in l. field, PLN in ex. *R.I.C. 131.* ............ | 20 | 40 |
| 736 | — VICTORIAE LAETAE PRINC. PERP. Two Victories supporting shield, inscribed VOT. / P. R., over altar ornamented with wreath, PLN in ex. *R.I.C. 182.* ............ | 20 | 40 |
| 737 | — VIRTVS EXERCIT. Vexillum, inscribed VOT. / XX., between two captives, PLON in ex. *R.I.C. 190.* ............ | 20 | 40 |

737A

| 737A | — BEATA TRANQVILLITAS. Altar, inscribed VOT / IS / XX., surmounted by globe and three stars, PLON in ex. *R.I.C. 236.* ............... | 20 | 40 |
|------|---------------------------------------------------------------------------------|------|-----|
| 738 | — CAESARVM NOSTRORVM around wreath containing VOT. / X., PLON and crescent in ex. *R.I.C. 292.* ............ | 20 | 40 |
| 738A | — PROVIDENTIAE CAESS. Gateway of military camp, PLON in ex. *R.I.C. 296.* ............ | 20 | 40 |
| 739 | **Constantius II,** 337-361 (Caesar 324-337). Æ 3, London (as Caesar). PROVIDENTIAE CAESS. Gateway of military camp, PLON in ex. *R.I.C. 298.* ............ | 35 | 85 |

|  | F | VF |
|--|---|----|
|  | £ | £ |

740    **Magnus Maximus,** usurper in the West, 383-388. *A' solidus,* London (?). RESTITVTOR REIPVBLICAE. Emperor stg. r., holding labarum and Victory, AVG in ex. *R.I.C. 1.* ..................................................................     *Unique*

*The attribution to London of this rare series has not been firmly established, though Maximus was certainly proclaimed emperor in Britain and it is well attested that the principal city of the British provinces bore the name 'Augusta' in the late Roman period (Ammianus Marcellinus XXVII, 8, 7; XXVIII, 3, 7).*

741

741    — VICTORIA AVGG. Two emperors enthroned facing, Victory hovering in background between them, AVGOB in ex. *R.I.C. 2b.* ..........................    7500   25000

*Maximus appears to have struck a similar type in the name of the eastern emperor Theodosius I (cf. R.I.C. 2a), though it is presently known only from a silver-gilt specimen preserved in the British Museum.*

742    *AR siliqua,* London (?). VOT. / V. / MVLT. / X. within wreath, AVG below. *R.I.C. 4.* .........................................................................................    1200    3400

742A   — VICTORIA AVGG. Victory advancing l., AVGPS in ex. *R.I.C. 3.* ......    1100    2800

# 4. IMITATIONS OF ROMAN COINS PRODUCED IN BRITAIN

At certain periods during the three and a half centuries of its occupation Roman Britain seems to have been the source of much local imitation of the official imported coinage. This began soon after the Claudian invasion in A.D. 43 when significant quantities of sestertii, dupondii and asses (especially the last) were produced in the newly conquered territory, as evidenced by the frequency of their occurrence in archaeological finds. The technical excellence of many of these 'copies', together with the surprising extent of their minting, would seem to indicate that some, at least, of these coins were produced with official sanction in order to make good an unexpected deficiency in the currency supply. Others are much poorer and well below weight, representing the 'unofficial' branch of this operation, some of it probably emanating from territory as yet unconquered. As conditions in the new province settled down rapid Romanisation and urbanisation of British society brought a general increase in wealth, and with it a much greater volume of currency flowing into the country. Local imitation now virtually ceased, except for the occasional activities of criminal counterfeiters, and this state of affairs lasted down to the great political crisis and financial collapse of the second half of the 3rd century. At this point large scale minting of imitations of the debased antoniniani of the late 260s and early 270s began in Britain and in the other northwestern provinces, all of which had been seriousy affected by the political dislocation of this turbulent era. This class of imitations is usually referred to as 'barbarous radiates', the emperor's spiky crown being a constant and conspicuous feature of the obverses. Most frequently copied were the antoniniani of the Gallic rulers Tetricus Senior and Tetricus Junior (ca. 270-273) and the posthumous issues of Claudius Gothicus (died 270). The quality of the 'barbarous radiates' is variable in the extreme, some exhibiting what appears to be a revival of Celtic art forms, others so tiny that it is virtually impossible to see anything of the design. Their production appears to have ended abruptly with Aurelian's reconquest of the western provinces in 273. A similar phenomenon, though on a lesser scale, occurred in the middle decades of the following century when normal life in Britain was again disrupted, not only by usurpation but additionally by foreign invasion. With supplies of currency from the Continent temporarily disrupted, local imitation, particularly of the 'Æ 2' and 'Æ 3' issues of Constantius II and the usurper Magnentius, began in earnest. How long this continued is difficult to determine as life in the island province was now subject to increasingly frequent episodes of dislocation. By now urban life in Britain was in serious decline and when Roman rule ended early in the 5th century, bringing a total cessation of currency supplies, the catastrophic decline in monetary commerce in the former provinces rendered it no longer necessary for the deficiency to be made good.

|  |  | F £ | VF £ |
|---|---|---|---|
| 743 | **Agrippa,** died 12 B.C. Æ as, of irregular British mintage, imitating the Roman issue made under Agrippa's grandson Caligula, A.D. 37-41. S. C. Neptune stg. l., holding dolphin and trident. .................................... | 65 | 160 |
|  | *The large official issue of Agrippa asses was made shortly before the Claudian invasion of Britain in A.D. 43 and would thus have comprised a significant proportion of the 'aes' in circulation at this time. In consequence, it would soon have become familiar to the new provincials providing an ideal prototype for imitation.* | | |
| 744 | **Claudius,** 41-54. Æ *sestertius,* of irregular British mintage. SPES AVGVSTA S. C. Spes walking l., holding flower. .................................. | 140 | 450 |
| 745 | Æ *dupondius,* of irregular British mintage. CERES AVGVSTA S. C. Ceres enthroned l., holding corn- ears and torch..................................... | 55 | 140 |

746

| 746 | Æ *as,* of irregular British mintage. S. C. Minerva advancing r., brandishing spear and holding shield. ......................................................................... | 50 | 130 |
|---|---|---|---|
|  | *This is by far the commonest of the Claudian imitations and the prototypes must have represented the bulk of the aes coinage carried by the legions at the time of the invasion. The martial type may well have been specially selected as a suitable theme for the initial import of coinage into the newly conquered territory.* | | |
| 747 | **Nero Claudius Drusus,** father of Claudius, died 9 B.C. Æ *sestertius,* of irregular British mintage. TI. CLAVDIVS CAESAR AVG. P. M. TR .P. IMP. S. C. Claudius seated l. on curule chair amidst arms ...................... | 175 | 450 |
|  | *This type was issued by Claudius half a century after his father's death and would thus have been prominently represented in the initial wave of coinage imported into the new province.* | | |
| 748 | **Antonia,** mother of Claudius, died A.D. 37. Æ *dupondius,* of irregular British mintage. TI. CLAVDIVS CAESAR AVG P.M. TR. P. IMP. P. P. S. C. Claudius stg. l., holding simpulum. ......................................................................... | 100 | 325 |
|  | *Another Claudian issue for a deceased parent, this represents one of only two dupondius types struck during this reign and would have entered Britain in significant quantities at the time of the invasion in A.D. 43.* | | |

749A                    749B                    749C

|                                                                              | F | VF |
|---|---|---|
|                                                                              | £ | £ |
| 749 'Barbarous radiates', ca. 270-273. British and Continental imitations of billon *antoniniani*, principally of Divus Claudius II (A), Tetricus Senior (B) and Tetricus Junior (C). The inscriptions are usually blundered and the types sometimes unrecognizable. British mintage can only be established by provenance. | 10 | 20 |
| 750 Barbarous 4th century, mostly of the second half of the century, and principally imitated from 'Æ 2' and 'Æ 3' issues of the later Constantinian period, notably those of Constantius II ('soldier spearing fallen horseman' type), and the usurpers Magnentius and Decentius ('two Victories' type). The copies, especially those of Magnentius and Decentius, are often of excellent style and execution, though the legends frequently contain small errors. Those of Constantius II are sometimes very barbarous and poorly struck, occasionally over regular issues of the earlier Constantinian period. Again, the likelihood of British mintage can only be established by provenance. | 15-20 | 20-25 |

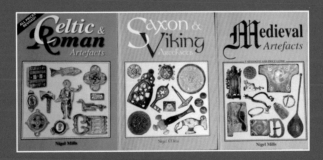

# ENGLISH HAMMERED COINAGE *c.*600-1662

84

## Grading of Hammered Coins

As the name suggests, hammered coins were struck by hand with a hammer. This can lead to the coin being struck off-centre, double struck, areas of the design not being struck up as well as cracks or other defects in the flan. It is important to take these factors into account along with surface wear, quality of the metal and patina when assessing the grade of this series. Value is considerably reduced if the coin is holed, pierced, plugged or mounted. Coins with proven provenance from important old collections will carry a price premium. For further detail on condition see pages ix to x.

**Extremely Fine**   **Very Fine**   **Fine**

William I PAXS type penny

Henry VIII 1st coinage gold Angel

Edward VI silver shilling

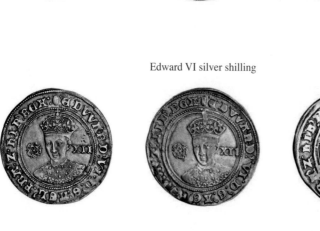

# EARLY & MIDDLE ANGLO-SAXON KINGDOMS & MINTS (c.650-973)

# EARLY ANGLO-SAXON PERIOD, *c*. 600-*c*. 775

The withdrawal of Roman forces from Britain early in the 5th century A.D. and the gradual decline of central administration resulted in a rapid deterioration of the money supply. The arrival of Germanic raiders and settlers, even in relatively small numbers, disrupted life and it was probably not until late in the 6th century that renewed political, cultural and commercial links with the kingdom of the Merovingian Franks led to the appearance of small quantities of Merovingian gold *tremisses* (one-third solidus) in England. A purse containing 37 such pieces (plus 3 gold blanks and 2 ingots) was found in the Sutton Hoo ship-burial; a further hoard of at least 60 Continental tremisses came to light in Norfolk in 2014. Native Anglo-Saxon gold shillings (*thrymsas*) were minted from the *c*.620s, initially in the style of their continental prototypes or copied from obsolete Roman coinage with others in pure Anglo-Saxon style. The mixed Crondall hoard of 101 gold coins (1 Byzantine, 24 Merovingian or Frankish, 69 Anglo-Saxon, 7 others) gives structure to the arrangement of thrymsas with types found in this hoard differentiated from those, some of the same date, that were not. By the middle of the 7th century the gold coinage was being increasingly debased with silver, and according to recent scientific analysis of grave goods gold had been superseded entirely by the 660s.

The silver coins, contemporary with the *deniers or denarii* of the Merovingian Franks, are the first English pennies, typically referred to as *sceats* or *sceattas* (pronounced 'skeets' or 'shatters' possibly meaning 'treasure' or 'wealth'); the singular is *sceat*. The term early-penny is now favoured. They provide important material for the student of Anglo-Saxon art. Indeed, it could be said that, until recently, the largely anonymous, anepigraphic, nature of the sceatta coinage detracted from its numismatic character, however, Anna Gannon's work on the subtle iconography of this period has elevated its status significantly.

The silver coins of the early ('primary') phase, *c*.680-710, are a transition from the gold coinage and are conservative in style. Those of the 'secondary' period, *c*.710-60, are far more diverse in design. Trading types were issued in substantial numbers (probably tens of millions) especially by the Frisians of the Low Countries ('Continental'), evidencing the significant volume of North Sea trade, and their central role in the economic resurgence. Early coins are of good silver content, though the quality deteriorates early in the 8th century, with weights then averaging around 1.00 g. The secondary types exist in numerous varieties, though the survival rate, for the non-trading types is low and for some types, extremely low. The designs on many of these mix Christian with pagan symbolism though the iconography is often, and probably intentionally, ambiguous. In this the coinage reflects the changes taking place during the period when Christianity was being adopted with the designs looking appealing to differing cultural strands in Anglo-Saxon England at the time. As well as the official issues there are mules and other varieties, which may be contemporary imitations; there is no clear line of demarcation. The 'eclectic' types are those which do not sit comfortably in the alphabetic Serial classification. However, Abramson's listing of varieties recognised here attempts to bring the eclectic issues into the general classification.

Many of the sceats were issued at the time of Aethelbald, King of Mercia, (A.D. 716-757) who was overlord of the southern English, but as few bear inscriptions it is only in recent years that research has enabled their correct dating and the attribution of certain types to specific areas. The Northumbrian issues are more literate and facilitate attribution to issuers. The Aston Rowant (Oxon.) hoard of 324 sceats, deposited *c*. 710, separates the primary and secondary phases. The sceatta 'penny' coinage came to an end *c*.780 when it was replaced by the broad flan penny initially in Kent before its wider adoption in Mercia. The Northumbrian kingdom continued to use the small flan sceatta which after 810 was increasingly a copper coinage, known as stycas, this ending with Danish conquest of York in 867.

Through recent detector finds and continued research, a definitive classification is evolving but remains fluid. The arrangement given below is informed by Michael Metcalf's work on the series, developing Rigold's alphabetical classification. In this listing, the primary sceats are followed by the Continental then the secondary and, finally, the eclectic. This is not chronologically precise as there is some overlap but has been adopted for ease of reference and identification. This list is more extensive than previously published in *Coins of England* but is not exhaustive. The reference Abr. refers to the type listing by Abramson; 'B.M.C.' to the type given in *British Museum Catalogue: Anglo-Saxon Coins*. The reference *M* is to an illustration, and *M. p.* to a page, in Metcalf (below).

Useful reference works include:

Abramson, T., *Sceatta List: An Illustrated and Priced Catalogue of Sceats for Collectors* (2017).

Abramson, T., *The Abramson Collection: Coins of Early Anglo-Saxon England and the North Sea Area*, SCBI, 69 (2018).

Gannon, A., *The Iconography of Early Anglo-Saxon Coinage* (2003).

Gannon, A., British Museum, Anglo Saxon Coins I, *SCBI* 63 (2013).

Lyon, S., 'The Lyon Collection of Anglo-Saxon Coins', *SCBI* 68, (2016).

Metcalf, D. M., *Thrymsas and Sceattas in the Ashmolean Museum,* Vols I-III.

Op den Velde, W., & Klaassen, C.J.F., *Sceattas and Merovingian Deniers from Domburg and Westenschovwen* (2004).

Rigold, S. E., 'The two primary series of sceattas', *B.N.J.,* XXX (1960).

Sutherland, C. H. V., *Anglo-Saxon Gold Coinage in the light of the Crondall Hoard* (1948).

ᚠᚪᚦᚻᚱᚲ·ᚷᛈᚾ�178ᛁ◊ᛋᚳᛄᛏᛒᛗᚻᚱ᛫ᚻᛉᚱᚠᛨᚪ

f  u  th  o  r  k  z  w  h  n  i  j  jh  p  x  s  t  b  e  m  l  ng  d  oe a Æ  ea  y

Early Anglo-Saxon Runes (Futhark)

## GOLD

752

|  | | F<br>£ | VF<br>£ |

**A.  EARLY PIECES, OF UNCERTAIN MONETARY STATUS**

751  Thrymsa. Name and portrait of Bishop Liudhard (chaplain to Queen Bertha of Kent). ℞. Cross. ............................................................................ *Extremely rare*

752  Solidus. Imitating solidi of Roman rulers. Blundered legends, some with runes. *Extremely rare*

753                 754                 758

**B.  CRONDALL TYPES, *c*. 620 – *c*. 645**

Twelve different types, which are almost certainly English, were found in the Crondall hoard of 1828. All are thrysmas, containing 40-70% gold.

| | | F | VF |
|---|---|---|---|
| 753 | 'Witmen' type. Bust r. with trident. ℞. Cross. Legend normally blundered. *M. 1-21* | 1100 | 4000 |
| 754 | London-derived type. Head r. with pseudo-legend. ℞. Cross. Pseudo-legend. *M. 22-32* | 1750 | 7500 |
| 755 | 'Licinius' type. Elegant imitation of Roman triens. Bust l. ℞. VOT XX. *M. 33-41* | 2250 | 10000 |
| 756 | 'LEMC' type. Head l. ℞. Maltese cross with letters L, E, M, C in angles, or cross on steps. *M. 42-9* | 1650 | 7250 |
| 757 | 'LONDINIV' type. Facing bust, crosslets l. and r. ℞. Tall cross, LONDVNIV and pseudo-legend around. *M. 51-7* | 2250 | 10000 |
| 758 | Eadbald of Kent (616-40). London. Bust r. AVDVARLD REGES. ℞. Cross on globule, LONDENVS. Usually garbled. *M. 50* | 4750 | 20000 |
| 758A | — Canterbury. As 758 but DOROVERNVS M. *M-* | 5250 | 22500 |
| 759 | Other crude types, usually with head or bust, ℞. Cross. *M. 58-72* | 850 | 3250 |

## C.   ULTRA-CRONDALL TYPES, *c*. 620 – *c*. 655

Thrymsas not represented in the Crondall hoard, but probably of the same date range.

760                          761

|  |  | F | VF |
|---|---|---|---|
|  |  | £ | £ |
| 760 | 'Benutigo' type. Bust r., blundered legend. R. Cross on steps, runic legend (Benutigoii?) | 2000 | 8500 |
| 761 | 'Wuneetton' type. Bust r., cross before. R. Cross. Blundered legend (WVNEETON or similar). *M. 77* | 1350 | 6000 |
| 762 | 'York' group, inscribed type, stylised face cross each side, lattice pattern below, R. uncertain blundered legend. *M. 76* | 2250 | 9500 |

762                          762B

| 762A | — uninscribed, similar, R., four 'faces' around central square or similar | 2500 | 10000 |
| 762B | — uninscribed, standing facing figure facing hold long cross each side, R., cross within inner circle, symbols around | 3250 | 14500 |
| 763 | — Bishop Paulinus of York (c.625-633), as 762, rev. :PAOLIENVS EP legend some letters inverted | 3750 | 16500 |

## D.   POST-CRONDALL TYPES, *c*. 655 – *c*. 675

Pale gold types, visibly debased and sometimes almost silvery, containing 10-35% gold. The description "standard" is a reference to the Roman legionary ensign bearing the legend e.g. VOTIS X MVLTIS XX also carried in Anglo-Saxon episcopal processions. The legend is reduced to TOTII on the coinage and may be described as the "votive standard".

764            764B            766            767

| 764 | 'Crispus' type. Helmeted bust, r. CRISPVS NOB CAES. R. Cross and XX in wreath, runic legend DESAIONA. *N.7* | 2250 | 9500 |
| 764A | 'Daisy and annulet-cross' type. Flower pattern. R. annulet Latin cross in pseudo wreath. | 2000 | 8500 |
| 764B | 'Head and annulet cross' type, bare head within coiled snake, R. similar to last. | 3250 | 14500 |
| 765 | 'Concordia' type. Radiate bust r. R. Clasped hands. *N.5* | 2500 | 10000 |
| 766 | 'Oath-taking' type. Bust r. or l. with hand placed against cross. R. Lyre-shaped object, or eight-rayed symbol. *N.6* | 1750 | 7500 |
| 767 | 'Two emperors' type. Helmeted bust r. R. Bust of angel with wings above two facing heads. *M. 79-80* | 900 | 3000 |

768A                 769                 771

| | | F | VF |
|---|---|---|---|
| | | £ | £ |
| 768 | 'Pada', Type Ia. Helmeted bust r. Ɍ. Runic PADA on panel. *M.p.73.* ..... | 1100 | 4000 |
| 768A | — Type Ib. Similar. Ɍ. Standard TTXX, PADA in runes in legend. *M. 81* | 900 | 3250 |
| 769 | — Type IIa. bust r. Ɍ. PADA in runes in field, blundered legend around, *M.p.73.* ....................................................................................... | 525 | 1650 |
| 770 | — Type III. bust r. Ɍ. Cross with annulets in angles, legend includes runic PADA and other lettering *M.p.73.* ................................... | 475 | 1500 |
| 771 | 'Vanimundus', Type A. bust r. holding sceptre. Ɍ. Cross, with CA in lower angles. VANIMVNDVS MONE. *M.p.82* ........................... | 750 | 3000 |
| 772 | — Type B. Similar. Ɍ. Small cross in double circle of dots. *M. 84* ......... | 675 | 2750 |

## SILVER

773

### SCEATTA COINAGE, *c.* 675 – *c.* 760
**A.     EARLY TRANSITIONAL TYPES BY THRYMSA MONEYERS, c.675 – c.685**

| 773 | 'Pada', Type III. As 770, but silver. *Abr. 1*, *M. 82, M. p. 73-9* ............... | 275 | 950 |
|---|---|---|---|
| 774 | 'Vanimundus', Type B. As 772, but silver. *Abr. 2*, *M. 85-7. M. p. 80-4* .. | 350 | 1200 |

**B.     PRIMARY PHASE, *c.* 680 – *c.* 710**
Minted in various regions of south-eastern and eastern England.

775

| 775 | **Series A 2a**. Radiate bust r., TIC. Ɍ. Standard, TOTII. Several varieties. *Abr. 3* ......70 | | 250 |
|---|---|---|---|

776                 777

| 776 | **Series BX**. Diademed bust r., VANTAVMA or similar. Ɍ. Bird r. above cross on steps, annulets and pellets in field vary. *Abr. 15, B.M.C. 26. M. 97-9, M. p. 99* | 90 | 325 |
|---|---|---|---|
| 777 | **Series BI**. Diademed head r. within serpent circle. Ɍ. Bird r. on cross. Some with symbols by bird. *Abr. 16, B.M.C. 27a. M. 100-106, M. 113-16* .............. | 40 | 135 |

777A: varieties                              778

|                                                                                      | F    | VF   |
|                                                                                      | £    | £    |

777A **Series BIIIA**, Type 27a. Diademed head r. with either protruding jaw or pointed nose, symbols before, serpent circle. R. Full bodied or linear bird on cross within serpent circle, annulets either side, pellets below. *Abr. 16.70-80, M. p. 158-65* .   60    200

778  **Series BZ**. Abstract facing head. R. Simplified bird on cross in linear style, blundered legend. *Abr. 17, BMC 29a, M. 138-9. M. p. 136-7* ..................   110   375

779 C1                              779 C2

779  **Series C**. Radiate bust r., similar to 775 but runic FMCF replaces TIC. R. Variety C1, standard, TOTII; variety C2, four crosses around standard, variety C2, cross abuts standard. *Abr. 4, B.M.C. 2b. M. 117-125, 132-2. M. P. 106-13* ...................   45    145

780                              781

780  Attributed to King Aethelred of Mercia (674-704). Degenerate head. R. 'Æthiliræd' in runes in two lines. *Abr. 92, M. 134-5, M. p. 120-4* ..............................   225   750

781  **Series F**. Bust r., with pelleted helmet, blundered legend. R. Small cross on steps, arrangement of surrounding annulets and letters "T" and "I" varies, as do styles. *Abr. 106, M. 136-7, M. p. 125-32* ...........................................   65    225

782: various styles

782  **Series Z**. Broad facing portrait (Christ?) with forked or straight beard. R. Hound running r., legs straight or crossed, tail curled beneath or above, erect ears sometimes with chevrons above, various styles known. Some coarse. *Abr. 102.10-60, BMC 66, M. 140-2, M. p. 137-8* .....................................   325   1100

782A                              783

782A **Series Z-related**. Skeletal hound r., perhaps copy of 782. R. Saltire standard or cross-crosslet design, various styles known. *Abr. 102.70-80, M. 143-4, M. p. 138-9*..........................................................................................   175   575

783  **'Vernus' group**, Types 2b, 3b and 91. Degenerate head r., VER before, execution deteriorates in later issues. R. Standard, various styles known. *Abr. 6, M. 146-8, M. p. 140-6* ..............................................................   50    175

784          785          786

|  | F £ | VF £ |
|---|---|---|

784   **'Saroaldo'**, Type 11. Bust r. becoming increasingly stylized R. Pseudo-legend
    SAROALDO(?) around standard. Some with FIT/RV inscribed (rare) or with saltire and
    pellets, various styles. *Abr. 7, M. 151-3, M. p. 147-51* ............................    80    300

785   **'Stepped cross'**, Type 53. Degenerate 'porcupine' head. R. Stepped cross,
    annulet at centre. *Abr. 91, M. 258-62, M. p. 140, M. p. 243-5.* ..................    60    200

786   **'SEDE'**. Type 89. Quilled serpent, pellet in mouth, coiled around cross.
    R. Small central saltire, S E D E in angles with saltires between.
    *Abr. 93, M. 263, M. p. 682* ........................................................................   350   1200

787: various styles

787   **Series W**. Half- to full-length figure, head r., holding long cross pommée or
    annulet cross either side. R. Cross crosslet on saltire. *Abr. 108, BMC 54,
    M. 155, M. p. 152-7* ...........................................................................   325   1100

788: Series W related

788   **Series W related**. Monogram (Marseilles?) or monster l. looking back R.
    Cross crosslet on saltire. *Abr. 53* ...........................................................   125    450

**C.**   **CONTINENTAL ISSUES, *c.* 695 – *c.* 740**
Most Continental sceattas emanate from the former Rhine mouth area, Frisia, particularly
the emporia of Domburg and Dorestad. The obverse motif of Series E, commonly
referred to as the "porcupine", is now recognized as a degenerate diademed bust. Series
D bust takes English Series C as its prototype retaining the runic inscription ÆPA.

790          790A *VICO*

790   **Series E**. Degenerate head enclosing three bars. R Votive standard
    with TOTII design, various styles. *Abr. 94* ..............................................    30    85

790A  —, **'Vico' type**. Degenerate head enclosing bars. R. 'Standard' with letters possibly
    reading VIC (*wic*, emporium) around central annulet. *Abr. 88, M. p. 211-16*    35    100

790B

790C

791

|  | | *F*<br>£ | *VF*<br>£ |
|---|---|---|---|
| 790B | —, variety D. Degenerate head, various symbols in field. R. 'Standard' with four pellets around central annulet. *Dorestad. Abr. 90, M. 209-11.* | 30 | 80 |
| 790C | —, variety E. Degenerate head. R. 'Standard' with four lines and central annulet. *Abr. 89, M. p. 216-19* | 30 | 85 |
| 790D | Later issues. Degenerate head. Innumerable varieties. R. 'Standard'. *Abr. 94-97, M. 214-53, M. p. 222-42.* | 30 | 80 |
| 791 | —, plumed bird, usually r. R. Standard with a variety of symmetrical geometric symbols. *Abr. 87, M. 190-3, M. p.206-11* | 45 | 150 |

792

792 var.

| 792 | **Series D**, Type 2c. Bust r. (types with bust l. are possibly English and imitative), runic ÆPA before bust. R. Plain cross with pellets in angles, pseudo-letters around. *Abr. 8, M. 158-80, M. p. 184-90.* | 30 | 95 |
|---|---|---|---|

793                          794

|     |                                                                                                     | F | VF |
|-----|-----------------------------------------------------------------------------------------------------|---|----|
|     |                                                                                                     | £ | £  |
| 793 | — Type 8. Crude standard with angular symbols. R. central cross pommée, pellets in angles. *Abr. 10, M. 183-6, M. p. 191-5* | 25 | 85 |
|     | A variety has a wheel device in standard, R. Bifurcated cross, chevrons above.                      |   |    |
| 794 | Type 10. Degenerate bust r., runic AEPA or APA. R. Profile 'moon' face, blundered legend. *Abr. 9, M. p.248.* | 110 | 425 |

795                          796

| 795 | **Interlace Cross Type** (formerly 'Maastricht' Type). Crude head l. or r. R. Quatrefoil interlaced cross. Some coins possibly English. *Abr. 60, M. 265-6, M. p. 258-60* | 110 | 425 |
|-----|---------------------------------------------------------------------------------------------------|-----|-----|
| 796 | **'Hexagon' Type** (formerly 'Herstal' Type and possibly a Denier). Hexagram enclosing central cross. R. Unbalanced radial arrangement, cross near centre and sometimes above. *Abr. 109, M. 325-8, M. p. 256-8* | 125 | 475 |

797                          797 (cruder style)

| 797 | **Series X.** Facing 'Wodan' head, of various styles. R. Crested monster r. or l., tail raised to mouth, claws below, prominent member, die mark below jaw. *Ribe, Jutland, M. 275-81, M. p. 275-86,* same cruder style possibly English. *Abr. 103-4, M. 282, M. p. 286-3* | 135 | 525 |
|-----|---------------------------------------------------------------------------------------------------|-----|-----|

**D.    SECONDARY PHASE, c. 710 – c. 760**

Die duplication is the exception in this coinage, with a substantial variation of execution and fabric within each type. It is assumed that quality deteriorates over time and late issues may be of more interest monetarily than aesthetically. This coinage was issued in all the main regions of southern and eastern England. Some boundaries between Series remain indistinct e.g. K and L, C and R.

800 varieties

| 800 | **Series G**, Type 3a. Diademed bust r., heavenward gaze, cross before. R. Standard with 3 or 4 saltires. *Abr. 21, M. 267-70, M. p. 266-72* | 60 | 175 |
|-----|---------------------------------------------------------------------------------------------------|----|-----|

801                801A                801B

|  | F £ | VF £ |
|---|---|---|

801    **Series H ('Hamwic')**, Type 39. Pecking bird. R. Celtic cross. *Abr. 46, M. 283-4,*
       *M. p. 324-5* ........................................................................................... 100    350
801A   — Type 49. 'Wodan' head, 5-11 bosses around. R. Pecking bird in various
       styles. *Abr. 48, M. 285-8, M. p. 325-32.* ................................................. 135    575
801B   — Type 48. Whorl of 3 wolf heads. R. Celtic cross. *Abr. 47, M. 289-92,*
       *M. p. 333-40.* ........................................................................................ 110    375

802                802A

802    **Series J ('York')**, Type 85. Large diademed head r. R. Outline bird on cross.
       *Abr. 18.20, M. 293-5, M. p. 345-50* ........................................................ 65    225
802A   — Type 37. Two diademed heads face-to-face. R. Four birds clockwise
       around cross. *Abr. 19.30, M. 296-300, M. p. 351-3* ................................. 75    275
802B   — Type 60. Diademed head r. R. Two serpents coiled clockwise with
       beaded bodies, heads central. *Abr. 18.10, M. p. 354-5* ...........................135    525

802C               802D

802C   — Type 72. Two diademed heads face-to-face. R. Bird r., looking back at serpent.
       *Abr. 19.10-20, M. 303, M. p. 355-6.* One variety has bird looking forward    110    375
802D   — Type 36. Diademed bust r., cross before. R. Two birds. *Abr. 20.10-30,*
       *M. 301-2, M. p. 361-4* ............................................................................. 80    325

803                803A

803    **Series K ('Kent')**, Type 33. Diademed bust r., cross before. R. Wolf's head
       with long tongue, l. or r. *Abr. 38, M. 306, M. p. 388-91* ........................... 150    575
803A   — Type 42. Diademed bust r. with bird, cross or flower. R. Hound 1.
       looking back, plant behind, various styles. *Abr. 41, M. 311-3, M. p. 391-5*    135    525
803B   — Type 75. Roulette wheel of 11 compartments . R. Hound 1. looking
       back, plant behind. *Abr. 41.50* ...............................................................175    625

803C

|  | F | VF |
|---|---|---|
|  | £ | £ |

803C — Type 32a. Bust r. with cross before, cupped in hand. ℞. Wolf curled
head to tail or wolf headed serpent. *Abr. 39, M. 309, 310, M. p. 395-402*      150      575

803D

803D — — Similar. ℞. Wolf-headed serpent r. or l. *Abr. 40, M. 310, M. p. 400*      110      400

803E: Series K, Type 20          obv var.

803E — Type 20. Bust r. cross or chalice before. ℞. Standing figure in crescent boat
holding cross and hawk. *Abr. 33, M. 314-18, M. p. 402-5*.......................      110      400

803F

803F — Type 16. Bust r. floral scroll before. ℞. Standing figure in crescent boat
holding cross and hawk. *Abr. 33.80, M. 314-18, M. p. 402-5*...................      125      425

804          804C          804D

804   **Series L ('London')**, Type 12. Bust r., LVNDONIA. ℞. Standing figure in
crescent boat holding two crosses. *Abr. 23, M. 319-22 M. p. 409-11* .......      150      575

804A — Type 13. Similar. ℞. Seated figure holding hawk and cross. *Abr. 23.20,
M. p. 409* ...........................................................................................      250      950

804B — Type 14. Similar, but bust l. ℞. Celtic cross. (as S.822). *Abr. 27.10, M. p. 427*      135      525

804C — Type 15. Diademed bust r. with cross, no legend. ℞. Standing figure
holding two crosses. *Abr. 35.20, M. 323-6* ............................................      85      325

804D — Type 16. Bust r. with floral scroll before. ℞. Standing figure holding
two crosses. *Abr. 35.40, M. 329-30*........................................................      90      350

804E — Type 17. Bust l. with long cross before. ℞. Standing figure holding two
crosses. *Abr. 36* .......................................................................................      95      375

804F      804G      804H

|  | | F £ | VF £ |
|---|---|---|---|
| 804F | — Type 18. Diademed bust l. or r. with chalice and sometimes cross above. R. Standing figure in crescent boat holding cross and bird. *Abr. 33.10-30, M. 331-3* | 90 | 350 |
| 804G | — Type 19. Diademed bust l. or r., long cross before. R. Standing figure in crescent boat holding cross and bird. *Abr. 33.40-80, 100-110, M. 335* .... | 110 | 400 |
| 804H | — Type 23e. Standing figure holding two long crosses. R. Whorl of 3 wolf heads. *Abr. 43, M. 359-62 M. p. 451-2* ..................................................... | 95 | 375 |

805

| 805 | **Series M**, Type 45. Sinuous animal r. R. Spiral vine. *Abr. 61, M. 363-6, M. p. 453-8* | 150 | 575 |
|---|---|---|---|

806: type 41a      type 41b

| 806 | **Series N**, Type 41. Two standing figures, one or both looking across or facing. R. Crested monster r. or l., looking back, claws beneath, tail raised, pellet outline. *Abr. 52, M. 368-72, M. p. 459-69.* ............................................................ | 110 | 400 |
|---|---|---|---|

807

| 807 | **Series O**, Type 38. Bust r. blundered legend or cable border. R. Bird r. in torc. *Abr. 58, M. 373-5, M. p. 470-2* ................................................. | 125 | 425 |
|---|---|---|---|
| 807A | — Type 21. Similar, but peg-nosed bust l. R. Standing figure with two crosses. *Abr. 59, M. 376, M. p. 472-4.*........................................................ | 175 | 625 |

807B

807C                    807D various

|       |                                                                 | F | VF |
|-------|-----------------------------------------------------------------|---|----|
|       |                                                                 | £ | £  |

807B — Type 40. Standing figure holding two long crosses. R. Monster l. looking
back, curled tail and foreleg raised, claw beneath, "feathered" coat below.
*Abr. 55, M. 379-81, M. p. 477-81, 490.* .................................................... 80 300

807C — Type 57. Peg-nosed bust r. in cable border. R. Monster looking back r.
or l. curled tail and foreleg raised, claw beneath, "feathered" coat below.
*Abr. 54, M. 377, M. p. 474-5.*.................................................................. 135 525

807D — Type 40 variety. Monster r., looking back, tail and crest raised, foreleg
raised behind head. R. Elaborate beaded standard in beaded circle, outer linear
border with annulets or standard, votive or beaded. *Abr. 57, M. p. 490* ... 150 575

808

808   **Series Q**, variety IA-D. Two Standing figures with long crosses. R. Monster r. or l.,
looking back, crest raised or lowered, tail raised, claws below, several varieties.
*Abr. 63.10-40, M. p. 488, 489, 491.* ......................................................... 175 650

808A                    808B

808A —, variety IE, Type 67. Diademed bust r., cross before. R. Walking bird l.,
pellets in field. *Abr. 63.50-70, M. 383, M. p. 490-1* ................................. 175 650

808B —, variety IF, Type 71. Standing facing figure with two crosses. R. Walking bird l.,
pellets in field. *Abr. 63.80, M. 384.* ......................................................... 275 900

808C                    808D

808C —, variety IG, Type 95. Facing head. R. Long-legged quadruped looking
back, crest intertwines legs, tail raised. *Abr. 63.100-110, M. p. 492.* ....... 300 1100

808D —, variety IH. Half-length profile figure holding cross r. R. Long-legged
quadruped looking back, crest raised, tail intertwines legs. *Abr. 63.90,
M. 385, M. p. 492*................................................................................... 275 1050

809

|  | | F<br>£ | VF<br>£ |
|---|---|---|---|

809    —, variety II. Quadruped l. or r., tail intertwines legs. R. Bird l. wings spread,
        cross by wing. *Abr. 64, M. p. 494* ............................................................    135    525

810

810    —, variety III. Quadruped l or r. with tail ending with triquetra. R. Bird l. or r.
        often with triquetra. *Abr.65, M. p. 496*......................................................    150    575

811

811    — variety IV. Bird or lion r. or l. R. Bird or lion r. or l. *Abr. 66, M. p. 499, 501*    125    525

812 mules of Series R and Q          812 Q/R mule

812    **Series R and Q** MULES, Type 73. Crude radiate bust r. or l. blundered runes.
        R. Quadruped or bird r. *M. 388, M.p.496-8 & 518,* vars. R/Q and Q/R mules.
        *Abr. 12, 67,*..........................................................................................    90    350

813 (R1)                  813 (R3)                  813 (R4)

813    **Series R.** Varieties R1-R6, bust r. on pyramidal neck. Epa in runes, sometimes
        retrograde. R. Standard, various angular symbols in and around. *Abr. 11,
        M. 391-428, M. p. 507-14* ........................................................................    45    135

813A: Series R7, Spi    813A: Series R10, Wigræd    813A: Series R11, Tilbeorht

813A   —, varieties R7-R12, Head r. or l. with no neck. Spi, Wigræd or Tilbeorht in
        runes r. or l. R. Standard with angular symbols. *Abr. 11, M. 391-428,
        M. p. 514-23* ..............................................................................................    50    175

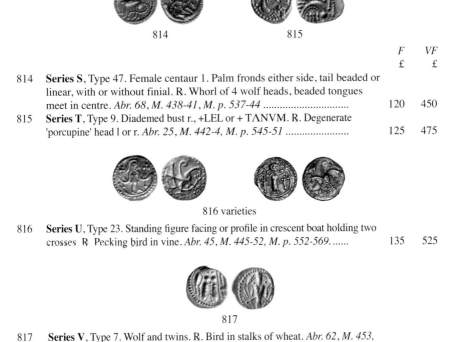

814                    815

|     |     | F<br>£ | VF<br>£ |
|-----|-----|-----|-----|
| 814 | **Series S**, Type 47. Female centaur 1. Palm fronds either side, tail beaded or linear, with or without finial. R. Whorl of 4 wolf heads, beaded tongues meet in centre. *Abr. 68, M. 438-41, M. p. 537-44* .............................. | 120 | 450 |
| 815 | **Series T**, Type 9. Diademed bust r., +LEL or + TΛNVM. R. Degenerate 'porcupine' head l or r. *Abr. 25, M. 442-4, M. p. 545-51* ...................... | 125 | 475 |

816 varieties

| 816 | **Series U**, Type 23. Standing figure facing or profile in crescent boat holding two crosses R Pecking bird in vine. *Abr. 45, M. 445-52, M. p. 552-569.* ...... | 135 | 525 |

817

| 817 | **Series V**, Type 7. Wolf and twins. R. Bird in stalks of wheat. *Abr. 62, M. 453, M. p. 570-5.* ....................................................................................... | 175 | 675 |

**E.   ECLECTIC SCEATTAS, *c.* 710 – *c.* 760**

Included here are groups of types, related often by a common reverse motif (Triquetras, Celtic cross, interlace, saltire, annulet cross groups and Type 70) that do not easily fit into the main alphabetical classification, even though there may be some features in common with or derived from the types therein. There are numerous 'mules' in this coinage, typically imitative combinations of known obverse and reverse types. Only a few of these are included.

820: C ARIP group, some varieties

| 820 | **'Carip' group**. Bust r., CARIP, often blundered. R. include pecking bird, wolf-serpent, or standing figure. *Abr. 26, M. 336-40, M. p. 416-21* ....... | 125 | 475 |

821: Triquetras group

|  | F £ | VF £ |
|---|---|---|

821  **'Triquetras' group**. Man and crosses, winged figure, facing bust, or pecking
bird. R. Interlaced cross with triquetra terminals, rosettes or pellets between.
*Abr. 110, M. p. 422-5.* .............................................................................  175    675

822: Celtic cross group, some obverse varieties

822: Celtic cross group, some reverse varieties

822  **'Celtic Cross' group**. Bust r. or l. with or without legend, cross or sprig
(34a(828A)) before; one or two standing figure(s) with long crosses, cross in
torc, wolf-worm or pecking bird. R. Celtic cross, void or with superimposed
pellet cross or cross pattée, rosettes in angles. *Abr. 27-31, M. p. 426-32.*   150    575

823: Rosette type, various styles

823  **'Rosette'**, Type 68, Series L-related. Bust r., one or two rosettes in field. R.
Standing figure usually with two crosses. *Abr. 32.30-50, M. 347, M. p. 433-4*   150    575

823A

823A  — Type 32b. Bust l. rosettes in field. R. Wolf-serpent within torc. *Abr. 32.10-20,
M. 307-8, M. p. 433-4* .........................................................................  175    650

824:Monita Scorum type                    824A

824  **'(Monita) Scorum' type**. Bust r., MONITA SCORVM. R. Degenerate 'porcupine'
head l., figure with two crosses, or triquetra cross. *Abr. 24, M. p. 435-6.*   325    1250
824A  — . Bust r., DE LVNDONIA. R. porcupine l., SCORVM. *Abr. 24.50, 25.50,
M. p. 436.* ..............................................................................................  350    1350

826: Hen type

|  | | F £ | VF £ |
|---|---|---|---|

825    **'Archer' group**. Kneeling archer r. R. Large bird (swan?) on branch r. or l.,
looking back. *Abr. 50, M. 349, M. p. 437-9*............................................    375    1500

826    **'Hen' type**. Hen r. or l. R. Large bird (swan?) on branch r. or l. looking back
and biting berries. *Abr. 51*....................................    225    900

827: Victory group

827    **'Victory'** Type 22. Victory standing with wreath. R. Standing figure
holding two crosses, winged figure in crescent boat, or diademed bust.
*Abr. 111, M. 350-1, M. p. 440-3*............................................    200    750

828: K/N group

828    **K/N related group**. Standing figure with two long crosses. R. Monster of Type
41 r. or l. looking back. *Abr. 37, M. p. 445.*............................................    110    400

829: Animal mask group

829    **'Animal mask' group**. Facing animal (feline?) with erect ears. R. Standing
figure with bird and cross, bird with cross before, segmented circle or monster.
*Abr. 112, M. 354-6 , M. p. 446-8*............................................    275    1000

830: K/R mule

830    **K/R mule**. Wolf worm curled r. or l. R. Standard with annulet cross or
central Annulet. *Abr. 42, M. p. 449.*............................................    125    475

831: Type 43

831    — Type 43. Monster of Type 40, l. looking back. R. Interlace cross.
(See also S.795.) *Abr. 54-58, M. p. 482*............................................    200    750

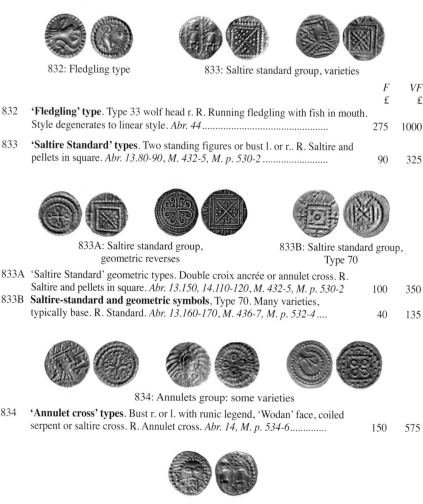

832: Fledgling type      833: Saltire standard group, varieties

|  | F £ | VF £ |
|---|---|---|
| 832 **'Fledgling' type**. Type 33 wolf head r. R. Running fledgling with fish in mouth. Style degenerates to linear style. *Abr. 44* | 275 | 1000 |
| 833 **'Saltire Standard' types**. Two standing figures or bust l. or r.. R. Saltire and pellets in square. *Abr. 13.80-90, M. 432-5, M. p. 530-2* | 90 | 325 |

833A: Saltire standard group,     833B: Saltire standard group,
geometric reverses            Type 70

| | | |
|---|---|---|
| 833A 'Saltire Standard' geometric types. Double croix ancrée or annulet cross. R. Saltire and pellets in square. *Abr. 13.150, 14.110-120, M. 432-5, M. p. 530-2* | 100 | 350 |
| 833B **Saltire-standard and geometric symbols**, Type 70. Many varieties, typically base. R. Standard. *Abr. 13.160-170, M. 436-7, M. p. 532-4* .... | 40 | 135 |

834: Annulets group: some varieties

| | | |
|---|---|---|
| 834 **'Annulet cross' types**. Bust r. or l. with runic legend, 'Wodan' face, coiled serpent or saltire cross. R. Annulet cross. *Abr. 14, M. p. 534-6* | 150 | 575 |

835: 'Wodan' head varieties

| | | |
|---|---|---|
| 835 **'Wodan' Head**, Type 30. Facing 'Wodan' head various styles some coarse. R. Two standing figures, standard or Series N, type 41 monster r. *Abr. 105, M. 429-31, M. p. 527-30.* | 175 | 675 |

836: Flying monster type

| | | |
|---|---|---|
| 836 **'Flying Monster'**. Monster in flight r. or l., looking back, tail erect. R. Swan-like bird r. or l., looking back, alternate with groups of pellets on limbs of central cross fourchée. *Abr. 107* | 150 | 575 |

# KINGS OF NORTHUMBRIA AND ARCHBISHOPS OF YORK

The issues associated with pre-Viking Northumbria comprise the York group of gold Shillings c. 630-80 (S.762-763), followed by silver sceattas which became increasingly debased after c. 810, becoming a copper alloy coin referred to as a Styca. There are two special presentation issues, Eanred's broad Penny and Wigmund's gold *Solidus,* for neither of which is there yet evidence of monetary use within the kingdom.

The stycas developed in two phases, becoming a robust currency of small-denomination coins, which seem to have been of great practical use. Production may have ceased early in Osberht's reign, although the old money may have continued in circulation until the Viking capture of York in 867. The official styca coinage, however, does appear to have been overwhelmed by irregular issues, which may reflect a period of civil war during the years c. 843 to c. 855.

James Booth's classification of the silver Sceatta coinage of the eighth century is used here, with newly discovered types and variants added ('Sceattas in Northumbria' in Hill and Metcalf, *Sceattas in England and on the Continent, BAR* 128 (1984), pp.71-111, and 'Coinage and Northumbrian History: c. 790-c. 810, in D.M. Metcalf, *Coinage in ninth-century Northumbria, BAR* 180 (1987), pp.57-90).

For the styca coinage of the *ninth-century* Elizabeth Pirie provides an indispensable illustrated corpus of the known material in her *Coins of the Kingdom of Northumbria c. 700-867,* 1996. Her classification is however over-complex for practical use, and several aspects of it, including her division of the coins of Aethelred II between his two reigns, have not been accepted by other scholars. The division here is that which is customarily adopted in volumes in the SCBI series. Moneyers' names are shown as they appear on the coinage.

Further reading: See SCBI 68, Lyon, C.S.S., *The Lyon Collection of Anglo-Saxon Coins* (2016). The introduction to this, sections 2 and 3, provides a useful up to date assessment of the Northumbrian Sceatta and Styca coinage along with illustrations of coins in the Lyon collection; Bude, R., *The joint coinage of Ecgberht and Eadberht of Northumbria,* in BNJ 86, 2016.

## SILVER SCEATTA COINAGE - A: REGAL ISSUES

846: Aldfrith

846    **Aldfrith** (685-705). ALδFRIDVS in semi-uncial lettering around central boss.
     R. Lion(?) l. triple tail above. *Abr. 69* ....................................................    300    1100

847 vars classes

847    **Eadberht** (737-758). Classes A-F. Small cross (mainly). R. Stylized stag, to
     l. or r., various ornaments. *Abr. 70* ......................................................    100    325

848

|  | F £ | VF £ |
|---|---|---|

848    **Aethelwald Moll** (759-765) ΛD+ELΛΑΓDRE (A and R inverted) around
       central boss. R. His son ΛEDILRED+R (second R reversed), around central
       cross. *Abr. 77* .....................................................................................    *Extremely rare*

849                          850                          851

849    **Alchred** (765-774). Small cross. R. Stylized stag to l. or r., cross below. *Abr. 71.*    275    900
850    **Aethelred I** (first reign, 774-779/80). R. Stylized stag to l. or r., triquetra
       below. *Abr. 72.*....................................................................................    400    1350
851    **Aelfwald I** (779/80-788). R. Stylized stag to l. or r., various ornaments,
       *Abr. 73*................................................................................................    425    1500

## SILVER SCEATTA COINAGE - B: JOINT ISSUES BY KINGS OF NORTHUMBRIA AND ARCHBISHOPS OF YORK

852                          854                          855

852    **Eadberht** with **Abp. Ecgberht** (737-758). Small cross. R. Mitred figure
       holding two crosses. *Abr.74* ....................................................................    175    500
853    **Aethelwald Moll** with **Abp. Ecgberht** (759-765). Cross each side. *Abr.76*    2000    7500
854    **Alchred** with **Abp. Ecgberht** (765-766). Cross each side. *Abr. 74* .......    275    900
855    **Aethelred I,** with **Abp. Eanbald I** (*c.* 779-780). Various motifs. *Abr. 78*    300    950

## SILVER SCEATTA COINAGE - C: REGAL ISSUES WITH NAMED MONEYERS

856

856    **Aethelred I** (second reign, 789-796). R. CEOLBALD, CVDHEARD, HNIFVLA,
       TIDVVLF, central motifs vary. *Abr.80, 82-84*..........................................    100    350

857    858

|     |                                                                           | F | VF |
|-----|---------------------------------------------------------------------------|------|------|
|     |                                                                           | £ | £ |
| 857 | – Base metal. R. 'Shrine', "CVDCLS" (the moneyer Cuthgils) ........... | 325 | 1100 |
| 858 | **Eardwulf** (first reign, 796-806). R. Small cross, CVDHEARD .......... | 2000 | 7500 |

**SPECIAL ISSUES**

863A

| 861A | **Eanred,** *c.* 830. Æ *penny.* Bust right. R. Cross, part moline part crosslet | 6500 | 27500 |
| 863A | **Abp. Wigmund** (837-849/50). *N solidus,* Facing bust. R. Cross in wreath | 45000 | 175000 |

**STYCA COINAGE - A: BASE SILVER REGAL ISSUES, *c.* 810 – *c.* 830**

859

| 859 | **Aelfwald II** (806-808). R. Small cross, CVDhEARD ......................... | 350 | 1250 |

860

| 860 | **Eanred** (810-841 (total reign)). R. CVDhEARD, CYNVVLF, DAEGBERCT, EADVINI,EDILECH, HERREÐ, [HEARDVVLF, correctly VVLFHEARD], HVAETRED, TIDVINI, VILHEAH, VVLFHEARD, various central motifs | 35 | 125 |

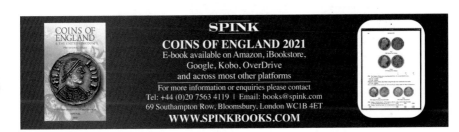

## STYCA COINAGE - B: BASE SILVER ARCHIEPISCOPAL ISSUES, *c. 830 – c. 867*

861

|   |   | F<br>£ | VF<br>£ |
|---|---|---|---|
| 861 | Abp. Eanbald II (796-835 (total tenure)). R. EODWVLF or EDILWEARD | 60 | 200 |

## STYCA COINAGE - C: COPPER ALLOY REGAL ISSUES, *c. 810 – c. 830*

862

| 862 | Eanred. R. ALDATES, BADIGILS, BROD(E)R, FORDRED, FVLCNOD, MONNE, ODILO, W(D)IHTRED, VVLFRED, various central motifs | 25 | 80 |
|---|---|---|---|

865

| 865 | Aethelred II (first reign, 841-843/4), R. ALGHERE, BRODER, COENRED, CVNEMVND, EANRED, FORDRED, HVNLAF, LEOFDEGN, MONNE, ODILO, VENDELBERHT, W(D)IHTRED, VVLFRED, VVLFSIG , various central motifs .......................................................................... | 25 | 70 |
|---|---|---|---|

866: varieties

| 866 | – Leofdegn's 'Special' motifs, R. Hound 1., LEOFDEGN ................... | 475 | 1850 |
|---|---|---|---|

866A

| 866A | –various elaborate cruciform central devices, LEOFDEGN ................. | 85 | 275 |
|---|---|---|---|

867              868              869

| 867 | Redwulf (843/4). R. ALGHERE, BROTHER, COENRED, CVDBEREhT, EANRED, FORDRED, HVAETNOD, MONNE ................................. | 35 | 130 |
|---|---|---|---|
| 868 | Aethelred II (second reign 843/4-849/50), R. EANVVLF, EARDVVLF, FORDRED, MONNE, ODILO, VVLFRED ......................................... | 25 | 75 |
| 869 | Osberht (849/50-867). R. EANVVLF, EDELHELM, MONNE, VINIBERHT, VVLFSIXT, VVLFRED ....................................................................... | 30 | 120 |

## STYCA COINAGE - D: COPPER ALLOY ARCHIEPISCOPAL ISSUES, *c.* 830 – *c.* 867

870

871

| | | F £ | VF £ |
|---|---|---|---|
| 870 | **Abp. Wigmund** (837-849/50). R. COENRED, EDELHELM, EDILVEARD, HVNLAF .......................................................................................... | 25 | 70 |
| 871 | **Abp. Wulfhere** (849/50-900). R. VVLFRED ..................................... | 65 | 225 |

## STYCA COINAGE - E: IRREGULAR ISSUES IN COPPER ALLOY, *c.* 843/4 – *c.* 855

| | | | |
|---|---|---|---|
| 872 | **Irregular Issues** (*c.*843/4-*c.*855). Various types; legends blundered..... | 20 | 65 |

In the kingdom of the Franks a reformed coinage of good quality *deniers* struck on broad flans had been introduced by Pepin in 755 and continued by his son Charlemagne and his descendants. A new coinage of *pennies* of similar size and weighing about 20 grains (1.3 gms) was introduced into England, probably by Offa (757-96), the powerful king of Mercia, c.780, though early pennies also exist of two little known kings of Kent, Heaberht and Ecgberht, of about the same period.

The silver penny (*Lat.* 'denarius', hence the *d.* of our £ *s. d.*) remained virtually the sole denomination of English coinage for almost five centuries, with the rare exception of occasional gold coins and the somewhat less rare silver halfpence. The penny reached a weight of 24 grains (c.1.55g), i.e., a 'pennyweight' during the reign of Alfred the Great. Silver pennies of this period normally bear the ruler's name, though not always his portrait, and the name of the moneyer responsible for their manufacture.

Pennies were issued by various rulers of the Heptarchy for the kingdoms of Kent, Mercia, East Anglia, Wessex and by the Danish settlers in the Danelaw and the Hiberno-Norse kings of York, and also by the Archbishops of Canterbury and a Bishop of London. Under Eadgar, who became the sole ruler of England, a uniform coinage was instituted throughout the country, and it was he who set the pattern for the 'reformed' coinage of the later Anglo-Saxon and Norman period.

Halfpence were issued by most rulers from the time of Alfred until the reform of Eadgar, c.871-973 for southern England, and although all are rare today, it is probable that reasonable quantities were made.

Nos. 873-1378 are all silver pennies except where stated.

NB. Many pennies of the early part of this period have chipped flans and prices should be reduced accordingly.

Further Reading: R. Naismith, *The Coinage of Southern England 796-865*, 2011; C.E. Blunt, B.H.I.H. Stewart & C.S.S. Lyon, *Coinage in Tenth-century England: From Edward the Elder to Edgar's Reform,* 1989.

## KINGS OF KENT

874　　　875

876　　　877

|  |  | F | VF |
|---|---|---|---|
|  |  | £ | £ |
| 873 | **Heaberht** (*c.* 765). Monogram for REX. ℞. Five annulets, each containing a pellet, joined to form a cross | 9000 | 37500 |
| 874 | **Ecgberht** (*c.* 780). Similar. ℞. Varied | 1350 | 5750 |
| 875 | **Eadberht Praen.** Type 1. (796-798). As illustration. ℞. Varied | 1250 | 5500 |
| 875A | — Type 2. (*c.* 798). His name around, Ⓜ in centre, ℞. Moneyer's name in angles of a tribrach | 1350 | 6000 |
| 876 | **Cuthred** (798-807). *Canterbury.* Various types without portrait | 750 | 3000 |
| 877 | — — Portrait. ℞. Cross and wedges or A | 1000 | 4500 |

878

880                                              881

|     |                                                                              | F    | VF   |
|-----|------------------------------------------------------------------------------|------|------|
|     |                                                                              | £    | £    |
| 878 | **Anonymous** (*c.* 822-823). *Canterbury.* As illustration or 'Baldred' style head | 975  | 4500 |
| 879 | **Baldred** (*c.* 823-825). *Canterbury.* diademed head r. R̃. DRVR CITS within inner circle | 1350 | 5750 |
| 880 | — Cross each side                                                            | 750  | 3000 |
| 881 | *Rochester.* Bust r. R̃. Cross moline or wheel design                        | 1250 | 5500 |

## ARCHBISHOPS OF CANTERBURY

882

| 881A | **Jaenberht** (765-792). New type (early). Under Ecgberht II of Kent (?). (before *c.* 780 ?) His name around small cross of pellets in centre. R̃. PONTIFEX in three lines | 1350 | 5750 |
|------|------|------|------|
| 882  | Under Offa of Mercia (*c.* 780-792) His name around central ornament or cross and wedges. R̃. OFFA REX in two lines | 950  | 4000 |
| 883  | — His name in three lines. R̃. OFFA or OFFA REX between the limbs of Celtic cross | 975  | 4250 |
| 884  | **Aethelheard** (el. 792, cons. 793, d. 805). With Offa as overlord. First issue (792-?), with title *Pontifex* | 900  | 3750 |

885                                              886

| 885  | — Second issue (?-796), with title *Archiepiscopus* | 800 | 3250 |
|------|------|------|------|
| 885A | — Third issue (*c.* 796-798), with title *Archiepiscopus*. His name and AR around EP in centre. R̃. Moneyer's name, EADGAR or CIOLHARD..... | 900 | 3750 |
| 886  | — With Coenwulf as overlord. (798-800 ?) Fourth Issue. As last. R̃. King's name in the angles of a tribrach | 850 | 3500 |

886A 887 888 (rev.)

| | | F | VF |
|---|---|---|---|
| | | £ | £ |
| 886A | — Fifth issue (c. 798-805?). As last R. Coenwulf's name around Ⓜ in centre | 675 | 2750 |
| 887 | **Wulfred** (805-832). group I (805-c. 810). As illustration. R. Crosslet, alpha-omega............................................................................................................... | 800 | 3500 |
| 888 | — Group II (c. 810). As last. R. DOROVERNIA C monogram .............. | 750 | 3250 |
| 889 | — Group III (pre- 823). Bust extends to edge of coin. R. As last ........... | 725 | 3000 |
| 890 | — Groups IV and V (c. 822-823). Anonymous under Ecgberht. Moneyer's name in place of the Archbishop's. R. DOROBERNIA CIVITAS in three or five lines ............................................................................................................ | 750 | 3500 |
| 891 | — Group VI (c. 823-825). Baldred type. Crude portrait. R. DRVR CITS in two lines................................................................................................................ | 1100 | 5000 |
| 892 | — Group VII (c. 832). Second monogram (Ecgberht) type. Crude portrait r., PLFRED. R. DORIB C. Monogram as 1035 ...................................... | 900 | 4000 |

893 894

| 893 | **Ceolnoth** (833-870). Group I with name CIALNOD. Tonsured bust facing. R. Varied ........................................................................................ | 675 | 2750 |
|---|---|---|---|
| 894 | — Group II. Similar but CEOLNOD. R. inscribed cross ........................ | 725 | 3000 |
| 894A | — —. O. as last, R. as 1054, cross fleury over floreate cross .................. | 1500 | 6000 |

895 896

| 895 | — Group III. Diad. bust r. R. Moneyer's name in and between lunettes . | 1000 | 5000 |
|---|---|---|---|
| 896 | **Aethelred** (870-889). Bust r. R. As illustration or with long cross with lozenge panel ........................................................................................... | 2250 | 10500 |
| 897 | — Cross pattée. R. ELF / STAN................................................................. | 1250 | 5500 |

898          900

| | | F | VF |
|---|---|---|---|
| | | £ | £ |
| 898 | **Plegmund** (890-914). DORO in circle. R. As illustration above, various moneyers | 900 | 3500 |
| 899 | — Similar, but title EPISC, and XDF in centre | 900 | 3500 |
| 900 | — Small cross pattée. R. moneyers name in two lines | 675 | 2750 |
| 901 | — Crosses moline and pommée on *obv.* | 900 | 4000 |
| 901A | — Halfpenny. As 900 | 1250 | 5250 |

## KINGS OF MERCIA

Until 825 Canterbury was the principal mint of the Kings of Mercia and some moneyers also struck coins for the Kings of Kent and Archbishops of Canterbury.

## GOLD

902          903

| | | | |
|---|---|---|---|
| 902 | **Offa** (757-796). Gold *dinar*. Copy of Arabic dinar of Caliph Al Mansur, dated 157 A.H. (A.D. 774), with OFFA REX added on *rev.* | 150000 | 750000 |
| 903 | Gold *penny*. Bust r., moneyer's name. R. Standing figure, moneyer's name | 45000 | 225000 |

*A copy of a solidus with a diademed bust appears to read CIOLHEARD and is probably Mercian of this or the following reign.*
For further information see: *The Coinage of Offa and his Contemporaries* by Derek Chick, 2010.

## SILVER

904          905

| | | | |
|---|---|---|---|
| 904 | **Offa** (757-796). Light Coinage. (*c.* 780?-792) *London and Canterbury.* Various types without portraits. Small flans | 475 | 1500 |
| 905 | — (*c.* 780?-792) *London and Canterbury.* Various types with portraits. Small flans | 750 | 3250 |

906                                          908

|                                                                                         | F £ | VF £ |
|-----------------------------------------------------------------------------------------|-----|------|
| 906 — East Anglia. Various types with portraits. R. Some with runic letters, small flans | 800 | 3500 |
| 907 — — Various types without portraits. R. often with runic letters, small flans       | 575 | 2000 |
| 908 Heavy Coinage (c. 792-796) London, Canterbury and East Anglia. Various types without portraits, large flans. | 550 | 1850 |

909                                          911

| 909 **Cynethryth** (wife of Offa). Coins as light coinage of Offa.With bust as illustration | 2000 | 7500 |
|------------------------------------------------------------------------------------------|------|------|
| 910 — O. without bust, as rev. of last, R, moneyers name on cross of lobes, usually EOBA | 1350 | 5500 |
| 911 **Eadberht** (Bishop of London, died 787/789). EADBERHT EP in three lines or ADBERHT in two lines within a beaded rectangle, EP below. R. various with name of Offa | 850 | 4250 |

912                                         912A

| 912 **Coenwulf, King of Mercia** (796-821). Gold *penny* or *Mancus* of 30 pence. London, diademed bust of Coenwulf right, finely drawn with four horizontal lines on the shoulders | 45000 | 225000 |
|------------------------------------------------------------------------------------------|-------|--------|
| 912A Penny Group I (796-805). *London.* Without portrait, three line inscription. R. Varied | 550 | 1850 |
| 913 — *Canterbury.* Name around ᴹ as illus. below. R. Moneyer's name in two lines | 575 | 2250 |

914                                          915

| 914 — *Both mints.* Tribrach type | 375 | 1250 |
|-----------------------------------|-----|------|
| 915 — Group II (c. 805-810). *Canterbury.* With portrait. Small flans. R. Varied but usually cross and wedges | 575 | 2250 |

916                                   919

|  | | *F* £ | *VF* £ |
|---|---|---|---|

916 — Groups III and IV (*c.* 810-820). *Canterbury.* Similar but larger flans. R. Varied    575    2250
917 — *Rochester.* Large diad. bust of coarse style. R. Varied. (Moneyers:
Dun, Ealhstan) .....................................................................................    625    2500
918 — *London.* With portrait generally of Roman style. R. Crosslet ............    750    3250
919 — *E. Anglia.* Crude diad. bust r. R. Moneyer's name LVL on leaves in
arms of cross .......................................................................................    575    2250
920 — — *O.* as last. R. Various types ...........................................................    550    2100

921                                   927

921 **Ceolwulf I** (821-823). *Canterbury.* Group I. Bust r. R. Varied.
(Moneyers: Oba, Sigestef) ........................................................................    1350    5750
922 — — Group II. *London.* Crosslet. R. Varied ..........................................    850    4000
923 — — Group III. Tall cross with MERCIORV. R. Crosslet. SIGESTEF
DOROBERNIA ......................................................................................    950    4250
924 — *Rochester.* Group I. Bust r. R. Varied.................................................    1100    5250
925 — — Group IIA. As last but head r. .........................................................    1100    5250
926 — — Group IIB. Ecclesiastical issue by Bp. of Rochester. With mint
name, DOROBREBIA, but no moneyer.................................................    1250    5750
927 — *East Anglia.* Crude style and lettering with coarse portrait. R. Varied    950    4250

928                                   929

928 **Beornwulf** (823-825). Group I. *East Anglia.* Bust r. R. Moneyer's name in
three lines ...............................................................................................    1350    5750
929 — Group II. *East Anglia* or *London.* R. Cross crosslet in centre .............    1250    5250
930 Group III. *East Anglia.* Similar to 928 but moneyer's name in two lines with
crosses between ......................................................................................    1200    5500
931 **Ludica** (825-827). *East Anglia.* Bust r. R. Moneyer's name in three lines
as 928 .....................................................................................................    6250    25000

932                              932A

|      |                                                                                           | F<br>£ | VF<br>£ |
|------|-------------------------------------------------------------------------------------------|--------|---------|
| 932  | — Similar. *East Anglia*. R. Moneyer's name around cross crosslet in centre, as 929 ........................................................................................ | 6750 | 27500 |
| 932A | *London*. Diademed bust r. R. LUNDONIA CIVIT in three lines. ....... | 7500 | 30000 |

933

| 933  | **Wiglaf,** first reign (827-829). *London*. Crude head r. R. Crosslet............ | 4250 | 15000 |

934                              935

| 934  | Second reign (830-840). *London*. Cross and pellets, or ⚹ R. Moneyer's name in three lines or between lunettes of pellets .................................... | 2000 | 7500 |
| 935  | **Berhtwulf** (840-852). Various types with bust........................................ | 1500 | 6750 |
| 936  | — without bust ......................................................................................... | 1200 | 5250 |
| 937  | As before. R. IAETHELWLF REX. cross pommée over cross pattée (crude die copying on obverse of Aethelwulf of Wessex) ...................... | 1100 | 4750 |

938 (rev. A)            939A            939B

| 938  | **Burgred (852-874)** Ia, 852-c.855, bust r, looks up, almond eye, r. A (MacKay P1) | 675 | 1750 |
| 939A | Ib, c.855-c.858-60, bust r, coarse style, annulet or almond eye, two panel or triangular tunic, r. A, C, D, (MacKay P2, P4)............................................ | 500 | 1200 |
| 939B | — — bust r, pellet in almond eye, low shoulders, high neck r. A, C (MacKay P3) | 600 | 1500 |

940A (rev. D)        940B (rev. C)        940C

|  | F £ | VF £ |
|---|---|---|

940A IIa, c.858/60-c.866, bust r, almond eye, neat bust, lips sometimes omitted,
r. A, C, D ( MacKay H1, H2) .................................................................... 350 1000

940B — —, bust r, as Aethelberht of Wessex Floreate type (S.1054), often six pellets
below neck, some coarse r. C  (MacKay H3-H4: coarse,H5) ................... 700 1600

940C — —, bust r, coarse style, large annulet eye, outward wedge lips,
r. A, C, D (MacKay V1) ........................................................................... 600 1500

941A        941B        942A

941A IIb, c.866-868/70, bust r, various styles incl. with large annulet eye, ill-
proportioned bust, realistic pointed nose narrow tunic, r. A, C, D (MacKay H6-8) 275 800

941B — —, bust r, outward or upward wedge lips, steeply angled diadem, various
styles, incl. with wide tunic, double inner-circle, narrow diameter i.c, r. D
(MacKay V2-4) ....................................................................................... 300 850

942A III, c.868/70-874, bust r, pellet eye, diadem cuts across eye, r. A, D (MacKay H10) 250 750

942B        942C        942D (rev. B)

942B — —, bust r, crescent below pellet eye, r. A, D (MacKay H11)............... 250 750

942C — —, bust r, pellet eye, small crescent above and below, r. A, often with six
pellets in one angle (MacKay H12) ......................................................... 225 700

942D — —, bust r, rather crude, steeply pitched diadem, outward or upward wedge
lips, r. A (MacKay V5) ........................................................................... 220 650

*Reverse types most commonly found are listed above; type A, closed lunettes (commonly found);
B, open at base and top (very rare); C, open at sides (rare); D, 'crooks' without lunettes semi-
circles (scarce); E, as D with large M symbol added above and below dividing legend (very rare).*
*Prices for Lunettes types can vary with rare types worth more than commoner types.*

| Lunette A | ................................................................................................. *from* | 250 | 650 |
|---|---|---|---|
| Lunette B | ................................................................................................. *from* | 600 | 2000 |
| Lunette C | ................................................................................................. *from* | 400 | 1000 |
| Lunette D | ................................................................................................. *from* | 300 | 850 |
| Lunette E | ................................................................................................. *from* | 950 | 3500 |

For further reading see; *MacKay, The Coinage of Burgred 852-874*, BNJ 85, 2015, pp 101-237.

| | | F | VF |
|---|---|---|---|
| | | £ | £ |
| 943 | **Ceolwulf II** (874-*c.* 880). Bust r. R. Two emperors seated. Victory above | 6500 | 27500 |

944

| 944 | — R. Moneyer's name in angles of long cross with lozenge centre ........ | 1750 | 7000 |
|---|---|---|---|
| 944A | — Halfpenny, similar to 944 ................................................................. | 3500 | 12500 |

## KINGS OF EAST ANGLIA

945                  947

| 945 | **Beonna,** King of East Anglia, *c.* 758. Æ sceat. Pellet in centre, Runic inscription. R. EFE in Roman characters around saltire cross. *Abr.113.10* | 750 | 2750 |
|---|---|---|---|
| 945A | — Similar. R. WILRED or WERFERTH in runic around pellet or cross. *Abr. 113.20-30* .................. | 850 | 3250 |
| 945B | — Similar. R. Interlace pattern (large flans). *Abr.113.40* ....................... | 1750 | 7500 |
| 945C | **Alberht** (749-?). Pellet in centre, AETHELBERT (runic) around R. Rosette in circle, TIAELRED (runic) around. *Abr. 114* ........................... | 4250 | 17500 |
| 946 | **Aethelberht** (d. 794). bust r. R. wolf and twins ..................................... | 8000 | 37500 |
| 946A | — King's name EDILBERHT around cross and pellets. R. Lozenge intersecting large cross fourchée, LVL in angles........................................................ | 5250 | 22500 |
| 947 | **Eadwald** (*c.* 798). King's name in three lines. R. Moneyer's name in quatrefoil, around cross or tribrach........................................................ | 950 | 4250 |
| 947A | — King's name around cross or Ᵽ in centre. R. Moneyer's name in quartrefoil | 975 | 4500 |

949              950 (obv,)            951

| 948 | **Aethelstan I** (*c.* 825-840). Bust r. or l. R. Crosslet or star ...................... | 1350 | 5500 |
|---|---|---|---|
| 949 | Bust r. R. Moneyer's name in three or four lines.................................... | 1350 | 5500 |
| 950 | Alpha or A. R. Varied................................................................. | 525 | 1750 |
| 951 | *O.* and *rev.* Cross with or without wedges or pellets in angles ................. | 525 | 1750 |
| 952 | — Similar, with king's name both sides ................................................. | 575 | 2000 |
| 952A | Name around ship in centre. R. Moneyer Eadgar, around cross of pellets or in two lines (Possibly the earliest of his coins.) ................................ | 6000 | 27500 |

953                                           954

|   |   | F | VF |
|---|---|---|---|
|   |   | £ | £ |
| 953 | **Aethelweard** (*c*. 840-*c*. 855), A, Omega or cross and crescents. R. Cross with pellets or wedges .......................................................................... | 975 | 4500 |
| 954 | **Edmund** (855-870). Alpha or A. R. Cross with pellets or wedges ......... | 425 | 1350 |
| 955 | — *O*. Varied. R. Similar....................................................................... | 425 | 1350 |

*For the St. Edmund coins and the Danish issues struck in East Anglia bearing the name of Aethelred I, see Danish East Anglia.*

# ANGLO-VIKING COINAGES *c*. 885-954

## DANISH EAST ANGLIA, *c*. 885-915

Following the treaty of Wedmore in 880 the Viking invaders were ceded control of Eastern Mercia including all territory east of Watling street. Coinage issued in this area after 880 initially imitated Wessex types of Alfred. Independent coinages were struck from early 880s in East Anglia, the east midlands and Northumbria.

| 956 | **Aethelstan II** Guthrum (878-890), Cross pattée. R. Moneyer's name in two lines....................................................................................... | 1750 | 8000 |
|---|---|---|---|
| 957 | **Oswald** (unknown except from his coins). Alpha or A. R. Cross pattée.. | 2500 | 10000 |
| 958 | — Copy of Carolingian 'temple' type. R Cross and pellets ..................... | 2500 | 10000 |
| 959 | **Aethelred** (*c*.870). As last, with name Aethelred. R. As last, or cross-crosslet | 1750 | 8000 |
| 959A | — As 954 ........................................................................................ | 1500 | 7000 |

Oswald and Aethelred, both unattested historically, are thought to be East Anglian kings in the period after the death of Eadmund in 870 before Guthrum took control of the East Anglia c.880.

960                                           962

| 960 | **St. Edmund,** memorial coinage, Æ *penny,* type as illus. above, various legends of good style ........................................................................... | 175 | 450 |
|---|---|---|---|
| 961 | — Similar, but barbarous or semi-barbarous legends............................. | 165 | 425 |
| 962 | *Halfpenny*. Similar ........................................................................ | 575 | 2000 |
| 963 | **St. Martin of Lincoln.** Sword dividing legend. R. Cross in voided cross. LINCOI A CIVIT. ................................................................................. | 3750 | 15000 |

## SOUTHERN DANELAW *c.* 880-910

965                                           970

|     |                                                                                                                                                      | *F*<br>£ | *VF*<br>£ |
|-----|------------------------------------------------------------------------------------------------------------------------------------------------------|----------|-----------|
| 964 | **Alfred.** Imitation of London Monogram types- see 1061, 1062, some very barbarous, bust usually right, R. *Londonia* monogram (wt. c.1.2-1.4g) ..   | 2250     | 7500      |
| 964A| — Similar, crude bust, blundered legends, R. *Lincolla* or *Roiseng* monogram (possibly an official issue, Chester?)......................           | 3500     | 13500     |
| 965 | — Similar to 1062, with moneyer's name (Aelfstan, Heawulf, Herewulf, Heremod, Winurdal) ................................                               | 3000     | 12500     |
| 966 | — Imitation of two line types (1066, 1069), small cross, R. some read REX DORO ................................                                       | 450      | 1350      |
| 967 | — Similar. R. 'St. Edmund type' A in centre...........................................                                                                | 750      | 3500      |
| 968 | — Imitation of Two Emperors type, as 943 and 964 ...............................                                                                      | 3750     | 15000     |
| 969 | *Halfpenny.* Imitation of London Monogram types - see 1063.................                                                                           | 950      | 3750      |
| 970 | — Imitation of two line types ................................                                                                                        | 750      | 3000      |

971                                           975

|     |                                                                                                                                                                     |      |       |
|-----|---------------------------------------------------------------------------------------------------------------------------------------------------------------------|------|-------|
| 971 | — Imitation of Oxford type, as 1071A, ELFRED between ORSNA and FORDA, R. Moneyer's name in two lines (sometimes divided by horizontal long cross)                   | 650  | 2250  |
| 972 | — *Halfpenny.* Similar, of very crude appearance ....................................                                                                               | 700  | 2500  |
| 973 | **Alfred/Archbishop Plegmund.** *Obv.* ELFRED REX PLEGN ..............                                                                                              | 1350 | 5750  |
| 974 | **Archbishop Plegmund.** Imitative of two line type, as 900 ...................                                                                                     | 725  | 2750  |
| 975 | **Earl Sihtric.** Type as 971. SCELDFOR between GVNDI BERTVS. R SITRIC COMES in two lines ................................                                           | 5250 | 20000 |

## COINAGES OF THE VIKING KINGDOM OF YORK, *c.* 895-920

*References are to 'The Classification of Northumbrian Viking Coins in the Cuerdale hoard', by*
*C. S. S. Lyon and B. H. I. H. Stewart, in Numismatic Chronicle, 1964, p. 281 ff.*

|  |  | F | VF |
|---|---|---|---|
|  |  | £ | £ |
| 975A | **Guthfrith.** GV DE F. RE Small cross. ℞. Moneyer's name in two lines. | 3750 | 15000 |
| 976 | **Siefred.** C. SIEFRE DIIS REX in two lines. ℞. EBRAICE CIVITAS (or contractions), small cross. *L. & S. Ia, Ie, Ii* | 550 | 2250 |
| 977 | — Cross on steps between. ℞. As last. *L. & S. If, Ij* | 725 | 3000 |
| 978 | — Long cross. ℞. As last. *L. & S. Ik* | 575 | 2500 |

979

980

984

| 979 | SIEFREDVS REX, cross crosslet within legend. ℞. As last. *L. & S. Ih...* | 475 | 1850 |
|---|---|---|---|
| 980 | SIEVERT REX, cross crosslet to edge of coin. ℞. As last. *L. & S. Ic, Ig, Im* | 450 | 1750 |
| 981 | — Cross on steps between. ℞. As last. *L. & S. Il* | 650 | 2750 |
| 982 | — Patriarchal cross. ℞. DNS DS REX, small cross. *L. & S. Va* | 450 | 1750 |
| 983 | — — ℞. MIRABILIA FECIT, small cross. *L. & S. VIb* | 575 | 2500 |
| 984 | REX, at ends of cross crosslet. ℞. SIEFREDVS, small cross. *L. & S. IIIa, b* | 475 | 1850 |
| 985 | — Long cross. ℞. As last. *L. & S. IIIc* | 450 | 1750 |
| 986 | *Halfpenny.* Types as 977, *L. & S. Ib;* 980, *Ic;* and 983, *VIb* | 750 | 2750 |
| 987 | **Cnut.** CNVT REX, cross crosslet to edge of coin. ℞. EBRAICE CIVITAS, small cross. *L. & S. Io, Iq* | 425 | 1650 |
| 988 | — — ℞. CVNNETTI, small cross. *L. & S. IIc* | 375 | 1350 |

989

993

| 989 | — Long cross. ℞. EBRAICE CIVITAS, small cross. *L. & S. Id, In, Ir....* | 240 | 800 |
|---|---|---|---|
| 990 | — — ℞. CVNNETTI, small cross. *L. & S. IIa, IId* | 200 | 525 |
| 991 | — Patriarchal cross. ℞. EBRAICE CIVITAS, small cross. *L. & S. Ip, Is* | 185 | 475 |
| 992 | — — ℞.— *Karolus* monogram in centre. *L. & S . It* | 900 | 3250 |
| 993 | — — ℞. CVNNETTI, small cross. *L. & S. IIb, IIe* | 190 | 450 |

995                                                998

|     |                                                                 | F £ | VF £ |
|-----|-----------------------------------------------------------------|-----|------|
| 994 | *Halfpenny.* Types as 987, *L. & S. Iq; 989, Id; 991, Is; 992, Iu; 993, IIb and e* | 650 | 2000 |
| 995 | *Halfpenny.* As 992, but CVNNETTI around *Karolus* monogram. *L. & S. IIf* | 675 | 2250 |
| 996 | **Cnut and/or Siefred.** CNVT REX, patriarchal cross. ℞. SIEFREDVS, small cross. *L. & S. IIId* | 475 | 1850 |
| 997 | — — ℞. DNS DS REX, small cross. *L. & S. Vc.* | 450 | 1750 |

1000                                               1002

|      |                                                                | F £ | VF £ |
|------|----------------------------------------------------------------|-----|------|
| 998  | — — ℞. MIRABILIA FECIT. *L. & S. VId*                          | 325 | 950  |
| 999  | EBRAICE C, patriarchal cross. ℞. DNS DS REX, small cross. *L. & S. Vb* | 450 | 1500 |
| 1000 | — — ℞. MIRABILIA FECIT. *L. & S. VIc*                           | 325 | 950  |
| 1001 | DNS DS REX in two lines. ℞. ALVALDVS, small cross. *L. & S. IVa* | 1350 | 5750 |
| 1002 | DNS DS O REX, similar. ℞. MIRABILIA FECIT. *L. & S. VIa*       | 525 | 1850 |
| 1003 | *Halfpenny.* As last. *L. & S. VIa*                            | 750 | 2250 |

1004                                               1006

|      |                                                                | F £ | VF £ |
|------|----------------------------------------------------------------|-----|------|
| 1004 | **'Cnut'.** Name blundered around cross pattée with extended limbs. ℞. QVENTOVICI around small cross. *L. & S. VII* | 950 | 3750 |
| 1005 | *Halfpenny.* Similar. *L. & S. VII*                            | 900 | 3000 |
| 1006 | **St. Peter coinage,** *c.* 905-915. Swordless type. Early issues. SCI PETRI MO in two lines. ℞. Cross pattée | 375 | 1200 |
| 1007 | — similar. ℞. 'Karolus' monogram                               | 975 | 4000 |
| 1008 | *Halfpenny.* Similar. ℞. Cross pattée                          | 750 | 2500 |

1009

| | F £ | VF £ |
|---|---|---|

1009 **Regnald** (blundered types). RAIENALT, head to l. or r. R. EARICE CT,
'Karolus' monogram ............................................................................. 3750 16500

1010

| | | |
|---|---|---|
| 1010 — Open hand. R. Similar ........................................................ | 1750 | 8000 |
| 1011 — Hammer. R. Bow and arrow ............................................. | 2500 | 10000 |
| 1012 Anonymous R. Sword ............................................................ | 1350 | 5750 |

## ENGLISH COINS OF THE HIBERNO-NORSE VIKINGS OF YORK c. 919-954

1015                                        1016

### EARLY PERIOD, c. 919-925

| | | |
|---|---|---|
| 1013 **Sihtric** (921-927). SITRIC REX, sword. R. cross, hammer, mallet or T (Lincoln) | 3000 | 12500 |
| 1014 **St. Peter coinage.** Sword type. Late issues SCI PETRI MO, sword and hammer. R. EBORACEI, cross and pellets ............................................. | 1100 | 4500 |
| 1015 — Similar. R. Voided hammer ................................................. | 1250 | 5500 |
| 1016 — Similar. R. Solid hammer ................................................... | 1350 | 5750 |

*St. Peter coins with blundered legends are rather cheaper.*

### LATER PERIOD, 939-954 (after the battle of Brunanburh, 937). Mostly struck at York.

| | | |
|---|---|---|
| 1017 **Anlaf Guthfrithsson,** 939-941. Flower type. Small cross, ANLAF REX TO D. R. Flower above moneyer's name ................................................. | 4750 | 18500 |
| 1018 — Circumscription type, with small cross each side, ANLAF CVNVNC, M in field on reverse *(Derby)* ............................................................ | 2750 | 12500 |
| 1018A — Two line type. ONLAF REX. Large letter both sides *(Lincoln?)* ........ | 2250 | 10000 |

1019                                    1020

|      |                                                                                 | F<br>£ | VF<br>£ |
|------|---------------------------------------------------------------------------------|--------|---------|
| 1019 | — Raven type. As illustration, ANLAF CVNVNC.................................... | 2000   | 9000    |
| 1020 | **Anlaf Sihtricsson,** first reign, 941-944. Triquetra type, ANLAF CVNVNC.       |        |         |
|      | R. Danish standard................................................................ | 1850   | 8000    |

1021                                    1022

| 1021 | — Circumscription type (a). Small cross each side, ANLAF CVNVNC, |      |      |
|------|-----------------------------------------------------------------|------|------|
|      | R. MONETR....................................................... | 2250 | 9500 |
| 1022 | — Cross moline type, ANLAF CVNVN C. R. Small cross............... | 2000 | 8500 |

1024

| 1023 | — Two line type. Small cross. R. ONLAF REX. R. Name in two lines .. | 2250 | 9500  |
|------|--------------------------------------------------------------------|------|-------|
| 1024 | **Regnald Guthfrithsson,** 943-944. Triquetra type. As 1020. REGNALD |      |       |
|      | CVNVNC ............................................................. | 4500 | 17500 |
| 1025 | — Cross moline type. As 1022, but REGNALD CVNVNC.................... | 4250 | 16500 |
| 1026 | **Sihtric Sihtricsson,** c. 942. Triquetra type. As 1020, SITRIC CVNVNC | 2500 | 12000 |
| 1027 | — Circumscription type. Small cross each side ...................... | 2500 | 12000 |

1027A

| 1027A | **Anonymous?** Two line type. Small cross ELTANGERHT. R. |      |       |
|-------|---------------------------------------------------------|------|-------|
|       | RERNART in two lines ................................... | 1100 | 4000  |
| 1028  | **Eric Blood-Axe,** first reign, 948. Two line type. Small cross, ERICVC REX |      |       |
|       | A; ERIC REX AL; or ERIC REX EFOR. R. Name in two lines ............. | 7250 | 30000 |

|  | F £ | VF £ |
|---|---|---|

1029 **Anlaf Sihtricsson,** second reign, 948-952. Circumscription type (b). Small cross each side, ONLAF REX, Ɽ. MONE.............................................. 2000 8500

1029A — Flower type. small cross ANLAF REX Ɽ. Flower above moneyer's name............................................................................................. 3250 13500

1029B — Two line type. Small cross, ONLAF REX. Ɽ. Moneyer's name in two lines......................................................................................... 2250 9500

1030

1030 **Eric Blood-Axe,** second reign, 952-954. Sword type. ERIC REX in two lines, sword between. Ɽ. Small cross ....................................................... 10500 45000

For more on the Anglo-Viking Coinages - see Blackburn M.A.S., *Viking Coinage in the British Isles (Spink 2011)*

# KINGS OF WESSEX, 786-924

## BEORHTRIC, 786-802

Beorhtric was dependent on Offa of Mercia and married a daughter of Offa.

1031

1031 As illustration.......................................................................................... 7500 35000
1032 Alpha and omega in centre. Ɽ. Omega in centre .................................. 7000 32500

## ECGBERHT, 802-839

King of Wessex only, 802-825; then also of Kent, Sussex, Surrey, Essex and East Anglia, 825-839, and of Mercia also, 829-830.

1035

1033 *Canterbury.* Group I. Diad. hd. r. within inner circle. Ɽ. Various............. 1350 5500
1034 — II. Non-portrait types. Ɽ. Various ................................................. 950 4250
1035 — III. Bust r. breaking inner circle. Ɽ. DORIB C .................................. 1250 5000
1036 *London.* Cross potent. Ɽ. LVN / DONIA / CIVIT .............................. 1650 7000
1037 — — Ɽ. REDMVND MONE around TA.............................................. 1250 5000

1041

|  | | F | VF |
|---|---|---|---|
|  | | £ | £ |
| 1038 | *Rochester,* royal mint. Non-portrait types with king's name ECGBEO RHT | 950 | 4250 |
| 1039 | — — Portrait types, ECGBEORHT....................................................... | 1300 | 5250 |
| 1040 | *Rochester,* bishop's mint. Bust r. ℞. SCS ANDREAS (APOSTOLVS).... | 1500 | 6000 |
| 1041 | *Winchester.* SAXON monogram or SAXONIORVM in three lines. ℞. Cross | 1300 | 5250 |

## AETHELWULF, 839-858

Son of Ecgberht; sub-King of Essex, Kent, Surrey and Sussex, 825-839; King of all southern England, 839-855; King of Essex, Kent and Sussex only, 855-858. No coins are known of his son Aethelbald who ruled over Wessex proper, 855-860.

1043                    1045

1047

| 1042 | *Canterbury.* Phase I (839-c. 843). Head within inner circle. ℞. Various. *Br. 3* | 750 | 3000 |
|---|---|---|---|
| 1043 | — — Larger bust breaking inner circle. ℞. A. *Br. 1 and 2* .................. | 800 | 3250 |
| 1044 | — — Cross and wedges. ℞. SAXONIORVM in three lines in centre. *Br. 10* | 625 | 2500 |
| 1045 | — — Similar, but OCCIDENTALIVM in place of moneyer. *Br. 11* .... | 675 | 2750 |
| 1046 | — Phase II (*c.* 843-848?). Cross and wedges. ℞. Various, but chiefly a form of cross or a large A. *Br. 4*................................................................ | 575 | 2250 |
| 1047 | — — New portrait, somewhat as 1043. ℞. As last. *Br. 7*..................... | 750 | 3250 |
| 1048 | — — Smaller portrait. ℞. As last, with *Chi/Rho* monogram. *Br. 7*....... | 800 | 3250 |

1049

1051

| | | F | VF |
|---|---|---|---|
| | | £ | £ |
| 1049 | — Phase III (*c*. 848/851-*c*. 855). DORIB in centre. ℞. CANT mon. *Br. 5* | 525 | 1850 |
| 1050 | — — CANT mon. ℞. CAN M in angles of cross. *Br. 6* | 700 | 2750 |
| 1051 | — Phase IV (*c*. 855-859). Mostly Canterbury rarely Rochester. New neat style bust ℞. Large voided long cross. *Br. 8* | 700 | 2750 |
| 1052 | *Winchester*. SAXON mon. ℞. Cross and wedges. *Br. 9* | 750 | 3000 |

## AETHELBERHT, 858-865

Son of Aethelwulf; sub-King of Kent, Essex and Sussex, 858-860; King of all southern England, 860-865/6.

1053

1053A (rev.)

| 1053 | Bust r., ℞ large voided long cross. Mostly Canterbury, also known for Rochester | 750 | 3000 |
|---|---|---|---|
| 1053A | *O*. As 1053, ℞ large cross pattée | 1500 | 6500 |

1054

| 1054 | *O*. Diad. bust r., ℞. Cross fleury over floreate cross | 1250 | 5250 |
|---|---|---|---|

**AETHELRED I, 865-871**

Son of Aethelwulf; succeeded his brother Aethelberht.

1055

|  | F | VF |
|---|---|---|
|  | £ | £ |
| 1055 As illustration, Wessex Lunettes, Canterbury, usually with bonnet ... | 850 | 3500 |
| 1055A— —, London obv. dies in style as Burgred ...................................... | 975 | 4000 |
| 1056 Similar, but moneyer's name in four lines, Canterbury or Winchester | 1250 | 5000 |

*For another coin with the name Aethelred see 959 under Viking coinages.*
For further reading see: *Lyons & MacKay,* BNJ 2007

## ALFRED THE GREAT, 871-899

Brother and successor to Aethelred, Alfred had to contend with invading Danish armies for much
of his reign. In 878 he and Guthrum the Dane divided the country, with Alfred holding all England
south and west of Watling Street. Alfred asserted over-lordship of Mercia and London from c.880.

**Types with portraits**

|  |  |  |
|---|---|---|
| 1057 | 1058 | 1061 |

| 1057 As illustration, Wessex Lunettes, Canterbury, bust with bonnet. r. R. As |  |  |
|---|---|---|
| Aethelred I. *Br. 1* (*name often* AELBRED)............................................... | 900 | 3250 |
| 1057A — —, London obv. dies in style as Burgred ............................................ | 950 | 3500 |
| 1058 — R. Long cross with lozenge centre, as 944, *Br. 5*............................... | 2250 | 9500 |
| 1059 — R. Two seated figures, as 943. *Br. 2*................................................. | 7500 | 30000 |
| 1060 — R. As Archbp. Aethered; cross within large quatrefoil. *Br. 3*.............. | 4500 | 17500 |

|  |  |
|---|---|
| 1062 | 1063 |

| 1061 *London.* Various busts. R. LONDONIA monogram, moneyer not named | 3000 | 12000 |
|---|---|---|
| *For contemporary Viking copies see 964.* |  |  |
| 1062 — R. Similar, but with moneyer's name (Tilewine) added ...................... | 3250 | 12500 |
| 1063 — *Halfpenny.* Bust r. or rarely l. R. LONDONIA monogram as 1061 .... | 1250 | 4500 |
| 1064 *Gloucester.* R. Æ GLEAPA in angles of three limbed cross.................... | 7500 | 30000 |

|   | F | VF |
|---|---|----|
|   | £ | £  |

**Types without portraits**
1065  King's name on limbs of cross, trefoils in angles. ℞. Moneyer's name in
quatrefoil. *Br. 4.* .................................................................................   3500  15000

1066                                                    1067

1066  Various styles, Cross pattée, legend in four parts. ℞. Moneyer's name in
two lines. *Br. 6* ....................................................................................   525   1750
1067  — As last, legend in three parts. ℞ as Edward the Elder, 1087 ...............   550   1850
1068  — *Halfpenny.* As 1066 .........................................................................   850   3000

1069

1069  *Canterbury.* As last but DORO added on *obv. Br. 6a* ............................   550   1850
1070  *Exeter?* King name in four lines. ℞. EXA vertical ...................................   5250  20000
1071  *Winchester?* Similar to last, but PIN ......................................................   5250  20000
1071A *Oxford.* Elfred between OHSNA and FORDA. ℞. Moneyer's name in
two lines (much commoner as a Viking Imitation - see 971) ...................   950   4000
1072  'Offering penny'. Very large and heavy. AELFRED REX SAXORVM in
four lines. ℞. ELIMO in two lines i.e. (*Elimosina,* alms) .......................   12500  52500
*For other pieces bearing the name of Alfred see under the Viking coinages.*
For further reading see: *Lyons & MacKay, The Lunettes Coinage of Alfred the Great* BNJ 2008.

## EDWARD THE ELDER, 899-924

Edward, the son of Alfred, aided by his sister Aethelflaed 'Lady of the Mercians', annexed all
England south of the Humber and built many new fortified boroughs to protect the kingdom.
**Rare types**

1074

1073  *Br. 1. Bath?* ℞. BA .............................................................................   2500  10500
1074  — *2. Canterbury.* Cross moline on cross pommée. ℞. Moneyer's name .   1500   6000

|                                                                                          | F    | VF    |
|                                                                                          | £    | £     |
| 1075 — *3. Chester?* Small cross. R. Minster .................................................. | 4250 | 17500 |
| 1076 — *4.* — Small cross. R. Moneyer's name in single line......................... | 1350 | 4750  |
| 1077 — *5.* — R. Two stars ............................................................................ | 2000 | 9500  |

1078                                             1079

| 1078 — *6.* — R. Flower above central line, name below ............................... | 2750 | 12500 |

1081                                             1083

| 1079 — *7.* — R. Floral design with name across field.................................... | 3000 | 13500 |
| 1080 — *8.* — R. Bird holding twig ............................................................... | 4500 | 20000 |
| 1081 — *9.* — R. Hand of Providence, several varieties................................. | 4000 | 16500 |
| 1082 — *10.* — R. City gate of Roman style................................................... | 2000 | 9500  |
| 1083 — *11.* — R. Anglo-Saxon burg............................................................ | 1850 | 8500  |

**Ordinary types**

1084                                             1087

| 1084 *Br. 12.* Bust l, var. styles R. Moneyer's name in two lines ...................... | 850   | 3500   |
| 1086 — *12a.* Similar, but bust r. of crude style ............................................. | 1100  | 4750   |
| 1087 — *13.* Small cross. R. Moneyers name in two lines............................... | 225   | 600    |
| 1087A — — As last, but in *gold* ........................................................................ | 27500 | 135000 |
| 1088 **Halfpenny**. Similar to 1087 .................................................................. | 950   | 3500   |
| 1088A — — R. Hand of Providence................................................................. | 1500  | 6000   |

Imitations of the types of Edward the Elder were also struck in the Danelaw territories. They are usually of lighter weight and coarser execution than the official Wessex issues of Edward the Elder.

## AETHELSTAN, 924-939

Aethelstan, the eldest son of Edward, completed the re-conquest of territories controlled by the Danes with the capture of York in 927. He decreed that money should be coined only in a borough, that every borough should have one moneyer and that some of the more important boroughs should have more than one moneyer.

1089      1093

|  |  | F £ | VF £ |
|---|---|---|---|
| 1089 | **Main issues.** Small cross. R. Moneyer's name in two lines | 275 | 700 |
| 1090 | Diad. bust r. R. As last | 1000 | 4500 |
| 1091 | — R. Small cross | 950 | 4000 |
| 1092 | Small cross both sides | 375 | 1200 |
| 1093 | — Similar, but mint name added | 425 | 1250 |
| 1094 | Crowned bust r. As illustration. R. Small cross | 750 | 2500 |

1095      1100

| 1095 | — Similar, but mint name added | 825 | 2750 |
|---|---|---|---|
| 1096 | **Local Issues.** *N. Mercian mints.* Star between two pellets. R. As 1089 | 900 | 3500 |
| 1097 | — Small cross. R. Floral ornaments above and below moneyer's name . | 950 | 4000 |
| 1098 | — Rosette of pellets each side | 425 | 1250 |
| 1099 | — Small cross one side, rosette on the other side | 450 | 1350 |
| 1100 | *N.E. mints.* Small cross. R. Tower over moneyer's name | 1100 | 4500 |

1102

| 1101 | Similar, but mint name added | 1250 | 4750 |
|---|---|---|---|
| 1102 | — Bust in high relief r. or l. R. Small cross | 975 | 4000 |
| 1103 | — Bust r. in high relief. R. Cross-crosslet | 975 | 4000 |
| 1104 | 'Helmeted' bust or head r. R. As last or small cross | 850 | 3250 |
| 1104A | **Halfpenny.** Small cross or floral lozenge. R. Moneyer's name in two lines . | 900 | 3000 |

Eadmund was a half brother of Aethelstan. At the start of his reign he lost the kingdom of York and faced renewed Viking incursions into North East England; however, by the end of his reign he had regained control of those territories.

1105                                         1106

| | F £ | VF £ |
|---|---|---|
| 1105 Small cross, rosette or annulet. ℞. Moneyer's name in two lines with crosses or rosettes between ....................................................................... | 275 | 700 |
| 1106 Crowned bust r. ℞. Small cross................................................................. | 850 | 3000 |

1107                                         1111

1112

| | F £ | VF £ |
|---|---|---|
| 1107 Similar, but with mint name ....................................................................... | 900 | 3250 |
| 1108 Small cross either side, or rosette on one side ......................................... | 475 | 1500 |
| 1109 Cross of five pellets. ℞. Moneyer's name in two lines ............................. | 425 | 1350 |
| 1110 Small cross. ℞. Flower above name......................................................... | 1350 | 5750 |
| 1111 'Helmeted' bust r. ℞. Cross-crosslet ....................................................... | 1000 | 4000 |
| 1112 **Halfpenny**. small cross, ℞. Moneyer's name in two lines or one line between rosettes....................................................................................... | 925 | 2750 |
| 1112A — Flower. ℞. As 1105 ........................................................................... | 1100 | 3500 |

Eadred was another of the sons of Edward. He faced renewed Viking attempts to recover York whose last king, Eric Bloodaxe, he drove out in 954 to finally secure Northumbria for the English.

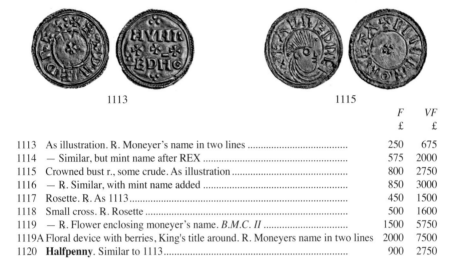

1113         1115

|  | F<br>£ | VF<br>£ |
|---|---|---|
| 1113   As illustration. Ṝ. Moneyer's name in two lines ...................................... | 250 | 675 |
| 1114   — Similar, but mint name after REX ...................................................... | 575 | 2000 |
| 1115   Crowned bust r., some crude. As illustration ........................................... | 800 | 2750 |
| 1116   — Ṝ. Similar, with mint name added ...................................................... | 850 | 3000 |
| 1117   Rosette. Ṝ. As 1113............................................................................. | 450 | 1500 |
| 1118   Small cross. Ṝ. Rosette .......................................................................... | 500 | 1600 |
| 1119   — Ṝ. Flower enclosing moneyer's name. *B.M.C. II* ............................... | 1500 | 5750 |
| 1119A Floral device with berries, King's title around. R. Moneyers name in two lines | 2000 | 7500 |
| 1120   **Halfpenny**. Similar to 1113.................................................................... | 900 | 2750 |

## HOWEL DDA, d. 949/950

Grandson of Rhodri Mawr, Howel succeeded to the kingdom of Dyfed *c.* 904, to Seisyllog *c.* 920 and became King of Gwynedd and all Wales, 942.

1121

1121   HOⱣÆL REX, small cross or rosette. Ṝ. Moneyer's name in two lines . .    17500   60000

## EADWIG, 955-959

Elder son of Eadmund, Eadwig lost Mercia and Northumbria to his brother Eadgar in 957.

1122        1123

| 1122   *Br. 1.* Type as illustration ........................................................................ | 700 | 2250 |
|---|---|---|
| 1123   — — Similar, but mint name in place of crosses ................................... | 850 | 2750 |

|        |                                                           | F     | VF    |
|        |                                                           | £     | £     |
| 1124   | — 2. As 1122, but moneyer's name in one line              | 1350  | 4500  |
| 1125   | — 3. Similar. R. Floral design                            | 1850  | 7000  |
| 1126   | — 4. Similar. R. Rosette or small cross                   | 825   | 2750  |
| 1127   | — 5. Bust r. R. Small cross                               | 8500  | 37500 |

1128

| 1128   | **Halfpenny**. Small cross. R. Flower above moneyer's name | 1250 | 4500 |
| 1128A  | — Similar. R. PIN (Winchester) across field                | 1350 | 4750 |
| 1128B  | — Star. R. Moneyer's name in two lines                     | 950  | 3500 |

# EADGAR, 959-975

King in Mercia and Northumbria from 957; King of all England 959-975. He was crowned King of England at Bath in 973 in the first coronation of an English King. His reign was largely free from Viking invasions, leading him to be given the sobriquet of 'The Peaceful'.

### PRE-REFORM COINAGE BEFORE 973
It is now possible on the basis of the lettering to divide up the majority of Eadgar's coins into issues from the following regions: N.E. England, N.W. England, York, East Anglia, Midlands, S.E. England, Southern England, and S.W. England. (See 'Anglo-Saxon Coins', ed. R. H. M. Dolley.)

1129

| 1129   | *Br I*. Small cross. R. Moneyer's name in two lines, crosses between, | | |
|        | trefoils top and bottom                                   | 225   | 600   |
| 1130   | — — R. Similar, but rosettes top and bottom (a N.W. variety) | 275 | 750   |
| 1131   | — — R. Similar, but annulets between                      | 275   | 750   |
| 1132   | — — R. Similar, but mint name between (a late N.W. type)  | 475   | 1500  |
| 1133   | — 2. — R. Floral design                                   | 1250  | 4750  |
| 1133A  | Voided cross, lys in angles, R. cross pattée dividing alpha and omega | 1350 | 5000 |
| 1134   | — 4. Small cross either side                              | 250   | 650   |

1135

| | F £ | VF £ |
|---|---|---|
| 1135 — — Similar, with mint name.................................................................... | 500 | 1650 |

1136                     1138

| | | |
|---|---|---|
| 1136 — — Rosette either side........................................................ | 300 | 950 |
| 1137 — — Similar, with mint name.............................................. | 525 | 1750 |
| 1138 — 5. Large bust to r. ℞. Small cross ...................................... | 950 | 3750 |
| 1139 — — Similar, with mint name.............................................. | 1350 | 5500 |
| 1140 **Halfpenny.** (8.5 grains / c.0.6 g)) *Br. 3*. Small cross. ℞. Flower above name | 975 | 3500 |

1140A                     1140B

| | | |
|---|---|---|
| 1140A — — ℞. Mint name around cross (Chichester, Wilton) ........................... | 1350 | 4750 |
| 1140B — Bust r. ℞. 'Londonia' monogram ......................................... | 1250 | 4500 |

For Eadgar 'reform' issues see next page.

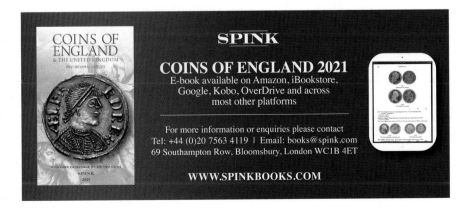

# KINGS OF ENGLAND, 973-1066

In 973 Eadgar introduced a new coinage. A royal portrait now became a regular feature and the reverses normally have a cruciform pattern with the name of the mint in addition to that of the moneyer. Most fortified towns of burghal status were allowed a mint, the number of moneyers varying according to their size and importance: some royal manors also had a mint and some moneyers were allowed certain ecclesiastical authorities. In all some seventy locations are recorded with striking coins in this period (see list of mints pp.144-46).

The control of the currency was retained firmly in the hands of the central government, unlike the situation in France and the Empire where feudal barons and bishops controlled their own coinage. Coinage types were changed at intervals to enable the Exchequer to raise revenue from new dies and periodic demonetisation of old coin types helped to maintain the currency in a good state. No halfpence were minted during this period. During the latter part of this era, full pennies were sheared into 'halfpennies' and 'farthings'. They are far rarer than later 'cut' coins.

**Further Reading**: On the initial reform of the coinage under Eadgar see K. Jonsson, *The NewEra: The Reformation of the Late Anglo-Saxon Coinage* (London: 1987). The nature and purpose of frequent periodic recoinages is explored by I. Stewart, 'Coinage and recoinage after Edgar's reform', in *Studies in Late Anglo-Saxon Coinage*, ed. K. Jonsson (Stockholm: 1990), 455-85. References to individual types for mints and moneyers for much of the first half of the period may be found in K. Jonsson, *Viking Age Hoards and Late Anglo-Saxon Coins* (Stockholm: 1986).

## EADGAR, 959-975 *(continued)*

**REFORM COINAGE, 973-975**

1141

|  | F<br>£ | VF<br>£ |
|---|---|---|
| 1141 **Penny**. Reform Small Cross type. Small diademed bust left. King's name 'Eadgar'. R. Small cross, name of moneyer and mint............................ | 950 | 3750 |

## EDWARD THE MARTYR, 975-978

The son of Eadgar by his first wife, Æthelflaed, Edward was murdered at Corfe in Dorset.

1142

| 1142 Sole type. As 1141, but reading 'Eadward'. .......................................... | 1750 | 5750 |
|---|---|---|

## LATE ANGLO-SAXON MINTS (973-1066)

1. Gothabyrig*
2. Launceston
3. Lydford
4. Barnstaple
5. Totnes
6. Exeter
7. Watchet
8. Taunton
9. Langport
10. Petherton
11. Crewkerne
12. Bridport
13. Axbridge
14. Ilchester
15. Miborne Port

16. Cadbury
17. Bruton
18. Dorchester
19. Wareham
20. Shaftesbury
21. Warminster
22. Bath
23. Bristol
24. Berkeley
25. Malmesbury
26. Wilton
27. Salisbury
28. Southampton
29. Winchester
30. Bedwyn

31. Cricklade
32. Oxford
33. Wallingford
34. Reading
35. Guildford
36. Chichester
37. Cissbury
38. Steyning
39. Lewes
40. Hastings
41. Romney
42. Lympne
43. Hythe
44. Dover
45. Sandwich

46. Canterbury
47. Rochester
48. Horndon
49. Southwark
50. London
51. Hertford
52. Aylesbury
53. Buckingham
54. Newport Pagnell
55. Bedford
56. Cambridge
57. Bury St Edmunds
58. Sudbury
59. Maldon
60. Colchester

61. Ipswich
62. Norwich
63. Thetford
64. Huntingdon
65. Northampton
66. Warwick
67. Worcester
68. Pershore
69. Winchcombe
70. Gloucester
71. Hereford
72. Grantham*
73. Shrewsbury
74. Chester
75. Stafford

76. Tamworth
77. Derby
78. Leicester
79. Nottingham
80. Melton Mowbray
81. Stamford
82. Newark
83. Torksey
84. Lincoln
85. Horncastle
86. Caistor
87. York
88. Wilton. Norfolk*
89. Frome
90. Droitwich

*Possible location of uncertain mint

Son of Eadgar by his second wife Ælfthryth, Æthelred ascended the throne on the murder of his half-brother. He is known to posterity as 'The Unready' from 'Unrede', meaning 'without counsel', an epithet gained from the weakness of his royal government. During this reign England was subjected to Viking raids of increasing frequency and strength, and a large amount of tribute was paid in order to secure peace. Large hoards have been found in Scandinavia and the Baltic region and coins are often found peck-marked. There is a high degree of regional variation in the style of dies, particularly in Last Small Cross type, for which readers are advised to consult the following paper: C.S.S. Lyon, '*Die cutting styles in the Last Small Cross issue of c.1009-1017...*', *BNJ* 68 (1998), 21-41.

1143                                    1144

|  | F £ | VF £ |
|---|---|---|
| 1143   First Small Cross type. Diademed bust left, usually with three pellets before in field. No line to indicate shoulder. *B.M.C I* | 800 | 2750 |
| 1144   First Hand type. Diademed bust right, without sceptre. ℞. Hand of providence between alpha and omega, issuing from cloud composed of parallel curved or angular lines. *B.M.C IIa* | 200 | 525 |
| 1145   — —, similar but bust left. *B.M.C IIb* | 675 | 2750 |

1146                                    1147

| 1146   Second Hand type. Diademed bust right, with sceptre. ℞. Hand of providence between alpha and omega, issuing from clouds with edges that billow outward. *B.M.C IId* | 175 | 475 |
|---|---|---|
| 1147   Benediction Hand type. *O*. as last. ℞. Hand gives Latin benediction, fields without alpha and omega. *B.M.C IIf* | 1350 | 4750 |

1148                                    1150

| 1148   Crux type. Bare-headed bust left, with sceptre. ℞. Voided short cross with letters C, R, V, X, in angles. *B.M.C IIIa* | 135 | 325 |
|---|---|---|
| 1149   Small Crux type. Reduced weight, small flans, sceptre inclined to bust such that the base penetrates drapery. | 140 | 350 |
| 1150   Intermediate Small Cross type. RX at end of legend separate letters. *B.M.C I* | 900 | 3250 |

1151

| | F | VF |
|---|---|---|
| | £ | £ |
| 1151  Long Cross type. Bare-headed bust left. R. Voided long cross. *B.M.C IVa* | 140 | 325 |

1152

| | F | VF |
|---|---|---|
| 1152  Helmet type. Armoured bust left in radiate helmet. *B.M.C VIII* ............... | 150 | 375 |
| 1153  As last but struck in gold. ........................................................................ | 45000 | 175000 |

1154

| | F | VF |
|---|---|---|
| 1154  Last Small Cross type. Diademed bust left, RX at end of legend ligated together as one letter-form. *B.M.C I* ...................................................................... | 130 | 300 |
| 1154A  — —, similar but bust right. ...................................................................... | 225 | 650 |
| 1155  — —, similar but bust to edge of coin...................................................... | 650 | 2250 |

1156

| | F | VF |
|---|---|---|
| 1156  Agnus Dei type. As illustration. *B.M.C X* ................................................ | 7500 | 30000 |

Son of King Swein Forkbeard of Denmark, Cnut was acclaimed king by the Danish fleet in England in 1014 but was forced to leave; Cnut returned and harried Wessex in 1015. Æthelred II died in 1016 and resistance to the Danes was continued by his son Eadmund Ironside, for whom no coins are known, but upon the latter's death in 1016 Cnut became undisputed king. The following year Cnut consolidated his position by marrying Emma of Normandy, the widow of Æthelred II.

There is a high degree of regional variation in the style of dies, particularly in Quatrefoil type, for which readers are advised to consult the following paper: M.A.S. Blackburn and C.S.S. Lyon, 'Regional die production in Cnut's Quatrefoil issue' in *Anglo-Saxon Monetary History*, ed. M.A.S. Blackburn (Leicester: 1986), 223-72. Some quatrefoil coins have pellets or a cross added in the obverse or reverse fields. There is considerable weight fluctuation within and between the types.

**Substantive types**

1157                                          1158

1159

|      |                                                          | F | VF |
|------|----------------------------------------------------------|---|----|
|      |                                                          | £ | £  |
| 1157 | Quatrefoil type (c.1017-23). Crowned bust left. *B.M.C. VIII* | 150 | 375 |
| 1158 | Pointed Helmet type (1024-1030). *B.M.C. XIV*            | 135 | 325 |
| 1159 | Short Cross type (c.1029-1035/6). *B.M.C. XVI*           | 125 | 275 |
| 1159A | — —, similar but sceptre replaced with a banner         | 750 | 3250 |

1160

**Posthumous type**

1160   Jewel Cross type. *B.M.C. XX*, style as 1163 in the name of Cnut. ........... 700   2500
*Type considered to have been struck under the auspices of his widow, Queen Emma of Normandy.*

Harold was the illegitimate son of Cnut by Ælfgifu of Northampton and was appointed regent on behalf of his half-brother Harthacnut. Queen Emma of Normandy initially held Wessex for her son, Harthacnut, but by 1037 she had been driven from the country and Harold had been recognised as king throughout England. The principal issue was the Jewel Cross type which is also found in the name of Cnut and Harthacnut, cf. nos. 1160 and 1166.

1163                                          1165

|      |                                                                                            | F<br>£ | VF<br>£ |
|------|--------------------------------------------------------------------------------------------|--------|---------|
| 1162 | Short Cross type (Autumn 1035). As 1159, but in the name of Harold.<br>B.M.C. IIIa .......... | 1350   | 5000    |
| 1163 | Jewel Cross type (c.1036-38). B.M.C. I.....................................                 | 300    | 950     |
| 1164 | Fleur-de-Lis type (1038-40). Armoured and diademed bust left. R. Voided<br>long cross, trefoil of pellets in each angle. B.M.C. V ........... | 275    | 900     |
| 1165 | — —, similar but fleur-de-lis between two pellets in each angle. B.M.C. V                  | 250    | 850     |

## HARTHACNUT, 1035-1042

Although Harthacnut was the only legitimate son of Cnut and his legitimate heir, the political situation in Denmark prevented him from leaving for England until 1040, by which time Harold had secured the kingdom. Harold's death allowed Harthacnut to reclaim England without bloodshed, but he himself died after two years of sole rule. The main variety of Harthacnut is the Arm and Sceptre type from his sole reign. The Jewel Cross type from the early period is also found in the name of Cnut and Harold I, cf. nos. 1160 and 1163.

**EARLY PERIOD (DURING REGENCY) 1035–7**

| 1166 | Jewel Cross type. As 1163, but in the name of Harthacnut. Diademed bust<br>left. B.M.C. I ........................................................................................ | 950 | 3250 |
|------|------------------------------------------------------------------------------------------------------------------------------------|-----|------|

1167

| 1167 | — —, similar but bust right. B.M.C I ........................................................ | 900 | 3000 |
|------|---------------------------------------------------------------------------------------------|-----|------|

1168

**SOLE REIGN 1040–42**

| 1168 | Arm and Sceptre type. King's name given as 'Harthacnut.' Diademed bust<br>left with sceptre in left hand, forearm visible across bust B.M.C. II ........ | 750 | 2250 |
|------|------------------------------------------------------------------------------------------------------------------------------------------------------|-----|------|

1169

|  | F | VF |
|  | £ | £ |

1169  — —, Similar but king's name given as 'Cnut'. ......................................  600  1750

1170

1170  **Danish types.** Types exist in the name of Harthacnut other than those listed
above and are Scandinavian in origin. ......................................................  300  825

# EDWARD THE CONFESSOR, 1042-1066

Son of Æthelred II and Emma of Normandy, Edward spent twenty-five years in Normandy
before he was adopted into the household of his half-brother Harthacnut in 1040. On the death of
Harthacnut, Edward was acclaimed king. He is known by the title 'The Confessor' owing to his
piety and he was canonised after his death. There is considerable weight fluctuation within and
between the types, which is often unaffected by the smallness of the flan, rather the coin might be
thicker to compensate.

Further reading: P. Seaby, 'The sequence of Anglo-Saxon types 1030–1050', *BNJ* 28 (1955-7),
111–46; T. Talvio, 'The design of Edward the Confessor's coins', in *Studies in Late Anglo-Saxon
Coinage*, ed. K. Jonsson (Stockholm: 1990), 489–99. A. Freeman. *The Moneyer and the Mint in
the Reign of Edward the Confessor: Parts 1 and 2*, (BAR) 1985.

1171                                              1172 (rev.)

1170A Arm and Sceptre type (1042). *B.M.C. IIIa* .............................................  1100  4500
1171  Pacx type (1042–4). Diademed bust left. R. Voided long cross. *B.M.C. IV*   200  525
1172  — —, Similar but R. voided short cross. *B.M.C. V* ..................................  225  625

1173

| | F £ | VF £ |
|---|---|---|
| 1173 Radiate/Small Cross type (1044–6). *B.M.C. I* | 140 | 375 |

1174

1175

| | F | VF |
|---|---|---|
| 1174 Trefoil Quadrilateral type (1046–8). *B.M.C. III* | 150 | 400 |
| 1175 Small flan type (1048–50). *B.M.C. II* | 130 | 325 |
| 1176 Expanding Cross type (1050–53). Light issue, small flans; weight approx. 1.10-1.30g. *B.M.C. V* | 150 | 450 |

1177

| | | |
|---|---|---|
| 1177 ——. Heavy issue, large flans; weight approx. 1.40-1.70g. *B.M.C. V* | 160 | 475 |
| 1178 ——, Similar but struck in gold | 47500 | 185000 |

1179

| | | |
|---|---|---|
| 1179 Pointed Helmet type (1053–6). Bearded bust right in pointed helmet. *B.M.C. VII* | 175 | 500 |
| 1180 ——, Similar but bust left. | 950 | 3500 |

1181

|  | | F<br>£ | VF<br>£ |
|---|---|---|---|
| 1181 | Sovereign/Eagles type (1056–9). King enthroned, holding orb. R. Cross,<br>eagles in angles *B.M.C. IX* ......................................................................... | 175 | 500 |

1182

| 1182 | Hammer Cross type (1059–62). *B.M.C. XI* .............................................. | 150 | 400 |
|---|---|---|---|

1183

| 1183 | Facing Bust/Small Cross type (1062–5). *B.M.C. XIII* ............................. | 140 | 375 |
|---|---|---|---|

1184

| 1184 | Pyramids type (1065–6). *B.M.C. XV* ....................................................... | 150 | 425 |
|---|---|---|---|

1185

| 1185 | Transitional Pyramids type (c.1065). *B.M.C. XIV* ................................... | 1750 | 6500 |
|---|---|---|---|

*Most York coins of this reign have an annulet in one quarter of the reverse.*

Harold was the son of Earl Godwine of Wessex, who had dominated the royal court, and was brother-in-law to Edward the Confessor. Harold successfully repulsed an invasion of Harald Hardrada of Norway, but was himself killed in the Battle of Hastings after a reign of ten months.

Further reading: H. Pagan, 'The coinage of Harold II', in *Studies in Late Anglo-Saxon Coinage*, ed. K. Jonsson (Stockholm: 1990), 177–205.

1186

1187

| | | F | VF |
| | | £ | £ |
| 1186 | Pax type. Crowned head left with sceptre. R. PAX across field. *B.M.C. I* | 1250 | 3500 |
| 1187 | — —, Similar but without sceptre. *B.M.C. Ia* | 1350 | 4500 |
| 1188 | — —, Similar but head right. *B.M.C. Ib* | 2750 | 9500 |

Cnut, Short Cross type (S.1159) - WULNOTH ON WINC:
*moneyer* Wulnoth    *mint* Winchester

William, Paxs type (S.1257) - LIFINC ON WINCE
*moneyer* Lifinc    *mint* Winchester

*Old English special letters found on Anglo-Saxon and Norman coins:*

| Letter | Name | Modern Equivalent |
|--------|------|-------------------|
| Æ | Ash | E |
| Ð | Eth | Th |
| ƿ (P) | Wynn | W |

In late Anglo-Saxon and Norman times coins were struck in the King's name at a large number of mints distributed in centres of population, and in times of emergency in places of refuge, across England and Wales. During the 10th century the use of a mint signature was sporadic but from the Reform type of Edgar the mint name is almost invariably given, usually in conjunction with that of the moneyer responsible, e.g. EDGAR ON BERCLE. At the peak, 71 mints struck the quatrefoil type of Cnut and 65 the PAXS type of William I and they provide a valuable insight into the economic and social structures of the period.

The output of the mints varied enormously and a dozen are exceptionally rare. Approximately 100,000 pennies survive, half of which emanate from the great centres of London, Canterbury, Lincoln, Winchester and York. At the other end of the scale a mint such as Rochester is known from about 500 coins, Derby from around 250, Guildford 100, Bedwyn 25, Horncastle 4 and Pershore 1. Many of these coins, particularly those from the great Scandinavian hoards, are in museum collections and are published in the Sylloge of Coins of the British Isles (SCBI) series.

There are too many type and mint combinations, over 1500 Saxon and 1000 Norman, to price each individually and our aim is to give an indication of value for the commonest Saxon and Norman type, in VF condition, for each of the 103 attested mints (excluding Baronial of Stephen's reign), and for a further 10 mints whose location or attribution is uncertain. The threshold VF price for a Norman coin exceeds that for a Saxon coin accounting for the difference in starting level. Prices for coins in lower grade would be less and there is a premium for the rarer types for each mint, but for many types, e.g. in the reigns of Harthacnut or Henry I, the value of the type itself far exceeds that of many of the constituent mints and a scarce mint is only worth a modest premium over a common one.

We also give the most characteristic mint signatures (often found abbreviated) and the reigns for which the mint is known. There are many pitfalls in identifying mints, not least that Saxon and Norman spelling is no more reliable than that of other ages and that late Saxon coins were widely imitated in Scandinavia. There is extensive literature and the specialist in this fascinating series can, for further details, consult J J North, *English Hammered Coinage Vol.1*.

| | | | | | |
|---|---|---|---|---|---|
| Alf | — | Alfred the Great | Hd1 | — | Harold I |
| EdE | — | Edward the Elder | HCn | — | Harthacnut |
| A'stn | — | Aethelstan | EdC | — | Edward the Confessor |
| Edm | — | Edmund | Hd2 | — | Harold II |
| Edw | — | Eadwig | W1 | — | William I |
| Edg | — | Edgar | W2 | — | William II |
| EdM | — | Edward the Martyr | H1 | — | Henry I |
| Ae2 | — | Aethelred II | St | — | Stephen |
| Cn | — | Cnut | | | |

Berkeley

Hastings

| | SAXON VF £ | NORMAN VF £ |
|---|---|---|
| Axbridge (AXAN, ACXEPO) Edg, Ae2, Cn, HCn | 4500 | — |
| Aylesbury (AEGEL, AEEL), Ae2, Cn, EdC | 4000 | — |
| Barnstable (BARD, BEARDA) Edw, Edg, Ae2-Hd1, EdC, W1, H1 | 1350 | 1750 |
| Bath (BADAN) EdE-A'stn, Edw-EdC, W1-St | 375 | 1000 |
| Bedford (BEDAN, BEDEFOR) Edw-St | 450 | 900 |
| Bedwyn (BEDEPIN) EdC, W1 | 2500 | 4000 |
| Berkeley (BEORC, BERCLE) EdC | 8500 | — |
| Bramber (BRAN) St | — | 3500 |
| Bridport (BRYDI, BRIPVT) A'stn, Ae2, Cn, HCn, EdC-W1 | 1500 | 1500 |
| Bristol (BRICSTO, BRVCSTO) Ae2-St | 500 | 800 |
| Bruton (BRIVT) Ae2, Cn, HCn, EdC | 2250 | — |
| Buckingham (BVCIN) Edg, EdM-Hd1, HCn, EdC | 3000 | — |
| Bury St.Edmunds (EDMVN, S.EDM) EdC, W1, H1, St | 1350 | 850 |
| Cadbury (CADANBY) Ae2, Cn | 8500 | — |
| Caistor (CASTR, CESTR) EdM, Ae2, Cn | 5000 | — |
| Cambridge (GRANTE) Edg-St | 325 | 1000 |
| Canterbury (DORO, CAENTPA, CNTL) Alf, A'stn, Edr, Edg-St | 275 | 575 |
| Cardiff (CIVRDI, CAIERDI) W1-H1, St, Mat | — | 1250 |
| Carlisle (CARD, EDEN) H1, St | — | 1250 |
| Castle Rising (RISINGE) St (type II-VII) | — | 1750 |
| Chester (LEIGE, LEGECE, CESTRE) A'stn, Edm, Edg-St | 400 | 800 |
| Chichester (CISSAN, CICEST) A'stn, Edg, Ae2-St | 400 | 700 |
| Christchurch (orig. Twynham) (TVEHAM, TPIN) W1, H1 | — | 3500 |
| Cissbury (SIDESTEB, SIDMES) Ae2, Cn | 3000 | — |
| Colchester (COLN, COLECES) Ae2-St | 350 | 700 |
| Crewkerne (CRVCERN) Ae2, Cn, Hd1 | 3500 | — |
| Cricklade (CROCGL, CRECCELAD, CRIC) Ae2-W2 | 1750 | 1750 |
| Derby (DEORBY, DERBI) A'stn, Edm, Edg-St | 1750 | 1750 |
| Dorchester (DORCE, DORECES) Ae2-H1 | 1500 | 1250 |
| Dover (DOFERA, DOFRN) A'stn, Edg, Ae2-St | 275 | 700 |
| Droitwich (PICC, PICNEH) EdC, Hd2 | 4500 | — |
| Dunwich (DVNE) St | — | 1350 |
| Durham (DVNE, DVRHAM, DVNHO) W1-St | — | 2250 |
| Exeter (EAXA, EAXCESTRE, IEXECE) Alf, A'stn, Edw-St | 300 | 750 |
| Frome (FRO) Cn, HCn, EdC | 4000 | — |
| Gloucester (GLEAP, GLEPECE, GLOPEC) Alf, A'stn, Edg-St | 450 | 800 |
| Grantham (GRANTHA, GRE) Ae2 | 6500 | — |
| Guildford (GYLD, GILDEFRI) EdM-W2 | 1750 | 3000 |
| Hastings (HAESTINGPOR, AESTI) Ae2-St | 400 | 900 |
| Hedon (HEDVN) St | — | 4000 |
| Hereford (HEREFOR, HRFRD) A'stn, Edg, Ae2-St | 600 | 900 |
| Hertford (HEORTF, HRTFI, RET) A'stn, Edw-EdC, W1-H1 | 350 | 1200 |
| Horncastle (HORN) EdM, Ae2 | 8500 | — |
| Horndon (HORNIDVNE) EdC | 8500 | — |
| Huntingdon (HVNTEN, HVTD) Edg, Ae2-St | 350 | 1000 |
| Hythe (HIĐEN, HIDI) EdC, W1, W2 | 3500 | 1200 |
| Ilchester (GIFELCST, GIVELC, IVELCS) Edg, Ae2-St | 700 | 1500 |
| Ipswich (GIPESWIC, GYPES) Edg-St | 350 | 800 |
| Langport (LANCPORT, LAGEPOR) A'stn, Cn-EdC | 2500 | — |
| Launceston (LANSTF, LANSA, SANCTI STEFANI) Ae2, W1-H1 | 4500 | 3000 |
| Leicester (LIHER, LEHRE, LEREC) A'stn, Edg, Ae2-St | 450 | 800 |
| Lewes (LAEPES, LEPEEI, LAPA) A'stn, Edg-St | 350 | 900 |
| Lincoln (LINCOLN, NICOLE) Edr, Edg-St | 275 | 575 |
| London (LVNDO, LVNDENE) Alf, A'stn, Edw-St | 275 | 575 |
| Louth (LVDE) Edm, Ae2 | 6500 | — |
| Lydford (LYDANFOR) Edg-EdC | 450 | — |
| Lympne (LIMENE, LIMNA) A'stn, Edg-Cn | 900 | — |
| Maldon (MAELDVN, MIEL) A'stn, Edg, Ae2-Hd1, EdC-W2 | 400 | 1500 |
| Malmesbury (MALD, MEALDMES, MELME) Edg, Ae2-W2, H1 | 2000 | 2500 |
| Marlborough (MAERLEBI) W1, W2 | — | 5000 |
| Melton Mowbray (MEDELTV) Ae2, Cn | 6500 | — |
| Milborne Port (MYLE) Ae2, Cn, EdC | 6500 | — |

| | SAXON VF £ | NORMAN VF £ |
|---|---|---|
| Newark (NEWIR, NIWOR) Edg-Cn | 6500 | — |
| Newcastle (CAST) St | — | 1750 |
| Newport (NIPANPO, NIPEPORT) Edw, Edg, EdC | 4500 | — |
| Northampton (HAMTVN, HMTI, NORHAM) Edw, Edg-St | 400 | 750 |
| Norwich (NORDPIC) A'stn-Edr, Edg-St | 275 | 575 |
| Nottingham (SNOTING) A'stn, Ae2-St | 1500 | 1500 |
| Oxford (OXNA, OCXEN, OXENFO) Alf, A'stn, Edr-St | 400 | 750 |
| Pembroke (PEI, PAN, PAIN) H1, St | — | 3500 |
| Pershore (PERESC) EdC | 9000 | — |
| Petherton (PEDR, PEDI) Cn, EdC | 8500 | — |
| Pevensey (PEFNESE, PEVEN) W1-St | — | 2250 |
| Reading (READIN, REDN) EdC | 6000 | — |
| Rhuddlan (RVDILI) W1 | — | 3500 |
| Rochester (ROFEC, ROFSC) A'stn, Edg-H1 | 500 | 1250 |
| Romney (RVMED, RVMNE) Ae2-H1 | 500 | 1000 |
| Rye (RIE) St | — | 2500 |
| Salisbury (SEREB, SEARB, SALEB) Ae2-EdC, W1-St | 450 | 700 |
| Sandwich (SANDPI) EdC, W1-St | 600 | 1000 |
| Shaftesbury (SCEFTESB, CEFT, SAFTE) A'stn, Edg-St | 450 | 800 |
| Shrewsbury (SCROB, SCRVBS, SALOP) A'stn, Edg, Ae2-St | 600 | 1000 |
| Southampton (HAMPIC, HAMTVN) A'stn, Edw-Cn | 600 | 1500 |
| Southwark (SVDBY, SVDGE, SVDPERC) Ae2-St | 275 | 575 |
| Stafford (STAFFO, STAEF) A'stn, Edg, Ae2-Hd1, EdC, W1-St | 750 | 1250 |
| Stamford (STANFORD) Edg-St | 275 | 700 |
| Steyning (STAENIG, STENIC) Cn-W2, St | 350 | 800 |
| Sudbury (SVDBI, SVBR) Ae2, Cn, EdC, W1-St | 600 | 900 |
| Swansea (SVENSEI) St | — | 3000 |
| Tamworth (TOMPEARÐ, TAMPRÐ) A'stn, Edg-Hd1, EdC, W1-St | 2000 | 1750 |
| Taunton (TANTVNE) Ae2-St | 1200 | 1000 |
| Thetford (ÐEOTFOR, DTF, TETFOR) Edg-St | 275 | 575 |
| Torksey (TVRC, TORC) EdM-Cn | 2500 | — |
| Totnes (DARENT, TOTANES, TOTNES) A'stn, Edw-HCn, W2, H1 | 600 | 1750 |
| Wallingford (PELINGA, PALLIG) A'stn, Edm, Edg, Ae2-H1 | 450 | 700 |
| Wareham (PERHAM, PERI) A'stn, Edg-St | 600 | 1200 |
| Warminster (PORIME) Ae2-Hd1, EdC | 3000 | — |
| Warwick (PAERINC, PERPIC, PAR) A'stn (?), Edg-St | 800 | 1250 |
| Watchet (PECED, PICEDI, WACET) Ae2-EdC, W1-St | 1500 | 1750 |
| Wilton (PILTVNE) Edg-St | 350 | 700 |
| Winchcombe (WENCLES, PINCEL, PINCL) Edg, Ae2, Cn, HCn-W1 | 2500 | 2000 |
| Winchester (PINTONIA, PINCEST) Alf, A'stn, Edw-St | 275 | 575 |
| Worcester (PIGER, PIHREC, PIREC) EdM, Ae2-St | 600 | 900 |
| York (EBORACI, EFORPIC, EVERWIC) A'stn, Edm, Edg-St | 275 | 750 |

*Mints of uncertain identification or location*

| | | |
|---|---|---|
| "Brygin" (BRYGIN) Ae2 | 3500 | — |
| "Dyr/Dernt" (DYR, DERNE, DERNT) EdC (East Anglia) | 1500 | — |
| "Weardburh" (PEARDBV) A'stn, Edg | 4500 | — |
| Abergavenny (?) (FVNI) W1 | — | 4000 |
| Gothabyrig (GEODA, GODABYRI, IODA) Ae2-HCn | 3000 | — |
| Eye (?) (EI, EIE) St | — | 3000 |
| Peterborough (?) (BVRI) W1, St | — | 3500 |
| Richmond, Yorks (?) (R1), St (type 1) | — | 1500 |
| St Davids (?) (DEVITVN) W1 | — | 3500 |
| Wilton, Norfolk (?) (PILTV) Ae2 (LSC) | 2500 | — |
| Bamborough (BCI, CIB, OBCI) Henry of Northumberland | — | 5500 |
| Corbridge (COREB) Henry of Northumberland | — | 5750 |

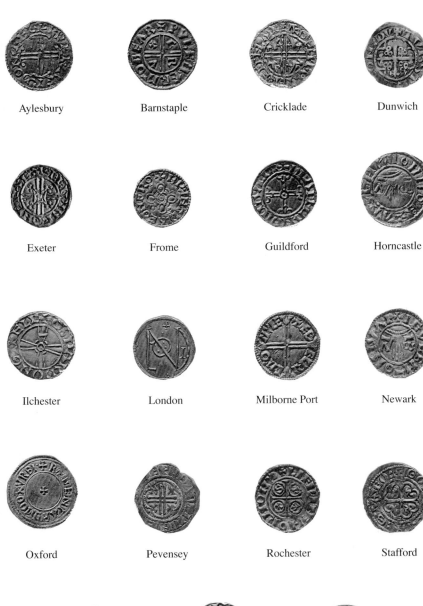

| Aylesbury | Barnstaple | Cricklade | Dunwich |
|---|---|---|---|
| Exeter | Frome | Guildford | Horncastle |
| Ilchester | London | Milborne Port | Newark |
| Oxford | Pevensey | Rochester | Stafford |

| Torksey | Winchcombe | York |
|---|---|---|

| | | | | | |
|---|---|---|---|---|---|
| 1. Launceston | 13. Bath | 25. Chichester | 37. London | 49. Huntingdon | 61. Rhuddlan |
| 2. Barnstaple | 14. Marlborough | 26. Steyning | 38. Hertford | 50. Bedford | 62. Chester |
| 3. Totnes | 15. Wilton | 27. Lewes | 39. Maldon | 51. Northampton | 63. Shrewsbury |
| 4. Exeter | 16. Salisbury | 28. Pevensey | 40. Colchester | 52. Warwick | 64. Stafford |
| 5. Watchet | 17. Christchurch | 29. Hastings | 41. Ipswich | 53. Worcester | 65. Tamworth |
| 6. Taunton | 18. Abergavenny* | 30. Romney | 42. Sudbury | 54. Winchcombe | 66. Leicester |
| 7. Bridport | 19. Winchester | 31. Hythe | 43. Cambridge | 55. Oxford | 67. Derby |
| 8. Dorchester | 20. Bedwyn | 32. Dover | 44. Bury | 56. Gloucester | 68. Nottingham |
| 9. Wareham | 21. Malmesbury | 33. Sandwich | 45. Thetford | 57. Hereford | 69. Lincoln |
| 10. Shaftesbury | 22. Cricklade | 34. Canterbury | 46. Norwich | 58. Cardiff | 70. York |
| 11. Ilchester | 23. Wallingford | 35. Rochester | 47. Stamford | 59. Pembroke | 71. Durham |
| 12. Bristol | 24. Guildford | 36. Southwark | 48. Peterborough | 60. St Davids* | 72. Carlisle |

*Possible location of uncertain mint*

William I maintained the Anglo-Saxon mint system and the practice of conducting frequent periodic recoinages by change of coin type. However, the twelfth-century witnessed a gradual transition from regional to centralised minting. Nearly seventy towns had moneyers operating under William I, but only thirty mint towns took part in the recoinage initiated by the Cross-and-Crosslets ('Tealby') coinage in 1158. Cut halfpennies and cut farthings were made during this period, but are scarce for all types up to BMC 13 of Henry I; cut coins are more frequently encountered for subsequent types.

Further reading: G.C. Brooke, *Catalogue of English Coins in the British Museum. The Norman Kings*, 2 volumes (London, 1916). (Abbr. BMC Norman Kings). I. Stewart, 'The English and Norman mints, c.600–1158', in *A New History of the Royal Mint,* ed. C.E. Challis (Cambridge, 1992), pp. 1–82.

## WILLIAM I, 1066-1087

Duke William of Normandy claimed the throne of England on the death of his cousin Edward the Confessor. An important monetary reform occurred towards the close of the reign with the introduction of the *geld de moneta* assessed on boroughs. This may be seen as part of the raft of administrative reforms initiated by William I, which included the compilation of Domesday Book in 1086.

The date of the Paxs type is central to the absolute chronology of this and the subsequent reign. which is now widely accepted.

1250             1251

| | | F £ | VF £ |
|---|---|---|---|
| 1250 | **Penny.** *B.M.C.* 1: Profile left type. | 475 | 1500 |

1252             1253

| | | | |
|---|---|---|---|
| 1251 | *B.M.C.* 2: Bonnet type. | 275 | 900 |
| 1252 | *B.M.C.* 3: Canopy type | 475 | 1500 |

1254             1255

| | | | |
|---|---|---|---|
| 1253 | *B.M.C.* 4: Two sceptres type. | 325 | 1100 |
| 1254 | *B.M.C.* 5: Two stars type. | 275 | 950 |
| 1255 | *B.M.C.* 6: Sword type. | 475 | 1500 |

| | | | F | VF |
|---|---|---|---|---|
| | | | £ | £ |
| 1256 | *B.M.C.* 7: Profile right type (lead die struck examples exist from the Thames) | | 525 | 1750 |
| 1257 | *B.M.C.* 8: Paxs type | | 250 | 700 |

## WILLIAM II, 1087-1100

Second son of William I was killed while hunting in the New Forest. Five of the thirteen coin types in the name of 'William' have been assigned to the reign of William II, although it remains uncertain whether the Paxs type of his father continued into his reign.

| 1258 | **Penny**. *B.M.C.* 1: Profile type. | 900 | 2750 |
|---|---|---|---|
| 1259 | *B.M.C.* 2: Cross in quatrefoil type. | 700 | 2000 |
| 1260 | *B.M.C.* 3: Voided cross type | 700 | 2000 |
| 1261 | *B.M.C.* 4: Cross pattée and fleury type. | 750 | 2250 |

| 1262 | *B.M.C.* 5: Cross fleury and piles type. | 800 | 2400 |
|---|---|---|---|

Henry was the third son of William I. Administrative reforms and military action to secure Normandy dominated the king's work. After the death of his son in 1120 Henry sought to guarantee the throne for his daughter Matilda, widow of German Emperor Henry V.

The coin types continue to be numbered according to BMC Norman Kings (London, 1916), but the order 1, 2, 3, 4, 5, 6, 9, 7, 8, 11, 10, 12, 13, 14, 15 is now accepted as a working hypothesis for the reign. Greater uncertainty pertains to the chronology of the coin types. The reign coincided with a period of monetary crisis. Scepticism concerning the quality of coinage led to the testing of coins by the public, hindering their acceptance in circulation. In response the government ordered all coins mutilated at issue to force the acceptance of damaged coins. Thus, a few coins of type 6 and all of those of types 7–14 have an official edge incision or 'snick'. Round halfpennies were produced and as some are found snicked they can be dated to the period when official mutilation of the coinage was ordered. In 1124 there was a general purge of moneyers in England as the royal government attempted to restore confidence in the coinage.

Further reading: M.A.S. Blackburn, 'Coinage and currency under Henry I; A review', *Anglo-Norman Studies* 13 (1991), 49–81. M.M. Archibald and W.J. Conte, 'Five round halfpennies of Henry I. A further case for reappraisal of the chronology of types', *Spink's Numismatic Circular* 98 (1990), 232–6, M. Allen 'Henry I Type 14', *BNJ* 79 (2009), 72-171.

1263          1263A          1264

| | F £ | VF £ |
|---|---|---|
| 1263 **Penny**. *B.M.C.* 1: Annulets type | 475 | 1750 |
| 1263A *B.M.C.* 2: Profile/cross fleury type | 325 | 1000 |

1265          1266

| | | |
|---|---|---|
| 1264 *B.M.C.* 3: Paxs type | 300 | 950 |
| 1265 *B.M.C.* 4: Annulets and piles type | 325 | 1000 |

1267          1268

| | | |
|---|---|---|
| 1266 *B.M.C.* 5: Voided cross and fleurs type | 750 | 2500 |
| 1267 *B.M.C.* 6: Pointing bust and stars type | 950 | 3250 |
| 1268 *B.M.C.* 7: Facing bust/quatrefoil with piles type | 375 | 1250 |

1269

1270

|  | | F | VF |
|---|---|---|---|
|  | | £ | £ |
| 1269 | *B.M.C.* 8: Large profile/cross and annulets type | 1100 | 4000 |
| 1270 | *B.M.C.* 9: Facing bust/cross in quatrefoil type | 675 | 2250 |

1271

1272

| 1271 | *B.M.C.* 10: Facing bust/cross fleury type | 275 | 950 |
|---|---|---|---|
| 1272 | *B.M.C.* 11: Double inscription type | 575 | 2000 |

1273

1274

| 1273 | *B.M.C.* 12: Small profile/cross and annulets type | 375 | 1100 |
|---|---|---|---|
| 1274 | *B.M.C.* 13: Star in lozenge fleury type | 400 | 1250 |

1275

1276

| 1275 | *B.M.C.* 14: Pellets in quatrefoil type | 225 | 750 |
|---|---|---|---|
| 1276 | *B.M.C.* 15: Quadrilateral on cross fleury type | 175 | 575 |

1277

1277A

| 1277 | *Round halfpenny*. Facing head. R. Cross potent with pellets in angles | 1750 | 5250 |
|---|---|---|---|
| 1277A | — —, As last but reverse from penny die of type 9 | 2500 | 7500 |

Stephen of Blois seized the English throne on the death of his uncle, Henry I, despite his oath to support Matilda, with whom he contended for power during his reign.

Substantive types BMC 1 and BMC 7 were the only nation-wide issues, the latter introduced after the conclusion of the final political settlement in 1153. The other substantive types, BMC 2 and BMC 6, were confined to areas in the east of England under royal control. In western England coinage was issued by or on behalf of the Angevin party (q.v. below). In areas without access to new dies from London, coinage was produced from locally made dies and initially based on the designs of regular coins of BMC 1. Particular local types were produced in the midlands and the north, associated with prominent magnates, in the king's name or occasionally in the name of barons. Entries contain references to the article by Mack (M).

Further reading: R.P. Mack, 'Stephen and the Anarchy 1135-54', *British Numismatic Journal* 35 (1966), 38–112. M.A.S. Blackburn, 'Coinage and currency', in *The Anarchy of King Stephen's Reign*, ed. E. King (Oxford, 1994), 145–205.

## SUBSTANTIVE ROYAL ISSUES

1278

|  | F | VF |
|---|---|---|
|  | £ | £ |
| 1278 **Penny**. *B.M.C.* 1: Cross Moline ('Watford') type (c.1136–45). Bust right holding sceptre.................................................................................... | 250 | 850 |
| 1279 — —, Similar but obv. reads PERERIC or PERERICM ........................ | 750 | 2750 |

1280

| 1280 *B.M.C.* 2: Voided cross and stars type (c.1145–50) ................................. | 275 | 950 |

1281                              1282

| 1281 *B.M.C.* 6: Cross and piles type (c.1150–54) ............................................ | 300 | 1000 |
| 1282 *B.M.C.* 7: Cross pommée (Awbridge) type (c.1154–58, largely posthumous) | 275 | 900 |
|      This type continued to be struck until 1158 in the reign of Henry II | | |

*The types designated BMC 3, 4 and 5 are non-substantive, listed as 1300–1302.*

= Regular mints of Stephen.

= Mints striking irregular coins including Angevin.

= Mints striking regular and irregular coins.

N.B. Attribution to some of the towns shown is uncertain.

Roxburgh
Bamborough
Corbridge
Newcastle
Carlisle
Durham
York
Hedon
Lincoln
Chester
Derby
Newark
Stafford
Tutbury
Nottingham
Shrewsbury
Leicester
Stamford
Castle Rising
Tamworth
Norwich
Peterborough
Thetford
Worcester
Warwick
Northampton
Huntingdon
Bury
Eye
Dunwich
Hereford
Cambridge
Ipswich
Bedford
Sudbury
Gloucester
Colchester
Cirencester
Oxford
Swansea
Cricklade
Pembroke
Malmesbury
Wallingford
London
Cardiff
Bristol
Bath
Marlborough
Southwark
Trowbridge
Canterbury
Sandwich
Watchet
Ilchester
Wilton
Dover
Wivelscombe
Shaftesbury
Salisbury
Winchester
Rye
Taunton
Bramber
Lewes
Sherborne
Southampton
Chichester
Hastings
Exeter
Dorchester
Wareham
Steyning
Pevensey
Launceston
Wight

# LOCAL AND IRREGULAR ISSUES OF THE CIVIL WAR

## COINS STRUCK FROM ERASED DIES LATE 1130s – *c*.1145

The association of these coins with the Interdict of 1148 is erroneous. Some of the marks that disfigured the dies were probably cancellation marks, but the exigencies of the civil war required the re-use of the dies. Other defacements may well be an overtly political statement.

1283               1288

|  |  | F £ | VF £ |
|---|---|---|---|
| 1283 | As 1278, but obverse defaced with long cross. *East Anglian mints.* (*M 137–47*) | 800 | 3500 |
| 1284 | – –, but king's bust defaced with cross. *Nottingham (M 149)* | 750 | 3500 |
| 1285 | – –, but sceptre defaced with bar or cross. *Nottingham, Lincoln, Stamford.* (*M 148, 150–54*) | 475 | 1650 |
| 1286 | – –, but obverse legend erased. *Nottingham (M 157)* | 575 | 2250 |
| 1286A | – –, but with defacement other than those noted above | 450 | 1500 |

### SOUTH EASTERN VARIANT

| 1287 | As 1278, but king holds mace instead of sceptre. *Canterbury (M 158)* ... | 900 | 4000 |
|---|---|---|---|

### EASTERN VARIANTS

| 1288 | As 1278, but R. has roundels in centre, on cross limbs or in angles. *Suffolk mints (M 159–68)* | 575 | 2250 |
|---|---|---|---|
| 1289 | – –, but R. Plain cross, fleurs in angles. *Lincoln (M 169–73)* | 550 | 2250 |
| 1290 | – –, but R. Plain cross superimposed on cross moline *(M 174)* | 525 | 2000 |
| 1290A | – –, but R. Quadrilateral over voided cross *(M 176)* | 800 | 3750 |
| 1290B | – –, but cross penetrating legend to edge, fleurs inverted in angles. *Lincoln. (M 186–7)* | 750 | 3500 |

### SOUTHERN VARIANTS

1291               1295

| 1291 | As 1278, but with large rosette of pellets at end of obverse legend *(M 184–5)* | 550 | 2000 |
|---|---|---|---|
| 1292 | – –, but with star at end of obverse legend *(M 187y)* | 500 | 1650 |
| 1293 | Bust r. or l., rosette in place of sceptre. R. As 1280, but solid cross. (*M 181–3*) | 650 | 2750 |
| 1295 | As 1278, but king wears collar of annulets. R. voided cross moline, annulet at centre. *Southampton. (M 207–212)* | 375 | 1500 |

|      |                                                                                                      | F<br>£ | VF<br>£ |
|------|------------------------------------------------------------------------------------------------------|--------|---------|
| 1296 | As 1278, but reverse cross penetrates legend with fleur-de-lis tips. *Leicester (M 177–8)* .......... | 700    | 2750    |
| 1297 | — —, but crude work. R. Voided cross, lis outward in angles. *Tutbury (M 179)* ...................... | 750    | 3250    |

1298                                                     1300

|      |                                                                                                        |      |       |
|------|--------------------------------------------------------------------------------------------------------|------|-------|
| 1298 | — —, but crude work. R. Voided cross with martlets in angles. *Derby Tutbury (M 175)* ............. | 2250 | 8500  |
| 1299 | — —, but R. plain cross with T-cross in each angle *(M 180)* ................... | 800  | 3000  |
| 1300 | *B.M.C.* 3: Facing bust. R. Cross pattée, fleurs inwards. *Northampton and Huntingdon (?) (M 67–71)* ..... | 900  | 3250  |

1301                                                     1302

|      |                                                                                                        |      |       |
|------|--------------------------------------------------------------------------------------------------------|------|-------|
| 1301 | *B.M.C.* 4: Lozenge fleury type. *Lincoln or Nottingham (M 72–5)* .......... | 475  | 1750  |
| 1302 | *B.M.C.* 5: Bust half-right. R. Lozenge in Cross Moline with fleurs. *Leicester (M 76)* ..... | 1100 | 4500  |
| 1303 | As 1280, but obverse legend ROBERTVS. *(M 269)* ............... | 3250 | 12500 |

### NORTH-EASTERN AND SCOTTISH BORDER VARIANTS

|      |                                                                                                        |      |       |
|------|--------------------------------------------------------------------------------------------------------|------|-------|
| 1304 | As 1278, but star before sceptre. R. Annulets at tips of fleurs *(M 188)* ... | 725  | 2750  |
| 1305 | — —, but voided cross penetrating legend to edge *(M 189–92)* ............... | 750  | 3000  |
| 1306 | — —, but crude style *(M 276–9, 281–2)* ................. | 575  | 2500  |
| 1307 | — —, but R. Cross with cross pattée and crescent in angles *(M 288)* ...... | 1650 | 5500  |
|      | **King David I of Scotland**                                                                            |      |       |
| 1308 | As 1278, but obverse legend DAVID REX *(M 280)* ............... | 1750 | 5250  |
|      | **Earl Henry of Northumberland (son of King David I of Scotland)**                                      |      |       |
| 1309 | As 1278, but legend hENRIC ERL *(M 283–5)* ..................... | 1750 | 5750  |
| 1310 | — —, Similar but reverse cross fleury *(M 286–7)* ............... | 1750 | 5750  |
| 1311 | As 1307, but obverse legend NENCI:COM *(M 289)* ............... | 2000 | 6500  |

### YORK ISSUES: THE ORNAMENTED GROUP ATTRIBUTED TO YORK (1140s)
**King Stephen**

|      |                                                                                                        |      |       |
|------|--------------------------------------------------------------------------------------------------------|------|-------|
| 1312 | As 1278, but obverse inscription NSEPEFETI, NSEPINEI or STIEFNER. R. ornamental letters WISÐGNOTA *(M 215–6)* ..... | 900  | 3500  |

1313             1315

|  | F<br>£ | VF<br>£ |
|---|---|---|
| 1313   Flag type. As 1278, but lance with pennant before face, star right. ℞. As<br>      1278, letters and four or eight ornaments in legend *(M 217)* ................. | 750 | 3000 |
| 1314   As 1278, but legend STEIN and pellet lozenge for sceptre-head *(M 218)* | 850 | 3250 |
| 1314A King standing facing, holding sceptre and standard with triple pennon. ℞.<br>      Cross pattée, crescents and quatrefoils in angles, ornaments in legend. .. | 3000 | 12000 |

**King Stephen and Queen Matilda**

| | | |
|---|---|---|
| 1315   Two full-length standing figures holding sceptre. ℞. Legend of ornaments.<br>      *(M 220)* ........................................................................................ | 3750 | 13500 |

1317            1320

**Eustace Fitzjohn**

| | | |
|---|---|---|
| 1316   EVSTACIVS, knight standing with sword. ℞. Cross in quatrefoil,<br>      EBORACI EDTS or EBORACI TDEFL *(M 221-222)* ........................... | 2000 | 8250 |
| 1317   — —, Similar but reverse legend ThOMHS FILIUS VLF *(M 223)* ........ | 2250 | 9500 |
| 1318   — —, Similar but reverse legend of ornaments and letters. *(M 224)* ....... | 1750 | 6750 |
| 1319   [EVSTA]CII. FII. IOANIS, lion passant right. ℞. Cross moline, ornaments in<br>      legend *(M 225)* ...................................................................................... | 2750 | 11000 |
| 1320   EISTAOhIVS, lion rampant right. ℞. Cross fleury, ornaments in legend *(M 226)* | 2500 | 10500 |

**William of Aumale, Earl of York**

| | | |
|---|---|---|
| 1320A WILLELMVS, Knight stg. r. holding sword. ℞. Cross in quatrefoil. As 1316 | 3250 | 12500 |

1322

**Rodbert III de Stuteville**

| | | |
|---|---|---|
| 1321   ROBERTVS IESTV, knight holding sword on horse right. ℞. as 1314.<br>      *(M 228)* ...................................................................................... | 5250 | 17500 |
| 1321A Type as 1312, but obverse legend RODBDS[T DE?] *(M 227)* ............... | 3250 | 12500 |

**Henry Murdac, Archbishop of York**

| | | |
|---|---|---|
| 1322   HENRICVS EPC, crowned bust, crosier and star before. ℞. similar to 1314<br>      but legend STEPHANVS REX *(M 229)* ................................................. | 3000 | 11000 |

**UNCERTAIN ISSUES**

|  |  | F | VF |
|---|---|---|---|
|  |  | £ | £ |
| 1323 | Obv. as 1278. R. Cross pattée with annulets in angles *(M 272)* | 675 | 2500 |
| 1324 | Obv. as 1275 (Henry I, *B.M.C.* 14), but reverse as last *(M 274 extr)* | 900 | 3000 |
| 1325 | Other miscellaneous types/varieties | 650 | 1500 |

# THE ANGEVIN PARTY

Matilda was the daughter of Henry I and widow of German Emperor Henry V (d.1125) and had been designated heir to the English throne by her father. Matilda was Countess of Anjou by right of her second husband Geoffrey of Anjou. Matilda arrived in England in pursuit of her inheritance in 1139 and established an Angevin court at Bristol and controlled most of south-western England. Matilda's cause was championed by her half-brother, Henry I's illegitimate son, Robert, Earl of Gloucester.

The initial phase of coinage in Matilda's name copied the designs of Stephen's BMC 1 and are dated to the early 1140s. The second type was only discovered in the Coed-y-Wenallt hoard (1980). A group of coins in the names of 'William' and 'Henry' and struck at the Angevin mints, particularly Hereford and Gloucester, are attributable, at least in part, to Earl William of Gloucester and Henry of Anjou (the future Henry II). Coins of Earl William, and his father Earl Robert, of the Lion type are now also known thanks to the discovery of the Box, Wiltshire hoard (1994). In addition to these great magnates a few minor barons placed their names on the coinage.

Further Reading: G. Boon, *Welsh Hoards 1979–81* (Cardiff, 1986). M.M. Archibald, 'The lion coinage of Robert Earl of Gloucester and William Earl of Gloucester', *British Numismatic Journal* 71 (2001), 71–86.

1326

**Matilda (in England 1139–48)**

| | | | |
|---|---|---|---|
| 1326 | As 1278, but cruder style, MATILDI IMP or variant (M 230–40) *Bristol, Cardiff, Monmouth, Oxford and Wareham.* | 2500 | 8000 |
| 1326A | — —, MATILDI IMP or IM.HE.MA. R. Cross pattée over fleury (Coed-y-Wenallt hoard). *Bristol and Cardiff.* | 2600 | 8250 |
| 1326B | — —, as last but triple pellets at cross ends (Coed-y-Wenallt hoard). *Bristol and Cardiff.* | 2600 | 8250 |

**Henry de Neubourg**

| | | | |
|---|---|---|---|
| 1326C | Similar type to 1326A but HENRICI dE NOVOB (Coed-y-Wenallt hoard) *Swansea.* | 2750 | 9000 |

**Issues in the name 'Henry' and 'William'**

| | | | |
|---|---|---|---|
| 1327 | As 1278, but HENRICVS or HENRICVS REX *(M 241–5). Hereford and Malmesbury.* | 1350 | 5500 |
| 1327A | As 1295, but HENRIC *(M 246). Gloucester.* | 1500 | 6000 |
| 1327B | As 1326A, but HENNENNVS | 1500 | 6000 |
| 1328 | Obv. as 1278, but HENRICVS. R. Cross crosslet in quatrefoil *(M 254). Gloucester.* | 1750 | 6500 |

1329

1331

|   |   | F £ | VF £ |
|---|---|---|---|

1329 — —, but HENRICVS or HENRICVS REX FVTVRVS Ɍ. Quadrilateral on
cross fleury *(M 248–53). Hereford, Cirencester (?) and Ilchester (?)* ..... 1350 5500

1330 Facing bust and stars, HENRICVS or HENRICVS RE. Ɍ. Quadrilateral on
cross botonnée *(M 255–8). Bristol, Ilchester (?) and Sherborne (?)*........ 1650 6500

1331 — —, Quadrilateral, on voided cross botonnée *(M 259–61)* .................. 1650 6500

1332 As 1329, but legend [WIL]LELM *(M 262)* ............................................. 1500 6000

1333 As 1330, but legend WILLELM or variant *(M 263). Cirencester (?)* ...... 1750 7000

1334 As 1331, but legend WILLELMVS *(M 264–8). Dorchester and Wareham* .. 1750 7000

**Earl Robert of Gloucester (1121/22–1147)**

1334A +ROB' COM' GLOC' lion passant right. Ɍ. Cross fleury ....................... 1650 6500

**Earl William of Gloucester (1147-1183)**

1334B +WILLEMVS, lion passant right. Ɍ. Cross fleury ................................. 1650 6500

**Brian Fitzcount, Lord of Wallingford (?)**

1335 As 1330, but legend B.R:C.I.T.B.R *(M 270)* ........................................... 3750 13500

1336

**Earl Patrick of Salisbury (?)**

1336 Helmeted bust r. with sword, star behind. Ɍ. As 1329. *(M 271)*............... 3500 12000

Tealby (1158-80)

Short Cross (1180-1247)

Voided Long Cross (1247-7

New coinage (1279-1327).

## HENRY II, 1154-1189

### CROSS-AND-CROSSLETS ('TEALBY') COINAGE, 1158-1180

Coins of Stephen's last type continued to be minted until 1158. Then a new coinage bearing Henry's name replaced the currency of the previous reign which contained a high proportion of irregular and sub-standard pennies. The new Cross and Crosslets issue is more commonly referred to as the 'Tealby' coinage, as over 6000 of these pennies were discovered at Tealby, Lincolnshire, in 1807. Twenty-nine mints were employed in this re-coinage, but once the re-minting had been completed not more than a dozen mints were kept open. The issue remained virtually unchanged for twenty-two years apart from minor variations in the king's portrait. The coins tend to be poorly struck on irregular flans.

Cut coins occur with varying degrees of frequency during this issue, according to the type and local area.

Further reading: *A Catalogue of English Coins in the British Museum. The Cross-and-Crosslet ("Tealby") Type of Henry II.* (London: 1951) by D.F. Allen.

| | | 1337 | 1338 | 1339 | | |
|---|---|---|---|---|---|---|
| | | | | | F | VF |
| | | | | | £ | £ |
| 1337 | Class A (1158-c.1163). No hair, no collar. Mantle falls from chin as two parallel lines between which is a line of pellets. | | | | 125 | 350 |
| 1338 | Class B (c.1162-c.1163). Similar, but mantle of two folds which meet at chin (various compositions) | | | | 135 | 400 |
| 1339 | Class C (c.1163-c.1167). Curl of hair at temple. Jewelled collar, mantle of many folds, field between sometimes jewelled, as is cuff | | | | 120 | 325 |

| | | 1340 | 1341 | | |
|---|---|---|---|---|---|
| 1340 | Class D (c.1167-c.1170). Jewelled collar continues down shoulder unbroken. Single curl of hair at temple, folds of mantle horizontal | | | 120 | 325 |
| 1341 | Class E (c.1170-c.1174). Similar to 1340. Jewelled collar only. Folds of mantle rise from hand to top of shoulder. | | | 120 | 325 |

1342

| | | | |
|---|---|---|---|
| 1342 | Class F (c.1174-c.1180). Similar to 1341, but hair falls in long ringlets from temple. | 110 | 300 |

**Mints and Moneyers for the Cross-and-Crosslets (Tealby) Coinage**

*From F £*

*London*: Accard (CD), Alwin (ABCDF), Edmund (ACDE), Geffrei (ACE), Godefrei (ACDEF), Godwin (BDE), Hunfrei (AC), Iohan (ACDEF), Lefwine (BCEF), Martin (ABC), Pieres (ACEF), Pieres Mer. (ABD), Pieres Sal. (AEF), Ricard (ABCD), Rodbert (AC), Swetman (ABC), Wid (A), *110*

*Canterbury*: Alferg (A), Goldhavoc (ABCDEF), Goldeep (C), Lambrin (F), Raul (CDEF), Ricard (ABCDEF), Ricard Mr. (ABCDE), Rogier (ABCDEF), Rogier F. (A), Willem (C), Wiulf (ABCDEF), *110*

*Bedford*: Arfin (A), *Extremely Rare*

*Bristol*: Elaf (ACF), Rogier (ADEF), Tancard (ABD), *250*

*Bury St Edmunds*: Henri (BDE), Raul (F), Willem (A), *140*

*Carlisle*: Willem (ACDEF), *140*

*Chester*: Andreu (A), Willem (AD), *220*

*Colchester*: Alwin (AC), Pieres (CE), *250*

*Durham*: Cristien (C), Iohan (B), Walter (A), *180*

*Exeter*: Edwid (AC), Guncelin (AC), Rainir (BC), Ricard (A), Rogier (AD), *220*

*Gloucester*: Godwin (A), Nicol (A), Rodbert (A), Sawulf (A), *275*

*Hereford*: Driu (AC), Osburn (A), Stefne (A), [ — ]ward (A), *250*

*Ilchester*: Adam (CDF), Reinard (A), Ricard (A), Rocelin (A), *220*

*Ipswich*: Nicole (BCDEF), Robert (CEF), Turstain (CF), *110*

*Launceston*: Willem (A), *Extremely Rare*

*Leicester*: Ricard (A), Robert (A), *250*

*Lewes*: uncertain (F), *Extremely Rare*

*Lincoln*: Andreu (ABCDE), Godric (ABCD), Lanfram (ABCDF), Raulf (ABCDEF), Raven (ACF), Swein (ACD), *140*

*Newcastle*: Willem (ACDEF), *150*

*Northampton*: Ingeram (AC), Iosep (A), Pieres (A), Reimund (AC), Stefne (A), Waltier (AC), Warnier (AC), *180*

*Norwich*: Gilebert (ABF), Herbert (ACD), Herbert R (A)., Hugo (ACF), Nicol (AC), Picot (ABC), Reiner (AD), Ricard (A), *180*

*Oxford*: Adam (ADE), Aschetil (A), Rogier (A), *220*

*Pembroke*: Walter (A), *Extremely Rare*

*Salisbury*: Daniel (A), Levric (A), *220*

*Shrewsbury*: Warin (A), *Extremely Rare*

*Stafford*: Colbrand (AC), Willem (C), *275*

*Thetford*: Siwate (ACD), Turstain (ACD), Willem (ACDF), Willem Ma (A), Willem De (A), *140*

*Wallingford*: Fulke (A), *Extremely Rare*

*Wilton*: Anschetil (A), Lantier (A), Willem (A), *220*

*Winchester*: Herbert (AC), Hosbert (ACD), Ricard (AE), Willem (AC), *140*

*York*: Cudbert (A), Gerrard (A), Godwin (AD), Griffin (AD), Herbert (ACD), Hervi (A), Iordan (A), Norman (A), Willem (A), Wulfsi (A), *140*

Letters in brackets after moneyer's name indicate Class known to exist for the mint and moneyer combination

## 'SHORT CROSS' COINAGE OF HENRY II (1180-1189)

In 1180 a coinage of new type, known as the Short Cross coinage, replaced the Tealby issue. The new coinage is remarkable in that it covers not only the latter part of the reign of Henry II, but also the reigns of his sons Richard and John and on into the reign of his grandson Henry III, and the entire issue bears the name 'hENRICVS'. There are no English coins with the names of Richard or John. The Short Cross coins can be divided chronologically into various classes: ten mints were operating under Henry II and tables of mints, moneyers and classes are given for each reign.

The Publishers acknowledge the work of the late Prof. Jeffrey Mass for re-organising and updating the shortcross series.

Further reading: *Sylloge of Coins of the British Isles Vol 56. The J.P. Mass Collection of English Short Cross Coins 1180 to 1247*. London 2002.

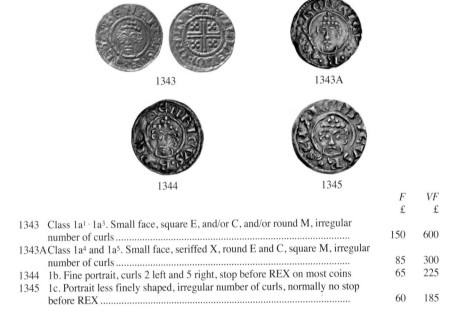

1343     1343A

1344     1345

| | | F £ | VF £ |
|---|---|---|---|
| 1343 | Class 1a¹ - 1a³. Small face, square E, and/or C, and/or round M, irregular number of curls | 150 | 600 |
| 1343A | Class 1a⁴ and 1a⁵. Small face, seriffed X, round E and C, square M, irregular number of curls | 85 | 300 |
| 1344 | 1b. Fine portrait, curls 2 left and 5 right, stop before REX on most coins | 65 | 225 |
| 1345 | 1c. Portrait less finely shaped, irregular number of curls, normally no stop before REX | 60 | 185 |

## RICHARD I, 1189-1199

Pennies of Short Cross type continued to be issued throughout the reign, all bearing the name hENRICVS. The coins of class 4, which have very crude portraits, continued to be issued in the early years of the next reign. The only coins bearing Richard's name are from his territories of Aquitaine and Poitou in western France.

1346     1347     1348A     1348C

| | | F | VF |
|---|---|---|---|
| 1346 | 2. Chin whiskers made of small curls, no side whiskers, almost always 5 pearls to crown, frequently no collar, sometimes RE/X | 110 | 375 |
| 1347 | 3. Large or small face, normally 7 pearls to crown, chin and side whiskers made up of small curls | 85 | 275 |

| | F | VF |
|---|---|---|
| | £ | £ |

1348A 4a. Normally 7 pearls to crown, chin and side whiskers made up of small
pellets, hair consisting of 2 or more non-parallel crescents left and right — 75 / 250

1348B 4a* Same as last, but with reverse colon stops (instead of single pellets) — 85 / 300

1348C 4b Normally 7 pearls to crown, chin and side whiskers made up of small
pellets, single (or parallel) crescents as hair left and right, frequent
malformed letters ............................................................................ — 70 / 225

## JOHN, 1199-1216

**'SHORT CROSS' COINAGE** *continued*. All with name hENRICVS
The Short Cross coins of class 4 continued during the early years of John's reign, but in 1205 a
re-coinage was initiated and new Short Cross coins of better style replaced the older issues. Coins of
classes 5a and 5b were issued in the re-coinage in which sixteen mints were employed. Only two of
these mints (London and Durham) were still working by the end of class 5. The only coins to bear
John's name are the pennies, halfpence and farthings issues for Ireland.

1349          1350A          1350B

1351          1352          1354

1349 4c. Reversed S, square face at bottom, 5 pearls to crown, normally single
crescents as hair left and right ................................................. 90 / 350

1350A 5a1 Reversed or regular S, irregular curved lines as hair (or circular curls
containing no pellets), cross pattée as initial mark on reverse, *London and
Canterbury* only.............................................................. 175 / 600

1350B 5a2 Reversed S, circular curls left and right (2 or 3 each side) containing
single pellets, cross pommée as initial mark on reverse ......................... 85 / 275

1350C 5a/5b or 5b/5a ................................................................ 65 / 200

1351 5b. Regular S, circular pelleted curls, cross pattée as initial mark on reverse 60 / 185

1352 5c. Slightly rounder portrait, letter X in the form of a St. Andrew's cross 55 / 160

1353 6a. Smaller portrait, with smaller letter X composed of thin strokes or,
later, short wedges ............................................................. 55 / 160

1354 6b. Very tall lettering and long rectangular face ..................................... 45 / 145

*For further reading and an extensive listing of the English Short Cross Coinage see:*
**Sylloge of Coins of the British Isles.** *The J. P. Mass Collection of English Short Cross
Coins 1180-1247*

## 'SHORT CROSS' COINAGE *continued* (1216-47)

The Short Cross coinage continued for a further thirty years during which time the style of portraiture and workmanship deteriorated. By the 1220s minting had been concentrated at London and Canterbury, one exception being the mint of the Abbot of Bury St. Edmunds.

Halfpenny and farthing dies are recorded early in this issue; a few halfpennies and now farthings have been discovered. See nos 1357 D-E.

|       | 1355 | 1355A | 1355B |
| --- | --- | --- | --- |

|                                                                                      | F | VF |
|                                                                                      | £ | £ |
| 1355  6c. Lettering now shorter, face narrow and triangular (also issued in the reign of John)...................................................................................... | 70 | 250 |
| 1355A 6c. orn. Various letters now ornamental in design, curls 3/3 left and right | 90 | 325 |
| 1355B 6x. Canterbury mint only, RE/X, curls 2/2, nostril pellets outside nose... | 475 | 1500 |
| 1355C 6d. Face less distinct in shape, N's containing a pellet along the crossbar | 85 | 275 |

|       | 1356A | 1356B | 1356C |
| --- | --- | --- | --- |

| 1356A 7a. Small compact face, letter A (rev. only) with top coming to a point under crossbar........................................................................................ | 35 | 125 |
| 1356B 7b. Letter A with square top, M appears as H (rev. only)......................... | 35 | 125 |
| 1356C 7c. Degraded portrait, letter A and M as in 7b, large lettering (rev. only) | 30 | 110 |

|       | 1357A | 1357C |
| --- | --- | --- |

| 1357A 8a. New portrait; letter X in shape of curule; cross pattée as initial mark on reverse (early style), or cross pommée (late style) ............................. | 135 | 450 |
| 1357B 8b. Degraded portrait, wedge-shaped X, cross pommée as initial mark .. | 50 | 175 |
| 1357C 8c. Degraded portrait, cross pommée X, cross pommée as initial mark .. | 50 | 175 |
| 1357D Round **Halfpenny** in style of class 7, initial mark in shape of up-turned crescent, London mint only (dated to 1222)............................................ | 3250 | 10000 |
| 1357E Round **Farthing** in style of class 7, initial mark in shape of up-turned crescent, London mint only (dated to 1222)............................................... | 2500 | 7500 |

**Mints and Moneyers for the Short Cross Coinage**

*Fine*

**Henry II:**
*London:* Aimer (1a-b), Alain (1a-b), Alain V (1a-b), Alward (1b), Davi (1b-c),
Fil Aimer (1a-b), Gefrei (1c), Gilebert (1c), Godard (1b), Henri (1a-b),
Henri Pi (1a), Iefrei (1a-b), Iohan (1a-b), Osber (1b), Pieres (1a-c),
Pieres M (1a-b), Randvl (1a-b), Ravl (1b-c), Reinald (1a-b), Willelm (1a-b)     50
*Carlisle:* Alain (1b-c)     85
*Exeter:* Asketil (1a-b), Iordan (1a-b), Osber (1a-b), Ravl (1b), Ricard (1b-c),
Roger (1a-c)     75
*Lincoln:* Edmvnd (1b-c), Girard (1b), Hvgo (1b), Lefwine (1b-c), Rodbert (1b),
Walter (1b), Will. D.F. (1b), Willelm (1b-c)     65
*Northampton:* Filip (1a-b), Hvgo (1a-b), Ravl (1a-c), Reinald (1a-c), Simvn (1b),
Walter (1a-c), Willelm (1a-b)     60
*Oxford:* Asketil (1b), Iefrei (1b), Owein (1b-c), Ricard (1b-c), Rodbert (1b),
Rodbt. F. B. (1b), Sagar (1b)     70
*Wilton:* Osber (1a-b), Rodbert (1a-b), Iohan (1a)     75
*Winchester:* Adam (1a-c), Clement (1a-b), Gocelm (1a-c), Henri (1a),
Osber (1a-b), Reinier (1b), Rodbert (1a-b)     60
*Worcester:* Edrich (1b), Godwine (1b-c), Osber (1b-c), Oslac (1b)     75
*York:* Alain (1a-b), Efrard (1a-c), Gerard (1a-b), Hvgo (1a-c), Hunfrei (1a-b),
Isac (1a-b), Tvrkil (1a-c), Willelm (1a-b)     60

**Richard I**
*London:* Aimer (2-4a), Fvlke (4a-b), Henri (4a-b), Ravl (2), Ricard (2-4b),
Stivene (2-4b), Willelm (2-4b)     70
*Canterbury:* Goldwine (3-4b), Hernavd (4b), Hve (4b), Ioan (4b), Meinir (2-4b),
Reinald/Reinavd (2-4b), Roberd (2-4b), Samvel (4b), Simon (4b), Vlard (2-4b)     80
*Carlisle:* Alein (3-4b)     125
*Durham:* Adam (4a), Alein (4a-b), Pires (4b)     150
*Exeter:* Ricard (3)     135
*Lichfield:* Ioan (2)     4500
*Lincoln:* Edmvnd (2), Lefwine (2), Willelm (2)     100
*Northampton:* Giferei (4a), Roberd (3), Waltir (3)     110
*Northampton or Norwich:* Randvl (4a-b), Willelm (4a-b)     100
*Shrewsbury:* Ive (4a-b), Reinald/Reinavd (4a-b), Willem (4a)     175
*Winchester:* Adam (3), Gocelm (3), Osbern (3-4a), Pires (4a), Willelm (3-4a)     80
*Worcester:* Osbern (2)     250
*York:* Davi (4a-b), Efrard/Everard (2-4b), Hvgo/Hve (2-4a), Nicole (4a-b),
Tvrkil (2-4a)     80

**John**
*London:* Abel (5c-6b), Adam (5b-c), Beneit (5b-c), Fvlke (4c-5b), Henri (4c-5b/5a),
Ilger (5b-6b), Ravf (5c-6b), Rener (5a/b-5c), Ricard (4c-5b), Ricard B (5b-c),
Ricard T (5a/b-5b), Walter (5c-6b), Willelm (4c-5b), Willelm B (5a/b-5c),
Willelm L (5b-c), Willelm T (5b-c)     45
*Canterbury:* Goldwine (4c-5c), Hernavd/Arnavd (4c-5c), Hve (4c-5c), Iohan (4c-5c),
Iohan B (5b-c), Iohan M (5b-c), Roberd (4c-5c), Samvel (4c-5c), Simon (4c-5c)     50
*Bury St Edmunds:* Fvlke (5b-c)     90
*Carlisle:* Tomas (5b)     110
*Chichester:* Pieres (5b/a-5b), Ravf (5b/a-5b), Simon (5b/a-5b), Willelm (5b)     80
*Durham:* Pieres (5a-6a)     90
*Exeter:* Gileberd (5a-b), Iohan (5a-b), Ricard (5a-b)     75

*Ipswich:* Alisandre (5b-c), Iohan (5b-c)    60
*Kings Lynn:* Iohan (5b), Nicole (5b), Willelm (5b)    125
*Lincoln:* Alain (5a), Andrev (5a-5c), Hve (5a/b-5c), Iohan (5a), Ravf (5a/b-5b),
Ricard (5a-5b/a), Tomas (5a/b-5b)    50
*Northampton:* Adam (5b-c), Roberd (5b), Roberd T (5b)    60
*Northampton or Norwich:* Randvl (4c)    80
*Norwich:* Gifrei (5a/b-5c), Iohan (5a-c), Renald/Renavd (5a-c)    60
*Oxford:* Ailwine (5b), Henri (5b), Miles (5b)    70
*Rochester:* Alisandre (5b), Hvnfrei (5b)    90
*Winchester:* Adam (5a-c), Andrev (5b-c), Bartelme (5b-c), Henri (5a), Iohan (5a-c),
Lvkas (5b-c), Miles (5a-c), Ravf (5b-c), Ricard (5a-b)    50
*York:* Davi (4c-5b), Nicole (4c-5c), Renavd (5b), Tomas (5a/b-5b)    50

## Henry III
*London:* Abel (6c-7a), Adam (7b-c), Elis (7a-b), Giffrei (7b-c), Ilger (6c-7b),
Ledvlf (7b-c), Nichole (7c-8c), Ravf (6c-7b), Ricard (7b), Terri (7a-b),
Walter (6b-c)    30
*Canterbury:* Arnold (6c/6x, 6x), Henri (6c-6c/d, 7a-c), Hivn/Ivn (6c-7b),
Iohan (6c-7c, 8b-c), Ioan Chic (7b-c), Ioan F. R. (7b-c), Nichole (7c, 8b-c),
Osmvnd (7b-c), Robert (6c, 7b-c), Robert Vi (7c), Roger (6c-7b),
Roger of R (7a-b), Salemvn (6x, 7a-b), Samvel (6c-d, 7a), Simon (6c-d, 7a-b),
Tomas (6d, 7a-b), Walter (6c-7a), Willem (7b-c, 8b-c), Willem Ta (7b-c)    30
*Bury St Edmunds:* Iohan (7c-8c), Norman (7a-b), Ravf (6c-d, 7a), Simvnd (7b-c),
Willelm (7a)    35
*Durham:* Pieres (7a)    80
*Winchester:* Henri (6c)    125
*York:* Iohan (6c), Peres (6c), Tomas (6c), Wilam (6c)    125

Irregular Local Issue
Rhuddlan (in chronological order)    95
Group I (c. 1180 – pre 1205) Halli, Tomas, Simond
Group II (c.1205 – 1215) Simond, Henricus

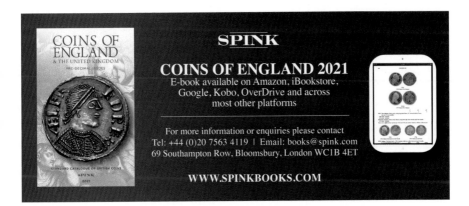

## 'LONG CROSS' COINAGE (1247-72)

By the middle of Henry's reign the Short Cross coinage in circulation was in a poor state and, in 1247, a new coinage was ordered with the cross on the reverse being extended to the edge of the coin in an attempt to prevent clipping. The earliest coins (1a) showed the names of the neither the mint nor the moneyer. Class 1b includes the name of the mint. From class 2 onwards all coins show the name of both the mint and the moneyer.

Following publication of the 1908 Brussels Hoard by Churchill and Thomas (2012) the classification of the Long Cross coinage was revised. This divided the Long Cross coinage into four phases: Phase I, 1247, Pre-provincial; Phase II, 1248-1250, Provincial when sixteen provincial mints, in addition to the main mints of London and Canterbury plus Bury St Edmunds were opened to facilitate the production and distribution of the new coins; Phase III, 1250-1272, The Post-provincial in which the mint of Durham re-opened operating intermittently; Phase IV, 1272-1280, Posthumous (see under Edward I on page 167) when the Long Cross coinage was continued in the name of Henry III through the first seven years of the reign of Edward I.

In Phases I and II the obverse features the King's head without a sceptre but during the Post-provincial phase, from class 4 onwards, the sceptre was re-introduced. No round Half-pennies or farthings were struck during the Long Cross coinage but cut halves and quarters were used in considerable numbers.

Mint marks feature on all coins from classes 1 to 4 inclusive and are an important aid to both chronology and identification. Five main varieties of mint mark exist.

          1             2             3             4             5

Further reading: Ron Churchill and Bob Thomas, *The Brussels Hoard of 1908. The Long Cross Coinage of Henry III*. 2012. *The Voided Long-Cross Coinage 1247-1279* by Christopher R. Wren

## THE LONG CROSS COINAGE, 1247-79

### PHASE I, 1247 PRE-PROVINCIAL PHASE

          1358                          1359

|      |                                                                              | F £ | VF £ |
|------|------------------------------------------------------------------------------|-----|------|
| 1358 | Class 1a. Obv. hENRICVS REX. Rev. ANG LIE TER CI'. *mm* 1.......... | 375 | 1500 |
| 1359 | Class 1b. Obv. hENRICVS REX ANG. Rev. LIE TER CI' LON (London),              |     |      |
|      | CAN (Canterbury - scarce) or AED (Bury St Edmunds - very rare). *mm* 1.       | 65  | 200  |
| 1359A| Class 1a/1b and 1b/1a mules ................................................ | 250 | 1000 |
| 1360 | Class 1b/2a mule. (London and Canterbury only)................................ | 55  | 175  |

1361

|      |                                                            |    |     |
|------|------------------------------------------------------------|----|-----|
| 1361 | Class 2a. Obv. hENRICVS REX TERCI'. *mm* 2.                 |    |     |
|      | Rev. Moneyer & mint. .........................................................| 35 | 110 |

## PHASE II, 1248-50 PROVINCIAL PHASE

1361A

|  | F<br>£ | VF<br>£ |
|---|---|---|

1361A Class 2b. Long, narrow bust, curly X or straight limbed X. Rev. Moneyer
& mint. *mm* 3. .................................................................................... 30    100

1362          1362A          1362B

1362   Class 3a1. Obv. hENRICVS REX III. Class 2 bust. *mm* 3. ................... 25    95
1362A Class 3a2. Bust altered, eyes are round comprising pellets in crescents;
often with a colon after REX. *mm* 3. ...................................................... 25    95
1362B Class 3ab. Neat 3a-3b transitional bust. *mm* 3. ........................................ 25    85

1363          1363A          1364

1363   Class 3b. Neat round bust; beard is three pellets either side of a large central
pellet. *mm* 3. ........................................................................................ 25    85
1363A Class 3bc. Smaller bust with necklines (sometimes vestigal). ENR usually
ligated. *mm* 4. ...................................................................................... 30    95
1364   Class 3c. Similar but coarser bust usually with necklines and a colon after REX.
Eyes are round comprising pellets in annulets. *mm* 4. ........................... 25    85

## PHASE III, 1250-72 POST-PROVINCIAL PHASE

1364A          1364B

1364A Class 3d1. Small neat bust generally with a pointed chin and neck lines. Most
have a colon after REX. *mm* 4. ............................................................ 30    95
1364B Class 3d2. Larger more rounded bust resembling class 4 coins. Ball tailed letter
R (R2). *mm* 4, with a few coins featuring *mm* 5. ..................................... 30    95

1365            1365a            1366            1366 detail

|                                                                              | F   | VF  |
|                                                                              | £   | £   |
| 1365  Class 4a. Bust similar to 3d2. King holds sceptre, crown has pellet ornaments. Legend starts at 1 o'clock. *mm* 5. | 110 | 375 |
| 1365A Class 4ab. As above but crown has end pellets and true central fleur. *mm* 5. | 110 | 375 |
| 1366  Class 4b. As above but crown has true half fleurs and central fleur. *mm* 5. | 225 | 750 |

1367            1367A            1367B            1367B detail

| 1367  Class 5a1. Legend starts at 10 o'clock. Large round bust, round eyes and half fleur at crown ends. No *mm* | 135 | 475 |
| 1367A Class 5a2. As above but crown has end pellets. Some with the letter X with one curved limb (Churchill/Thomas Class 5a3). | 25 | 80 |
| 1367B Class 5a4. As above but with a jewelled crown | 225 | 750 |

1368            1368A            1368A detail

| 1368  Class 5b1. Large oval bust, sometimes narrower with more pointed chin. Half fleur crown ends. | 150 | 525 |
| 1368A Class 5b2. As above but crown with end pellets. | 25 | 70 |

1369

| 1369  Class 5c. Similar but with almond eyes or wedge tailed R., variety with disjointed central fleur and/or no stalks | 25 | 70 |

1370      1370A      1370B      1370B detail

|  | F £ | VF £ |
|---|---|---|
| 1370 Class 5d1. Completely new and very coarse bust with crude central fleur and half fleur ends often with unusual mint spellings. | 100 | 325 |
| 1370A Class 5d2. As above but bust is more realistic and less crude. | 60 | 175 |
| 1370B Class 5d3. The "Beri" type; much neater and more pleasing. Central fleur has distinctly pointed ends. | 60 | 175 |

1371      1372      1373      1374

1372 detail      1373 detail

|  | F £ | VF £ |
|---|---|---|
| 1371 Class 5e. Bust similar to 5d3 (but Canterbury busts usually coarser) but with jewelled crown. | 150 | 525 |
| 1372 Class 5f. New large and round bust similar to those from 5a to 5c with a double banded crown and a low central fleur. | 25 | 70 |
| 1373 Class 5g. Similar bust but crown has thick single band with low central fleur. | 25 | 70 |
| 1374 Class 5h. Similar but coarser with 'heavier' features and a more pointed chin. Crown fleur comprises three pellets often with one or more individual stalks, possibly posthumous. | 45 | 165 |

1375

| | F £ | VF £ |
|---|---|---|
| 1375 Gold Penny of 20 pence. As illustration. | 75000 | 300000 |

## Mints, Moneyers and Classes for the Long Cross Coinage

Question marks appear against certain sub classes eg Lincoln 3bc for Walter. In such cases, whilst the Brussels Hoard contained no specimens and whilst no specimen is known to Churchill and Thomas, it is thought feasible that coins of this sub-class were struck and examples may exist.

*Fine*
*From £*

*London*; Anonymous 1a, 1b, 1a/b, 1b/a.
Nicole (1b/2-5c2), Henri (3a1-5g), Davi (3d1-5f), Ricard (3d1/2-5g),
Note. Of the above four moneyers, only Nicole is known for class 4ab
Walter (5c2-5g), Willem (5c2-5g), Ion (5c3-5g), Thomas (5g), Robert (5g),
Renaud (5g-7), Phelip (7). ........................................................................ 25
Note: Coins of 5a4 and 5d1 are not known for London and coins of 5d2 are excessively rare.

*Canterbury*: Anonymous 1b. Nicole (1b/2-5g), Gilbert (1b/2-3ab, 3b-5c, 5d3-5g),
Willem (1b/2, 2b-5g), Ion (4ab-5c, 5d2-5g), Robert/Roberd (5c-5d1, 5d3-5h)
Walter (5c-5g), Ambroci (5g), Alein (5g-5h), Ricard (5h), Roger (5h). ........................... 25
Note: No coin of class 2a is known for Willem but one may exist; coins of classes 4a, 4b, 5a1 and 5b1 are not known for any Canterbury moneyer and class 5a4 is known only for Nicole and Ion.

*Bury St Edmunds*: Ion (2a-3d2, 4ab, 5a2 and 5a3), Randulf (5b2-5c, 5d3, 5f), Renaud (5g),
Stephane (5g), Ion/Iohs (5g-7), Ioce (7). ........................................................ 25

*Durham*: Ricard (5a3, 5b2 & 5c), Roger (5g), Wilelm (5g), Roberd/Robert (6, 7). ................ 50

*Bristol*: Elis (3ab, b, bc, c), Henri (3ab, b), Iacob (3ab, b, bc, c), Roger (3b, bc),
Walter (3ab, b, bc). ............................................................................ 60

*Carlisle*: Adam (3ab, b, bc), Ion (3ab, b, bc, c), Robert (3ab, b, bc), Willem (3ab, b). .......... 80

*Exeter*: Ion (2b, 3a, a2, ab, b), Philip (2b, 3a, a2, ab, b), Robert (2b, 3a1, a2, ab, b),
Walter (2b2, 3a1, a2, ab, b). .................................................................. 50

*Gloucester*: Ion (2b, 3a1, a2, ab, b, c), Lucas (2b2, 3a1, a2, ab, b, c),
Ricard (2b, 3a1, a2, ab, b, c), Roger (2b, 3a1, a2, ab, b, c). ................................... 50

*Hereford*: Henri (3ab, b, c), Ricard (3ab, b, c), Roger (3ab, b, c), Walter (3ab, b, c). .......... 70

*Ilchester*: Huge (3a2, ab, b, bc, c), Ierveis (3a2, ab, b, bc, c), Randvlf (3a2, ab, b, bc, c),
Stephe (3a2, ab, b, bc, c). ..................................................................... 70

*Lincoln*: Ion (2b, 3a1, a2, ab, b, bc, c), Ricard (2b, 3a1, a2, ab, b, bc, c),
Walter (2b, 3a1, a2, ab, b, bc, c), Willem (2b, 3a1, a2, ab, b, bc, c). .......................... 30

*Newcastle*: Adam (3ab, b, c), Henri (3ab, b, c), Ion (3ab, b, c), Roger (3ab, b, c). ............... 40

*Northampton*: Lucas (2b, 3a1, a2, ab, b, bc, c), Philip (2b, 3a1, a2, ab, b, bc, c),
Tomas (2b, 3a1, a2, ab, b, bc, c), Willem (2b, 3a1, a2, ab, b, bc, c). ........................... 40

*Norwich*: Huge (2b, 3a1, a2, ab, b, bc, c), Iacob (2b, 3a1, a2, ab, b, bc, c),
Ion (2b, 3a, a2, ab, b, bc, c),Willem (2b, 3a1, a2, ab, b, bc, c). ............................... 40

*Oxford*: Adam (2b, 3a1, a2, ab, b, bc, c), Gefrei (2b, 3a1, a2, ab, b, bc, c),
Henri (2b, 3a1, a2, ab, b, bc, c), Willem (2b, 3a1, a2, ab, b, bc, c). ........................... 40

*Shrewsbury*: Lorens (3ab, b, bc, c), Nicole (3ab, b, bc, c), Peris (3ab, b, bc, c),
Ricard (3ab, b, bc, c). ......................................................................... 70

*Wallingford*: Alisandre (3ab, b), Clement (3ab, b), Ricard (3ab, b), Robert (3ab, b). ............ 70

*Wilton*: Huge (3ab, b, bc, c), Ion (3ab, b, bc, c), Willem (3ab, b, bc, c). ...................... 70

*Winchester*: Huge (2b, 3a1, a2, ab, b, bc, c), Iordan (2b, 3a1, a2, ab, b, bc, c),
Nicole (2b, 3a1, a2, ab, b, bc, c), Willem (2b, 3a1, a2, ab, b, bc, c). .......................... 40

*York*: Alain (2b, 3a1, a2, ab, b, bc), Ieremie (2b, 3a1, a2, ab, b, bc), Ion (2b, 3a1,
a2, ab, b, bc), Rener (2b, 3a1, a2, ab, b, bc), Tomas (3a2, ab, b, bc, c). ....................... 30

## COINAGE IN THE NAME OF HENRY III 1272-1279

## LONG CROSS COINAGE, 1247-79 *(continued)*

## PHASE IV, POSTHUMOUS PHASE

These coins were struck between 1272 and 1279 during the reign of Edward I but they bear the name of Henry III. It is most likely that class 5h were also struck during these years but there are no means of separating the coins struck under Edward I from those struck before the death of Henry III; we have, therefore, included all coins of class 5h as being part of the Henry III Phase III.

The earliest coinage of Edward I, in the name of Henry III (Class 5i and 6), is of coarse style and was struck at London, Bury St. Edmunds and Durham only. Class 7, also only from these mints, is of neater style. In 1279 the Long Cross coinage was abandonned and a new coinage introduced.

Cut Halfpennies and Farthings also occur for this issue.

| 1376 | 1377 | 1378 |

|  | F<br>£ | VF<br>£ |
|---|---|---|
| 1376 Class 5i. Even more degraded than 5h. Most coins have ENR ligated and the line of pellets below the crown band is either missing or in a format other than a simple line of three, possibly posthumous............................................. | 225 | 750 |
| 1377 Class 6. Crude bust with almond shaped eyes and realistic hair reaching the level of the King's mouth. Lombardic N's feature in the reverses of the coins of Bury St Edmunds................................................................ | 30 | 90 |
| 1378 Class 7. More realistic busts (several varieties) with shorter hair reaching the King's nose. Sometimes with Lombardic N's and V's... | 80 | 300 |

## Mints, Moneyers, and Classes for Edward I 'Long Cross' Coinage

| | | |
|---|---|---|
| *London:* Phelip (VII), Renaud (VII) ....................................................*from* | 65 | |
| *Bury St. Edmunds:* Ioce (VII), Ion or Ioh (VI, VII) ...........................................*from* | 25 | |
| *Durham:* Roberd (VI), Robert (VII) ...............................................*from* | 250 | |

**NEW COINAGE** (from 1279).

A major re-coinage was embarked upon in 1279 which introduced new denominations. In addition to the penny, halfpence and farthings were also minted and, for the first time, a fourpenny piece called a 'Groat', wt. 89 grs., (from the French *Gros*).

The groats, though ultimately unsuccessful, were struck from more than thirty obverse dies and form an extensive series with affinities to the pence of classes 1c to 3g. The chronology of this series has now been definitively established (see Allen, M. The Durham Mint, pp. 172-179).

As mint administration was now very much centralised, the practice of including the moneyer's name in the coinage was abandoned (except for a few years at Bury St. Edmunds). Several provincial mints assisted with the re-coinage during 1279-81, then minting was again restricted to London, Canterbury, Durham and Bury.

The provincial mints were again employed for a subsidiary re-coinage in 1300 in order to remint lightweight coins and the many illegal *esterlings* (foreign copies of the English pennies, mainly from the Low Countries), which were usually of poorer quality than the English coins.

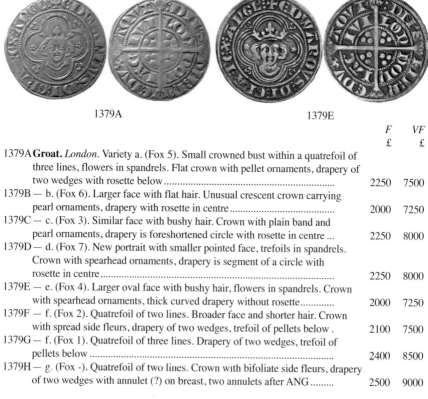

1379A                                    1379E

|  | F £ | VF £ |
|---|---|---|
| 1379A **Groat**. *London*. Variety a. (Fox 5). Small crowned bust within a quatrefoil of three lines, flowers in spandrels. Flat crown with pellet ornaments, drapery of two wedges with rosette below | 2250 | 7500 |
| 1379B — b. (Fox 6). Larger face with flat hair. Unusual crescent crown carrying pearl ornaments, drapery with rosette in centre | 2000 | 7250 |
| 1379C — c. (Fox 3). Similar face with bushy hair. Crown with plain band and pearl ornaments, drapery is foreshortened circle with rosette in centre ... | 2250 | 8000 |
| 1379D — d. (Fox 7). New portrait with smaller pointed face, trefoils in spandrels. Crown with spearhead ornaments, drapery is segment of a circle with rosette in centre | 2250 | 8000 |
| 1379E — e. (Fox 4). Larger oval face with bushy hair, flowers in spandrels. Crown with spearhead ornaments, thick curved drapery without rosette | 2000 | 7250 |
| 1379F — f. (Fox 2). Quatrefoil of two lines. Broader face and shorter hair. Crown with spread side fleurs, drapery of two wedges, trefoil of pellets below . | 2100 | 7500 |
| 1379G — f. (Fox 1). Quatrefoil of three lines. Drapery of two wedges, trefoil of pellets below | 2400 | 8500 |
| 1379H — g. (Fox -). Quatrefoil of two lines. Crown with bifoliate side fleurs, drapery of two wedges with annulet (?) on breast, two annulets after ANG | 2500 | 9000 |

*Edward I groats were often mounted as brooches and gilt. Such specimens are worth considerably less*

1381      1382      1383

| | | F £ | VF £ |
|---|---|---|---|

1380 **Penny.** *London.* Class 1a. Crown with plain band, ЄDW RЄX; Lombardic
Ⴈ on *obv;* pellet 'barred' S on rev. A with sloping top ............................ 275 1350
1381  — 1b. — ЄD RЄX; no drapery on bust, Roman N ................................. 900 4500
1382  — 1c. — ЄDW RЄX; Roman N, normal or reversed; small lettering ..... 30 140
1383  — 1d. — ЄDW R;—; large lettering and face ........................................ 25 125

1384      1385      1386

1384  — — — Annulet below bust .................................................. 110 450
1385  — 2a. Crown with band shaped to ornaments; usually broken left petal
to central fleur portrait as ld. N usually reversed ...................... 20 80
1386  — 2b. — tall bust; long neck; N reversed ................................... 20 75

1388

1387  — 3a. Crescent-shaped contraction marks; pearls in crown, drapery is
foreshortened circle with hook ends ......................................... 25 100
1388  — 3b. — — drapery is segment of a circle, pearls in crown ................... 25 100
1389  — 3c. — normal crown; drapery in one piece, hollowed in centre.......... 20 75

1391      1392      1394

1390  — 3d. — — drapery in two pieces, broad face ....................................... 20 75
1391  — 3e. — long narrow face (Northern mints) ......................................... 20 75
1392  — 3f. — broad face, large nose, rougher work, late S first used.............. 25 100
1393  — 3g. — Spread crown small neat bust, narrow face ............................ 20 70
1394  — 4a. Comma-shaped contraction mark, late S always used, C and Є open 20 75

| | | | |
|---|---|---|---|
| 1395 | 1396 | 1397 | 1398 |

|  |  | F | VF |
|---|---|---|---|
|  |  | £ | £ |
| 1395 | — 4b. Similar, but face and hair shorter | 20 | 70 |
| 1396 | — 4c. Larger face with more copious hair; nick to band of crown | 25 | 90 |
| 1397 | — 4d. Pellet at beginning of *obv.* and *rev.* legend | 20 | 70 |
| 1398 | — 4e. Three pellets on breast, ropy hair, pellet in *rev.* legend (no pellets on Bury or Durham) | 25 | 80 |

| | |
|---|---|
| 1399 | 1400 |

| 1399 | — 5a. Well spread coins, pellet on breast, face as 1398, A normally unbarred | 30 | 110 |
|---|---|---|---|
| 1400 | — 5b. Coins more spread, tall lettering, long narrow face, pellet on breast | 25 | 100 |

| | | |
|---|---|---|
| 1401 | 1402 | 1403 |

| 1401 | — 6a. Smaller coins, smaller lettering with closed E (from now on) initial cross almost plain, crown with wide fleurs, crude appearance | 95 | 375 |
|---|---|---|---|
| 1402 | — 6b. Initial cross pattée | 50 | 200 |
| 1403 | — 7a. Rose on breast (except Bury), short hair; almond-shaped eyes, double barred N | 40 | 150 |

| | | |
|---|---|---|
| 1404 | 1406 | 1406A |

| 1404 | — 7b. Rose on breast (London only) longer hair, new crown | 45 | 175 |
|---|---|---|---|
| 1405 | — 8a. Crown resembling 7b with central fleur usually broken | 25 | 85 |
| 1406 | — 8b. Similar to 1405 with wider drapery, top-tilted S | 25 | 85 |
| 1406A | — 8c — — Crown with very arched band | 25 | 100 |

1407

|        |                                                                                           | *F*<br>£ | *VF*<br>£ |
|--------|-------------------------------------------------------------------------------------------|----------|-----------|

1407  — 9a. Drapery of two wedges, pellet eyes, crown of 8a-b or new flatter
one; often star on breast ...........................................................................  20    65

1408  — 9b. Small coins; Roman N, normal, un-barred, or usually of pot-hook
form; often star or (very rarely) pellet on breast. Some Durham coins are
from locally made dies...............................................................................  20    65

1408A– 9c. Larger crude lettering with barred A and abbreviation marks.
(only found in combination with dies of 9b or 10ab, except Bury)..........  35    125

1409 - 10ab                              1409B - 10ab

1409  — 10ab. ЄDWARD. Bifoliate crown (converted 9b or new taller one).
Narrow incurved lettering.............................................................................  20    60

1409A — 10ab. Similar with annulet on breast or a pellet each side of head
and on breast ...............................................................................................  100   350

1409B — 10ab. ЄDWAR (rarely ЄDWR). Similar to 1409. A few early coins
have the trifoliate crown of 9b...................................................................  20    60

1410                              1411

Crown 1          Crown 2          Crown 3          Crown 4          Crown 5

1410  — 10cf1. Crown 1 (Axe-shaped central fleur, wedge-shaped petals).
ЄDWA from now on. Stub-tailed. R. ........................................................  20    60

1411  — 10cf2. Crown 2 (Well-shaped central lis, no spearheads). Spreading hair.  20    60

1413                                                      1414

|  | F £ | VF £ |
|---|---|---|
| 1412 — 10cf3. Crown 3 (Left-hand arrowhead inclines to right). Early coins have the broken lettering of 10cf2; later have new lettering with round-backed Є. | 20 | 60 |
| 1413 — 10cf4. Crown 4 (Neat with hooked petal to right-hand side fleur) | 25 | 80 |
| 1414 — 10cf5. Crown 5 (taller and more spread, right-hand ornament inclines to left). Later coins are on smaller flans. | 20 | 65 |

*Some of the coins of class 10cf3 (c.1307-9), and all of the coins of classes 10cf4 and 10cf5 (c.1309-10), were struck in the reign of Edward II.*

*For a more detailed classification of Class 10, see 'Sylloge of British Coins, 39, The J. J. North Collection, Edwardian English Silver Coins 1279-1351', The Classification of Class 10, c. 1301-10, by C. Wood.*

*Prices are for full flan, well struck coins.*

*The prices for the above types are for London. For coins of the other mints see following pages; types are in brackets, prices are for the commonest type of each mint.*

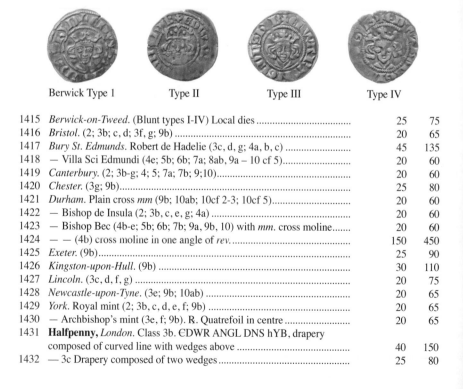

Berwick Type 1          Type II          Type III          Type IV

| 1415 | *Berwick-on-Tweed.* (Blunt types I-IV) Local dies | 25 | 75 |
|---|---|---|---|
| 1416 | *Bristol.* (2; 3b; c, d; 3f, g; 9b) | 20 | 65 |
| 1417 | *Bury St. Edmunds.* Robert de Hadelie (3c, d, g; 4a, b, c) | 45 | 135 |
| 1418 | — Villa Sci Edmundi (4e; 5b; 6b; 7a; 8ab, 9a – 10 cf 5) | 20 | 60 |
| 1419 | *Canterbury.* (2; 3b-g; 4; 5; 7a; 7b; 9;10) | 20 | 60 |
| 1420 | *Chester.* (3g; 9b) | 25 | 80 |
| 1421 | *Durham.* Plain cross *mm* (9b; 10ab; 10cf 2-3; 10cf 5) | 20 | 60 |
| 1422 | — Bishop de Insula (2; 3b, c, e, g; 4a) | 20 | 60 |
| 1423 | — Bishop Bec (4b-e; 5b; 6b; 7b; 9a, 9b, 10) with *mm*. cross moline | 20 | 60 |
| 1424 | — — (4b) cross moline in one angle of *rev.* | 150 | 450 |
| 1425 | *Exeter.* (9b) | 25 | 90 |
| 1426 | *Kingston-upon-Hull.* (9b) | 30 | 110 |
| 1427 | *Lincoln.* (3c, d, f, g) | 20 | 75 |
| 1428 | *Newcastle-upon-Tyne.* (3e; 9b; 10ab) | 20 | 65 |
| 1429 | *York.* Royal mint (2; 3b, c, d, e, f; 9b) | 20 | 65 |
| 1430 | — Archbishop's mint (3e, f; 9b). R. Quatrefoil in centre | 20 | 65 |
| 1431 | **Halfpenny,** *London.* Class 3b. ЄDWR ANGL DNS hYB, drapery composed of curved line with wedges above | 40 | 150 |
| 1432 | — 3c Drapery composed of two wedges | 25 | 80 |

1434A

| | F | VF |
|---|---|---|
| | £ | £ |
| 1433 — 3g. New wide crown, thick-waisted S, drapery as 3b | 25 | 80 |
| 1433A — — 4c. Narrower crown, drapery of two unequal wedges | 30 | 110 |
| 1433B — — Similar, pellet before LON | 40 | 140 |
| 1434 — 4e. Single-piece collar with (usually) three pellets on breast | 45 | 160 |
| 1434A — 6. Small face with short hair, large coarse crown, closed Є | 50 | 175 |
| 1435 — 7. Larger face with square jaw, open Є, usually double-barred N | 40 | 135 |
| 1436 — 8. Similar, new crown with straight sides | 45 | 160 |
| 1437 — 10. ЄDWAR R ANGL DNS hYB, bifoliate or trifoliate crown, new waisted letters | 30 | 100 |

*The above prices are for London; halfpence of the mints given below were also struck.*

| | F | VF |
|---|---|---|
| 1438 *Berwick-on-Tweed.* (Blunt types I, II and III) | 85 | 275 |
| 1439 *Bristol.* Class 3c, 3g, 4c | 40 | 125 |
| 1440 *Lincoln.* Class 3c | 45 | 150 |
| 1441 *Newcastle.* Class 3e, single pellet in each angle of *rev.* | 60 | 175 |
| 1442 *York.* Class 3c-e | 40 | 125 |

1443A        1445

| | F | VF |
|---|---|---|
| 1443 **Farthing,** *London.* Class 1a. Base silver issue (6.65 grains), ЄDWARDVS RЄX. bifoliate crown with no intermediate jewels, inner circle. R. LONDONIЄNSIS, (rarely LONDRIЄNSIS), | 60 | 200 |
| 1443A — 1c. Similar trifoliate crown | 35 | 135 |
| 1444 — 2. Smaller face, trifoliate crown with intermediate jewels | 25 | 90 |
| 1445 — 3c. New tapering face, wide at top, crown with curved band | 25 | 100 |
| 1445A — 3de. Sterling silver issue (5.51 grains.) Є R ANGLIЄ bust (usually) to bottom of coin, no inner circle. R. LONDONIЄNSIS | 25 | 110 |
| 1446 — 3g. Similar, new wide crown with curving side fleurs. | 25 | 90 |
| 1446A — 4de. Similar to 3de. R. CIVITAS LONDON | 35 | 135 |
| 1446B — 5. Similar, crude wide crown. | 35 | 135 |
| 1447 — 6-7. New large face with wide cheeks, pellet or almond eyes | 25 | 90 |
| 1448 — 8. Similar, small rounded face, tall crude crown | 30 | 135 |
| 1449 — 9a. Є R ANGL DN, small tapering face, (a variety has the face of class 6-7) | 40 | 150 |
| 1449A — 9b. Small ugly face, usually wide crown with outwards-sloping sides.. | 45 | 175 |
| 1450 — 10 ЄDWARDVS REX (-, A, AN or ANG,) large bust within inner circle. *Type 1450 often appears on oval flans.* | 25 | 90 |

*It is now thought that the order of London Farthings is class 4de, 6-7, 5, 9a, 8, 9b*

1446                           1452

|                                                                  | F | VF |
|                                                                  | £ | £ |
| 1451  *Berwick-on-Tweed.* (Blunt type I, IIIb) ................................................ | 125 | 450 |
| 1452  *Bristol.* Class 2, 3c, 3de ................................................................. | 35 | 125 |
| 1453  *Lincoln.* Class 3de ........................................................................... | 35 | 125 |
| 1453A *Newcastle.* Class 3de, R NOVI CASTRI ........................................ | 200 | 750 |
| 1454  *York.* Class 2, 3c, 3de ..................................................................... | 40 | 150 |

For further information see: *Farthings and Halfpennies, Edward I and II,* P. and B  R Withers, 2001

## EDWARD II, 1307-27

The coinage of this reign differs only in minor details from that of Edward I. No groats were issued in the years *c.* 1282-1351.

1458 (12a)          1459 (13)          1460 (14)

1461 (15a)          1462 (15b)         1463 (15c)

| 1455 | **Penny,** *London.* Class 11a. Broken spear-head or pearl on l. side of crown; long narrow face, straight-sided N; round back to C and Є .................... | 20 | 75 |
| 1456 | — 11b. — Є with angular back (till 15b), N with well-marked serifs (late) | 25 | 80 |
| 1457 | — 11c. — — A of special form .............................................................. | 45 | 150 |
| 1458 | — 12a. Central fleur of crown formed of three wedges; thick cross *mm*. | 25 | 90 |
| 1458A | — 12b — Crown with diamond-shaped petals and cruciform central fleur; cross of four wedges *mm* ........................................................................ | 50 | 175 |
| 1458B | — 12c — Crown with heart-shaped petals; cross pattée *mm* .................. | 60 | 225 |
| 1459 | — 13. Central fleur of crown as Greek double axe ................................. | 25 | 75 |
| 1460 | — 14. Crown with tall central fleur; large smiling face with leering eyes | 20 | 75 |
| 1461 | — 15a. Small flat crown with both spear-heads usually bent to l.; face of 14 | 25 | 85 |
| 1462 | — 15b. — very similar, but smaller face ................................................. | 25 | 80 |
| 1463 | — 15c. — large face, large Є ................................................................. | 25 | 85 |

| Berwick Type V | Type VI | Type VII |
|---|---|---|

|  | F | VF |
|---|---|---|
|  | £ | £ |
| 1464 *Berwick-on-Tweed.* (Blunt types V, VI and VII) Local dies except V ...... | 50 | 150 |
| 1465 *Bury St. Edmunds.* (11; 12; 13; 14; 15)................................................. | 20 | 75 |
| 1466 *Canterbury.* (11; 12a; 13; 14; 15) ......................................... | 20 | 75 |
| 1467 *Durham.* King's Receiver (11a), *mm.* plain cross .................................... | 20 | 75 |
| 1468 — Bishop Bec. (11a), *mm.* cross moline ................................................ | 20 | 75 |
| 1469 — Bishop Kellawe (11; 12a; 13), crozier on *rev.* .................................. | 25 | 80 |
| 1470 — Bishop Beaumont (13; 14; 15), *mm.* lion with lis............................. | 25 | 90 |
| 1471 *mm.* plain cross (11a, 14, 15c) ................................................... | 45 | 150 |

1472

| 1472 **Halfpenny,** *London.* Class 10-11, ЄDWARDVS REX (-, A, AN, ANG, ANGL or ANGLI,) bifoliate or trifoliate crown ..................................... | 45 | 175 |
|---|---|---|
| 1473 — *Berwick-on-Tweed.* (Blunt type V) ..................................................... | 125 | 450 |

1474

| 1474 **Farthing,** *London.* Class 11, 13, ЄDWARDVS REX (-, A, AN, or AG), face with pellet eyes............................................................................. | 30 | 100 |
|---|---|---|
| 1475 — *Berwick-on-Tweed.* (Blunt type V) ..................................................... | 175 | 550 |

During Edward's early years small quantities of silver coins were minted following the standard of the previous two reigns, but in 1335 halfpence and farthings were produced which were well below the .925 Sterling silver standard. In 1344 an impressive gold coinage was introduced comprising the Double Florin or Double Leopard valued at six shillings, and its half and quarter, the Leopard and the Helm. The design of the Florin was based on the contemporary gold of Philip de Valois of France.

The first gold coinage was not successful and it was replaced later the same year by a heavier coinage, the Noble, valued at 6s. 8d, i.e., 80 pence, half a mark or one third of a pound, together with its fractions. The Noble was lowered in weight in two stages over the next few years, being stabilised at 120 grains in 1351. With the signing of the Treaty of Bretigny in 1360 Edward's title to the Kingdom of France was omitted from the coinage, but it was resumed again in 1369.

In 1344 the silver coinage had been re-established at the old sterling standard, but the penny was reduced in weight to just over 20 grains and in 1351 to 18 grains. Groats were minted again in 1351 and were issued regularly henceforth until the reign of Elizabeth.

Subsequent to the treaty with France which gave England a cross-channel trading base at Calais, a mint was opened there in 1363 for minting gold and silver coins of English type. In addition to coins of the regular English mints, the Abbot of Reading also minted silver pence, halfpence and farthings with a scallop shell in one quarter of the reverse while coins from Berwick display one or two boar's or bear's heads.

There is evidence of re-use of dies at later periods, e.g. 3rd coinage halfpennies.

For further study of the English Hammered Gold Coinage see: *Sylloge of Coins of the British Isles, 47: The Herbert Schneider Collection Volume One*, by Peter Woodhead. 1996.

*Mintmarks*

| 6 | 1 | 2 | 3 | 74 | 4 | 5 | 7a |
|---|---|---|---|---|---|---|---|

| | | | | |
|---|---|---|---|---|
| 1334-51 | Cross pattée (6) | 1356 | Crown (74) |
| 1351-2 | Cross 1 (1) | 1356-61 | Cross 3 (4) |
| 1351-7 | Crozier on cross end (76a, *Durham*) | 1361-9 | Cross potent (5) |
| 1352-3 | Cross 1 broken (2) | 1369-77 | Cross pattée (6) |
| 1354-5 | Cross 2 (3) | | Plain cross (7a) |

*The figures in brackets refer to the plate of mintmarks in Appendix IV.*

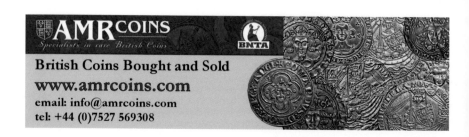

# GOLD
## (No gold coinage issued before 1344)

**THIRD COINAGE, 1344-51, First period, 1344**

|      | 1476 | 1477 | 1478 |
|------|------|------|------|
|      |      |      | F    VF |
|      |      |      | £    £  |

| | | F | VF |
|---|---|---|---|
| 1476 | **Double-florin (Double Leopard).** (=6s.; wt. 108 grs., 6.99g.). King enthroned beneath canopy; crowned leopard's head each side. ℞. Cross in quatrefoil | 90000 | 375000 |
| 1477 | **Florin.** Leopard sejant with banner l. ℞. Somewhat as last ..................... | 30000 | 150000 |
| 1478 | **Half-florin.** Helmet on fleured field. ℞. Floriate cross ........................... | 17500 | 80000 |

**Second period, 1344-46**

| | | F | VF |
|---|---|---|---|
| 1479 | **Noble** (=6s. 8d., wt. 138.46 grs., 8.97g.). King stg. facing in ship with sword and shield. ℞. L in centre of royal cross in tressure................................. | 22500 | 110000 |
| 1479A | **Half-noble.** Similar ................................................................ | 7500 | 30000 |
| 1480 | **Quarter-noble.** Shield in tressure. ℞. As last......................................... | 2500 | 9500 |

1481

1482

**Third period, 1346-51**

| | | F | VF |
|---|---|---|---|
| 1481 | **Noble** (wt. 128.59 grs., 8.33g.). As 1479, but Є in centre; large letters ... | 2750 | 11000 |
| 1482 | **Half-noble.** Similar ................................................................ | 2250 | 9000 |
| 1483 | **Quarter-noble.** As 1480, but Є in centre ................................................. | 375 | 1500 |

## FOURTH COINAGE, 1351-77

*Reference:* L. A. Lawrence, *The Coinage of Edward III from 1351.*
**Pre-treaty period, 1351-61.** With French title.

|      |                                                                                                          | *F*<br>£ | *VF*<br>£ |
|------|----------------------------------------------------------------------------------------------------------|----------|-----------|
| 1484 | **Noble** (wt. 120 grs., 7.77g.), series B (1351). Open Є and C, Roman M; *mm.* cross 1 (1)              | 1100     | 4000      |
| 1485 | — — *rev.* of series A (1351). Round lettering, Lombardic M and N; closed inverted Є in centre            | 1250     | 4500      |
| 1486 | C (1351-1352). Closed Є and C, Lombardic M; *mm.* cross 1 (1)                                            | 950      | 3500      |
| 1487 | D (1352-1353). *O.* of series C. R. *mm.* cross 1 broken (2)                                             | 1350     | 5000      |

1490                                    1498

|      |                                                                                                          | *F*<br>£ | *VF*<br>£ |
|------|----------------------------------------------------------------------------------------------------------|----------|-----------|
| 1488 | E (1354-1355). Broken letters, V often has a nick in r. limb; *mm.* cross 2 (3)                          | 900      | 3250      |
| 1489 | F (1356). *mm.* crown (74)                                                                                | 1000     | 3750      |
| 1490 | G (1356-1361). *mm.* cross 3 (4). Many varieties                                                         | 850      | 3000      |
| 1491 | **Half-noble,** B. As noble with *rev.* of series A, but closed Є in centre not inverted                 | 750      | 2750      |
| 1492 | C. *O.* as noble. *Rev.* as last                                                                         | 850      | 3000      |
| 1493 | E. As noble                                                                                               | 1000     | 3500      |
| 1494 | G. As noble. Many varieties                                                                               | 700      | 2400      |
| 1495 | **Quarter-noble,** B. Pellet below shield. R. Closed Є in centre                                         | 375      | 950       |
| 1496 | C. *O.* of series B. *Rev.* details as noble                                                             | 450      | 1100      |
| 1497 | E. *O.* as last. *Rev.* details as noble, pellet in centre                                               | 400      | 1000      |
| 1498 | G. *mm.* cross 3 (4). Many varieties                                                                     | 350      | 900       |

**Transitional treaty period, 1361.** French title omitted, replaced by that of Aquitaine on the noble and (rarely) on the half-noble, but not on the quarter-noble; irregular sized letters; *mm.* cross potent (5).

1499

|      |                                                                                                          |      |      |
|------|----------------------------------------------------------------------------------------------------------|------|------|
| 1499 | **Noble.** R. Pellets or annulets at corners of central panel                                            | 1050 | 3750 |

1504

|      |                                                                          | F £ | VF £ |
|------|--------------------------------------------------------------------------|-----|------|
| 1500 | **Half-noble.** Similar .............................................. | 550 | 1750 |
| 1501 | **Quarter-noble.** Similar. Many varieties. Pellet and rarely Є in centre.... | 325 | 850 |

**Treaty period, 1361-69.** Omits FRANC, new letters, usually curule-shaped X; *mm.* cross potent(5).

| 1502 | **Noble.** *London.* Saltire or nothing before ЄDWARD.............................. | 950 | 3500 |
|------|---------------------------------------------------------------------------------------|-----|------|
| 1503 | — Annulet before ЄDWARD (with, rarely, crescent on forecastle)......... | 900 | 3250 |
| 1504 | *Calais.* C in centre of *rev.,* flag at stern of ship ..................................... | 950 | 3500 |
| 1505 | — — without flag....................................................... | 975 | 3750 |

1506                                            1508

| 1506 | **Half-noble.** *London.* Saltire before ЄDWARD ...................................... | 650 | 2000 |
|------|-----------------------------------------------------------------------------------------|------|------|
| 1507 | — Annulet before ЄDWARD ................................................. | 700 | 2250 |
| 1508 | *Calais.* C in centre of *rev.,* flag at stern of ship ................................. | 900 | 3250 |
| 1509 | — — without flag............................................................ | 950 | 3500 |
| 1510 | **Quarter-noble.** *London.* As 1498. Ŗ. Lis in centre............................ | 300 | 750 |
| 1511 | — — annulet before ЄDWARD ................................................ | 300 | 750 |
| 1512 | *Calais.* Ŗ. Annulet in centre.................................................... | 350 | 900 |
| 1513 | — — cross in circle over shield ................................................ | 325 | 850 |
| 1514 | — Ŗ. Quatrefoil in centre; cross over shield ........................................ | 425 | 1100 |
| 1515 | — — crescent over shield........................................................ | 450 | 1250 |

**Post-treaty period, 1369-1377.** French title resumed.

| 1516 | **Noble.** *London.* Annulet before ЄD. Ŗ. Treaty period die...................... | 1350 | 5250 |
|------|------------------------------------------------------------------------------------------|------|------|
| 1517 | — — — crescent on forecastle................................................. | 1100 | 4250 |
| 1518 | — — post-treaty letters. Ŗ. Є and pellet in centre.................................. | 1000 | 4000 |
| 1519 | — — — Ŗ. Є and saltire in centre........................................... | 1100 | 4250 |
| 1520 | *Calais.* Flag at stern. Ŗ. Є in centre............................................... | 1050 | 4000 |

1521

|  |  | F | VF |
|---|---|---|---|
|  |  | £ | £ |
| 1521 | — — *Rev.* as 1518, with Є and pellet in centre | 975 | 3750 |
| 1522 | — As 1520, but without flag. ℞. Є in centre | 1100 | 4250 |
| 1523 | **Half-noble.** *London. O.* Treaty die. *Rev.* as 1518 | 1750 | 6500 |
| 1524 | *Calais.* Without AQT, flag at stern. ℞. Є in centre | 1650 | 6000 |
| 1525 | — — ℞. Treaty die with C in centre | 1750 | 6500 |

## SILVER

**FIRST COINAGE, 1327-35** (0.925 fineness)

|  | 1526 | 1530 |  |  |
|---|---|---|---|---|
| 1526 | **Penny.** *London.* As Edw. II; Fox class XVd with Lombardic Ո's | | 325 | 1000 |
| 1527 | *Bury St. Edmunds.* Similar | | 425 | 1350 |
| 1528 | *Canterbury; mm.* cross pattée with pellet centre | | 250 | 900 |
| 1529 | — — three extra pellets in one quarter | | 225 | 850 |
| 1530 | *Durham.* ℞. Small crown in centre | | 575 | 1850 |
| 1530A | *Reading.* ℞. Escallop in 2nd quarter | | 625 | 2000 |
| 1531 | *York.* As 1526, but quatrefoil in centre of *rev;* three extra pellets in TAS quarter | | 175 | 600 |
| 1532 | — — — pellet in each quarter of *mm.* | | 175 | 600 |

|  | 1535 | 1537 | 1539 |  |  |
|---|---|---|---|---|---|
| 1534 | — — — Roman N's on *obv.* | | | 175 | 600 |
| 1535 | *Berwick* (1333-1342, Blunt type VIII). Bear's head in one quarter of *rev.* | | | 575 | 1750 |
| 1536 | **Halfpenny.** *London.* Indistinguishable from EDWARD II (cf. 1472) | | | 45 | 175 |
| 1537 | *Berwick* (Bl. VIII). Bear's head in one or two quarters | | | 100 | 350 |
| 1538 | **Farthing.** *London.* Indistinguishable from those of EDWARD II (cf. 1474) | | | 30 | 100 |
| 1539 | *Berwick* (Bl. VIII). As 1537 | | | 90 | 325 |

1540                                      1542

|  | F £ | VF £ |
|---|---|---|

**SECOND COINAGE, 1335-43** (0.833 fineness)

1540 **Halfpenny.** *London.* ЄDWARDVS RЄX AN(G). Six-pointed star after
AN and before LON. Bifoliate or trifoliate crown. .................................. 25 | 85

1540A — — New tall crown. Star of eight or six points after ANG and DON
and before CIVI or none on rev. ................................ 25 | 90

1541 *Reading.* Escallop in one quarter, star before or after mint ..................... 175 | 575

1542 **Farthing.** *London.* A (N), six-pointed star after A (rarely omitted) and
before LON, flat crown.......................................................... 25 | 85

1542A — ANG, star after ANG and before LON or after DON, tall crown........ 25 | 90

**THIRD OR FLORIN COINAGE, 1344-51.** Bust with bushy hair. (0.925 fine, 20 grs., 1.30g.)

1543                                      1544

Reverses: I. Lombardic n  II. Roman N. III. Reversed N. IV. Reversed Double-barred N.

1543 **Penny.** Fox proposed 'Class XVI'. *London.* Class 1. ЄDW, Lombardic N. Rev. I. | 25 | 100
1544 — — Class 2, ЄDWA, Lombardic N. Rev. I, II. ........................................ 25 | 95
1545 — — Class 3. ЄDW. Roman N. Rev. I, II, III. ........................................ 25 | 95
1546 — — Class 4. ЄDW. Reversed N. Rev. I, II, III, IV (doubtful) .............. 20 | 95
1546A — Unusual types designated A to E. ........................................ 35 | 135
1547 — Canterbury. Class 2. as 1544. Rev. I. ................................................. 80 | 250
1548 — — Class 4. as 1546 Rev. I............................................................. 65 | 200
1549 *Durham,* Sede Vacante (possibly 1345 issues of Bishop Richard de Bury
or Bishop Hatfield). A, ЄDWR rev. No marks ....................................... 30 | 110
1550 — — B, similar, ЄDWAR R................................................................ 45 | 150
1551 — Bp. Hatfield. C, similar, but pellet in centre of *rev.* ........................... 50 | 160
1552 — — — Crozier on *rev.*.................................................................. 50 | 160
1553 — — — — with pellet in centre of *rev.* ............................................... 60 | 175
1554 — — D, ЄDWARDVS RЄX AIn, crozier on *rev.* ................................. 95 | 325

1555

1555 *Reading. obv.* as 1546. Ɍ. Escallop in one quarter.................................. 225 | 850
1555A — — ЄDWARDVS RЄX AnG. Rev. as 1555....................................... 275 | 1000
1556 *York. obv.* as 1546. Ɍ. Quatrefoil in centre ...................................... 30 | 100

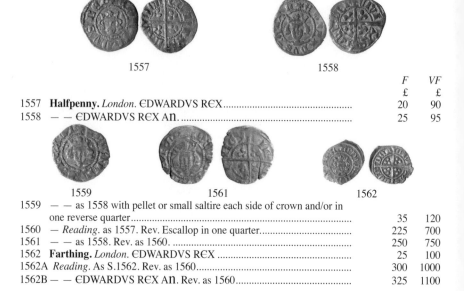

1557                                    1558

| | F £ | VF £ |
|---|---|---|
| 1557 **Halfpenny.** *London.* ЄDWARDVS RЄX............................................... | 20 | 90 |
| 1558 — — ЄDWARDVS RЄX AΠ. ....................................................... | 25 | 95 |

1559                    1561                            1562

| | | |
|---|---|---|
| 1559 — — as 1558 with pellet or small saltire each side of crown and/or in one reverse quarter....................................................................... | 35 | 120 |
| 1560 — *Reading.* as 1557. Rev. Escallop in one quarter................................. | 225 | 700 |
| 1561 — — as 1558. Rev. as 1560. .............................................................. | 250 | 750 |
| 1562 **Farthing.** *London.* ЄDWARDVS RЄX ................................................. | 25 | 100 |
| 1562A *Reading.* As S.1562. Rev. as 1560............................................... | 300 | 1000 |
| 1562B — — ЄDWARDVS RЄX AΠ. Rev. as 1560.......................................... | 325 | 1100 |

## FOURTH COINAGE, 1351-77
*Reference:* L. A. Lawrence, *The Coinage of Edward III from 1351.*
*A large variety of mules exist between styles and issue.*

**Pre-treaty period, 1351-61.** With French title.

1563                                    1565

1567

| | | |
|---|---|---|
| 1563 **Groat** (=4d., 72 grs., 4.66g.). *London,* series B (1351). Roman M, open C and Є; *mm.* cross 1 ............................................................. | 135 | 525 |
| 1564 — — — crown in each quarter............................................................... | 2500 | 9500 |
| 1565 — C (1351-2). Lombardic M, closed Ꞓ and Є, R with wedge-shaped tail; *mm.* cross 1 ...................................................................... | 45 | 210 |
| 1566 — D (1352-3). R with normal tail; *mm.* cross 1 or cross 1 broken (2)..... | 50 | 225 |
| 1567 — E (1354-5). Broken letters, V often with nick in r. limb; *mm.* cross 2 (3) | 40 | 185 |

|      |                                                              | F<br>£ | VF<br>£ |
|------|--------------------------------------------------------------|----|-----|
| 1568 | — — — lis on breast | 45 | 200 |
| 1569 | — F (1356). *mm.* crown (74) | 65 | 240 |

1570                    1572

|      |                                                              |    |     |
|------|--------------------------------------------------------------|----|-----|
| 1570 | — G (1356-61). Usually with annulet in one quarter and sometimes under bust, *mm.* cross 3 (4). Many varieties | 40 | 175 |
| 1571 | *York,* series D. As London | 175 | 750 |
| 1572 | — E. As London | 60 | 250 |

1573                    1581

|      |                                                              |    |     |
|------|--------------------------------------------------------------|----|-----|
| 1573 | **Halfgroat.** *London,* series B. As groat | 85 | 300 |
| 1574 | — C. As groat | 30 | 120 |
| 1575 | — D. As groat | 35 | 135 |
| 1576 | — E. As groat | 35 | 130 |
| 1577 | — F. As groat | 40 | 135 |
| 1578 | — G. As groat | 35 | 125 |
| 1579 | — — — annulet below bust | 40 | 140 |
| 1580 | *York,* series D. As groat | 70 | 250 |
| 1581 | — E. As groat | 60 | 200 |
| 1582 | — — — lis on breast | 65 | 225 |
| 1583 | **Penny.** *London.* Series A (1351). Round letters, Lombardic m and n, annulet in each quarter; *mm.* cross pattée | 80 | 275 |

1584              1585              1591

|      |                                                              |    |     |
|------|--------------------------------------------------------------|----|-----|
| 1584 | — C. Details as groat, but annulet in each quarter | 20 | 95 |
| 1585 | — D. Details as groat, but annulet in each quarter | 25 | 100 |
| 1586 | — E. Sometimes annulet in each quarter | 20 | 95 |
| 1587 | — F. Details as groat | 20 | 95 |
| 1588 | — G. Details as groat | 20 | 90 |

|  |  | F £ | VF £ |
|---|---|---|---|
| 1589 | — — — annulet below bust | 25 | 100 |
| 1590 | — — — saltire in one quarter | 30 | 135 |
| 1591 | *Durham,* Bp. Hatfield. Series A. As 1583, but extra pellet in each quarter, VIL LA crozier DVRRЄM and VIL crozier LA DVRRЄM | 70 | 275 |
| 1592 | — C. Details as groat. ꝶ. Crozier, CIVITAS DVNЄLMIЄ | 25 | 110 |
| 1593 | — D — — — | 30 | 125 |
| 1594 | — E — — — | 35 | 135 |
| 1595 | — F — ꝶ. Crozier, CIVITAS DVRЄMЄ | 30 | 125 |
| 1596 | — G — — — | 30 | 125 |
| 1597 | — — — — — annulet below bust | 35 | 135 |
| 1598 | — — — — — saltire in one quarter | 45 | 175 |
| 1599 | — — — — — annulet on each shoulder | 35 | 150 |
| 1600 | — — — — — trefoil of pellets on breast | 35 | 150 |
| 1601 | — — — ꝶ. Crozier, CIVITAS DVRЄLMIЄ | 45 | 175 |
| 1602 | *York,* Royal Mint. Series D | 30 | 110 |
| 1603 | — — E | 25 | 100 |
| 1604 | — Archb. Thoresby. Series D. ꝶ. Quatrefoil in centre | 30 | 120 |
| 1605 | — — G — | 25 | 100 |
| 1606 | — — — annulet or saltire on breast | 30 | 125 |

1607    1609    1609A

| 1607 | **Halfpenny.** *London.* Series E. ЄDWARDVS RЄX An | 60 | 225 |
|---|---|---|---|
| 1608 | — G, but with *obv.* of F (*mm.* crown). Annulet in one quarter | 135 | 475 |
| 1609 | **Farthing.** *London.* Series E. ЄDWARDVS RЄX | 95 | 375 |
| 1609A | — — Series G. Annulet in one quarter | 110 | 450 |

**Transitional treaty period, 1361.** French title omitted, irregular sized letters; *mm.* cross potent (5).

| 1610 | **Groat.** *London.* Annulet each side of crown | 325 | 1250 |
|---|---|---|---|

1611    1612    1615

| 1611 | **Halfgroat.** Similar, but only seven arches to tressure | 135 | 525 |
|---|---|---|---|
| 1612 | **Penny,** *London.* Omits RЄX, annulet in two upper qtrs. of *mm.* | 110 | 450 |
| 1613 | *York,* Archb. Thoresby. Similar, but quatrefoil enclosing pellet in centre of *rev.* | 50 | 185 |
| 1614 | *Durham.* Bp. Hatfield. Similar. ꝶ. Crozier, CIVITAS DORЄLMЄ | 65 | 250 |
| 1615 | **Halfpenny.** Two pellets over *mm.,* ЄDWARDVS RЄX An | 175 | 750 |

**Treaty period, 1361-69.** French title omitted, new letters, usually 'Treaty' X, rarely curule chair X *mm.* cross potent (5).

|                                                         | F £ | VF £ |
|---------------------------------------------------------|-----|------|
| 1616  **Groat,** *London.* Many varieties ........................................ | 65  | 250  |
| 1617  — Annulet before ЄDWARD ............................. | 70  | 275  |
| 1618  — Annulet on breast ......................................... | 100 | 375  |

1617                                      1618

| 1619  *Calais.* As last ................................................................. | 110 | 400 |

1620                                1626

| 1620  **Halfgroat,** *London.* As groat ................................. | 55  | 185 |
| 1621  — — Annulet before ЄDWARDVS ...................................... | 60  | 200 |
| 1622  — — Annulet on breast ........................................... | 65  | 225 |
| 1623  *Calais.* As last ........................................... | 110 | 375 |
| 1624  **Penny,** *London.* ЄDWARD AПGL R, etc ............................. | 35  | 140 |
| 1625  — — — pellet before ЄDWARD ............................. | 45  | 175 |
| 1626  *Calais.* R. VILLA CALCSIE ........................ | 150 | 575 |
| 1627  *Durham.* R. CIVITAS DVПЄLMIS ....................... | 55  | 185 |
| 1628  — R. Crozier, CIVITAS DVRЄMЄ ........................ | 40  | 150 |
| 1629  *York,* Archb. Thoresby. Quatrefoil in centre of *rev.,* ЄDWARDVS DЄI G RЄX AП.................. | 40 | 150 |
| 1630  — — — ЄDWARDVS RЄX AПGLI .............................. | 30  | 120 |
| 1631  — — — — quatrefoil before ЄD and on breast ..................................... | 35  | 130 |
| 1632  — — — — annulet before ЄD........................ | 35  | 140 |
| 1633  — — — ЄDWARD AПGL R DПS HYB .......................... | 40  | 150 |
| 1634  **Halfpenny.** ЄDWARDVS RЄX AП, pellet stops ..................... | 30  | 110 |

1635                                      1636

| 1635  — Pellet before ЄD, annulet stops ......................................... | 30  | 110 |
| 1636  **Farthing.** ЄDWARDVS RЄX, pellet or no stops ................................. | 175 | 750 |

**Post-treaty period, 1369-77.** French title resumed, X like St. Andrew's cross; *mm.* 5, 6, 7a.

1637              1639

| | | *F* £ | *VF* £ |
|---|---|---|---|
| 1637 | **Groat.** Various readings, *mm.* cross pattée | 85 | 350 |
| 1638 | — — row of pellets across breast (chain mail) | 275 | 900 |
| 1639 | — row of annulets below bust (chain mail); *mm.* cross potent with four pellets | 375 | 1100 |
| 1640 | **Halfgroat.** Various readings | 100 | 325 |

1641             1643

| | | | |
|---|---|---|---|
| 1640A | — Thin portrait of Richard II | 135 | 500 |
| 1641 | — row of pellets one side of breast (chain mail) | 150 | 575 |
| 1642 | **Penny,** *London.* No marks on breast | 50 | 225 |
| 1643 | — Pellet or annulet on breast | 50 | 225 |
| 1644 | — Cross or quatrefoil on breast | 45 | 185 |
| 1645 | *Durham,* Bp. Hatfield. *mm.* 7a, CIVITAS DVnOLM, crozier | 40 | 160 |
| 1646 | — — — — annulet on breast | 40 | 175 |
| 1647 | — — — — lis on breast | 40 | 175 |
| 1648 | *York.* Archb. Thoresby or Neville. ℞. Quatrefoil in centre | 30 | 135 |
| 1649 | — — — lis on breast | 40 | 150 |
| 1650 | — — — annulet on breast | 35 | 140 |
| 1651 | — — — cross on breast | 40 | 160 |

1652

| | | | |
|---|---|---|---|
| 1652 | **Farthing.** ЄDWARD RЄX ANGL, large head without neck | 275 | 950 |

*For further reading see:*
Halfpennies and Farthings of Edward III and Richard II. *Paul and Bente R. Withers, 2002.*

There was no change in the weight standard of the coinage during this reign and the coins evolve from early issues resembling those of Edward III to late issues similar to those of Henry IV.

There is no overall, systematic classification of the coins of Richard II but a coherent scheme for the gold coinage has been worked out and is published in the Schneider Sylloge (SCBI 47). This classification has been adopted here.

Reference: *Silver coinages of Richard II, Henry IV and V.* (B.N.J. 1959-60 and 1963).

*Mintmark:* cross pattée (6)

## GOLD

|  | | F | VF |
|---|---|---|---|
|  | | £ | £ |
| 1653 | **Noble,** *London.* Style of Edw. III. IA. Lis over sail .................................. | 1350 | 5000 |

1654          1658

| 1654 | — IB. Annulet over sail .............................................................. | 1250 | 4250 |
|---|---|---|---|
| 1655 | French title omitted. IIA. Crude style, saltire over sail. IIB. Fine style, trefoil over sail. IIC. Porcine style, no mark over sail ........................... | 1250 | 4250 |
| 1656 | French title resumed. IIIA. Fine style, no marks ..................................... | 1250 | 4250 |
| 1657 | — IIIB. Lis on rudder. IIIC. Trefoil by shield ........................................ | 1350 | 4500 |
| 1658 | Henry IV style. IVA. Escallop on rudder. IVB. Crescent on rudder......... | 1750 | 6500 |
| 1659 | *Calais.* With altered obverse of Edw. III, Edw. III lettering.................... | 2250 | 8000 |
| 1660 | Style of Edw. III. IB. New lettering. Voided quatrefoil over sail ........... | 1350 | 5250 |

1661

| 1661 | French title omitted. IIA. Crude style, no marks. IIB. Fine style, trefoil over sail. IIC. Porcine style, no marks...................................................... | 1250 | 4250 |
|---|---|---|---|
| 1662 | French title resumed. IIIA. Fine style, no marks ..................................... | 1250 | 4250 |
| 1663 | — IIIB. Lion on rudder. IIIC. Two pellets by shield .............................. | 1350 | 5250 |

| | F £ | VF £ |
|---|---|---|

1664 **Half-noble,** *London.* With altered *obv.* of Edw. III. Usually muled with
*rev.* or altered *rev.* of Edw. III ................................................................ 1350 5250

1665                                                  1673

| 1665 | Style of Edw. III. IB. No marks or saltire over sail | 1250 | 4500 |
|---|---|---|---|
| 1666 | French title omitted. IIA. New style, no marks | 1300 | 5000 |
| 1667 | French title resumed. IIIA. No marks. IIIB. Lion on rudder | 1250 | 4500 |
| 1668 | Henry IV style. IVB. Crescent on rudder | 1500 | 6000 |
| 1669 | *Calais.* Mule with *obv.* or *rev.* of Edw. III | 1600 | 6500 |
| 1670 | Style of Edw. III. IB. Quatrefoil over sail | 1500 | 6000 |
| 1671 | Late style. French title. IIIA. No marks. IIIB. Saltire by rudder | 1450 | 5750 |
| 1672 | **Quarter-noble,** *London.* IA. R̅ in centre of *rev.* | 500 | 1350 |
| 1673 | IB Lis in centre of *rev.* | 450 | 1250 |
| 1674 | — lis or cross over shield | 500 | 1350 |

1675                                               1677

| 1675 | IIIA. Pellet in centre of *rev.* | 450 | 1250 |
|---|---|---|---|
| 1676 | IIIB. Trefoil of annulets over shield or trefoils in spandrels | 575 | 1500 |
| 1677 | IVA. Escallop over shield | 500 | 1350 |

# SILVER

1680

|      |                                                                     | F    | VF   |
| ---- | ------------------------------------------------------------------- | ---- | ---- |
|      |                                                                     | £    | £    |
| 1678 | **Groat.** I. Style of Edw. III, F *(i.e. et)* before FRANC, etc. .................. | 450  | 1850 |
| 1679 | II. New lettering, retrograde Z before FRANC, etc. ........................... | 375  | 1650 |
| 1680 | III. Bust with bushy hair, 'fishtail' serifs to letters ............................. | 425  | 1750 |
| 1681 | IV. New style bust and crown, crescent on breast ............................. | 950  | 3750 |

1682

| 1682 | **Halfgroat.** II. New lettering; with or without French title ................. | 200 | 750  |
| ---- | --------------------------------------------------------------------------- | --- | ---- |
| 1683 | III. As 1680 ..................................................................... | 225 | 800  |
| 1684 | — — with *obv.* die of Edw. III (1640A) ............................................ | 250 | 900  |
| 1685 | IV. As 1681, with or without crescent on breast................................ | 450 | 1500 |
| 1686 | **Penny,** *London.* I Lettering as 1678, RICARDVS REX ANGLIE..... | 160 | 650  |
| 1688 | — II. As 1679, Z FRANC lis on breast ............................................. | 175 | 700  |

1688

| 1689 | — III. As 1680, RICARD REX AnGLIE, fish-tail letters ................. | 200 | 750 |
| ---- | ----------------------------------------------------------------------- | --- | --- |
| 1690 | *York.* I. Early style, usually with cross or lis on breast, quatrefoil in centre of *rev.*............................................................................................ | 65 | 300 |
| 1691 | — II. New bust and letters, no marks on breast ............................. | 65 | 300 |

1692

1692  — Local dies. Pellet above each shoulder, cross on breast, REX AnGLIE
         or AnGILIE ........................................................................   80   375
1693  — — — RЄX DNS ЄB ...................................................   90   400
1694  — — — RЄX AnG FRAnC.............................................  100   425
1695  — III. As 1680, RЄX AnGL Z FRAnC (scallop after TAS) ..............   90   400
1696  — IV. Very bushy hair, new letters, Ŗ. R in centre of quatrefoil........  135   575
1697  *Durham.* Cross or lis on breast, DVnOLM ......................................  125   500

1698            1699

1698  **Halfpenny.** Early style. LONDON, saltire or annulet (rare) on breast ....   45   160
1699  Intermediate style. LOnDOn, no marks on breast .....................................   35   135
1700  Type III. Late style. Similar, but fishtail letters ...........................................   35   135
1700A Type IV. Short, stubby lettering .................................................................   40   140

1701            1704A

1701  **Farthing.** Small bust and letters................................................................  110   475
1703  Similar but no neck ......................................................................................  110   475
1704  Rose in each angle of *rev.* instead of pellets .............................................  150   575
1704A Large head with broad face as Henry IV ...................................................  225   900

For further reading see:
*Halfpennies and Farthings of Edward III and Richard II. P. and B. R. Withers, 2002.*

## HENRY IV, 1399-1413

In 1412 the standard weights of the coinage were reduced, the noble by 12 grains and the penny by 3 grains, partly because there was a scarcity of bullion and partly to provide revenue for the king, as Parliament had not renewed the royal subsidies. As in France, the royal arms were altered, three fleur-de-lis taking the place of the four or more lis previously displayed.

*Mintmark:* cross pattée (6)

### GOLD

**HEAVY COINAGE, 1399-1412**

1706                1707

|  | | F | VF |
|---|---|---|---|
|  | | £ | £ |
| 1705 | **Noble** (120 grs., 7.77g.), *London.* Old arms with four lis in French quarters; crescent or annulet on rudder | 6000 | 17500 |
| 1706 | — New arms with three lis; crescent, pellet or no marks on rudder | 5250 | 16500 |
| 1707 | *Calais.* Flag at stern, old arms; crown on or to l. of rudder | 7000 | 20000 |

1709

| 1708 | — — new arms; crown or saltire on rudder | 6000 | 17500 |
|---|---|---|---|
| 1709 | **Half-noble,** *London.* Old arms | 4750 | 16500 |
| 1710 | — new arms | 4500 | 16000 |
| 1711 | *Calais.* New arms | 6250 | 20000 |
| 1712 | **Quarter-noble,** *London.* Crescent over old arms | 1200 | 4250 |
| 1713 | — — — new arms | 1100 | 4000 |
| 1714 | *Calais.* New arms. R. *Mm.* crown | 1350 | 5000 |

1715

|  | | F | VF |
|--|--|---|----|
|  | | £ | £ |

**LIGHT COINAGE, 1412-13**

1715  **Noble** (108 grs., 6.99g.). Trefoil, or trefoil and annulet, on side of ship.
R. Trefoil in one quarter.......................................................................... 1500  5250

1716  **Half-noble.** Similar, but always with annulet ......................................... 2250  8000

1717

1717  **Quarter-noble.** Trefoils, or trefoils and annulets beside shield, lis above. R.
Lis in centre ........................................................................................... 650  2000

## SILVER

**HEAVY COINAGE, 1399-1412**

1718  **Halfgroat** (36 grs., 2.33g.). Star on breast ............................................. 1650  5500

1718A — Muled with Edw. III (1640A) *obv.*...................................................... 650  2250

1719  **Penny,** *London.* Similar, early bust with long neck................................. 800  2750

1720  — later bust with shorter neck, no star on breast ..................................... 750  2500

1722                          1723                          1725

1722  *York*  Bust with broad face, round chin...................................................... 450  1350

1723  **Halfpenny.** Early small bust......................................................................... 175  650

1724  — later large bust, with rounded shoulders,............................................. 200  700

1725  **Farthing.** Face without neck ........................................................................ 950  3000

## LIGHT COINAGE, 1412-13

1726

1732

|      |                                                                                              | F £  | VF £ |
|------|----------------------------------------------------------------------------------------------|------|------|
| 1726 | **Groat** (60 grs., 3.88g.). I. Pellet to l., annulet to r. of crown; altered die of Richard II | 1500 | 7000 |
| 1727 | New dies; II. Annulet to l., pellet to r. of crown, 8 or 10 arches to tressure               | 1250 | 6250 |
| 1728 | — III. Similar but 9 arches to tressure                                                      | 1000 | 5250 |
| 1729 | **Halfgroat.** Pellet to l., annulet to r. of crown                                          | 850  | 3000 |
| 1730 | Annulet to l., pellet to r. of crown                                                         | 750  | 2500 |
| 1731 | **Penny,** *London*. Annulet and pellet by crown; trefoil on breast and before CIVI          | 675  | 2250 |
| 1732 | — — annulet or slipped trefoil before LON                                                    | 750  | 2500 |
| 1733 | — Pellet and annulet by crown                                                                | 750  | 2500 |
| 1734 | *York*. Annulet on breast. R. Quatrefoil in centre                                           | 425  | 1100 |
| 1735 | *Durham*. Trefoil on breast, DVnOLM                                                          | 375  | 1000 |

1737

1738

|      |                                                                       | F £ | VF £ |
|------|-----------------------------------------------------------------------|-----|------|
| 1737 | **Halfpenny.** New dies; annulets by crown or neck, or no marks       | 200 | 700  |
| 1738 | **Farthing.** Face, no bust; trefoil after RCX                        | 750 | 2500 |

For further information see:
*Halfpennies and Farthings of Henry IV, V and VI.* P. and B. R. Withers, 2003.

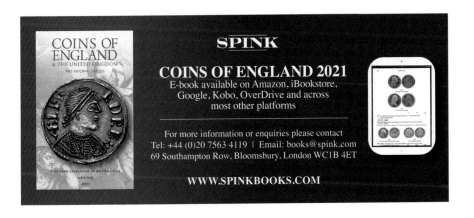

There was no change of importance in the coinage of this reign. There was, however, a considerable development in the use of privy marks which distinguished various issues, except for the last issue of the reign when most marks were removed. The Calais mint, which had closed in 1411, did not re-open until just before the end of the reign. There is now some uncertainty as to whether types A and B of Henry V should be given to Henry IV.

*Mintmarks*

Cross pattée (4)    Pierced cross with    Pierced cross (18).
pellet centre (20)

# GOLD

|  | | F | VF |
|---|---|---|---|
|  | | £ | £ |
| 1739 | **Noble.** A. Quatrefoil over sail and in second quarter of *rev.* Short broad letters, no other marks | 1750 | 6500 |
| 1740 | — B. Ordinary letters; similar, or with annulet on rudder | 1250 | 4500 |
| 1741 | — C. Mullet by sword arm, annulet on rudder | 1100 | 4250 |

1742                                                 1744

| 1742 | — — — broken annulet on side of ship | 1000 | 4000 |
|---|---|---|---|
| 1743 | —D. Mullet and annulet by sword arm, trefoil by shield, broken annulet on ship | 1100 | 4250 |
| 1744 | — E. Mullet, or mullet and annulet by sword arm, trefoil by shield, pellet by sword point and in one quarter, annulet on side of ship | 1100 | 4250 |
| 1745 | — — Similar, but trefoil on ship instead of by shield | 1250 | 4500 |
| 1746 | — F. Similar, but no pellet at sword point, trefoil in one quarter | 1350 | 5000 |
| 1747 | — G. No marks; annulet stops, except for mullet after first word | 1750 | 6500 |
| 1748 | **Half Noble.** B. As noble; Hen. IV *rev.* die | 2000 | 7250 |
| 1749 | — C. Broken annulet on ship, quatrefoil below sail | 1100 | 3500 |
| 1750 | — — Mullet over shield, broken annulet on *rev.* | 900 | 3000 |
| 1751 | — F. Similar, but no annulet on ship, usually trefoil by shield | 1000 | 3250 |
| 1752 | — F/E. As last, but pellet in 1st and annulet in 2nd quarter | 1200 | 3750 |

1753                                      1756

|   |   | F | VF |
|---|---|---|---|
|   |   | £ | £ |
| 1753 | — G. As noble, but quatrefoil over sail, mullet sometimes omitted after first word of *rev.* | 1100 | 3500 |
| 1754 | **Quarter Noble.** A. Lis over shield and in centre of *rev.* Short broad letters; quatrefoil and annulet beside shield, stars at corners of centre on *rev.* | 675 | 1750 |
| 1755 | — C. Ordinary letters; quatrefoil to l., quat. and mullet to r. of shield | 475 | 1250 |
| 1756 | — — — annulet to l., mullet to r. of shield | 375 | 900 |
| 1757 | — F. Ordinary letters; trefoil to l., mullet to r. of shield | 425 | 1000 |
| 1758 | — G. — no marks, except mullet after first word | 450 | 1200 |

## SILVER

1759

| | | | |
|---|---|---|---|
| 1759 | **Groat.** A. Short broad letters; 'emaciated' bust | 675 | 3000 |
| 1760 | — — muled with Hen. IV *obv* | 900 | 4000 |
| 1761 | — — muled with Hen. IV *rev* | 750 | 3250 |

1762B                                     1767

| | | | |
|---|---|---|---|
| 1762 | B. Ordinary letters; 'scowling' bust | 240 | 950 |
| 1762A | — — mullet in centre of breast | 275 | 1100 |
| 1762B | — — mullet to r. of breast | 300 | 1250 |
| 1763 | — — muled with Hen. IV | 475 | 1850 |
| 1764 | C. Normal 'frowning' bust | 185 | 750 |
| 1765 | — — mullet on r. shoulder | 150 | 600 |
| 1766 | — — R muled with Hen. IV | 450 | 1750 |
| 1767 | G. Normal 'frowning' bust; no marks | 200 | 800 |
| 1768 | **Halfgroat.** A. As groat, but usually with annulet and pellet by crown | 525 | 2250 |

|                                                                                          | F | VF |
|                                                                                          | £ | £ |
| 1769 B. Ordinary letters; no marks | 225 | 850 |
| 1770  — — muled with Hen. IV *obv.* | 750 | 3000 |
| 1771 C. Tall neck, broken annulet to l. of crown | 100 | 425 |
| 1772  — — — mullet on r. shoulder | 110 | 450 |

1774                          1775                              1788

| 1773  — — — mullet in centre of breast | 100 | 425 |
| 1774 F. Annulet and trefoil by crown, mullet on breast | 95 | 375 |
| 1775 G. New neat bust: no marks | 90 | 350 |
| 1776 **Penny.** *London.* Altered Hen. IV *obv.* with mullet added to l. of crown .. | 450 | 1750 |
| 1777  — A. Letters, bust and marks as 1768 | 250 | 950 |
| 1778  — C. Tall neck, mullet and broken annulet by crown | 45 | 175 |
| 1779  — D. Similar, but whole annulet | 50 | 200 |
| 1780  — F. Mullet and trefoil by crown | 50 | 200 |
| 1781  — G. New neat bust, no marks, DI GRA | 60 | 225 |
| 1782 *Durham.* C. As 1778 but quatrefoil at end of legend | 45 | 185 |
| 1783  — D. As 1779 | 45 | 185 |
| 1784  — G. Similar, but new bust. R. Annulet in one qtr. | 45 | 200 |
| 1785 *York.* C. As 1778, but quatrefoil in centre of *rev.* | 40 | 175 |
| 1786  — D. Similar, but whole annulet by crown | 40 | 175 |
| 1787  — E. As last, but pellet above mullet | 60 | 240 |
| 1788  — F. Mullet and trefoil by crown | 40 | 175 |
| 1789  — — Trefoil over mullet to l., annulet to r. of crown | 50 | 225 |
| 1790  — G. Mullet and trefoil by crown (London dies) | 45 | 185 |

1791                          1796                              1798

| 1791  — — Mullet and lis by crown, annulet in one qtr. (usually local dies) .... | 40 | 175 |
| 1792 **Halfpenny.** A. Emaciated bust, annulets by crown | 175 | 650 |
| 1793  — altered dies of Hen. IV | 225 | 800 |
| 1794 C. Ordinary bust, broken annulets by crown | 30 | 110 |
| 1795 D. Annulets, sometimes broken, by hair | 35 | 120 |
| 1796 F. Annulet and trefoil by crown | 35 | 120 |
| 1797 G. New bust; no marks, (usually muled with Henry VI annulet *rev.*) ...... | 50 | 175 |
| 1797A **Farthing.** *London.* B. Very large head | 475 | 1750 |
| 1798  — G. Small face with neck | 350 | 1250 |
| 1798A *Calais.* G. as 1798, VILLA CALIS | 450 | 1650 |

For further information see:
*Halfpennies and Farthings of Henry IV, V and VI.* P and B. R. Withers, 2003.

The supply of gold began to dwindle early in the reign, which accounts for the rarity of gold after 1426. The Calais mint had reopened just before the death of Henry V and for some years a large amount of coin was struck there. It soon stopped minting gold; the mint was finally closed in 1440. A royal mint at York was opened for a short time in 1423/4.

Marks used to denote various issues become more prominent in this reign and can be used to date coins to within a year or so.

Reference: C. A. Whitton, *The Heavy Coinage of Henry VI*. (B.N.J. 1938-41).

## Mintmarks

| 136 | 7a | 105 | 18 | 133 | 8 | 9 | 15 |

| | |
|---|---|
| 1422-7 | Incurved pierced cross (136) |
| 1422-3 | Lis (105, York) |
| 1422-60 | Plain cross (7a, intermittently |
| | Lis (105, on gold) |
| 1422-27 | Pierced cross (18) |
| 1460 | Lis (105, on rev. of some groats) |

| | |
|---|---|
| 1422-34 | Cross pommée (133) |
| 1427-34 | Cross patonce (8) |
| | Cross fleury (9) |
| 1434-35 | Voided cross (15) |
| 1435-60 | Cross fleury (9) |

For Henry VI (second reign 1470-71), restoration mintmarks see page 220.

## GOLD

1799

**Annulet issue, 1422-c.1430**

| | | F £ | VF £ |
|---|---|---|---|
| 1799 | **Noble.** *London.* Annulet by sword arm, and in one spandrel on *rev.;* trefoil stops on *obv.* with lis after hЄnRIC, annulets on *rev.,* with mullet after IhC | 1100 | 3500 |
| 1800 | — Similar, but *obv.* from Henry V die | 1750 | 6000 |
| 1801 | — As 1799, but Flemish imitative coinage | 900 | 2500 |

1802

| | | | |
|---|---|---|---|
| 1802 | *Calais.* As 1799, but flag at stern and C in centre of *rev* | 1100 | 4000 |

|      |                                                      | F    | VF   |
|------|------------------------------------------------------|------|------|
|      |                                                      | £    | £    |
| 1803 | — — with h in centre of *rev.* | 1000 | 3750 |
| 1804 | *York.* As London, but with lis over stern | 1500 | 5250 |

1805

| 1805 | **Half-noble.** *London.* As 1799 | 900 | 2750 |
| 1806 | — Similar, but *obv.* from Henry V die | 1100 | 4000 |
| 1807 | *Calais.* As noble, with C in centre of *rev.* | 1350 | 5000 |
| 1808 | — — with h in centre of *rev.* | 1250 | 4500 |
| 1809 | *York.* As noble | 1500 | 5250 |
| 1810 | **Quarter-noble.** *London.* Lis over shield; *mm.* large lis | 300 | 750 |
| 1811 | — — — trefoil below shield | 300 | 800 |
| 1812 | — — — pellet below shield | 325 | 825 |
| 1813 | *Calais.* Three lis over shield; *mm.* large lis | 375 | 950 |

1814                                        1819

| 1814 | — Similar but three lis around shield | 350 | 900 |
| 1815 | — As 1810, but much smaller *mm.* | 300 | 800 |
| 1816 | *York.* Two lis over shield | 400 | 1000 |

**Rosette-mascle issue, c.1430-31**

| 1817 | **Noble.** *London.* Lis by sword arm and in *rev.* field; stops, rosettes, or rosettes and mascles | 1750 | 6000 |
| 1818 | *Calais.* Similar, with flag at stern | 2000 | 7500 |
| 1819 | **Half-noble.** *London.* Lis in *rev.* field; stops, rosettes and mascles | 2250 | 9000 |
| 1820 | *Calais.* Similar, flag at stern; stops, rosettes | 3000 | 12000 |
| 1821 | **Quarter-noble.** *London.* As 1810; stops, as noble | 900 | 3000 |
| 1822 | — without lis over shield | 950 | 3250 |
| 1823 | *Calais.* Lis over shield, rosettes r. and l., and rosette stops | 950 | 3250 |

**Pinecone-mascle issue, c.1431-2/3**

1824

|   |   | F | VF |
|---|---|---|---|
|   |   | £ | £ |
| 1824 | **Noble.** Stops, pinecones and mascles ..................................................... | 1750 | 6000 |
| 1825 | **Half-noble.** *O.* Rosette-mascle die. R. As last ........................................ | 3000 | 12000 |
| 1826 | **Quarter-noble.** As 1810, but pinecone and mascle stops ...................... | 950 | 3250 |

1828

**Leaf-mascle issue, c.1432/3-6**

| 1827 | **Noble.** Leaf in waves; stops, saltires with two mascles and one leaf ....... | 3250 | 13000 |
|---|---|---|---|
| 1828 | **Half-noble.** (Fishpool hoard and Reigate hoard) .................................... | 3000 | 12500 |
| 1829 | **Quarter-noble.** As 1810; stops, saltire and mascle; leaf on inner circle of *rev.* | 900 | 3000 |

**Leaf-trefoil issue, c.1436-8**

| 1830 | **Noble.** Stops, leaves and trefoils ............................................................. | 2500 | 11000 |
|---|---|---|---|
| 1830A | **Half-noble.** ............................................................................................. | 3000 | 12000 |
| 1831 | **Quarter-noble.** Similar ......................................................................... | 900 | 3000 |

**Trefoil issue, 1438-43**

| 1832 | **Noble.** Trefoil to left of shield and in *rev.* legend ..................................... | 2500 | 11000 |
|---|---|---|---|

**Leaf-pellet issue, 1445-54**

| 1833 | **Noble.** Annulet, lis and leaf below shield .............................................. | 3000 | 12500 |
|---|---|---|---|

**Cross-pellet issue, 1454-61**

| 1834 | **Noble.** Mascle at end of *obv.* legend....................................................... | 3250 | 13500 |
|---|---|---|---|

*Muling exists in Henry VI coins spanning two or three issues. Full flan coins in the smaller denominations are difficult to find.*

## SILVER

**Annulet issue, 1422-30**

1835                                    1836

|  | | F | VF |
|---|---|---|---|
|  | | £ | £ |
| 1835 | **Groat.** *London.* Annulet in two quarters of *rev.* | 50 | 175 |
| 1836 | *Calais.* Annulets at neck. R. Similar | 45 | 160 |
| 1837 | — — no annulets on *rev.* | 65 | 250 |

1838

| 1838 | *York.* Lis either side of neck. R. As 1835 | 650 | 2500 |
|---|---|---|---|
| 1839 | **Halfgroat.** *London.* As groat | 40 | 125 |

1840                                    1843

| 1840 | *Calais.* As 1836 | 30 | 110 |
|---|---|---|---|
| 1841 | — — no annulets on *rev.* | 40 | 125 |
| 1843 | *York.* As groat | 750 | 3250 |

1845

| 1844 | **Penny.** *London.* Annulets in two qtrs. | 30 | 120 |
|---|---|---|---|
| 1845 | *Calais.* Annulets at neck. R. As above | 30 | 100 |

|      |                                                           | F £ | VF £ |
|------|-----------------------------------------------------------|-----|------|
| 1847 | *York.* As London, but lis at neck ................................. | 650 | 2500 |
| 1848 | **Halfpenny.** *London.* As penny ......................... | 20  | 80   |
| 1849 | *Calais.* Similar, but annulets at neck ..................... | 20  | 80   |

1850                1852

|       |                                                          | F £ | VF £ |
|-------|----------------------------------------------------------|-----|------|
| 1850  | *York.* Similar, but lis at neck ................................ | 525 | 1750 |
| 1851  | **Farthing.** *London.* As penny, but *mm.* cross pommée ......................... | 120 | 475 |
| 1852  | *Calais.* Similar, but annulets at neck ..................... | 175 | 650 |
| 1852A | *York.* Similar, but lis at neck ................................. | 575 | 2250 |

**Annulet-trefoil sub-issue**

1854                                        1855

| 1854 | **Groat.** *Calais.* As 1836 but trefoil to l. of crown, R trefoil after POSVI and only one annulet ........................ | 65 | 210 |
|------|--------------------------------------------------------------------------|----|-----|
| 1855 | **Halfgroat.** *Calais.* Similar, usually a mule with annulet issue............... | 55 | 175 |
| 1856 | **Penny.** *Calais.* Similar, only one annulet on *rev* ...................................... | 90 | 350 |

**Rosette-mascle issue, 1430-31.** All with rosettes (early) or rosettes and mascles somewhere in the legends.

| 1858 | **Groat.** *London.* ...................................................... | 55 | 200 |
|------|-----------------------------------------------------------|----|-----|

1859                                        1861

| 1859 | *Calais.* ......................................................... | 50  | 185 |
|------|------------------------------------------------------------|-----|-----|
| 1860 | — mascle in two spandrels ....................................... | 65  | 200 |
| 1861 | **Halfgroat.** *London.* ............................................. | 110 | 350 |

1862                     1870                  1872

|  |  | F<br>£ | VF<br>£ |
|---|---|---|---|
| 1862 | *Calais.* | 45 | 150 |
| 1863 | — mascle in two spandrels | 50 | 165 |
| 1864 | **Penny.** *London.* | 135 | 475 |
| 1865 | *Calais.* | 35 | 130 |
| 1866 | *York.* Archb. Kemp. Crosses by hair, no rosette | 30 | 120 |
| 1867 | — — Saltires by hair, no rosette | 35 | 135 |
| 1868 | — — Mullets by crown | 30 | 120 |
| 1869 | *Durham.* Bp. Langley. Large star to l. of crown, no rosette, DVnOLMI | 65 | 200 |
| 1870 | **Halfpenny.** *London.* | 30 | 100 |
| 1871 | *Calais.* | 25 | 90 |
| 1872 | **Farthing.** *London.* | 175 | 625 |
| 1873 | *Calais. Mm.* cross pommée | 225 | 800 |

**Pinecone-mascle issue, 1431-32/3.** All with pinecones and mascles in legends.

1874                                1876

| 1874 | **Groat.** *London.* | 50 | 175 |
|---|---|---|---|
| 1875 | *Calais.* | 45 | 165 |
| 1876 | **Halfgroat.** *London.* | 60 | 175 |
| 1877 | *Calais.* | 45 | 150 |
| 1878 | **Penny.** *London.* | 55 | 185 |
| 1879 | *Calais.* | 40 | 135 |
| 1880 | *York.* Archb. Kemp. Mullet by crown, quatrefoil in centre of *rev.* | 40 | 140 |
| 1881 | — — rosette on breast, no quatrefoil | 40 | 140 |
| 1882 | — — mullet on breast, no quatrefoil | 45 | 160 |
| 1883 | *Durham.* Bp. Langley. DVnOLMI | 55 | 185 |

1884                        1886

|  |  | F | VF |
|  |  | £ | £ |
| 1884 | **Halfpenny.** *London.* | 25 | 100 |
| 1885 | *Calais.* | 25 | 100 |
| 1886 | **Farthing.** *London.* | 175 | 625 |
| 1887 | *Calais. Mm.* cross pommée | 225 | 800 |

**Leaf-mascle issue, 1432/3-6.** Usually with a mascle in the legend and a leaf somewhere in the design.

| 1888 | **Groat.** *London.* Leaf below bust, all appear to read DONDON | 325 | 1000 |
| 1889 | — — *rev.* of last or next coinage | 135 | 525 |

1890                                      1892

| 1890 | *Calais.* Leaf below bust, and usually below MЄVM | 110 | 350 |
| 1891 | **Halfgroat.** *London.* Leaf under bust, pellet under TAS and DON | 150 | 575 |
| 1892 | *Calais.* Leaf below bust, and sometimes on *rev.* | 125 | 450 |
| 1893 | **Penny.** *London.* Leaf on breast, no stops on *rev.* | 85 | 300 |
| 1894 | *Calais.* Leaf on breast and below SIЄ | 90 | 325 |
| 1895 | **Halfpenny.** *London.* Leaf on breast and on *rev.* | 35 | 110 |
| 1896 | *Calais.* Leaf on breast and below SIЄ | 75 | 225 |

1897                                      1902

**Leaf-trefoil issue, 1436-8.** Mostly with leaves and trefoil of pellets in the legends.

| 1897 | **Groat.** *London.* Leaf on breast | 85 | 250 |
| 1898 | — without leaf on breast | 85 | 250 |
| 1899 | *Calais.* Leaf on breast | 225 | 750 |
| 1900 | **Halfgroat.** *London.* Leaf on breast; *mm.* plain cross | 85 | 300 |
| 1901 | — *O. mm.* cross fleury; leaf on breast | 75 | 250 |
| 1902 | — — without leaf on breast | 80 | 275 |
| 1902A | *Calais.* leaf on breast, mule with leaf mascle *rev.* | 175 | 650 |

|                                                                                          | F | VF |
|------------------------------------------------------------------------------------------|---|----|
|                                                                                          | £ | £  |
| 1903 **Penny.** *London.* Leaf on breast.............................................................. | 110 | 325 |
| 1903A *Calais.* Similar ............................................................................. | 275 | 750 |
| 1904 *Durham.* Bp. Neville. Leaf on breast. R. Rings in centre, no stops, DVnOLM | 125 | 375 |

1905                        1907

| 1905 **Halfpenny.** *London.* Leaf on breast ....................................................... | 25 | 100 |
|----------------------------------------------------------------------------------------------------|----|-----|
| 1906 — without leaf on breast........................................................................... | 30 | 110 |
| 1906A *Calais.* leaf on breast, mule with leaf mascle rev. .................................... | 110 | 350 |
| 1907 **Farthing.** *London.* Leaf on breast; stops, trefoil and saltire on *obv.*........ | 275 | 950 |

**Trefoil issue, 1438-43.** Trefoil of pellets either side of neck and in legend, leaf on breast.

1910

| 1908 **Groat.** *London.* Sometimes a leaf before LON....................................... | 80 | 250 |
|---------------------------------------------------------------------------------------------|----|-----|
| 1909 — Fleurs in spandrels, sometimes extra pellet in two qtrs. ...................... | 85 | 275 |
| 1910 — Trefoils in place of fleurs at shoulders, none by neck, sometimes extra pellets.......................................................................................... | 90 | 300 |
| 1911 *Calais.*.................................................................................................... | 250 | 850 |

1911A

| 1911A **Halfgroat.** *London.* Similar, but trefoil after DEUM and sometimes after POSVI Mule only with leaf trefoil *obv.*................................................. | 135 | 475 |
|--------------------------------------------------------------------------------------------------------------------------------------------------------------------------------|-----|------|
| 1911B — *Calais. Obv.* Similar to 1911, mule with leaf mascle *rev.*.................... | 275 | 1000 |
| 1911C **Penny.** *Calais.* Trefoils by neck, leaf on breast ..................................... | 475 | 1500 |
| 1912 **Halfpenny.** *London.* ............................................................................. | 25 | 110 |

1912A

| 1912A **Farthing.** *London.* ................................................................................... | 300 | 1100 |
|------------------------------------------------------------------------------------------------------------------|-----|------|

**Trefoil pellet issue, 1443-5**

1913

|  | | F<br>£ | VF<br>£ |
|---|---|---|---|
| 1913 | **Groat.** Trefoils by neck, pellets by crown, small leaf on breast; sometimes extra pellet in two quarters ........................................................ | 135 | 425 |

1915                                    1917

**Leaf-pellet issue, 1445-54.** Leaf on breast, pellet each side of crown, except where stated.

| 1914 | **Groat.** AПGL; extra pellet in two quarters ............................................. | 60 | 225 |
|---|---|---|---|
| 1915 | *Similar,* but AПGLI............................................................................ | 60 | 210 |
| 1916 | — — trefoil in *obv.* legend ........................................................ | 75 | 275 |
| 1917 | Leaf on neck, fleur on breast, R often extra pellet in two quarters.......... | 60 | 225 |
| 1918 | As last, but two extra pellets by hair....................................... | 225 | 750 |
| 1919 | **Halfgroat.** As 1914 *mm.* Cross patonce .................................................. | 85 | 325 |
| 1920 | Similar, but *mm.* plain cross, some times no leaf on breast, no stops....... | 70 | 250 |
| 1921 | **Penny.** *London.* Usually extra pellets in two quarters............................ | 60 | 225 |
| 1922 | — — pellets by crown omitted.............................................................. | 65 | 275 |
| 1923 | — — trefoil in legend........................................................................ | 75 | 300 |
| 1924 | *York,* Archb. Booth. R. Quatrefoil and pellet in centre ........................... | 40 | 145 |
| 1925 | — — two extra pellets by hair (local dies).............................................. | 40 | 145 |
| 1926 | *Durham,* Bp. Neville. Trefoil in *obv.* legend. R. Two rings in centre of cross | 65 | 200 |

1928                          1930

| 1927 | — — Similar, but without trefoil............................................................. | 65 | 200 |
|---|---|---|---|
| 1928 | **Halfpenny.** Usually extra pellet in two quarters ...................................... | 25 | 95 |
| 1929 | — *mm.* plain cross ........................................................................... | 25 | 95 |
| 1930 | **Farthing.** As last ................................................................................ | 275 | 950 |

## Unmarked issue, 1453-4

|      |      |
| ---- | ---- |
| 1931 | 1935 |

|      |                                                                 | F £ | VF £ |
| ---- | --------------------------------------------------------------- | --- | ---- |
| 1931 | **Groat**. No marks on *obv.;* two extra pellets on *rev.*      | 325 | 1250 |
| 1932 | — four extra pellets on *rev.*                                  | 375 | 1350 |
| 1933 | **Halfgroat.** As 1931                                          | 350 | 1250 |

## Cross-pellet issue, 1454-61

|      |                                                                                                         | F £ | VF £ |
| ---- | ------------------------------------------------------------------------------------------------------- | --- | ---- |
| 1934 | **Groat.** Saltire either side of neck, pellets by crown, leaf and fleur on breast, extra pellets on *rev.* | 375 | 1100 |
| 1935 | Saltire on neck, no leaf, pellets by crown, usually mullets in legend; extra pellets on *rev.*          | 125 | 375  |
| 1936 | — Similar, but mascles in place of mullets on *obv.*                                                     | 125 | 375  |
| 1937 | — — pellets by hair instead of by crown                                                                 | 150 | 525  |
| 1938 | **Halfgroat.** Saltire on neck, pellets by crown and on *rev.*, mullets in legend                       | 275 | 950  |

|      |      |      |
| ---- | ---- | ---- |
| 1940 | 1943 | 1944 |

|      |                                                                                                        | F £ | VF £ |
| ---- | ------------------------------------------------------------------------------------------------------ | --- | ---- |
| 1939 | **Penny.** *London.* Saltire on neck, pellets by crown and on *rev.*, mascle(s), or mullet and mascle in legend | 135 | 475  |
| 1940 | *York.* Archb. Wm. Booth. Saltires by neck, usually leaf on breast, pellets by crown. R. Cross in quatrefoil in centre. | 70  | 250  |
| 1941 | *Durham.* Bp. Laurence Booth. Saltire and B or B only at neck, pellets by crown. R. Rings in centre    | 75  | 275  |
| 1942 | **Halfpenny.** Saltires by neck, usually two extra pellets on *rev.*                                   | 30  | 110  |
| 1943 | Similar, but saltire on neck, sometimes mullet after hЄnRIC                                             | 25  | 100  |
| 1944 | **Farthing**. Saltire on neck, usually pellets by crown and on *rev.*, but known without either.       | 300 | 1050 |

For further information see:
*Halfpennies and Farthings of Henry IV, V and VI.* P. and B. R. Withers, 2003.

## Lis-pellet issue, 1456-61

1945

|      |                                                                 | F £ | VF £ |
| ---- | --------------------------------------------------------------- | --- | ---- |
| 1945 | **Groat.** Lis on neck; pellets by crown. R. Extra pellets      | 225 | 800  |

## EDWARD IV, First Reign, 1461-70

In order to increase the supply of bullion to the mint the weight of the penny was reduced to 12 grains in 1464, and the current value of the noble was raised to 8s. 4d. Later, in 1465, a new gold coin was issued, the Ryal or 'Rose Noble', weighing 120 grains and having a value of 10s. However, as 6s. 8d. had become the standard professional fee the old noble was missed, and a new coin was issued to take its place, the Angel of 80 grains.

Royal mints were set up in Bristol, Coventry, Norwich and York to help with the recoinage. The Coventry and Norwich mints were not open for long, but the York and Bristol mints remained open until 1471 and 1472 respectively.

*Reference:* C. E. Blunt and C. A Whitton, *The Coinage of Edward IV and Henry VI (Restored),* B.N.J. 1945-7.

### Mintmarks

| 105 | 9 | 7a | 33 | 99 | 28 | 74 | 11 |
|---|---|---|---|---|---|---|---|

| | | | | |
|---|---|---|---|---|
| 1461-4 | Lis (105) | 1467-70 | Lis (105, *York*) | |
| | Cross fleury (9) | 1467-8 | Crown (74) | (often |
| | Plain cross (7a) | | Sun (28) | combined) |
| 1464-5 | Rose (33 and 34) | 1468-9 | Crown (74) | (sometimes |
| 1464-7 | Pall (99, *Canterbury*) | | Rose (33) | combined) |
| 1465-6 | Sun (28) | 1469-70 | Long cross | |
| 1466-7 | Crown (74) | | fitchee (l.c.f) (11) | (often |
| | | | Sun (28) | combined) |

## GOLD

**HEAVY COINAGE, 1461-4**

1946

| | | F | VF |
|---|---|---|---|
| | | £ | £ |
| 1946 | **Noble** (=6s. 8d., wt. 108 grs., 6.99g.). Normal type, but *obv.* legend commences at top left, lis below shield; *mm.*-/lis (Spink's sale May 1993) | 4000 | 16500 |
| 1947 | — Quatrefoil below sword arm; *mm.* rose/lis | 4500 | 17500 |
| 1948 | — R. Roses in two spandrels; *mm.* rose | 5000 | 18500 |
| 1949 | **Quarter-noble** | 1750 | 6000 |

1950

| | F £ | VF £ |
|---|---|---|

## LIGHT COINAGE, 1464-70

| | | F £ | VF £ |
|---|---|---|---|
| 1950 | **Ryal** or rose-noble (=10s., wt. 120 grs., 7.77g), *London*. As illustration. Large fleurs in spandrels; *mm.* 33-74 .................................................. | 1100 | 3500 |
| 1951 | — — Small trefoils in spandrels; *mm.* 74-11 ...................................... | 1100 | 3500 |

1952

| 1952 | — Flemish imitative coinage (mostly 16th cent. on a large flan)............. | 750 | 2500 |
|---|---|---|---|
| 1953 | *Bristol.* B in waves, large fleurs; *mm.* sun, crown ................................... | 1250 | 4250 |
| 1954 | — — small fleurs in spandrels; *mm.* sun, crown .................................... | 1350 | 4500 |
| 1955 | *Coventry.* C in waves; *mm.* sun................................................................ | 1650 | 5500 |
| 1956 | *Norwich.* Ꞃ in waves; *mm.* sun, rose ...................................................... | 1750 | 6000 |
| 1957 | *York.* Є in waves, large fleurs in spandrels, *mm.* sun, lis ......................... | 1200 | 3750 |
| 1958 | — — small fleurs, *mm.* sun. lis ................................................................ | 1250 | 4000 |
| 1959 | **Half-ryal.** *London.* As 1950 ........................................................................ | 750 | 2250 |
| 1960 | *Bristol.* B in waves; *mm.* sun, sun/crown................................................. | 1250 | 4500 |
| 1961 | *Coventry.* C in waves; *mm.* sun.................................................................. | 5250 | 17500 |
| 1962 | *Norwich.* Ꞃ in waves; *mm.* rose ............................................................... | 3500 | 12500 |

1963             1965

|  | F £ | VF £ |
|---|---|---|
| 1963 *York.* Є in waves; *mm.* 28, 105, 33/105 ................................................. | 900 | 2750 |
| 1963A Similar but lis instead of Є in waves (probably York) ............................ | 1000 | 3500 |
| 1964 **Quarter-ryal.** Shield in tressure of eight arcs, rose above. ℞. Somewhat as half ryal; *mm.* sun/rose ........................................................ | 1250 | 4500 |
| 1965 Shield in quatrefoil. Є above, rose on l., sun on r.; *mm.* 33/28-74/33 ...... | 450 | 1200 |
| 1966 — — sun on l., rose on r.; *mm.* 74-11 ...................................................... | 475 | 1250 |

1967

| 1967 **Angel** (=6s. 8d., wt. 80 grs., 5.18g). St. Michael spearing dragon. R. Ship, rays of sun at masthead, large rose and sun beside mast; *mm.*-/33 ...................... | 9500 | 37500 |
|---|---|---|
| 1968 — — small rose and sun at mast; *mm.*-/74 ............................................. | 10000 | 40000 |

## SILVER

1969              1972

### HEAVY COINAGE, 1461-4

| 1969 **Groat** (60 grs., 3.88g.). Group I, lis on neck, pellets by crown; *mm.* 9, 7a, 105, 9/105 ................................................................................................ | 120 | 400 |
|---|---|---|
| 1970 — Lis on breast, no pellets; *mm.* plain cross, 7a/105 ............................... | 135 | 450 |
| 1971 — — with pellets at crown; *mm.* plain cross ............................................ | 150 | 525 |
| 1972 II, quatrefoils by neck, crescent on breast; *mm.* rose .............................. | 110 | 375 |
| 1973 III, similar but trefoil on breast; *mm.* rose ............................................... | 120 | 400 |

1974

1979

|  | | F | VF |
|---|---|---|---|
|  | | £ | £ |
| 1974 | — — — eye in *rev.* inner legend, *mm.* rose | 100 | 375 |
| 1975 | — Similar, but no quatrefoils by bust | 175 | 625 |
| 1976 | — — Similar, but no trefoil on breast | 150 | 525 |
| 1977 | IV, annulets by neck, eye after TAS; *mm.* rose | 225 | 750 |
| 1978 | **Halfgroat.** I, lis on breast, pellets by crown and extra pellets in two qtrs.; *mm.* 9, 7a | 475 | 2000 |
| 1979 | II, quatrefoils at neck, crescent on breast; *mm.* rose | 325 | 1100 |
| 1980 | III, similar, but trefoil on breast, eye on rev.; *mm.* rose | 275 | 900 |
| 1981 | — Similar, but no mark on breast | 275 | 900 |
| 1982 | IV, annulets by neck, sometimes eye on *rev.*; *mm.* rose | 325 | 1100 |
| 1983 | **Penny** (15 grs.). *London.* I, marks as 1978, but mascle after RЄX; *mm.* plain cross | 375 | 1350 |
| 1984 | II, quatrefoils by neck; *mm.* rose | 250 | 850 |

1985                    1991                    1994

| 1985 | III, similar, but eye after TAS; *mm.* rose | 275 | 900 |
|---|---|---|---|
| 1986 | IV, annulets by neck; *mm.* rose | 325 | 1050 |
| 1987 | *York,* Archb. Booth. Quatrefoils by bust, voided quatrefoil in centre of *rev.; mm.* rose | 125 | 350 |
| 1988 | *Durham. O.* of Hen. VI. R. DVnOLIn | 120 | 325 |
| 1988A | (ca.1461-c.1462). Local dies, mostly with rose in centre of rev.; *mm.* 7a, 33 | 35 | 140 |
| 1989 | **Halfpenny.** I, as 1983, but no mascle | 65 | 225 |
| 1990 | II, quatrefoils by bust; *mm.* rose | 35 | 125 |
| 1991 | — saltires by bust; *mm.* rose | 35 | 125 |
| 1992 | III, no marks by bust; *mm.* rose | 35 | 135 |
| 1992A | — saltires by bust, eye after TAS, *mm.* rose | 100 | 500 |
| 1993 | IV, annulets by bust; *mm.* rose | 35 | 135 |
| 1994 | **Farthing.** I, pellets by crown, extra pellets on rev., with or without lis on breast | 375 | 1250 |
| 1994A | II. saltires by bust; *mm.* rose | 400 | 1350 |
| 1994B | III, no marks by bust; *mm.* rose | 375 | 1250 |

**LIGHT COINAGE, 1464-70.** There is a great variety of groats and we give only a selection. Some have pellets in one quarter of the reverse, or trefoils over the crown; early coins have fleurs on the cusps of the tressure, then trefoils or no marks on the cusps, while the late coins have only trefoils.

|  |  | F | VF |
|---|---|---|---|
|  |  | £ | £ |
| 1995 | **Groat** (48 grs., 3.11g). *London.* Annulets at neck, eye after TAS; *mm.* 33 (struck from heavy dies, IV) | 135 | 500 |
| 1996 | — — — Similar, but new dies, eye after TAS or DON | 120 | 425 |
| 1997 | — Quatrefoils at neck, eye; rose (heavy dies, III) | 100 | 350 |
| 1998 | — — — Similar, but new dies, eye in *rev.* legend | 120 | 425 |
| 1999 | — No marks at neck, eye; *mm* rose | 135 | 500 |
| 2000 | — Quatrefoils at neck, no eye; *mm.* 33, 74, 28, 74/28, 74/33, 11/28 | 45 | 165 |

2001                                                         2002

| 2001 | — — — rose or quatrefoil on breast; *mm.* 33, 74/28 | 50 | 175 |
|---|---|---|---|
| 2002 | — No marks at neck; *mm.* 28, 74, 11/28, 11 | 60 | 200 |
| 2003 | — Trefoils or crosses at neck; *mm.* 11/33, 11/28, 11 | 50 | 200 |

2004                                                         2014

| 2004 | *Bristol.* B on breast, quatrefoils at neck; *mm.* 28/33, 28, 28/74, 74, 74/28 | 65 | 225 |
|---|---|---|---|
| 2005 | — — trefoils at neck; *mm.* sun | 80 | 300 |
| 2006 | — — no marks at neck; *mm.* sun | 135 | 525 |
| 2007 | — Without B, quatrefoils at neck; *mm.* sun | 120 | 425 |
|  | *Bristol is variously rendered as* BRESTOLL, BRISTOLL, BRESTOW, BRISTOW. |  |  |
| 2008 | *Coventry.* C on breast, quatrefoils at neck, COVETRE; *mm.* 28/33, 28... | 135 | 450 |
| 2009 | — — Local dies, similar; *mm.* rose | 165 | 575 |
| 2010 | — — — as last, but no C or quatrefoils | 175 | 625 |
| 2011 | Norwich. Ⴖ on breast, quatrefoils at neck, ⴖORWIC or ⴖORVIC, *mm.* 28/33, 28 | 125 | 350 |
| 2012 | *York.* Ɛ on breast, quatrefoils at neck, ƐBORACI; *mm.* 28, 105/74, 105, 105/28 | 65 | 225 |
| 2013 | — Similar, but without Ɛ on breast, *mm.* lis | 90 | 300 |
| 2014 | — Ɛ on breast, trefoils at neck; *mm.* 105/28, 105 | 75 | 250 |

2016                                          2035

|      |                                                                                                              | F £ | VF £ |
|------|--------------------------------------------------------------------------------------------------------------|-----|------|
| 2015 | **Halfgroat.** *London.* Annulets by neck (heavy dies); *mm.* 33 ................... | 275 | 900 |
| 2016 | — Quatrefoils by neck; *mm.* 33/-, 28/-, 74, 74/28 ................................. | 60 | 165 |
| 2017 | — Saltires by neck; *mm.* 74, 74/28 .............................................. | 65 | 170 |
| 2018 | — Trefoils by neck; *mm.* 74, 74/28, 11/28 ......................................... | 65 | 170 |
| 2019 | — No marks by neck; *mm.* 11/28 ................................................ | 85 | 250 |
| 2020 | *Bristol.* Saltires or crosses by neck; *mm.* 33/28, 28, 74, 74/-................... | 125 | 525 |
| 2021 | — Quatrefoils by neck; *mm.* 28/-, 74, 74/- ....................................... | 110 | 475 |
| 2022 | — Trefoils by neck; *mm.* crown .................................................. | 125 | 525 |
| 2023 | — No marks by neck; *mm.* 74/28 ................................................ | 150 | 575 |
| 2024 | *Canterbury,* Archb. Bourchier (1464-7). Knot below bust; quatrefoils by neck; *mm.* 99/-, 99, 99/33, 99/28 .................................. | 55 | 160 |
| 2025 | — — — quatrefoils omitted *mm.* 99 ............................................ | 55 | 160 |
| 2026 | — — — saltires by neck; *mm.* 99/-, 99/28 ..................................... | 65 | 180 |
| 2026A| — — — trefoils by neck; *mm.* 99................................................. | 70 | 200 |
| 2027 | — — — wedges by hair and/or neck; *mm.* 99, 99/–, 99/33, 99/28 ......... | 50 | 165 |
| 2028 | — — As 2024 or 2025, but no knot................................................ | 60 | 175 |
| 2029 | — (1467-9). Quatrefoils by neck; *mm.* 74, 74/- ................................. | 60 | 175 |
| 2030 | — — Saltires by neck; *mm.* 74/-, 74 ........................................... | 60 | 175 |
| 2031 | — — Trefoils by neck; *mm.* 74, 74/-, 74/28, 33 ................................. | 55 | 160 |
| 2032 | — No marks by neck; *mm.* sun.................................................. | 85 | 275 |
| 2033 | *Coventry.* Crosses by neck; *mm.* sun ........................................... | 750 | 2250 |
| 2034 | *Norwich.* Quatrefoils or saltires by neck; *mm.* sun ........................... | 675 | 2000 |
| 2035 | *York.* Quatrefoils by neck; *mm.* sun, lis, lis/- ................................ | 110 | 425 |
| 2036 | — Saltires by neck; *mm.* lis ................................................... | 100 | 400 |
| 2037 | — Trefoils by neck; *mm.* lis, lis/- .............................................. | 150 | 575 |
| 2038 | — Є on breast, quatrefoils by neck; *mm.* lis/- .................................. | 110 | 425 |
| 2039 | **Penny** (12 grs., 0.77g.), *London.* Annulets by neck (heavy dies); *mm.* rose | 275 | 900 |
| 2040 | — Quatrefoils by neck; *mm.* 74, sun. crown ................................... | 70 | 260 |
| 2041 | — Trefoil and quatrefoil by neck; *mm.* crown................................... | 75 | 275 |
| 2042 | — Saltires by neck; *mm.* crown ............................................... | 75 | 275 |
| 2043 | — Trefoils by neck; *mm.* crown, long cross fitchée ............................ | 85 | 300 |
| 2044 | — No marks by neck; *mm.* long cross fitchée .................................. | 125 | 400 |
| 2045 | *Bristol.* Crosses, quatrefoils or saltires by neck, BRISTOW; *mm.* crown | 275 | 1000 |
| 2046 | — Quatrefoils by neck; BRI(trefoil)STOLL ..................................... | 300 | 1100 |
| 2047 | — Trefoil to r. of neck BRISTOLL .............................................. | 300 | 1100 |
| 2048 | *Canterbury,* Archb. Bourchier. Quatrefoils or saltires by neck, knot on breast; *mm.* pall................................................... | 70 | 250 |
| 2049 | — — Similar, but no marks by neck ............................................. | 70 | 250 |
| 2050 | — — As 2048, but no knot....................................................... | 75 | 275 |
| 2051 | — — Crosses by neck, no knot ................................................. | 70 | 250 |
| 2052 | — Quatrefoils by neck; *mm.* crown............................................. | 135 | 475 |
| 2053 | — King's Receiver (1462-4). Local dies, mostly with rose in centre of rev.; *mm.* 7a, 33................................................... | 35 | 140 |

| | | F £ | VF £ |
|---|---|---|---|
| 2054 | — *Durham*, Bp. Lawrence Booth (1465-70). B and D by neck, B on *rev.; mm.* 33 | 35 | 150 |
| 2055 | — — Quatrefoil and B by neck; *mm.* sun | 35 | 140 |
| 2056 | — — B and quatrefoil by neck; *mm.* crown | 40 | 150 |
| 2057 | — — D and quatrefoil by neck; *mm.* crown | 40 | 150 |
| 2058 | — — Quatrefoils by neck; *mm.* crown | 35 | 140 |
| 2059 | — — Trefoils by neck; *mm.* crown | 40 | 150 |
| 2060 | — Lis by neck; *mm.* crown | 35 | 130 |
| 2061 | *York*, Sede Vacante (1464-5). Quatrefoils at neck, no quatrefoil in centre of *rev.; mm.* sun, rose | 40 | 160 |
| 2062 | — Archb. Neville (1465-70). Local dies, G and key by neck, quatrefoil on *rev.; mm.* sun, plain cross | 35 | 120 |

2063

| | | | |
|---|---|---|---|
| 2063 | — — London-made dies, similar; *mm.* 28, 105, 11 | 40 | 140 |
| 2064 | — — Similar, but no marks by neck; *mm.* large lis | 40 | 160 |
| 2065 | — — — Quatrefoils by neck; *mm.* large lis | 40 | 160 |
| 2066 | — — — Trefoils by neck; *mm.* large lis | 40 | 150 |

2068                     2077

| | | | |
|---|---|---|---|
| 2067 | **Halfpenny,** *London*. Saltires by neck; *mm.* 34, 28, 74 | 25 | 110 |
| 2068 | — Trefoils by neck; *mm.* 28, 74, 11 | 25 | 110 |
| 2069 | — No marks by neck; *mm.* 11 | 30 | 125 |
| 2070 | *Bristol*. Crosses by neck; *mm.* crown | 110 | 400 |
| 2071 | — Trefoils by neck; *mm.* crown | 100 | 375 |
| 2072 | *Canterbury*. Archb. Bourchier. No marks; *mm.* pall | 75 | 275 |
| 2072A | — — — Trefoils by neck, *mm.* pall | 75 | 275 |
| 2073 | — Saltires by neck; *mm.* crown | 65 | 200 |
| 2074 | — — Trefoils by neck; *mm.* crown | 65 | 200 |
| 2074A | *Norwich*. Quatrefoils by neck., *mm.* Sun | 300 | 950 |
| 2074B | — — Trefoils by neck; *mm.* crown | 325 | 1000 |
| 2075 | *York*. Royal mint. Saltires by neck; *mm.* lis/-, sun/- | 50 | 185 |
| 2076 | — — Trefoils by neck; *mm.* lis/- | 45 | 160 |
| 2077 | **Farthing,** *London*. ЄDWARD DI GRA RЄX, trefoils by neck, *mm.* crown | 425 | 1350 |

*Full flan coins are difficult to find in the smaller denominations.*

For further information see:
*Halfpennies and Farthings of Edward IV to Henry VII*. P. and B. R. Withers, 2004; also *The English Long-Cross Pennies 1279-1489* by Christopher R. Wren

The coinage of this short restoration follows closely that of the previous reign. Only angel gold was issued, the ryal being discontinued. Many of the coins have the king's name reading hεnRICV — another distinguishing feature is an R that looks like a B.

*Mintmarks*

Cross pattée (6)                 Rose (33, Bristol)
Restoration cross (13)          Lis (105)
Trefoil (44 and 45)            Short cross fitchée (12)

## GOLD

2078

| | | F | VF |
|---|---|---|---|
| | | £ | £ |
| 2078 | **Angel,** *London.* As illus.; *mm.* -/6, 12, 105, none | 1350 | 5000 |
| 2079 | *Bristol.* B in waves; *mm.* -/13, none | 2750 | 9000 |
| 2080 | **Half-angel,** *London.* As 2078; *mm.* -/6, -/13, -/105 | 4500 | 12500 |
| 2081 | *Bristol.* B in waves; *mm.* -/13 | 6000 | 17500 |

## SILVER

2082                    2084          2089

| | | F | VF |
|---|---|---|---|
| 2082 | **Groat,** *London.* Usual type; *mm.* 6, 6/13, 6/105, 13, 13/6, 13/105, 13 /12 | 200 | 600 |
| 2083 | *Bristol.* B on breast; *mm.* 13, 13/33, 13/44, 44, 44/13, 44/33, 44/12 | 375 | 1250 |
| 2084 | *York.* Є on breast; *mm.* lis, lis/sun | 225 | 650 |
| 2085 | **Halfgroat,** *London.* As 2082; *mm.* 13, 13/- | 350 | 1000 |
| 2086 | *York.* Є on breast; *mm.* lis | 750 | 2500 |
| 2087 | **Penny,** *London.* Usual type; *mm.* 6, 13, 12 | 325 | 1100 |
| 2087A | *Bristol.* Similar; *mm.* 12 | 525 | 1650 |
| 2088 | *York.* G and key by neck; *mm.* lis | 250 | 850 |
| 2089 | **Halfpenny,** *London; mm.* 12, 13, | 175 | 575 |
| 2090 | *Bristol.* Similar; *mm.* cross | 350 | 1100 |

The Angel and its half were the only gold denominations issued during this reign. The main types and weight standards remained the same as those of the light coinage of Edward's first reign. The use of the 'initial mark' as a mintmark to denote the date of issue was now firmly established.

### Mintmarks

| 33 | 105 | 12 | 55 | 44 | 55 | 28 | 56 | 17 |
|----|-----|----|----|----|----|----|----|----|

| 30 | 37 | 6 | 18 | 19 | 20 | 31 | 11 | 38 |
|----|----|---|----|----|----|----|----|----|

| | | |
|---|---|---|
| 1471-83 | Rose (33, *York & Durham*) | |
| | Lis (105, *York*) | |
| 1471 | Short cross fitchee (12) | |
| 1471-2 | Annulet (large, 55) | |
| | Trefoil (44) | |
| | Rose (33, *Bristol*) | |
| 1471-3 | Pansy (30, *Durham*) | |
| 1472-3 | Annulet (small, 55) | |
| | Sun (28, *Bristol*) | |
| 1473-7 | Pellet in annulet (56) | |
| | Cross and four pellets (17) | |
| | Cross in circle (37) | |

| | |
|---|---|
| 1473-7 | Cross pattée (6) |
| | Pierced cross 1 (18) |
| 1477-80 | Pierced cross and pellet (19) |
| | Pierced cross 2 (18) |
| | Pierced cross, central pellet (20) |
| | Rose (33, *Canterbury*) |
| 1480-3 | Heraldic cinquefoil (31) |
| | Long cross fitchee (11, *Canterbury*) |
| 1483 | Halved sun and rose (38) |
| | (Listed under Ed. IV/V.) |

## GOLD

2091

2093

| | | F | VF |
|---|---|---|---|
| | | £ | £ |
| 2091 | **Angel.** *London.* Type as illus.; *mm.* 12, 55, 56, 17, 18, 19, 31 .............. | 900 | 3000 |
| 2092 | *Bristol.* B in waves; *mm.* small annulet ................................. | 3500 | 12500 |
| 2093 | **Half-angel.** As illus.; *mm.* 55, cross in circle, 19, 20/19, 31 ............. | 800 | 2500 |
| 2094 | King's name and title on rev.; *mm.* 12/- ................................. | 850 | 2750 |
| 2095 | King's name and the title both sides; *mm.* 55/- ......................... | 900 | 3000 |

## SILVER

2097

|  | | F £ | VF £ |
|---|---|---|---|
| 2096 | **Groat,** *London.* Trefoils on cusps, no marks by bust; *mm.* 12-37 ........... | 65 | 225 |
| 2097 | — — roses by bust; *mm.* pellet in annulet ............................................. | 150 | 575 |
| 2098 | — Fleurs on cusps; no marks by bust; *mm.* 18-20 .................................. | 65 | 240 |
| 2099 | — — pellets by bust; *mm.* pierced cross ................................................. | 85 | 300 |
| 2100 | — — rose on breast; *mm.* 31 ................................................................. | 75 | 275 |

2101                                        2107

| 2101 | *Bristol.* B on breast no marks by bust; *mm.* 33, 33/55, 28/55, 55, 55/-, 28 | 175 | 650 |
|---|---|---|---|
| 2102 | *York.* Є on breast no marks by bust; *mm.* lis ............................................ | 225 | 725 |
| 2103 | **Halfgroat,** *London.* As 2096; *mm.* 12-31 ................................................. | 65 | 250 |
| 2104 | *Bristol.* B on breast; *mm.* 33/12 .................................................................. | 375 | 1200 |
| 2105 | *Canterbury.* Archb. Bourchier. As 2103; *mm.* 33, 11, 11/31, 31 ............. | 50 | 175 |
| 2106 | — C on breast; *mm.* rose ............................................................................... | 45 | 160 |
| 2107 | — — R. C in centre; *mm.* rose ...................................................................... | 45 | 160 |
| 2108 | — — R. Rose in centre; *mm.* rose ................................................................ | 45 | 160 |
| 2109 | *York.* No. Є on breast; *mm.* lis .................................................................... | 275 | 950 |
| 2110 | **Penny,** *London.* No marks by bust; *mm.* 12-31 ...................................... | 75 | 275 |
| 2111 | *Bristol.* Similar; *mm.* rose ........................................................................... | 300 | 1000 |
| 2112 | *Canterbury.* Archb. Bourchier. Similar; *mm.* 33, 11 .................................. | 75 | 275 |
| 2113 | — C on breast; *mm.* rose ............................................................................... | 85 | 325 |
| 2114 | *Durham,* Bp. Booth (1471-6). No marks by neck; *mm.* 12, 44 ................. | 35 | 120 |

2115                                        2116

| 2115 | — — D in centre of *rev.;* B and trefoil by neck; *mm.* 44, 33, 56 ............. | 35 | 120 |
|---|---|---|---|
| 2116 | — — — two lis at neck; *mm.* rose ............................................................... | 35 | 130 |
| 2117 | — — — crosses over crown, and on breast; *mm.* rose ............................... | 35 | 130 |
| 2118 | — — — crosses over crown, V under CIVI; *mm.* rose, pansy ................. | 40 | 130 |
| 2119 | — — — B to l. of crown, V on breast and under CIVI ............................ | 35 | 120 |

|      |                                                              | F | VF |
|------|--------------------------------------------------------------|---|----|
|      |                                                              | £ | £  |
| 2120 | — — — As last but crosses at shoulders                       | 35 | 120 |
| 2121 | — — R̞. D in centre; *mm.* rose                               | 35 | 130 |
| 2122 | — Bp. Dudley (1476-83). V to r. of neck; as last             | 40 | 130 |

2123                     2125                              2131

|        |                                                                        | F | VF |
|--------|------------------------------------------------------------------------|---|----|
| 2123   | — — D and V by neck; as last, but *mm.* 31                              | 35 | 120 |

*Nos. 2117-2123 are from locally-made dies.*

| 2124   | *York,* Archb. Neville (1471-2). Quatrefoils by neck. R̞. Quatrefoil; *mm.* 12 (over lis) | 45 | 175 |
| 2125   | — — Similar, but G and key by neck; *mm.* 12 (over lis)                 | 35 | 120 |
| 2126   | — Neville suspended (1472-5). As last, but no quatrefoil in centre of *rev.* | 40 | 150 |
| 2126A  | — — no marks by bust, similar; *mm.* annulet                           | 45 | 165 |
| 2127   | — — No marks by neck, quatrefoil on *rev.; mm.* 55, cross in circle, 33.. | 35 | 120 |
| 2128   | — — Similar but Є and rose by neck; *mm.* rose                         | 30 | 110 |
| 2129   | — Archb. Neville restored (1475-6). As last, but G and rose            | 35 | 120 |
| 2130   | — — Similar, but G and key by bust                                     | 30 | 110 |
| 2131   | — Sede Vacante (1476). As 2127, but rose on breast; *mm.* rose         | 45 | 165 |
| 2132   | — Archb. Lawrence Booth (1476-80). B and key by bust, quatrefoil on *rev.; mm.* 33, 31 | 30 | 110 |
| 2133   | — Sede Vacante (1480). Similar, but no quatrefoil on rev.; *mm.* rose   | 40 | 150 |

2134                              2140

|        |                                                                        | F | VF |
|--------|------------------------------------------------------------------------|---|----|
| 2134   | — Archb. Rotherham (1480-3). T and slanting key by neck, quatrefoil on *rev.; mm.* 33 | 35 | 120 |
| 2135   | — — — Similar, but star on breast                                      | 45 | 165 |
| 2136   | — — — Star on breast and to r. of crown                               | 50 | 175 |
| 2137   | **Halfpenny,** *London.* No marks by neck; *mm.* 12-31                 | 25 | 90 |
| 2138   | — Pellets at neck; *mm.* pierced cross                                 | 30 | 110 |
| 2139   | *Canterbury* (Archbishop Bourchier). C on breast and in centre of *rev.; mm.* rose | 85 | 300 |
| 2140   | — C on breast only; *mm.* rose                                        | 75 | 225 |
| 2141   | — Without C either side; *mm.* 11                                     | 80 | 250 |
| 2142   | *Durham,* Bp. Booth. No marks by neck. R̞. DЄRA̅ M, D in centre; *mm.* rose | 200 | 750 |
| 2142A  | — — Lis either side of neck. R̞. with or without D in centre          | 225 | 850 |
| 2142B  | — — B to l. of crown, crosses at shoulders. R̞. with or without D. in centre; *mm.* rose | 225 | 850 |
| 2143   | — — — Bp. Dudley V to l. of neck; as last                             | 200 | 800 |

*Full flan coins are very difficult to find in the small denominations.*

On 12th February 1483, the prolific cinquefoil coinage of Edward IV came to an end and an indenture between the king and the new master of the mint, Bartholomew Reed, saw the introduction of the sun and rose mintmark.

Edward IV died on 9th April 1483, but the sun and rose coinage continued, essentially unaltered, through the short reign of Edward V and into the reign of Richard III, ending with the indenture of 20th July 1483, with Robert Brackenbury, who had been Richard's ducal treasurer, and the introduction of the boar's head mintmark.

New dies prepared after the accession of Richard III on 26th June 1483, bear his name but coins of the sun and rose coinage struck under Edward IV and Edward V can only be distinguished by arranging the dies in sequence. This is possible for the angels (Schneider Sylloge, SCBI 47, p.41) but has not yet been achieved for the silver coinage.

*Mintmark:* Halved sun and rose.

## GOLD

2144A

|  | | F<br>£ | VF<br>£ |
|---|---|---|---|
| 2144 | **Angel.** Type As 2091, reading EDWARD DEI GRA (Edward IV).......... | 5250 | 15000 |
| 2144A | — Similar but reading EDWARD DI GRA (Edward V)......................... | 13500 | 40000 |
| 2145 | **Half-angel.** As 2093 (probably Edward IV)............................................ | 5750 | 17500 |

## SILVER

2146

| 2146 | **Groat.** *London,* pellet below bust, reading EDWARD or EDVARD ....... | 1100 | 4000 |
|---|---|---|---|
| 2146A | — — No pellet below, reading EDWARD or EDWRD ........................... | 1000 | 3750 |
| 2147 | **Penny.** *London* As 2110 ........................................................................ | 1350 | 5750 |
| 2148 | **Halfpenny.** *London* As 2137 ................................................................ | 300 | 950 |

Richard's coinage follows the pattern of previous reigns. The portrait on the silver denominations remains stylised, though increasingly distinctive. It can be divided into three types according to mintmark. Type 1, the first sun and rose coinage, lasted 24 days to 20th July 1483. Type 2, the boar's head coinage, was issued until about June 1484. Type 3, the second sun and rose coinage, was struck until the end of the reign (Schneider Sylloge, SCBI 47, pp. 41-2).

It is evident that coin dies were stored in a 'loose-box' system which led to extensive muling between types. As an interim measure, after the indenture of 20th July 1483, at least eleven existing sun and rose obverse dies, both gold and silver, were overpunched with the boar's head mark. The seven overpunched groat dies included four Edward IV/V dies, then still in use, and three dies of Richard III type 1.

*Mintmarks*

| SR1 | BH1 | BH2 | SR2 | SR3 | 105 | 33 |

Halved sun and rose, 1, 2 and 3.
Boar's head, 1 (62) 2 (63).
Lis (105, *Durham*)
Rose only (33).

## GOLD

2150                          2152

|  |  | F | VF |
|---|---|---|---|
|  |  | £ | £ |
| 2149 | **Angel.** 1. Reading RICARD. R. R and rose by mast; *mm.* sun and rose 1 | 6000 | 22500 |
| 2150 | — 2a. Reading EDWARD. R. E and rose or R and rose by mast; *mm.* boar's head 1 over sun and rose 1/sun and rose 1 | 7500 | 27500 |
| 2151 | — 2b. Reading RICARD. R. R and rose by mast; mm. boar's head 1 over sun and rose 1/sun and rose 1, boar's head 1, boar's head 2 (often muled) | 5500 | 20000 |
| 2152 | — 3. Reading RICARD or RICAD; *mm.* sun and rose 2 | 5250 | 18000 |

2153

| 2153 | **Half-angel.** 2b. R. R and rose by mast; *mm.* boar's head 1 | 9500 | 32500 |

## SILVER

2154

2155

|  | | F £ | VF £ |
|---|---|---|---|
| 2154 | **Groat.** 1. *London.* Reading RICARD; *mm.* sun and rose 1 ...................... | 750 | 2400 |
| 2155 | — 2a. Reading EDWARD; *mm.* boar's head 1 over sun and rose 1/sun and rose 1 | 1350 | 4250 |

2156 - BH2

2158 - SR3

| 2156 | — 2b. Reading RICARD; *mm.* boar's head 1 over sun and rose 1/sun and rose 1, boar's head 1, boar's head 2 (often muled) ......................... | 850 | 2750 |
|---|---|---|---|
| 2157 | — 3. *mm.* sun and rose 2, sun and rose 3 ................................................ | 700 | 2000 |
| 2158 | — — Pellet below bust, *mm.* sun and rose 2, sun and rose 3 .................. | 750 | 2250 |
| 2159 | *York.* 3. *mm.* sun and rose 2/- ....................................................................... | 2000 | 6500 |

2161

2164

2166

| 2160 | **Halfgroat.** *London.* 2a. Reading EDWARD; *mm.* boar's head 1 over sun and rose 1/- (the *mm.* is indistinct) ............................................................... | 2000 | 6500 |
|---|---|---|---|
| 2161 | — 2b. Reading RICARD; *mm.* boar's head 2/- ...................................... | 1500 | 5500 |
| 2162 | — 3. *mm.* sun and rose 2, sun and rose 2/- ........................................... | 1350 | 5000 |
| 2163 | — — Pellet below bust; *mm.* sun and rose 2 ......................................... | 1500 | 5500 |
| 2164 | **Penny.** *London.* 2a. Reading EDWARD; *mm.* boar's head 1 over sun and rose 1/- .......................................................................................................... | 2000 | 6500 |
| 2165 | — 2b. Reading RICARD; *mm.* boar's head 1/- ....................................... | 1750 | 5750 |
| 2166 | *York.* Archb. Rotherham. T and upright key at neck. R. Quatrefoil in centre; *mm.* boar's head 1/- ................................................................................... | 400 | 1250 |
| 2167 | — — *mm.* rose/- ..................................................................................... | 350 | 1100 |
| 2168 | — No marks at neck; *mm.* sun and rose 2/- ............................................ | 475 | 1500 |

2169

2171

| 2169 | *Durham.* Bp. Sherwood. S on breast. R. D in centre; *mm.* lis/-............... | 275 | 950 |
|---|---|---|---|
| 2170 | **Halfpenny.** *London.* 2b. No marks by neck; *mm.* boar's head 1/- .......... | 325 | 1000 |
| 2171 | — 3. *mm.* sun and rose 2/- ........................................................................ | 275 | 900 |
| 2171A | **Farthing.** *London.* 3. *mm.* sun and rose 2/-............................................. | 1750 | 4500 |

## HENRY VII, 1485-1509

For the first four years of his reign Henry's coins differ only in name and mintmark from those of his predecessors, but from 1489 radical changes were made in the coinage. On the Groat and subsequently on the lesser denominations the traditional open crown was replaced with an arched imperial crown. Though the pound sterling had been a denomination of account for centuries, a pound coin had never been minted. Now a magnificent gold pound was issued, and, from the design of the king enthroned in majesty, was called a 'Sovereign'. A small simplified version of the Sovereign portrait was at the same time introduced on the silver pence. The reverse of the gold 'Sovereign' had the royal arms set in the centre of a Tudor rose. A few years later the angel was restyled and St. Michael, who is depicted about to thrust Satan into the Pit with a cross-topped lance, is no longer a feathered figure but is clad in armour of Renaissance style. A gold ryal of ten shillings was also minted again for a brief period.

The other major innovation was the introduction of the shilling (testoon) in the opening years of the 16th century. It is remarkable for the very fine profile portrait of the king which replaces the representational image of a monarch that had served on the coinage for the past couple of centuries. This new portrait was also used on groats and halfgroats but not on the smaller denominations.

*Mintmarks*

| 39 | 41 | 40 | 42 | 33 | 11 | 7a | 123 |

| 105 | 76b | 31 | 78 | 30 | 91 | 43 | 57 |

| 85 | 94 | 118 | 21 | 33 | 53 |

| 1485-7 | Halved sun and rose (39) | 1495-8 | Pansy (30) |
|---|---|---|---|
| | Lis upon sun and rose (41) | | Tun (123, *Canterbury*) |
| | Lis upon half rose (40) | | Lis (105, York) |
| | Lis-rose dimidiated (42) | 1498-9 | Crowned leopard's head (91) |
| | Rose (33, *York*) | | Lis issuant from rose (43) |
| 1487 | Lis (105) | | Tun (123, *Canterbury*) |
| | Cross fitchée (11) | 1499-1502 | Anchor (57) |
| 1487-8 | Rose (33) | 1502-4 | Greyhound's head (85) |
| | Plain cross (7a, *Durham*) | | Lis (105, profile issue only) |
| 1488-9 | No marks | | Martlet (94, *York*) |
| 1489-93 | Cinquefoil (31) | 1504-5 | Cross-crosslet (21) |
| | Crozier (76b, *Durham*) | 1504-9 | Martlet (94, (York, Canterbury) |
| 1492 | Cross fitchée (11, gold only) | | Rose (33, *York* and |
| 1493-5 | Escallop (78) | | *Canterbury*) |
| | Dragon (118, gold only) | 1505-9 | Pheon (53) |
| | Lis (105, *Canterbury and York* | | |
| | Tun (123, *Canterbury*) | | |

# GOLD

|                                                                                                                                                         | F £      | VF £     |
|---------------------------------------------------------------------------------------------------------------------------------------------------------|----------|----------|
| 2172 **Sovereign** (20s; wt. 240 grs., 15.55g). Group I. Large figure of king sitting on backless throne. R. Large shield crowned on large Tudor rose. *mm.* 31 .. | 125000   | 525000   |
| 2173 — Group II. Somewhat similar but throne has narrow back, lis in background. R. Large Tudor rose bearing small shield. *mm.* -/11 ............       | 90000    | 375000   |

2174

| 2174 — III. King on high-backed very ornamental throne, with greyhound and dragon on side pillars. R. Shield on Tudor rose; *mm.* dragon ............ | 37500 | 150000 |
| 2175 — IV. Similar but throne with high canopy breaking legend and broad seat, *mm.* 105/118, (also with no *obv.* i.c. *mm.* 105/118, very rare) .................. | 35000 | 135000 |
| 2176 — Narrow throne with a portcullis below the king's feet (like Henry VIII); *mm.* 105/21, 105/53 .................................................................. | 20000 | 85000 |
| 2177 **Double-sovereign** and **Treble-sovereign** from same dies as 2176. These piedforts were probably intended as presentation pieces *mm.* 105/21, 105/53 | 95000 | 425000 |

2178

| 2178 **Ryal** (10s.). As illustration: *mm.* -/11 ....................................................... | 27500 | 135000 |
| 2179 **Angel** (6s. 8d). I. Angel of old type with one foot on dragon. R. PER CRVCEM. etc., *mm.* 39, 40, (also muled both ways)............................... | 1350 | 5500 |
| 2179A — With Irish title, and legend over angel head. mm. 33/-........................ | 1500 | 6000 |
| 2180 — — Name altered from RICARD? and h on *rev.* from R. mm. 41/39, 41/40, 41/-, 39/?.................................................................................. | 1750 | 6500 |

2181            2183

2187

|  |  | *F*<br>£ | *VF*<br>£ |
|---|---|---|---|
| 2181 | II. As 2179, but *mm.* none. 31/-. ............................................................ | 1200 | 4500 |
| 2181A | II/III mule. *mm.* 31/78, R̴. PER CRUC or AVTƐM TRAⱧS .................... | 1250 | 4750 |
| 2182 | As 2181. R̴. IhC AVTƐM TRAⱧSIƐⱧS etc.; *mm.* none, 31/- .................. | 1350 | 5000 |
| 2183 | III. New dies, angel with both feet on dragons; (large straight lettering)<br>*mm.* 78-85 except 91 (many mules exist) ................................................ | 900 | 2750 |
| 2183A | — Angel with very small wings. *mm.* escallop ......................................... | 1000 | 3250 |
| 2184 | — — R̴. IhC AVTƐM TRAⱧSIƐⱧS, etc.; *mm.* escallop ......................... | 1200 | 4250 |
| 2185 | IV. Small square lettering; *mm.* 85 (also muled with 2183) ..................... | 900 | 2750 |
| 2186 | — Tall thin lettering; *mm.* 21 (also muled with 2185 obv.) ..................... | 900 | 2750 |
| 2187 | V. Large crook-shaped abbreviation after hƐⱧRIC; *mm.* 21 and 53<br>(combinations and mules exist) ................................................................ | 850 | 2500 |
| 2188 | **Half-angel or angelet.** I. *Mm.* 39, 41, (old dies RIII altered) .................. | 1350 | 5000 |
| 2189 | III. Angel with both feet on dragon: *mm.* 30, 57/30, 30/85 ..................... | 750 | 2500 |
| 2190 | IV. Small square lettering; *mm.* rose *mm.* -/85 ......................................... | 725 | 2400 |
| 2191 | — *Obv.* as last. R̴. Tall thin lettering; *mm.* 33/21 ................................. | 725 | 2400 |
| 2192 | V. As angel; *mm.* pheon, cross-crosslet .................................................... | 700 | 2250 |

## SILVER

**Facing bust issues.** Including 'Sovereign' type pennies.

| 2193 | **Groat.** I. Open crown; *mm.* 40 (rose on bust), 39-42 and none (combinations) | 110 | 425 |
|---|---|---|---|

2194                  2195

| 2194 | — — crosses or saltires by neck, 41, 40, 105-33 and none (combinations) | 110 | 425 |
|---|---|---|---|
| 2195 | IIa. Large bust with out-turned hair, crown with two plain arches; *mm.*<br>none, 31, 31/-, 31/78 ................................................................................ | 85 | 300 |

2198A                      2199                      2201

|      |                                                                                                                                    |   F   |   VF   |
|------|------------------------------------------------------------------------------------------------------------------------------------|-------|--------|
|      |                                                                                                                                    |   £   |   £    |
| 2196 | — — similar but crosses by neck; *mm.* none, -/105 ............................... | 100 | 350 |
| 2197 | — — R. Portcullis over long cross; *mm.* -/lis ......................................... | 3500 | 10000 |
| 2198 | IIIa. Bust as IIa. Crown with two jewelled arches, *mm.* 31 ..................... | 300 | 900 |
| 2198A | IIIb. Similar, but new bust with realistic hair *mm.* 78, 30 ...................... | 80 | 275 |
| 2199 | IIIc. Bust as IIIb, but crown with one plain and one jewelled arch, *mm.* 30-21 and none ................ | 70 | 250 |
| 2199A | IIId. As last, but plainer letters. mm 57, 85, 33 and none ........................ | 80 | 275 |
| 2200 | IVa. Wide single arch crown; arch is single or double bar with 4 crockets; *mm.* 85, 85/33, 21 ................ | 90 | 325 |
| 2201 | IVb. — Similar, but arch is double bar with 6 uprights or crockets as jewels; *mm.* 85, 21/85, 21 ................ | 100 | 375 |
| 2202 | **Halfgroat,** *London.* I. Open crown, tressure unbroken; *mm.* 40/-, 40/39 (R. III mule) ................ | 325 | 1350 |
| 2203 | — IIIa. Double arched crown, rosettes on tressure; mm. escallop ........... | 150 | 575 |
| 2204 | — IIIb. Similar, nothing on tressure. R. Lozenge panel in centre; *mm.* lis | 40 | 160 |
| 2205 | — — Similar, but also with lis on breast; mm. lis ................................... | 45 | 175 |
| 2206 | — IIIc. Unarched crown with tressure broken. R. Lozenge panel in centre; *mm.* lis ................ | 35 | 150 |
| 2206A | — — — Similar but smaller dies and much smaller lettering ................ | 50 | 175 |

2208                           2211

|      |                                                                                                                                    |   |   |
|------|------------------------------------------------------------------------------------------------------------------------------------|-----|-----|
| 2207 | *Canterbury,* Archb. Morton. I. Open crown, crosses by neck. R. M in centre; *mm.* tun/- ................ | 60 | 185 |
| 2208 | — — II. Similar, but double-arched crown; no *mm.* ............................... | 60 | 185 |
| 2209 | III King and Archb. jointly. As last but without M; (a) early lettering, trefoil stops; *mm.* lis, tun and lis/lis ................ | 50 | 175 |
| 2210 | — — (b) ornate lettering, rosette stops; *mm.* tun, lis in combinations ..... | 40 | 145 |
| 2211 | — — (c) — saltire or no stops; *mm.* 123, 123 & 30/123 ........................ | 40 | 145 |
| 2212 | *York,* Royal mint. (a) Double-arched crown, lis on breast (rarely omitted). R. Lozenge panel in centre; *mm.* lis ................ | 65 | 225 |
| 2213 | — — (b) Similar, but unarched crown, tressure broken, *mm.* lis. ........... | 50 | 175 |

|       |                                                                                                      | *F* £ | *VF* £ |
|-------|------------------------------------------------------------------------------------------------------|-------|--------|
| 2214  | — Archb. Savage. (a) Double-arched crown, keys at neck, no tressure; ornate lettering; *mm.* martlet | 45    | 160    |
| 2215  | — — (b) Similar, but fleured tressure, small square lettering; *mm.* martlet                          | 50    | 175    |
| 2216  | — — (c) As last, but tall thin lettering; *mm.* martlet                                               | 50    | 175    |
| 2217  | — As last but no keys; *mm.* martlet                                                                  | 60    | 185    |

2221                                        2226

|       |                                                                                                                                          | *F* | *VF* |
|-------|------------------------------------------------------------------------------------------------------------------------------------------|-----|------|
| 2218  | **Penny.** Old type. London; *mm.* 40/-                                                                                                   | 200 | 750  |
| 2219  | — — — crosses by bust, mm. small cross (obv.)                                                                                             | 250 | 900  |
| 2220  | — *Canterbury*, Archb. Morton. Open crown, *mm.* tun/- R. M in centre .                                                                   | 200 | 850  |
| 2221  | — — King and Archb. jointly, arched crown; *mm.* tun, tun/-                                                                               | 110 | 425  |
| 2222  | — *Durham*, Bp. Sherwood. S on breast. R. D in centre; *mm.* 7a/-                                                                         | 110 | 425  |
| 2223  | — *York*, Archb. Rotherham. With or without cross on breast, *mm.* 33/-, T and cross or key at neck. R. h in centre                      | 55  | 200  |
| 2224  | — — — T and trefoil at neck. R. Quatrefoil in centre and two extra pellets; *mm.* 39/-                                                    | 50  | 185  |
| 2225  | 'Sovereign' type. *London*. Early lettering, no stops, no pillars to throne; no *mm.*                                                     | 135 | 475  |
| 2226  | — — — single pillar on king's right side, trefoil stops; no *mm.* or 31/-..                                                              | 50  | 200  |
| 2227  | — — Ornate letters, rosette stops, single pillar; *mm.* lis (can be muled with above)                                                    | 75  | 275  |
| 2228  | — — saltire stops or none, two pillars; *mm.* none, -/30                                                                                  | 50  | 200  |
| 2229  | — — Similar, but small square lettering; no *mm.*                                                                                         | 55  | 225  |
| 2230  | — — Similar, but lettering as profile groats two double pillars; *mm.* 21, 53, none (sometimes on one side only)                         | 50  | 200  |

2231                          2233                          2235

|       |                                                                                                                                | *F* | *VF* |
|-------|--------------------------------------------------------------------------------------------------------------------------------|-----|------|
| 2231  | — *Durham*, Bp. Sherwood. Crozier to r. of king, throne with one pillar. R. D and S beside shield                             | 45  | 185  |
| 2232  | — — Throne with two pillars, no crozier. R. As last                                                                           | 50  | 200  |
| 2233  | — — Bp. Fox. Throne with one pillar. R. Mitre above shield, RD or DR at sides, no *mm.*                                        | 40  | 145  |
| 2234  | — — Similar, but two pillars                                                                                                  | 45  | 160  |
| 2235  | *York*, Archb. Rotherham. Keys below shield; early lettering, trefoil stops, no pillars to throne, no *mm.*                   | 40  | 150  |
| 2236  | — — — single pillar                                                                                                           | 35  | 140  |
| 2237  | — — — — ornate lettering, rosette or no stops,                                                                                | 35  | 140  |
| 2238  | — — — two pillars sometimes with crosses between legs of throne                                                               | 35  | 140  |

2239                    2244A                    2245

2249                          2250

|      |                                                                                      | F | VF |
|------|--------------------------------------------------------------------------------------|-----|-----|
|      |                                                                                      | £ | £ |
| 2239 | **Halfpenny,** *London*. I. Open crown; *mm.* 40, 42 .................................. | 45 | 175 |
| 2240 | — — — trefoils at neck; no *mm.*, rose ...................................... | 50 | 185 |
| 2241 | — — — crosses at neck; *mm.* rose, cross fitchée.......................... | 40 | 145 |
| 2242 | — II. Double arched crown; *mm.* cinquefoil, none ............................... | 30 | 100 |
| 2243 | — — — saltires at neck; no *mm.* ........................................... | 30 | 100 |
| 2244 | — IIIa. Crown with single arch, ornate lettering; no *mm.*, pansy............ | 25 | 90 |
| 2244A| — IIIb. Similar but with rosette stops; *mm.* none, rose, lis ..................... | 35 | 110 |
| 2245 | — IIIc. Much smaller portrait; *mm.* pheon, lis, none ............................. | 25 | 90 |
| 2246 | *Canterbury,* Archb. Morton. I. Open crown, crosses by neck; ℞. M in centre | 95 | 350 |
| 2247 | — — II. Similar, but arched crown, saltires by bust; *mm.* profile eye (82) | 90 | 325 |
| 2247A| — — — no marks at neck ........................................................ | 85 | 300 |
| 2248 | — III. King and Archb. Arched crown; *mm.* lis, none............................ | 40 | 150 |
| 2249 | *York,* Archb. Savage. Arched crown, key below bust to l or r. *mm.* | | |
|      | martlet ........................................................................................... | 110 | 375 |
| 2250 | **Farthing,** *London*. hᴇɴRIC DI GRA Rᴇx (A), arched crown ............. | 525 | 1500 |

*No.s 2239-49 have *mm.* on *obv.* only.

**Profile issue**

| 2251 | **Testoon** (ls.). Type as groat. hᴇɴRIC (VS); *mm.* lis ............... | 15000 | 40000 |
|------|------------------------------------------------------------------------|-------|-------|
| 2252 | — hᴇɴRIC VII; *mm.* lis ........................................................... | 16000 | 45000 |

2253                                    2254

| 2253 | — hᴇɴRIC SᴇᴘTIM; *mm.* lis ................................................ | 17500 | 52500 |
|------|------------------------------------------------------------------------|-------|-------|
| 2254 | **Groat,** *Tentative issue* (contemporary with full-face groats). Double band | | |
|      | to crown, hᴇɴRIC VII; *mm.* none, 105/-, -/105: 105/85, 105, 85, 21 ..... | 275 | 1000 |
| 2255 | — — — tressure on *obv.;* *mm.* cross-crosslet.......................... | 2250 | 8500 |
| 2256 | — — hᴇɴRIC (VS); *mm.* 105, -/105, 105/ 85, none ............................. | 475 | 1500 |
| 2257 | — — hᴇɴRIC SᴇᴘTIM; *mm.* -/105.............................................. | 2000 | 7500 |

2258

|      |                                                                                     | F<br>£ | VF<br>£ |
|------|-------------------------------------------------------------------------------------|--------|---------|
| 2258 | *Regular issue.* Triple band to crown; *mm.* 21, 53 (both *mm.*s may occur on *obv.* or *rev.* or both) | 135 | 425 |
| 2259 | **Halfgroat,** *London.* As last; *mm.* 105, 53/105, 105/53, 53 | 90 | 325 |
| 2260 | — — no numeral after King's name, no *mm.,* -/lis | 375 | 1250 |
| 2261 | *Canterbury,* King and Archb. As London, but *mm.* 94, 33, 94/33 | 80 | 275 |

2262                              rev. enlarged

| 2262 | *York,* Archb. Bainbridge. As London, but two keys below shield; *mm.* 94, 33, 33/94 | 65 | 250 |

2263

| 2263 | — — XB beside shield; *mm.* rose/martlet | 185 | 650 |
| 2263A | — — Similar but two keys below shield *mm.* rose(?)/martlet | 225 | 800 |

Henry VIII is held in ill-regard by numismatists as being the author of the debasement of England's gold and silver coinage; but there were also other important numismatic innovations during his reign. For the first sixteen years the coinage closely followed the pattern of the previous issues, even to the extent of retaining the portrait of Henry VII on the larger silver coins.

In 1526, in an effort to prevent the drain of gold to continental Europe, the value of English gold was increased by 10%, the sovereign to 22s. 0d. and the angel to 7s. 4d., and a new coin valued at 4s. 6d.—the Crown of the Rose—was introduced as a competitor to the French *écu au soleil*. The new crown was not a success and within a few months it was replaced by the Crown of the Double Rose valued at 5s but made of gold of only 22 carat fineness, the first time gold had been minted below the standard 23c. At the same time the sovereign was again revalued to 22s. 6d. and the angel to 7s. 6d., with a new coin, the George Noble, valued at 6s. 8d. (one-third pound).

The royal cyphers on some of the gold crowns and half-crowns combine the initial of Henry with those of his queens: Katherine of Aragon, Anne Boleyn and Jane Seymour. The architect of this coinage reform was the chancellor, Cardinal Thomas Wolsey, who besides his other changes had minted at York a groat bearing his initials and cardinal's hat in addition to the other denominations normally authorised for the ecclesiastical mints.

When open debasement of the coinage began in 1544 to help finance Henry's wars, the right to coin of the archbishops of Canterbury and York and of the bishop of Durham was not confirmed. Instead, a second royal mint was opened in the Tower as in subsequent years were six others, at Southwark, York, Canterbury, Bristol, Dublin and Durham House in the Strand. Gold, which fell to 23c. in 1544, 22c. in 1545, and 20c. in 1546 was much less debased than silver which declined to 9oz 2dwt. in 1544, 6oz 2dwt. in 1545 and 4oz 2dwt. in 1546. At this last standard the blanched silver surface of the coins soon wore away to reveal the copper alloy beneath which earned for Henry the nickname 'Old Coppernose'.

*Mintmarks*

| | | | | | | | |
|---|---|---|---|---|---|---|---|
| 53 | 69 | 70 | 108 | 33 | 94 | 73 | 11 |
| 105 | 22 | 23 | 30 | 78 | 15 | 24 | 110 |
| 52 | 72a | 44 | 8 | 65a | 114 | 121 | 90 |
| 36 | 106 | 56 | S | E | 116 | 135 | |

1509-26

Pheon (53)
Castle (69)
Castle with H (70, gold)
Portcullis crowned (108)
Rose (33, *Canterbury*)
Martlet (94, *Canterbury*)
Pomegranate (73, but broader, *Cant.*)
Cross fitchée (11, *Cant.*)
Lis (105, *Canterbury, Durham*)

1509-14    Martlet (94, *York*)
1509-23    Radiant star (22, *Durham & York*)
1513-18    Crowned T (135, *Tournai*)
1514-26    Star (23, *York & Durham*)
              Pansy (30, *York*)
              Escallop (78, *York*)
              Voided cross (15, *York*)
1523-26    Spur rowel (24, *Durham*)

| 1526-44 | Rose (33) |
| | Lis (105) |
| | Sunburst 110) |
| | Arrow (52) |
| | Pheon (53) |
| | Lis (106) |
| | Star (23, *Durham*) |
| 1526-9 | Crescent (72a, *Durham*) |
| | Trefoil (44 variety, *Durham*) |
| | Flower of eight petals and circle centre (*Durham*) |
| 1526-30 | Cross (7a, sometimes slightly voided, *York*) |
| | Acorn (65a, *York*) |

| 1526-32 | Cross patonce (8, *Cant.*) |
| | T (114, *Canterbury*) |
| | Uncertain mark (121, *Canterbury*) |
| 1529-44 | Radiant star (22, *Durham*) |
| 1530-44 | Key (90, *York*) |
| 1533-44 | Catherine wheel (36, *Canterbury*) |
| 1544-7 | Lis (105 and 106) |
| | Pellet in annulet (56) |
| | S (Southwark) |
| | Є or E (Southwark) |
| 1546-7 | WS monogram (116, *Bristol*) |

# GOLD

**FIRST COINAGE, 1509-26**

2265

| | | F £ | VF £ |
|---|---|---|---|
| 2264 | **Sovereign** (20s; wt. 240grs., 15.55g.). Similar to last sov. of Hen. VII; *mm.* 108 | 10000 | 40000 |
| 2264A | **Ryal** (10s.) King in ship holding sword and shield. ℞. Similar to 1950, *mm.*-/108 .................................. | *Extremely rare* | |
| 2265 | **Angel** (6s. 8d.). As Hen. VII, but hℇnRIC? VIII DI GRA RℇX, etc.; *mm.* 53, 69, 70, 70/69, 108, ℞. May omit h and rose, or rose only; *mm.* 69, 108 | 900 | 2750 |
| 2266 | **Half-angel.** Similar (sometimes without VIII), *mm.* 69, 70, 108/33, 108 | 750 | 2250 |

**SECOND COINAGE, 1526-44**

2267

| | | | |
|---|---|---|---|
| 2267 | **Sovereign** (22s. 6d; wt. 240grs., 15.55g.). As 2264, ℞. single or double tressure *mm.* 110, 105, 105/52 .................................. | 9000 | 37500 |
| 2268 | **Angel** (7s. 6d.). As 2265, hℇnRIC VIII D(I) G(RA) R(ℇX) etc,; *mm.* 110, 105 .................................. | 1250 | 4500 |

|                                                                                      | F    | VF    |
|                                                                                      | £    | £     |
| 2269 **Half-angel.** Similar; *mm.* lis .................................................................... | 1350 | 4750  |

2270

2272

| 2270 | **George-noble** (6s. 8d.). As illustration; *mm.* rose ............................... | 9000  | 37500 |
| 2270A | — Similar, but more modern ship with three masts, without initials hR. R. | | |
| | St. George brandishing sword behind head.......................................... | 10500 | 45000 |
| 2271 | **Half-George-noble.** Similar to 2270 *mm* rose, lis............................... | 7500  | 35000 |
| 2272 | **Crown of the rose** (4s. 6d., 23 c. 3 $^1/_2$ gr.). As illustration; *mm.* rose, | | |
| | two legend varieties ................................................................. | 6000  | 22500 |
| 2273 | **Crown of the double-rose** (5s., 22 c). Double-rose crowned, hK (Henry and | | |
| | Katherine of Aragon) both crowned in field. R. Shield crowned; *mm.* rose | 800 | 2750 |

2274

2285

| 2274 | — hK both sides; *mm.* rose/lis, lis, arrow ............................................ | 800  | 2750  |
| 2275* | — hK/hA or hA/hK; *mm.* arrow............................................... | 2500 | 9500  |
| 2276* | — hR/hK or hI/hR; *mm.* arrow ............................................... | 1100 | 3500  |
| 2277 | — hA (Anne Boleyn); *mm.* arrow....................................... | 3750 | 13500 |
| 2278 | — hA/hR; *mm.* arrow................................................................. | 2500 | 9500  |
| 2279 | — hI (Jane Seymour); *mm.* arrow ......................................... | 950  | 3250  |
| 2280* | — hK/hI; *mm.* arrow ................................................................. | 1250 | 3750  |
| 2281 | — hR/hI; *mm.* arrow ................................................................. | 1100 | 3500  |
| 2282 | — hR (Rex); *mm.* arrow................................................................. | 900  | 3000  |
| 2283 | — — *mm.* pheon ........................................................................ | 1100 | 3500  |
| 2284 | **Halfcrown.** Similar but king's name henric 8 on *rev.,* no initials; *mm.* rose | 1350 | 5000  |
| 2285 | — hK uncrowned on *obv.; mm.* rose.................................................... | 725  | 2250  |
| 2286 | — hK uncrowned both sides; *mm.* rose/lis, lis, arrow .......................... | 725  | 2250  |
| 2287 | — hI uncrowned both sides; *mm.* arrow ............................................... | 800  | 2500  |
| 2288 | — hR uncrowned both sides; hIB RCX; *mm.* pheon ........................... | 900  | 3000  |

*The hK initials may on later coins refer to Katherine Howard (Henry's fifth wife).

## THIRD COINAGE, 1544-7

2291

| | | F | VF |
|---|---|---|---|
| | | £ | £ |
| 2289 | **Sovereign,** I (20s., Wt. 200 grs., 12.96g., 23 ct.). Large module, similar to 2291 but king with large head; *mm.* lis ............................................ | 32500 | 150000 |
| 2290 | II (20s., wt. 200 or 192 grs., 23, 22 or 20 ct.). *Tower.* As illustration; *mm.* lis, pellet in annulet/lis ............................................................... | 6500 | 25000 |
| 2291 | — *Southwark.* Similar; *mm.* S, Є/S.................................................... | 6250 | 22500 |
| 2292 | — — Similar but Є below shield; *mm.* S/Є........................................ | 7000 | 27500 |
| 2293 | — *Bristol.* As London but *mm.* WS/- .................................................. | 12500 | 45000 |

| | 2294 | | 2303 | |
|---|---|---|---|---|

| | | F | VF |
|---|---|---|---|
| 2294 | **Half-sovereign** (wt. 100 or 96 grs., 6.22g.), *Tower.* As illus.; *mm.* lis, pellet in annulet ........................................................................................... | 900 | 3000 |
| 2295 | — Similar, but with annulet on inner circle (either or both sides)........ | 950 | 3250 |
| 2296 | *Southwark. mm.* S............................................................................... | 950 | 3250 |
| 2297 | — Є below shield; *mm.* S, Є, S/Є, Є/S, (known without sceptre; *mm.* S) ............................................................................................... | 900 | 3000 |
| 2298 | *Bristol.* Lombardic lettering; *mm.* WS, WS/-...................................... | 1750 | 6500 |
| 2299 | **Angel** (8s., 23 c). Annulet by angel's head and on ship, hЄnRIC' 8; *mm.* lis ............................................................................................... | 900 | 2750 |
| 2300 | — Similar, but annulet one side only or none.................................... | 950 | 2850 |
| 2300A | — Similar, but three annulets on ship, *mm.* lis ................................. | 1250 | 4500 |
| 2301 | **Half-angel.** Annulet on ship; *mm.* lis................................................. | 750 | 2250 |
| 2302 | — No annulet on ship; *mm.* lis............................................................. | 800 | 2500 |
| 2303 | — Three annulets on ship; *mm.* lis...................................................... | 900 | 2750 |

2304                                              2309

|       |                                                                                                       | *F*   | *VF*  |
|       |                                                                                                       | £     | £     |
| 2304  | **Quarter-angel** Angel wears armour; *mm.* lis ................................................       | 850   | 2500  |
| 2304A | — Angel wears tunic; *mm.* lis ..............................................................          | 900   | 2750  |
| 2305  | **Crown,** *London.* Similar to 2283, but hЄnRIC' 8 ; Lombardic lettering; *mm.* 56                   | 625   | 2250  |
| 2306  | — without RVTILAnS; *mm.* 56.......................................................                    | 650   | 2400  |
| 2307  | — — — with annulet on inner circle .....................................................              | 650   | 2400  |
| 2307A | — King's name omitted. DEI GRA both sides, *mm.* 56 ........................                          | 750   | 3000  |
| 2308  | — *Southwark.* As 2306; *mm.* S, Є, E/S, Є/-, E/Є ...........................                         | 700   | 2750  |
| 2309  | *Bristol.* hЄnRIC VIII. ROSA etc. ᚱ. D G, etc.; *mm.*-/WS ..................                          | 625   | 2250  |
| 2309A | — — with initials H R transposed on  rev.............................................                 | 700   | 2750  |
| 2310  | — Similar but hЄnRIC(VS) 8 ᚱ. DЄI) G(RA); *mm.* -/WS, WS ...........                                  | 625   | 2250  |
| 2311  | **Halfcrown,** *London.* Similar to 2288; *mm.* 56, 56/-................................              | 475   | 1500  |
| 2312  | — — with annulet on inner circle *mm.* 56..............................................               | 500   | 1600  |
| 2313  | *Southwark.* As 2311; *mm.* S ...................................................................      | 525   | 1750  |
| 2314  | — *O.* hЄnRIC 8 ROSA SINЄ SPIn. ᚱ. DЄI GRA, etc.; *mm.* Є ...........                                | 525   | 1750  |
| 2315  | *Bristol. O.* RVTILAnS, etc. ᚱ. hЄnRIC 8; *mm.* WS/-...........................                       | 675   | 2250  |

*For other gold coins in Henry's name see page 221-2.*

## SILVER

**FIRST COINAGE, 1509-26**

2316                                              2322

|       |                                                                                                       |     |      |
|-------|-------------------------------------------------------------------------------------------------------|-----|------|
| 2316  | **Groat.** Portrait of Hen. VII. *London* mm. 53, 69, 108, 108 over 135.......                        | 125 | 450  |
| 2317  | — *Tournai; mm.* crowned T. ᚱ. CIVITAS TORnACЄn*, dated 1513 ...                                     | 975 | 3500 |
| 2318  | **Halfgroat.** Portrait of Hen. VII. London; *mm.* 108, 108/- ......................                  | 135 | 500  |
| 2319  | — *Canterbury,* Archb. Warham. POSVI *rev.; mm.* rose ..........................                      | 150 | 650  |
| 2320  | — — — WA above shield; *mm.* martlet ..................................................                | 130 | 475  |
| 2321  | — — — WA beside shield; *mm.* cross fitchee.........................................                   | 130 | 475  |
| 2322  | — — CIVITAS CAnTOR *rev.,* similar; *mm.* 73, 105, 11/105 .................                            | 85  | 300  |
| 2323  | — *York,* POSVI *rev.,* Archb. Bainbridge (1508-14). Keys below shield; *mm.* martlet .................................................................. | 110 | 350  |
| 2324  | — — — XB beside shield no keys; *mm.* martlet ...................................                     | 125 | 450  |
| 2325  | — — — Archb. Wolsey (1514-30). Keys and cardinal's hat below shield; *mm.* 94, 22........................................................................ | 225 | 750  |
| 2326  | — — CIVITAS ЄBORACI *rev.* Similar; *mm.* 22, 23, 30, 78, 15, 15/78..                                 | 75  | 275  |
| 2327  | — — As last with TW beside shield; *mm.* voided cross..........................                       | 125 | 450  |
| 2327A | — *Tournai.* As 2317................................................................................   | 950 | 3000 |

*\*Non-portrait groats and half-groats exist of this mint, captured during an invasion of France in
1513. (Restored to France in 1518.)*

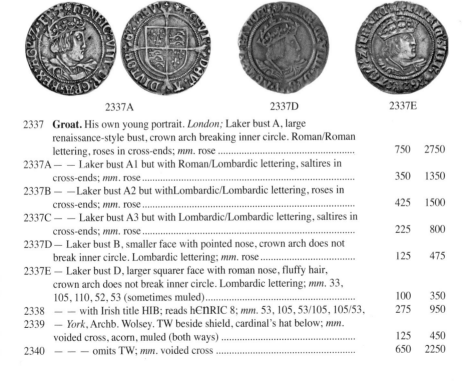

|       |      | 2328 | 2332 | 2334 | 2336 |       |       |
|-------|------|------|------|------|------|-------|-------|

|                                                                                                          | F<br>£ | VF<br>£ |
|----------------------------------------------------------------------------------------------------------|--------|---------|
| 2328 **Penny,** 'Sovereign' type, *London; mm.* 69, 108 /-, 108/108 .................... | 60 | 175 |
| 2329 — *Canterbury.* WA above shield; *mm.* martlet......................................... | 175 | 650 |
| 2330 — — — WA beside shield; *mm.* 73/- ................................................. | 90 | 325 |
| 2331 — *Durham,* Bp. Ruthall (1509-23). TD above shield; *mm.* lis................ | 45 | 150 |
| 2332 — — — TD beside shield; above or below horizontal line *mm.* lis, radiant star | 45 | 150 |
| 2333 — — Bp. Wolsey (1523-9). DW beside shield, cardinal's hat below;<br>*mm.* spur rowel...... | 250 | 800 |
| 2334 **Halfpenny.** Facing bust, hEnRIC DI GRA REX (AGL). *London;*<br>*mm.* 69, 108/- ...................................................................................... | 35 | 135 |
| 2335 — *Canterbury.* WA beside bust; *mm.* 73/-, 11 ...................................... | 80 | 275 |
| 2335A — *York.* Key below bust, *mm.* star, escallop............................................. | 100 | 350 |
| 2336 **Farthing.** *mm.* 108/-, hEnRIC DI GRA REX, portcullis.<br>R. CIVITAS LOnDON, rose in centre of long cross ............................. | 275 | 850 |

## SECOND COINAGE, 1526-44

|                                   | 2337A | 2337D | 2337E |
|-----------------------------------|-------|-------|-------|

|                                                                                                          | F<br>£ | VF<br>£ |
|----------------------------------------------------------------------------------------------------------|--------|---------|
| 2337 **Groat.** His own young portrait. *London;* Laker bust A, large<br>renaissance-style bust, crown arch breaking inner circle. Roman/Roman<br>lettering, roses in cross-ends; *mm.* rose .................................................... | 750 | 2750 |
| 2337A — — Laker bust A1 but with Roman/Lombardic lettering, saltires in<br>cross-ends; *mm.* rose ...................................................................................... | 350 | 1350 |
| 2337B — —Laker bust A2 but withLombardic/Lombardic lettering, roses in<br>cross-ends; *mm.* rose ...................................................................................... | 425 | 1500 |
| 2337C — — Laker bust A3 but with Lombardic/Lombardic lettering, saltires in<br>cross-ends; *mm.* rose ...................................................................................... | 225 | 800 |
| 2337D — Laker bust B, smaller face with pointed nose, crown arch does not<br>break inner circle. Lombardic lettering; *mm.* rose ................................... | 125 | 475 |
| 2337E — Laker bust D, larger squarer face with roman nose, fluffy hair,<br>crown arch does not break inner circle. Lombardic lettering; *mm.* 33,<br>105, 110, 52, 53 (sometimes muled)........................................................ | 100 | 350 |
| 2338 — — with Irish title HIB; reads hEnRIC 8; *mm.* 53, 105, 53/105, 105/53, | 275 | 950 |
| 2339 — *York,* Archb. Wolsey. TW beside shield, cardinal's hat below; *mm.*<br>voided cross, acorn, muled (both ways) ................................................... | 125 | 450 |
| 2340 — — — omits TW; *mm.* voided cross ........................................ | 650 | 2250 |

2341          2343          2345

|                                                                                                          | F | VF |
|----------------------------------------------------------------------------------------------------------|------|------|
|                                                                                                          | £ | £ |
| 2341 **Halfgroat.** *London;* type as groats, Lombardic lettering both sides.                             |      |      |
| *mm.* rose to arrow or none (sometimes muled).......................................... | 65 | 225 |
| 2341A — — Mainly Roman letters on obv. or on both sides, *mm.* rose ............. | 110 | 425 |
| 2342 As 2341 with Irish title HIB; *mm.* pheon.................................................... | 475 | 1500 |
| 2343 — *Canterbury*, Archb. Warham (—1532). R. CIVITAS CAΠTOR, WA |      |      |
| beside shield; *mm.* 121, 121/-, 121/33, 8, 8/T, T........................................ | 60 | 200 |
| 2344 — — — nothing by shield; *mm.* 121/- ................................................... | 70 | 250 |
| 2345 — — Archb. Cranmer (1533—). TC beside shield; *mm.* 36, 36/-............ | 60 | 185 |
| 2346 — *York,* Archb. Wolsey (—1530). R. CIVITAS ЄBORACI, TW |      |      |
| beside shield, hat below; *mm.* 15/-, 15..................................................... | 65 | 200 |
| 2347 — — Sede Vacante (1530/1). No marks; *mm.* key................................... | 70 | 225 |
| 2348 — — Archb. Lee (1531-44). EL or LE beside shield; *mm.* key .............. | 60 | 185 |

2349          2358          2362

|                                                                                                          | F | VF |
|----------------------------------------------------------------------------------------------------------|------|------|
| 2349 **Penny.** 'Sovereign' type h . D . G . ROSA SIΠЄ SPIΠA, *London;* |      |      |
| *mm.* rose to arrow (*obv.* only), *mm.* lis both sides.................................... | 50 | 175 |
| 2350 — *Canterbury.* WA beside shield; *mm.* 121/-, 8/-, T/-............................ | 150 | 525 |
| 2351 — — TC beside shield; *mm.* 36/- ............................................................ | 225 | 750 |
| 2352 — *Durham,* Bp. Wolsey (—1529). TW beside shield, hat below; *mm.* 23, |      |      |
| 23/44, 23/-, 72a/-, 44, 44/-, 72a/44 (muled with 2333 *obv.*, *mm.* 24/44).. | 40 | 140 |
| 2353 — — Sede Vacante (1529-30). No marks; *mm.* 23/-, 22/-....................... | 45 | 150 |
| 2354 — — Bp. Tunstall (1530—). CD beside shield; *mm.* 23, 23/-, 22/-, 22 ... | 40 | 140 |
| 2355 — *York.* EL beside shield; *mm.* key/-................................................... | 475 | 1500 |
| 2356 **Halfpenny.** Facing bust, h D G ROSA SIЄ SPIA. *London;* sometimes |      |      |
| annulet in centre of rev. *mm.* rose to arrow, arrow/- ................................. | 30 | 135 |
| 2357 — *Canterbury.* WA beside bust; *mm.* 121/-, 8/-, T/-............................. | 150 | 525 |
| 2358 — — TC beside bust; *mm.* 36/- ............................................................. | 35 | 140 |
| 2359 — *York.* TW beside bust; *mm.* acorn/- ............................................... | 85 | 300 |
| 2359A — — —; key below bust.......................................................................... | 125 | 450 |
| 2360 — — Sede Vacante. Key below bust; *mm.* 15/-..................................... | 60 | 185 |
| 2361 — — EL or LE beside bust; *mm.* key/- ................................................ | 35 | 140 |
| 2362 **Farthing.** O. RVTILANS ROSA, portcullis; *mm.* 105/-, 110/-. R. |      |      |
| DEO GRACIAS, long cross with pellet in each angle ............................ | 325 | 750 |
| 2363 — — *mm.* arrow/- R. DEO GRACIAS, rose on long cross .................... | 375 | 900 |
| 2363A — *Canterbury.* O. Similar. R. Similar. *mm.* 36/- ................................. | 900 | 2500 |

2364

|  | F | VF |
|  | £ | £ |

**THIRD COINAGE, 1544-7** (Silver progressively debased. 9oz (2dwt), 6oz (2dwt) 4oz (2dwt)).

2364  **Testoon.** *Tower.* hЄnRIC'. VIII, etc. R. Crowned rose between crowned h
    and R.POSVI, etc.; *mm*. lis, lis and 56, lis/two lis ....................................   1500   6500

2365  — hЄnRIC 8, *mm*. 105 and 56, 105/56, 105 and 56/56, 56 ...................   950   4000

2366  — — annulet on inner circle of rev. or both sides; *mm*. pellet in annulet   1000   4250

2367

2367  — *Southwark.* As 2365. R. CIVITAS LonDon; *mm*. S, Є, S/Є, Є/S ....   950   4000

2368  — *Bristol. mm*.-/WS monogram. (Tower or local dies.)...........................   1750   6000

2369 Bust 1        2374 Bust 2

2369  **Groat.** *Tower.* As ill. above, busts 1, 2, 3; *mm*. lis/-, lis............................   125   575

2369A  Bust 1, R. As second coinage; i.e. saltires in forks; *mm*. lis ...................   150   700

2370  Bust 2 or 3 annulet on inner circle, both sides or rev. only ....................   135   625

2371  *Southwark.* As 2367, busts 1, 2, 3, 4; no *mm*. or lis/-; S or S and Є or
    Є in forks .................................................................................................   125   575

2372  *Bristol. Mm*.-/WS monogram, Bristol bust and Tower bust 2 or 3 .........   125   575

2373  *Canterbury.* Busts 1, 2, (2 var); no *mm*, or lis/– .....................................   125   575

2374  *York.* Busts 1 var., 2, 3, no *mm*..............................................................   125   575

2377          2384

|  |  | F | VF |
|---|---|---|---|
|  |  | £ | £ |
| 2375 | **Halfgroat.** *Tower.* As 2365, bust 1; *mm.* lis, none ................................ | 75 | 350 |
| 2376 | *Southwark.* As 2367, bust 1; no *mm.*; S or Є and S in forks................. | 100 | 425 |
| 2377 | *Bristol. Mm.-*/WS monogram ........................................................................ | 70 | 325 |
| 2378 | *Canterbury.* Bust 1; no *mm.*........................................................................ | 60 | 275 |
| 2379 | *York.* Bust 1; no *mm.*................................................................................... | 75 | 350 |
| 2380 | **Penny.** *Tower.* Facing bust; no *mm.* or lis/- ............................................ | 50 | 225 |
| 2381 | *Southwark.* Facing bust; *mm.* S/-, Є/-, -/Є............................................... | 85 | 325 |
| 2382 | *Bristol.* Facing bust; no *mm.* (Tower dies or local but truncated at neck) | 60 | 250 |
| 2383 | *Canterbury.* Facing bust; no *mm.*............................................................... | 50 | 200 |
| 2384 | *York.* Facing bust; no *mm.*.......................................................................... | 55 | 225 |

2385          2388A

| 2385 | **Halfpenny.** *Tower.* Facing bust; pellet in annulet in *rev.* centre, no *mm.* or lis/- ................................................................................. | 75 | 225 |
|---|---|---|---|
| 2386 | *Bristol.* Facing bust; no *mm.*....................................................................... | 90 | 300 |
| 2387 | *Canterbury.* Facing bust; no *mm.*, (some read H 8).................................. | 60 | 185 |
| 2388 | *York.* Facing bust; no *mm.*.......................................................................... | 50 | 165 |
| 2388A | **Farthing** *obv.* Rose. R. Cross and pellets.............................................. | 900 | 2500 |

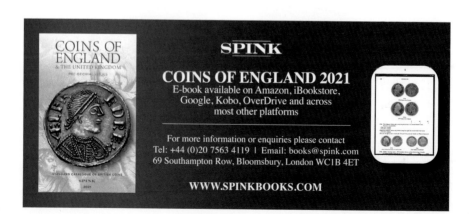

These coins were struck during the reign of Edward VI but bear the name and portrait of Henry VIII, except in the case of the half-sovereigns which bear the youthful head of Edward.

*Mintmarks*

| 56 | 105 | 52 | K | E | 116 |

| 66 | 115 | 33 | 122 | t | 94 |

## GOLD

|  |  | F | VF |
|---|---|---|---|
|  |  | £ | £ |
| 2389 | **Sovereign** (20 ct.), *London*. As no. 2290, but Roman lettering; *mm*. lis.. | 7000 | 27500 |
| 2390 | — *Bristol*. Similar but *mm*. WS | 12500 | 45000 |

2391

2393

| 2391 | **Half-sovereign.** As 2294, but with youthful portrait with sceptre. *Tower*; *mm*. 52, 105, 94 (various combinations) | 800 | 2750 |
|---|---|---|---|
| 2391A | — Similar but no sceptre; *mm*. 52, 52/56 | 850 | 2850 |
| 2392 | — — — K below shield; *mm*.-/K, none,. E/- | 825 | 2800 |
| 2393 | — — — grapple below shield; *mm*. 122, none, 122/-, -/122. | 850 | 2850 |
| 2394 | — *Southwark. Mm.* E, E/-, -/E, Є /E. Usually Є or E (sometimes retro-grade) below shield (sceptre omitted; *mm*. -/E) | 800 | 2750 |
| 2394A | — — — R. As 2296; *mm*.-/S | 900 | 3000 |

2395

|  | F | VF |
|---|---|---|
|  | £ | £ |
| 2395 **Crown.** Similar to 2305. *London; mm.* 52, 52/-, -/K, 122, 94, ................. | 575 | 2000 |
| 2396 — Similar but transposed legends without numeral; *mm.* -/arrow .......... | 600 | 2250 |
| 2396A — As 2395, but omitting RVTILANS; *mm.* arrow ................................ | 600 | 2250 |
| 2396B Similar, but RVTILANS both sides; *mm.* arrow ...................................... | 750 | 2750 |
| 2397 — *Southwark.* Similar to 2396; *mm.* E ...................................... | 675 | 2500 |
| 2398 — — King's name on *obv.*; *mm.* E/-, -/E.................................... | 600 | 2250 |
| 2399 **Halfcrown.** Similar to 2311. *London; mm.* 52, K/-, 122/-, 94, -/52 ........ | 575 | 1750 |
| 2399A As last but E over h on *rev.*, *mm.* 56/52.................................... | 900 | 3000 |
| 2399B As 2399 but RVTILANS etc. on both sides, *mm.* arrow .......................... | 625 | 2250 |
| 2400 — *Southwark. mm.* E, E/-, -/E ................................................ | 600 | 2000 |

# SILVER

AR (4oz .333)

| 2401 **Testoon.** *Tower.* As 2365 with lozenge stops one side; -/56, 56 .......... | 2250 | 9500 |
|---|---|---|

2403                2403 Bust 4                2403 Bust 6

*Some of the Bristol testoons, groats and halfgroats with WS monogram were struck after the death of Henry VIII but cannot easily be distinguished from those struck during his reign.*

| 2403 **Groat.** *Tower.* Busts 4, 5, 6 (and, rarely, 2). R. POSVI, etc.; *mm.* 105-94 and none (frequently muled)........................................................ | 100 | 550 |
|---|---|---|
| 2404 — *Southwark.* Busts 4, 5, 6. R. CIVITAS LONDON; no *mm.* -/E; lis/-, -/lis, K/E; roses or crescents or S and Є in forks, or rarely annulets ....... | 90 | 475 |
| 2405 — *Durham House.* Bust 6. R. REDDE CVIQVE QVOD SVVM EST; *mm.* bow.................................................................................. | 275 | 900 |
| 2406 — *Bristol. mm.* WS on *rev.* Bristol bust B, Tower bust 2 and 3 .............. | 110 | 575 |
| 2407 — — *mm.* TC on *rev.* Similar, Bristol bust B .......................................... | 125 | 625 |
| 2408 — *Canterbury.* Busts 5, 6; no *mm.* or rose/- .......................................... | 90 | 475 |
| 2409 — *York.* Busts 4, 5, 6; no *mm.* or lis/-, -/lis.............................................. | 90 | 475 |

2411                          2416

|  | | F | VF |
|---|---|---|---|
|  | | £ | £ |
| 2410 | **Halfgroat.** Bust 1. *Tower.* POSVI, etc.; *mm.* 52, 52/-, 52/K , -/K, 52/122, 122, -/122 | 90 | 400 |
| 2411 | — *Southwark.* CIVITAS LONDON; *mm.* E, -/E, none, 52/E, K/E | 65 | 225 |
| 2412 | — *Durham House.* ꝶ. REDD, etc.; *mm.* bow, -/bow | 425 | 1500 |
| 2413 | — *Bristol. Mm.* WS on *rev.* | 75 | 350 |
| 2414 | — — *mm.* TC on *rev.* | 90 | 400 |
| 2415 | — *Canterbury.* No *mm.* or t/-, -/t, | 50 | 200 |
| 2416 | — *York.* No *mm.*, bust 1 and three-quarter facing | 70 | 300 |

2417                     2418

| 2417 | **Penny.** *Tower.* CIVITAS LONDON. Facing bust; *mm.* 52/-, -/52, -/K, 122/-, -/122, none | 50 | 200 |
|---|---|---|---|
| 2418 | — — three-quarter bust; no *mm.* | 50 | 200 |
| 2419 | — *Southwark.* As 2417; *mm.* E, -/E | 55 | 225 |
| 2420 | — *Durham House.* As groat but shorter legend; *mm.* -/bow | 475 | 1500 |

2421                     2426                 2428

| 2421 | — *Bristol.* Facing busts, as 2382 but showing more body, no *mm.* | 75 | 300 |
|---|---|---|---|
| 2422 | — *Canterbury.* Similar to 2417 | 50 | 200 |
| 2423 | — — three-quarter facing bust; no *mm.* | 55 | 225 |
| 2424 | — *York.* Facing bust; no *mm.* | 50 | 200 |
| 2425 | — — three-quarter facing bust; no *mm.* | 65 | 275 |
| 2426 | **Halfpenny.** *Tower. mm* 52?, none | 45 | 150 |
| 2427 | — *Canterbury.* No *mm.*, sometimes reads H8 | 50 | 165 |
| 2428 | — *York.* No *mm.* | 45 | 150 |

The 4 oz. 2.5dwt coins of Henry VIII and those issued under Edward in 1547 and 1548 caused much disquiet, yet at the same time government was prevented by continuing financial necessity from abandoning debasement. A stratagem was devised which entailed increasing the fineness of silver coins, thereby making them appear sound, while at the same time reducing their weight in proportion so that in practice they contained no more silver than hitherto. The first issue, ordered on 24th January 1549, at 8 oz.2 dwt. fine produced a shilling which, at 60 gr., was so light that it was rapidly discredited and had to be replaced in April by another at 6 oz. 2 dwt. Weighing 80 gr., these later shillings proved acceptable.

Between April and August 1551 the issue of silver coins was the worst ever – 3 oz. 2dwt. fine at 72s per lb. before retrenchment came in August, first by a 50% devaluation of base silver coin and then by the issue of a fine standard at 11oz. 1dwt. 'out of the fire'. This was the equivalent of 11oz.3dwt. commixture, and means that since sterling was only 11oz. 2dwt., this issue, which contained four new denominations – the crown, halfcrown, sixpence and threepence – was in effect the finest ever issued under the Tudors.

Some base 'pence' were struck in parallel with the fine silver, but at the devalued rate, they and the corresponding 'halfpence' were used as halfpence and farthings respectively.

The first dates on English coinage appear in this reign, first as Roman numerals and then on the fine issue crowns and halfcrowns of 1551-3, in Arabic numerals.

## Mintmarks

| 66 | 52 | 35 | 115 | E | 53 | 122 |
|----|----|----|-----|---|----|-----|

| t | T | 111 | Y | 126 | 94 | 91A |
|---|---|-----|---|-----|----|----|

| 92 | 105 | y | 97 | 123 | 78 | 26 |
|----|-----|---|----|-----|----|----|

| | | | | |
|---|---|---|---|---|
| 1547-8 | Arrow (52) | | | |
| | E (Southwark) | | | |
| 1548-50 | Bow (66, *Durham House*) | 1550 | Martlet (94) |
| 1549 | Arrow (52) | 1550 | Leopard's head (91A) |
| | Grapple (122) | 1550-1 | Lion (92) |
| | Rose (35, *Canterbury*) | | Lis (105, *Southwark*) |
| | TC monogram (115, *Bristol*) | | Rose (33) |
| | Pheon (53) | 1551 | Y or y (117, *Southwark*) |
| | t or T (*Canterbury*) | | Ostrich's head (97, gold only) |
| 1549-50 | Swan (111) | 1551-3 | Tun (123) |
| | Roman Y (*Southwark*) | | Escallop (78) |
| 1549-50 | 6 (126 gold only) | 1552-3 | Pierced mullet (26, *York*) |

# GOLD

**First period, Apr. 1547-Jan. 1549**

2430

| | | F | VF |
|---|---|---|---|
| | | £ | £ |

2429   **Half-sovereign** (20 c). As 2391, but reading EDWARD 6. Tower; *mm.*
      arrow ...................................................................................................... 2250    9000

2430   — *Southwark* (Sometimes with E or Є below shield); *mm.* E................ 1750    6500

2431   **Crown.** RVTILANS, etc., crowned rose between ER both crowned. Ɍ.
      EDWARD 6, etc., crowned shield between ER both crowned; *mm.* arrow,
      E over arrow/- ...................................................................................... 2000    7500

2431A— *Obv.* as last. Ɍ. As 2305, *mm.* 52/56 .................................................. 1750    6500

2432   **Halfcrown.** Similar to 2431, but initials not crowned; *mm.* arrow .......... 1500    4500

2432A—*Southwark.* Similar. *mm.* –/E .............................................................. 1500    4500

**Second period, Jan. 1549-Apr. 1550**

2433

2433   **Sovereign** (22 ct). As illustration; *mm.* arrow, –/arrow, Y, ...................... 6500   20000

2434   **Half-sovereign.** Uncrowned bust. *Tower.* TIMOR etc., MDXLIX on
      *obv. mm.* arrow......................................................................................... 3500   12500

2435

2435   — — SCVTVM, etc., as illustration; *mm.* arrow, **6,** Y ............................. 2000    7000

|      |                                                                                 | F<br>£ | VF<br>£ |
|------|---------------------------------------------------------------------------------|-------|-------|
| 2436 | — *Durham House*. Uncrowned, 1/2 length bust with MDXLVIII at end of *obv*. legend; *mm*. bow; SCVTVM etc. | 7500 | 27500 |
| 2437 | — Normal, uncrowned bust. LVCERNA, etc., on *obv.; mm*. bow | 6500 | 22500 |
| 2437A | — Normal, uncrowned bust. SCVTVM, etc. but with *rev.* as 2440, *mm*. bow | 5250 | 17500 |

2438                                                   2441

|      |                                                                                 | F | VF |
|------|---------------------------------------------------------------------------------|-------|-------|
| 2438 | — *London, Southwark*. Crowned bust. EDWARD VI, etc. R. SCVTVM, etc.; *mm*. 52, 122, 111/52, 111, Y, 94 | 1850 | 6500 |
| 2439 | — *Durham House*. Crowned, half-length bust; *mm*. bow | 7500 | 27500 |
| 2440 | — — King's name on *obv*. and *rev.; mm*. bow (mule of 2439/37) | 8000 | 30000 |
| 2441 | **Crown.** Uncrowned bust, as 2435; *mm*. 6, Y, 52/-, Y/- | 2250 | 8500 |
| 2442 | — Crowned bust, as 2438; *mm*. 52, 122, 111, Y (usually *obv*. only) | 2000 | 7500 |
| 2443 | **Halfcrown.** Uncrowned bust; R. As 2441, *mm*. arrow, Y, Y/-, 52/- | 2250 | 8500 |
| 2444 | — Crowned bust, as illus. above; *mm*. 52, 52/111, 111, 122, Y, Y/- | 1650 | 5750 |
| 2445 | — Similar, but king's name on *rev., mm*. 52, 122 | 1750 | 6000 |

**Third period, 1550-3, Fine Gold (23 ct.)**

| 2446 | **Sovereign** (30s., 240grs., 15.55g.). King on throne; *mm*. 97, 123 | 30000 | 125000 |
|------|---------------------------------------------------------------------------------|-------|-------|

2444                                                   2448

| 2447 | **Double sovereign.** From the same dies, *mm*. 97 | 100000 | 450000 |
|------|---------------------------------------------------------------------------------|-------|-------|
| 2448 | **Angel** (10s.). As illustration; *mm*. 97, 123 | 12500 | 40000 |
| 2449 | **Half-angel.** Similar, *mm*. 97 | 11000 | 37500 |

2450

|  | F £ | VF £ |
|---|---|---|

## Crown Gold (22 ct.)

2450 **Sovereign**. (=20s., 174.6 grs., 11.31g.). Half-length
figure of king r., crowned and holding sword and orb. ℞. Crowned shield
with supporters; *mm*. y, tun ........................................................................ 7250 21000

2451

| 2451 | **Half-sovereign**. As illustration above; *mm*. y, tun ................................... | 1850 | 6500 |
|---|---|---|---|
| 2452 | **Crown**. Similar, but *rev*. SCVTVM etc., *mm*. y, tun ............................... | 2000 | 7500 |
| 2453 | **Halfcrown**. Similar, *mm*. tun, y................................................................ | 2500 | 8500 |

*\*Small denominations often occur creased or straightened.*

# SILVER

**First period, Apr. 1547-Jan. 1549**

2454                                        2455

| 2454 | **Groat.** Crowned bust r. *Tower.* ℞. Shield over cross, POSVI, etc.; *mm*. arrow | 750 | 4500 |
|---|---|---|---|
| 2455 | — As last, but EDOARD 6, *mm*. arrow..................................................... | 850 | 5000 |
| 2456 | *Southwark*. *Obv*. as 2454. ℞. CIVITAS LONDON; *mm*.-/E or none, sometimes S in forks............................................................................... | 750 | 4500 |
| 2457 | **Halfgroat.** *Tower*. *Obv*. as 2454; *mm*. arrow .......................................... | 650 | 2500 |
| 2458 | *Southwark*. As 2456; *mm*. arrow, E on reverse only ............................... | 575 | 2000 |

2459                              2462

|  | F | VF |
|---|---|---|
|  | £ | £ |
| 2459 *Canterbury*. Similar. No *mm*., reads EDOARD or EDWARD (rare) ....... | 450 | 1500 |
| 2460 **Penny**. *Tower*. As halfgroat, but E.D.G. etc. R. CIVITAS LONDON; *mm*. arrow ............................................................................................................ | 450 | 1500 |
| 2461 *Southwark*. As last, but *mm*. -/E................................................................. | 500 | 1650 |
| 2462 *Bristol*. Similar, but reads ED6DG or E6DG no *mm*................................ | 450 | 1500 |
| 2463 **Halfpenny**. *Tower*. *O*. As 2460, *mm*. E (?). R. Cross and pellets ........... | 575 | 1750 |
| 2464 *Bristol*. Similar, no *mm*. but reads E6DG or EDG.................................. | 650 | 2000 |

## Second period, Jan. 1549-Apr. 1550

At all mints except Bristol, the earliest shillings of 1549 were issued at only 60 grains but of 8 oz. 2 dwt standard. This weight and size were soon increased to 80 grains, (S.2466 onwards), but the fineness was reduced to 6 oz. 2 dwt so the silver content remained the same. Dies, mm G were prepared for a coinage of 80gr shillings at York, but were not used. Coins from the *mm* are found suitably overmarked, from other mints, S.2466-8. The shilling bust types are set out in *J. Bispham 'The Base Silver Shillings of Edward VI; BNJ 1985*.

Bust 1                    2465A                    Bust 2

**First Issue, 60 grs., 3.88g., 8oz. 2 dwt.**

| 2465 **Shilling**. *Tower*. Broad bust with large crown. *Obv*. TIMOR etc. MDXLIX. R. Small, oval garnished shield dividing ER. EDWARD VI etc., *mm*. 52, no *mm*, Bust 1; *mm*, –/52, Bust 2 (very rare) ...................... | 275 | 1350 |
|---|---|---|
| 2465A *Southwark*. As last, Bust 1, *mm*. Y, EY/Y .............................................. | 250 | 1250 |
| 2465B *Canterbury*. As last, Bust 1, *mm*. -/rose ................................................... | 275 | 1500 |

2465C

| 2465C *Durham House*. Bust with elaborate tunic and collar TIMOR etc. MDXLIX. R. Oval shield, very heavily garnished in different style. EDWARD VI etc., *mm*. bow (2469) ............................................................. | 275 | 1500 |
|---|---|---|

**Second Issue, debased, 80 grs., 5.18g., 6oz. 2 dwt.**

Bust 3               Bust 4

Bust 5          2466C            2468

2472

|   |   | F | VF |
|---|---|---|---|
|   |   | £ | £ |
| 2466 | *Tower.* Tall, narrow bust with small crown. *Obv.* EDWARD VI etc. MDXLIX or MDL. Ɍ. As 2465 but TIMOR etc., Busts 3, 4 and 5, *mm.* 52-91a (frequently muled) | 175 | 900 |
| 2466A | — *Obv.* as last, MDXLIX. Ɍ. Heavily garnished shield, Durham House style, Bust 3 *mm.* grapple | 375 | 1750 |
| 2466B | *Southwark.* As 2466, Busts 3, 4 and 5 *mm.* Y, Y/swan | 175 | 900 |
| 2466C | — — — Bust 4; Ɍ. as 2466A. *mm.* Y | 375 | 1750 |
| 2467 | *Bristol. Obv.* similar to 2466, Bust 3 or local die Ɍ. Shield with heavy curved garniture or as 2466, *mm.* TC, or TC over G | 950 | 3750 |
| 2468 | *Canterbury.* As 2466, Bust 3 and 4 *mm.* T, T/t, t/T, t or t over G | 210 | 1050 |
| 2470 | *Durham House.* Bust as 2465C. INIMICOS etc., no date. Ɍ. EDWARD etc. | 225 | 1100 |
| 2472 | — Bust similar to 2466. EDWARD VI etc. Ɍ. INIMICOS etc. | 200 | 1000 |
| 2472A | — As last but legends transposed | 300 | 1500 |
| 2472B | *Tower.* Elegant bust with extremely thin neck. Bust 6, Ɍ. As 2466, *mm.* martlet | 450 | 2250 |
| 2472C | *Southwark.* As last, Bust 6, *mm.* Y | 250 | 1250 |

*For coins of Edward VI countermarked, see p. 236*

**Third period, 1550-3**

**Very base issue (1551) ca. 70grs., ca. 4.88g., 3oz. 2 dwt.**

2473 Bust 6      2474      2476

|  | F £ | VF £ |
|---|---|---|
| 2473 **Shilling**, *Tower*. As 2472B. MDL or MDLI, *mm.* lion, rose, lion/rose .... | 175 | 950 |
| 2473A *Southwark*. As last, *mm.* lis/Y, Y/lis, lis ...................................................... | 175 | 950 |
| 2474 **Base Penny**. *London. O.* Rose. ℞. Shield; *mm.* escallop (*obv.*)................ | 55 | 250 |
| 2475  — — *York. Mm.* mullet (*obv.*) as illustration ............................................ | 50 | 225 |
| 2476 **Base Halfpenny**. As penny, but single rose ............................................. | 325 | 1500 |

\* The base penny and halfpenny were used as halfpenny and farthing respectively.
Note: Irish very base shillings exist which are all dated MDLII, a date that does not occur for
English issued shillings.

**Fine silver issue, (1551-3) 460grs., 30g., 11oz. 3 dwt.**

2478

| 2478 **Crown**. King on horseback with date below horse. ℞. Shield on cross; *mm.* y. 1551; tun, 1551-3 (1553, wire line inner circle may be missing) . | 975 | 3500 |
|---|---|---|

2479

| 2479 **Halfcrown**. Walking horse with plume; *mm.* y, 1551 .............................. | 650 | 2000 |
|---|---|---|
| 2480 Galloping horse without plume; *mm.* tun, 1551-3 ..................................... | 675 | 2250 |

2482

2483                           2484

|   |   | F | VF |
|---|---|---|---|
|   |   | £ | £ |
| 2481 | Large walking horse without plume; *mm*. tun, 1553 .................................. | 1000 | 3750 |
| 2482 | **Shilling**. Facing bust, rose l., value XII r. *mm*. y, tun (several bust varieties) | 125 | 525 |
| 2483 | **Sixpence**. *London*. Similar value VI, as illustration; *mm*. y/-, -/y, y, tun (bust varieties) ............................................................................................ | 135 | 575 |
| 2484 | *York*. As last, but rev. reads CIVITAS ЄBORACI; *mm*. mullet............... | 275 | 1350 |

2485                           2486

| 2485 | **Threepence**. *London*. As sixpence, but value III; *mm*. tun ...................... | 200 | 1000 |
|---|---|---|---|
| 2486 | *York*. As 2484, but III by bust .................................................. | 475 | 2500 |

2487                           2487A

| 2487 | **Penny**. 'Sovereign' type; *mm*. tun ............................................................... | 1350 | 4750 |
|---|---|---|---|
| 2487A | **Farthing**. *O*. Portcullis, R Cross and Pellets ......................................... | 1500 | 5000 |

# SPINK

## LONDON
## 1666

# THE COINS OF ENGLAND COLOURING BOOK

# SPINK BOOKS ARE PROUD TO PRESENT THE FIRST EVER
## COINS OF ENGLAND COLOURING BOOK
### A COLOURING BOOK FOR ALL AGES

**22 FULL PAGE ILLUSTRATIONS**
FILLED WITH A SELECTION OF OUR NATION'S MOST BEAUTIFUL COIN DESIGNS
EACH COLOURING DESIGN IS ACCOMPANIED BY A SHORT PAGE OF HISTORICAL CONTEXT

ISBN: 978-1-912667-40-6
**RRP: £6.99**

Mary brought English coins back to the sterling standard and struck all her gold coins at the traditional fineness of 0.995. The mintmarks usually appear at the end of the first or second word of the legends.

Pomegranate     Halved rose and castle

## GOLD

2488

|  | F<br>£ | VF<br>£ |
|---|---|---|
| 2488   **'Fine' Sovereign** (30s.). Queen enthroned. ℞. Shield on rose, MDLIII, MDLIIII and undated, *mm.* pomegranate, half-rose (or mule) | 8500 | 25000 |
| 2489   **Ryal** (15s.). As illus, MDLIII. ℞. As 1950 but A DNO etc. *mm.* pomegranate/- | 27500 | 90000 |

2489

2490

|  | | F | VF |
|---|---|---|---|
|  | | £ | £ |
| 2490 | **Angel** (10s.). Class I, annulet stops; *mm*. pomegranate............................ | 2000 | 5500 |
| 2490A | — Class II, pellet stops, *mm*. pomegranate (often muled with class I reverse) | 2100 | 5750 |
| 2490B | — Class III, pellet stops, large Roman letters, *mm*. half-rose and castle . | 2250 | 6000 |
| 2491 | **Half-angel**. Similar; *mm*. pomegranate, pomegranate/- ........................... | 6500 | 17500 |

## SILVER

2492

| 2492 | **Groat**. Crowned bust l. R. VERITAS, etc.; *mm*. pomegranate, pomegranate/- ......................................................................................... | 135 | 575 |
|---|---|---|---|
| 2493 | **Halfgroat**. Similar............................................................................... | 675 | 2500 |
| 2494 | **Penny**. Similar, but M. D. G. ROSA, etc. ............................................... | 575 | 2250 |

2495

| 2495 | — As last. R. CIVITAS LONDON; no *mm*............................................... | 575 | 2250 |

The groats and smaller silver coins of this period have Mary's portrait only, but the shillings and sixpences show the bust of the queen's husband, Philip of Spain.

*Mintmarks*

Lis (105           Half-rose and castle

## GOLD

2496A

| | | F | VF |
|---|---|---|---|
| | | £ | £ |
| 2496 | **Angel**. As illustration; wire line inner circles, calm sea, *mm*, lis .......... | 5750 | 20000 |
| 2496A | — — New-style, large wings, wire line i.c. ........................................ | 6000 | 21000 |
| 2496B | — — As above but beaded i.c. ............................................................... | 6250 | 22000 |
| 2497 | **Half-angel**. Similar to 2496 ................................................................. | 13500 | 42500 |

## SILVER

2497A

| | | | |
|---|---|---|---|
| 2497A | **Halfcrown (Pattern)**. As illustration. Bust of Philip r., crown above, date 1554 below. R. Bust of Mary l. crown and date 1554 above, without mark of value, no *mm*.............................................................................. | 13500 | 45000 |
| 2498 | **Shilling**. Busts face-to-face, full titles, undated, no *mm*. ..................... | 400 | 2000 |
| 2499 | — — — also without mark of value ..................................................... | 450 | 2250 |

2500

|      |                                                        | F | VF |
|------|--------------------------------------------------------|------|-------|
|      |                                                        | £ | £ |
| 2500 | — — 1554 ............................................................. | 400 | 2000 |
| 2501 | — English titles only 1554, 1555 ............................................ | 425 | 2000 |
| 2501A | — — undated............................................................ | 525 | 2500 |
| 2502 | — — without mark of value, 1554, 1555 (rare)................................. | 450 | 2250 |
| 2503 | — — date below bust, 1554, 1555 ............................................. | 3250 | 12500 |
| 2504 | — — As last, but without ANG., 1555............................................ | 3750 | 13500 |

2505

2506

| | | | |
|------|--------------------------------------------------------|------|-------|
| 2505 | **Sixpence**. Similar. Full titles, 1554 (and undated?).............................. | 350 | 1750 |
| 2506 | — English titles only, 1555 (no *mm.*, rare), 1557 (*mm*. lis, rounder garnishing) | 325 | 1650 |
| 2506A | — As last but heavy beaded i.c. on obv. 1555. (Irish 4d. obv. mule) .... | 375 | 1850 |
| 2507 | — — date below bust, 1554, 1557 (very rare) ................................... | 1050 | 4500 |

2508

2510A

| | | | |
|------|--------------------------------------------------------|------|-------|
| 2508 | **Groat**. Crowned bust of Mary 1. Ŗ. POSVIMVS etc. (several legend vars.); | | |
|      | *mm*. lis................................................................. | 125 | 525 |
| 2509 | **Halfgroat**. Similar, but POSVIM, *mm*. lis ............................................ | 525 | 2000 |
| 2510 | **Penny**. Similar to 2495, but P. Z. M. etc.; *mm*. lis................................ | 375 | 1600 |
| 2510A | **Base penny**, but P. Z. M . etc.; *mm*. halved rose and | | |
|      | castle or castle/–, (used as a halfpenny)............................................... | 65 | 250 |

Elizabeth's coinage is particularly interesting on account of the large number of different denominations issued. 'Crown' gold coins were again issued as well as the 'fine' gold denominations. In 1560 the base shillings of Edward VI's second and third coinages were called in and countermarked for recirculation at reduced values. Smaller debased coins were also devalued but not countermarked. The old debased groat became a three halfpence and other coins in proportion. The normal silver coinage was initially struck at 0.916 fineness as in the previous reign but between 1560 and 1577 and after 1582 the old sterling standard of 0.925 was restored. Between 1578 and 1582 the standard was slightly reduced and the weights were reduced by 1/32nd in 1601. Gold was similarly reduced slightly in quality 1578-82, and there was a slight weight reduction in 1601.

To help alleviate the shortage of small change, and to avoid the expense of minting an impossibly small silver farthing, a threefarthing piece was introduced to provide change if a penny was tendered for a farthing purchase. The sixpence, threepence, threehalfpence and threefarthings were marked with a rose behind the queen's head to distinguish them from the shilling, groat, half-groat and penny.

Coins of exceedingly fine workmanship were produced in a screw press introduced by Eloye Mestrelle, a French moneyer, in 1561. With parts of the machinery powered by a horse-drawn mill, the coins produced came to be known as 'mill money'. Despite the superior quality of the coins produced, the machinery was slow and inefficient compared to striking by hand. Mestrelle's dismissal was engineered in 1572 and six years later he was hanged for counterfeiting.

*Mintmarks*

| 1ST ISSUE | 2ND ISSUE | | 3RD & 4TH ISSUES | | | | |
|---|---|---|---|---|---|---|---|
| 106 | 21 | 94 | 23 | 53 | 33 | 107 | 92 |
| | | | 74 | 71 | 77 | 65b | 27 |

| 5TH ISSUE | | | 6TH ISSUE | | | | |
|---|---|---|---|---|---|---|---|
| 7 | 14 | 113 | 60 | 54 | 79 | 72b | 86 |

| 7TH ISSUE | | | | | | |
|---|---|---|---|---|---|---|
| 1 | 2 | 123 | 124 | 90 | 57 | 0 |

First Issue
1558-60    Lis (106)
Second Issue
1560-1    Cross crosslet (21)
         Martlet (94)
Third & Fourth Issue
1560-6    Star (23, milled)
1561-5    Pheon (53)
1565      Rose (33)
1566      Portcullis (107)
1566-7    Lion (92)
1567-70   Coronet (74)

Lis (106, milled)
1569-71   Castle (71)
1572-3    Ermine (77)
1573-4    Acorn (65b)
1573-8    Eglantine (27)
Fifth Issue
1578-9    Greek cross (7)
1580-1    Latin cross (14)
1582      Sword (113)
Sixth Issue
1582-3    Bell (60)
1582-4    A (54)

1584-6    Escallop (79)
1587-9    Crescent (72b)
1590-2    Hand (86)
1592-5    Tun (123)
1594-6    Woolpack (124)
1595-8    Key (90)
1598-1600 Anchor (57)
1600      0
Seventh Issue
1601-2    1
1602      2

N.B. *The dates for* mms *sometimes overlap. This is a result of using up old dies, onto which the new mark was punched.*

# GOLD

**HAMMERED COINAGE**

**First to Fourth issues, 1559-78.** ('Fine' gold of 0.994. 'Crown' gold of 0.916 fineness. Sovereigns of 240 grs., 15.55g.). Mintmarks; lis to eglantine.

|  | | *F*<br>£ | *VF*<br>£ |
|---|---|---|---|
| 2511 | **'Fine' Sovereign** (30 s.) Queen enthroned, tressure broken by throne, reads Z not ET, no chains to portcullis. R. Arms on rose; *mm*. lis............ | 10500 | 35000 |

2512

| 2512 | — — Similar but ET, chains on portcullis; *mm*. crosslet ......................... | 8000 | 22500 |
|---|---|---|---|

2513

| 2513 | **Angel**. St. Michael. R. Ship. Wire line inner circles; *mm*. lis.................. | 1750 | 6000 |
|---|---|---|---|
| 2513A | — Similar, but beaded i.c. on *obv*., *mm*. lis ............................................. | 2000 | 7500 |
| 2514 | — — Similar, but beaded inner circles; ship to r.; *mm*. 106, 21, 74, 27,.. | 1200 | 3750 |
| 2515 | — — — Similar, but ship to l.; *mm*. 77-27 .............................................. | 1250 | 4000 |
| 2516 | **Half Angel**. As 2513, wire line inner circles; *mm*. lis ............................ | 2500 | 9000 |
| 2516A | — As last, but beaded i.c.s, legend ends. Z.HIB .................................... | 1750 | 6500 |

2517

| 2517 | — As 2514, beaded inner circles; *mm*. 106, 21, 74, 77-27 ....................... | 1000 | 3250 |
|---|---|---|---|
| 2518 | **Quarter Angel**. Similar; *mm*. 74, 77-27............................................... | 1000 | 3250 |
| 2519 | **Half Pound** (10 s.) Young crowned bust l. R. Arms. Wire line inner circles; *mm*. lis ........................................................................................ | 7500 | 22500 |

2520

| | | F | VF |
|---|---|---|---|
| | | £ | £ |
| 2520 | — Similar, but beaded inner circles; *mm.* 21, 33-107 .............................. | 1750 | 5250 |
| 2520A | — — Smaller bust; *mm.* lion .................................................................... | 2000 | 6500 |
| 2520B | — — Broad bust, ear visible; *mm.* 92, 74, 71........................................ | 1850 | 5750 |
| 2521 | **Crown**. As 2519; *mm.* lis............................................................................ | 4500 | 15000 |
| 2522 | — Similar to 2520; *mm.* 21, 33-107 ...................................................... | 1100 | 3750 |
| 2522A | — Similar to 2520B; *mm.* 74, 71, 92..................................................... | 1100 | 3750 |
| 2523 | **Half Crown**. As 2519; *mm.* lis .................................................................. | 3750 | 12500 |

2524

| | | | |
|---|---|---|---|
| 2524 | — Similar to 2520; *mm.* 21, 33-107 (2 busts) ........................................ | 1100 | 3750 |
| 2524A | — Similar to 2520B; *mm.* 107-71 ............................................................ | 1250 | 4000 |

**Fifth Issue, 1578-82** (`Fine' gold only of 0.992). *Mms* Greek cross,
Latin cross and sword.

| | | | |
|---|---|---|---|
| 2525 | **Angel**. As 2514; *mm.* 7, 14, 113 ................................................................ | 1100 | 3500 |
| 2526 | **Half Angel**. As 2517; *mm.* 7, 14, 113 ...................................................... | 950 | 3000 |
| 2527 | — Similar, but without E and rose above ship; *mm.* latin cross ............. | 1100 | 3500 |
| 2528 | **Quarter Angel**. As last; *mm.* 7, 14, 113 .................................................. | 1000 | 3250 |

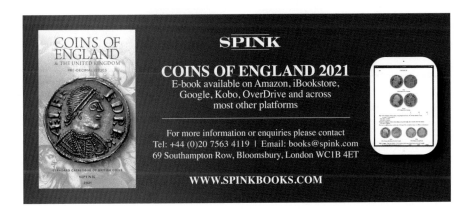

**Sixth Issue, 1583-1600** (`Fine' gold of 0.995, `crown' gold of 0.916; pound of 174.5 grs. wt.). Mintmarks: bell to **O**.

2529

| | F £ | VF £ |
|---|---|---|
| 2529 **Sovereign** (30 s:). As 2512, but tressure not normally broken by back of throne; *mm.* 54-123 ................................................................................ | 7000 | 20000 |

2530

| | F £ | VF £ |
|---|---|---|
| 2530 **Ryal** (15 s.). Queen in ship. R. Similar to 1950; *mm.* 54-86 (*rev.* only) .. | 17500 | 50000 |

*Note: Contemporary imitations of the Elizabeth Ryal are known for the Low Countries.*

2531

| | | |
|---|---|---|
| 2531 **Angel**. As 2514; *mm.* 60-123, 90-**O** ........................................................ | 1100 | 3500 |
| 2532 **Half Angel**. As 2517; *mm.* 60-86, 90-57 .................................................... | 1000 | 3250 |

2535

|  |  | F | VF |
|---|---|---|---|
|  |  | £ | £ |
| 2533 | **Quarter Angel**. As 2518; *mm.* 60-123, 90-57/–.................................... | 950 | 3000 |
| 2534 | **Pound** (20 s.). Old bust l., with elaborate dress and profusion of hair; *mm.*, lion and tun/tun, 123-**O** ........................................................................ | 3500 | 10500 |
| 2535 | **Half Pound**. Similar; *mm.* tun................................................................ | 2500 | 8000 |
| 2535A | — Similar but smaller bust with less hair; *mm.* 123-**O** .......................... | 2400 | 7500 |

2536

| 2536 | **Crown**. Similar to 2534; *mm.* 123-90. **O** ............................................... | 2250 | 7000 |
|---|---|---|---|
| 2537 | **Half Crown**. Similar; *mm.* -/123, 123-0, **O** ......................................... | 1350 | 4500 |

**Seventh Issue, 1601-3** ('Fine' gold of 0.994, 'crown' gold of 0.916; Pound of 172 gr.). Mintmarks: **1** and **2**

| 2538 | **Angel**. As 2531; *mm.* **1, 2** ......................................................................... | 2000 | 6500 |
|---|---|---|---|
| 2539 | **Pound**. As 2534; *mm.* **1, 2** ....................................................................... | 3750 | 12500 |
| 2540 | **Half Pound**. As 2535A; *mm.* **1, 2**.............................................................. | 4500 | 15000 |
| 2541 | **Crown**. As 2536; *mm.* **1, 2** ....................................................................... | 3000 | 9500 |
| 2542 | **Half Crown**. As 2537; *mm.* **1, 2**............................................................... | 2500 | 8000 |

**MILLED COINAGE, 1561-70**

2543

| 2543 | **Half Pound**. Crowned bust l.; *mm.* star, lis............................................ | 3500 | 10000 |
|---|---|---|---|
| 2544 | **Crown**. Similar; *mm.* star, lis ................................................................. | 3250 | 9000 |
| 2545 | **Half Crown**. Similar; *mm.* star, lis ......................................................... | 4500 | 13500 |

For further details on the Gold milled coinage, *see* D. G. Borden & I.D. Brown *'The milled coinage of Elizabeth I'*. BNJ 53, 1983

## SILVER
### HAMMERED COINAGE
#### Countermarked Edward VI base shillings (1560)

2546                              2547

|  | Fair £ | F £ |
|---|---|---|
| 2546 **Fourpence-halfpenny**. Edward VI 2nd period 6oz and 8oz shillings .... cmkd on obv. with a portcullis; *mm*. 66, –/33, 52, t, 111, Y and 122 | 900 | 3750 |
| 2547 **Twopence-farthing**. Edward VI 3rd period 3 oz. shillings .................... countermarked on obverse with a seated greyhound; *mm*. 92. 105, 35 and 87 | 1350 | 5250 |
| N.B. *Occasionally the wrong countermark was used* | | |

**First Issue, 1559-60** (.916 fine, shillings of 96 grs., 6.22g.)

2549                              2551

1A          1B          1D          2A          2B

|  | F £ | VF £ |
|---|---|---|
| 2548 **Shilling**. Without rose or date. ELIZABET(H), wire line inner circles, pearls on bodice, busts 1A, and 1B; *mm*. lis. ...................................... | 900 | 3500 |
| 2549 — Similar, ELIZABETH, wire line and beaded inner circles, busts 1A, 1D, 2A and 2B; *mm*. lis.............................................................................. | 200 | 1100 |

1F                 1E 2550 only               1G

|  |  | F £ | VF £ |
|---|---|---|---|
| 2550 | **Groat**. Without rose or date, wire line or no inner circle, (busts 1F and 1E); *mm*. lis | 150 | 700 |
| 2551 | — Similar, wire line and beaded inner circles, bust 1F; *mm*. lis........... | 110 | 450 |
| 2551A— | — Small bust 1G and shield (from halfgroat punches); *mm*. lis...... | 125 | 575 |

2551A              2552             2553

| 2552 | **Halfgroat**. Without rose or date, wire line inner circles; *mm*. lis......... | 200 | 900 |
|---|---|---|---|
| 2553 | **Penny**. Without rose or date, wire line inner circles; *mm*. lis............... | 450 | 1500 |
| 2554 | — Similar but dated 1558 on *obv*.; *mm*. lis.......................................... | 900 | 3500 |
| 2554A— | Similar to 2553, but wire line and beaded inner circles.; *mm*. lis .... | 500 | 1750 |

**Second Issue, 1560-1** (0.925 fineness, shilling of 96 grs., 6.22g.)

2555           2557

2558

3A            3B            3C            3J

| 2555 | **Shilling**. Without rose or date, beaded inner circles. ET instead of Z busts 3A, 3B, 3C and 3J; *mm*. 21, 94 ...................................................... | 120 | 550 |
|---|---|---|---|
| 2555A— | large bust with pearls on bodice as 2548; *mm*. 21, bust 1A, 94, bust 1B | 150 | 900 |
| 2556 | **Groat**. Without rose or date, bust as 2551; *mm*. 21, 94 ........................ | 75 | 300 |
| 2557 | **Halfgroat**. Without rose or date; *mm*. 21, 94........................................ | 40 | 175 |
| 2558 | **Penny**. Without rose or date (three bust varieties); *mm*. 21, 94............ | 35 | 135 |

**Third and Fourth Issues, 1561-77** (Same fineness and weight as last)

2559                     2561                     2561B

|      |                                                                              | F<br>£ | VF<br>£ |
|------|------------------------------------------------------------------------------|--------|---------|
| 2559 | **Sixpence**. With rose and date, large flan (inner beaded circle 19mm), large bust 3D with hair swept back, 1561; *mm.* pheon | 135 | 675 |
| 2560 | — Similar, small bust 1F, 1561; *mm.* pheon | 75 | 325 |

3D 2559 only              1F 2560              3E 2561B only

2562                                    4B 2562

| 2561   | — Smaller flan (inner beaded circle 17.5mm). Small bust 1F, 1561-6; *mm.* 53-107 | 70  | 300  |
| 2561B  | — Similar, very large bust 3E, 1563-5; *mm.* pheon | 90  | 425  |
| 2562   | — Intermediate bust 4B, ear shows, 1566-73; *mm.* 92-77 | 65  | 275  |
| 2562A  | — Similar, without date; *mm.* lion, coronet, ermine | 900 | 3250 |

2563              5A 2563                     2565

| 2563 | — Larger bust 5A, 1573-7; *mm.* 77-27 | 65 | 275 |
| 2564 | **Threepence**. With rose and date 1561, large flan (inner circle 15mm.); *mm.* pheon | 55 | 250 |
| 2565 | — smaller flan (inner circle 14mm.). Regular bust, 1561-7; *mm.* 53-92 . | 50 | 225 |

2566      2567

2570      2571

|  | | F | VF |
|---|---|---|---|
|  | | £ | £ |
| 2566 | — taller bust, ear shows, 1567-77; *mm.* 74-27 ........................................ | 45 | 210 |
| 2566A | — Similar, without rose, 1568; *mm.* coronet ........................................... | 325 | 1100 |
| 2567 | **Halfgroat**. Without rose or date; *mm.* 107-71 ........................................ | 50 | 225 |
| 2568 | **Threehalfpence**. With rose and date 1561, large flan (inner circle 12.5mm.) *mm.* pheon ...................................................................................... | 50 | 225 |
| 2569 | — — Smaller flan (inner circle 10.5-11.5mm.); 1561-2, 1564-78; *mm.* 53-27 | 45 | 200 |
| 2570 | **Penny**. Without rose or date; *mm.* 33 71, 65b, 27 .................................... | 40 | 150 |
| 2571 | **Threefarthings**. With rose and date 1561-2, 1564, 1567, 1568, 1572-7; *mm.* 53, 74, 77-27 ....................................................................... | 65 | 250 |

**Fifth Issue, 1578-82** (0.921 fineness, "shilling" of 95.6 grs., 6.19g.)

2572      2573

| 2572 | **Sixpence**. As 2563, 1578-82; *mm.* 7-113.............................................. | 55 | 240 |
|---|---|---|---|
| 2573 | **Threepence**. As 2566, 1578-82; *mm.* 7-113 .......................................... | 45 | 225 |

2574      2575

| 2574 | **Threehalfpence**. As 2569, 1578-9, 1581-2; *mm.* 7-113 ......................... | 50 | 240 |
|---|---|---|---|
| 2575 | **Penny**. As 2570; *mm.* 7-113 ................................................................ | 40 | 150 |
| 2576 | **Threefarthings**. As 2571, 1578-9, 1581-2; *mm.* 7-113 ......................... | 65 | 250 |

**Sixth Issue, 1582-1600** (0.925 fineness, shilling of 96 grs., 6.22g.)

| 2577 | 2578 |
| 2581 | 6A | 6B | 6C |

| | | F | VF |
| | | £ | £ |
| 2577 | **Shilling**. Without rose or date, ELIZAB; busts 3B and 6A ear concealed, *mm.* 60-72b. Bust 6B. Ear shows, *mm.* 79-**0** (mules occur) | 110 | 525 |
| 2578 | **Sixpence**. As 2572, ELIZABETH, 1582, 1583 *mm.* bell | 75 | 325 |
| 2578A | — Similar, ELIZAB, 1582-1589; *mm.* 60-72b | 65 | 275 |
| 2578B | — Similar, but bust 6C 1589-1600, *mm.* 72b-**0** | 65 | 275 |
| 2579 | **Halfgroat**. Without rose or date, two pellets behind bust. ℞. CIVITAS LONDON; *mm.* 60-**0** (*mm.* bell sometimes without pellets or with ··/II). | 35 | 135 |
| 2580 | **Penny**. Without rose or date. ℞. CIVITAS LONDON; *mm.* 60-**0**; 90-**0** on obv only | 40 | 150 |
| 2581 | **Halfpenny**. Portcullis. ℞. Cross and pellets; *mm.* none, 54-**0** | 35 | 135 |

**Seventh Issue, 1601-2** (0.925 fineness, shilling of 92.9 grs., 6.02)

2582

| 2582 | **Crown**. As illustration, *mm.* **1** | 1750 | 4500 |
| 2582A | – Similar, *mm.* **2** | 3250 | 12500 |

2583                                    2588

|       |                                                                      | F | VF |
|-------|----------------------------------------------------------------------|------|-------|
|       |                                                                      | £ | £ |
| 2583  | **Halfcrown**. As illustration, *mm*. **1**                          | 950  | 3000  |
| 2583A | – Similar, *mm*. **2**                                               | 3250 | 13500 |
| 2584  | **Shilling**. As 2577; bust 6B *mm*. **1, 2**                        | 110  | 525   |
| 2585  | **Sixpence**. As 2578B, 1601-2; *mm*. **1, 2**                       | 65   | 275   |
| 2586  | **Halfgroat**. As 2579, *mm*. **1, 2**                              | 35   | 135   |
| 2587  | **Penny**. As 2580, *mm*. **1, 2**                                  | 40   | 150   |
| 2588  | **Halfpenny**. As 2581, *mm*. **1, 2**                             | 35   | 135   |

**MILLED COINAGE 1561-71**

|      |                                                                                        | F | VF |
|------|----------------------------------------------------------------------------------------|------|------|
| 2589 | **Shilling**. Without rose or date; *mm*. star. Plain dress, large size (over 31 *mm*.) | 1100 | 3750 |
| 2590 | — decorated dress, large size                                                          | 475  | 1750 |
| 2591 | — — intermediate size (30-31 *mm*.)                                                    | 350  | 1200 |
| 2592 | — — small size (under 30 *mm*.)                                                        | 325  | 950  |

2593                                          2594

|      |                                                                                | F | VF |
|------|--------------------------------------------------------------------------------|------|------|
| 2593 | **Sixpence**. Small bust, large rose. R. Cross fourchee, 1561 *mm*. star         | 135  | 575  |
| 2594 | Tall narrow bust with plain dress, large rose, 1561-2; *mm*. star               | 125  | 550  |

2595                                          2596

|      |                                                                                     | F | VF |
|------|-------------------------------------------------------------------------------------|------|------|
| 2595 | — similar, but decorated dress, 1562                                                 | 120  | 525  |
| 2596 | Large broad bust, elaborately decorated dress, small rose, 1562; *mm*. star          | 120  | 525  |
| 2597 | — — cross pattée on *rev*., 1562, 64 *mm*. star                                      | 135  | 575  |

2599

|  | F<br>£ | VF<br>£ |
|---|---|---|
| 2598 — similar, pellet border, 1562-4 | 150 | 625 |
| 2598A Bust with low ruff, raised rim, 1564, 1566 (both overdates) | 175 | 675 |
| 2599 Small bust, 1567-8, ℞. As 2593; *mm*. lis | 110 | 500 |

2600                                  2601

| 2600 Large crude bust breaking legend; 1570, *mm*. lis; 1571/0, *mm*. castle<br>(over lis) | 375 | 1500 |
|---|---|---|
| 2601 **Groat**. As illustration | 200 | 800 |
| 2602 **Threepence**. With rose, small bust with plain dress, 1561 | 225 | 900 |
| 2603 Tall narrow decorated bust with medium rose, 1562 | 135 | 700 |
| 2604 Broad bust with very small rose, 1562 | 150 | 750 |
| 2605 Cross pattée on *rev*., 1563, 1564/3 | 250 | 1000 |

2606

| 2606 **Halfgroat**. As groat | 200 | 800 |
|---|---|---|
| 2607 **Threefarthings**. E . D . G . ROSA, etc., with rose. ℞. CIVITAS LONDON,<br>shield with 1563 above | 3500 | 9000 |

Further reading:

*The Hammered Silver Coins produced at the Tower Mint during the reign of Elizabeth I.*
I. D. Brown, C. H. Comber and W. Wilkinson. 2006.

*The Milled Coinage of Elizabeth I.* D. G. Borden and I. D. Brown. *BNJ* 53, 1983

## EAST INDIA COMPANY TRADE COINAGE - 'Portcullis money'

Trade coins of 8, 4, 2, and 1 Testerns were coined at the Tower Mint in 1600/1 for the first voyage of the incorporated 'Company of Merchants of London Trading into the East Indies'. The coins bear the royal arms on the obverse and a portcullis on the reverse and have the *mm*. **O**. They were struck to the weights of the equivalent Spanish silver 8, 4, 2 and 1 reales.

2607A

|  | F | VF |
|---|---|---|
|  | £ | £ |
| 2607A  Eight testerns | 6500 | 18500 |

2607B

| | F | VF |
|---|---|---|
| 2607B  Four testerns | 2750 | 8500 |

2607C

2607D

| | F | VF |
|---|---|---|
| 2607C  Two testerns | 2500 | 7500 |
| 2607D  One testern | 2250 | 6000 |

## JAMES I, 1603-25

With the accession of James VI of Scotland to the English throne, the royal titles and coat of arms are altered on the coinage; on the latter the Scottish rampant lion and the Irish harp now appear in the second and third quarters. In 1604 the weight of the gold pound was reduced and the new coin became known as the 'Unite'. Fine gold of 0·979 and crown gold of 0·916 fineness were both issued, and a gold four-shilling piece was struck 1604-19. In 1612 all the gold coins had their values raised by 10%; but in 1619 the Unite was replaced by a new, lighter 20s. piece, the 'Laurel', and a lighter rose-ryal, spur-ryal and angel were minted.

In 1613 the king granted Lord Harington a licence to coin farthings of copper as a result of repeated public demands for a low value coinage; this was later taken over by the Duke of Lennox. Towards the end of the reign coins made from silver sent to the mint from the Welsh mines had the Prince of Wales's plumes inserted over the royal arms.

*Mintmarks*

| 125 | 105 | 33 | 79 | 84 | 74 | 90 |
|---|---|---|---|---|---|---|
| 60 | 25 | 71 | 45 | 32 | 123 | 132 |
| 72b | 7a | 16 | 24 | 125 | 105 | 46 |

First coinage
1603-4    Thistle (125)
1604-5    Lis (105)

Second coinage
1604-5    Lis (105)
1605-6    Rose (33)
1606-7    Escallop (79)
1607      Grapes (84)
1607-9    Coronet (74)

1609-10   Key (90)
1610-11   Bell (60)
1611-12   Mullet (25)
1612-13   Tower (71)
1613      Trefoil (45)
1613-15   Cinquefoil (32)
1615-16   Tun (123)
1616-17   Book on lectern (132)

1617-18   Crescent (72b, gold)

1618-19   Plain cross (7a)
1619      Saltire cross (16, gold)

Third coinage
1619-20   Spur rowel (24)
1620-1    Rose (33)
1621-3    Thistle (125)
1623-4    Lis (105)
1624      Trefoil (46)

# GOLD

**FIRST COINAGE, 1603-4** (Obverse legend reads D' . G' . ANG : SCO : etc.)

|  |  | F | VF |
|---|---|---|---|
|  |  | £ | £ |
| 2608 | **Sovereign** (20s; 171.9 grs., 11.14g.). King crowned r., half-length, first bust with plain armour. R. EXVRGAT, etc.; *mm*. thistle ............................... | 4000 | 13500 |
| 2609 | — second bust with decorated armour; *mm*. thistle, lis.......................... | 4500 | 14500 |

2610                                                   2611

| 2610 | **Half-sovereign.** Crowned bust r. R. EXVRGAT, etc.; *mm*. thistle .......... | 6500 | 20000 |
|---|---|---|---|
| 2611 | **Crown.** Similar. R. TVEATVR, etc.; *mm*. 125, 105/125 ........................ | 3000 | 9500 |
| 2612 | **Halfcrown.** Similar; *mm*. thistle, lis...................................................... | 1500 | 4500 |

**N.B.** *The Quarter-Angel of this coinage is considered to be a pattern (possibly a later strike), although coin weights are known.*

**SECOND COINAGE, 1604-19** (Obverse legend reads D' G' MAG : BRIT : etc.)

2613

| 2613 | **Rose-ryal** (30s., 33s. from 1612; 213.3 grs., 13.83g.) (Fine gold, 23 ct.). King enthroned. R. Shield on rose; *mm*. 33-90, 25-132 ......................... | 4250 | 13500 |
|---|---|---|---|

2614

|  | | *F*<br>£ | *VF*<br>£ |
|---|---|---|---|
| 2614 | **Spur ryal** (15s., 16s. 6d. from 1612). King in ship; *mm.* 33, 79, 74, 25-32, 132 ........................................................................................................ | 8500 | 27500 |
| 2615 | **Angel** (10s., 11s. from 1612). Old type but larger shield; *mm.* 33-74, 60-16............................................................................................................ | 1350 | 4500 |
| 2616 | — — pierced for use as touch-piece ........................................................ | 600 | 1850 |
| 2617 | **Half-angel** (5s., 5s. 6d. from 1612; 154.8 grs., 10.03 g.) (Crown gold, 22 ct.). Similar; *mm.* 71-132, 7a, 16 ........................................................ | 4000 | 12500 |
| 2618 | **Unite** (20s., 22s. from 1612). Half-length second bust r. R. FACIAM etc.; *mm.* lis or rose............................................................................... | 800 | 2250 |

2619

| 2619 | — fourth bust; *mm.* rose to cinquefoil...................................................... | 700 | 1850 |
|---|---|---|---|
| 2620 | — fifth bust; *mm.* cinquefoil to saltire.................................................... | 700 | 1850 |
| 2621 | **Double-crown**. Third bust r. R. HENRICVS, etc.; *mm.* lis or rose ......... | 575 | 1850 |

2623

| 2622 | Fourth bust; *mm.* rose to bell ................................................................. | 550 | 1750 |
|---|---|---|---|
| 2623 | Fifth bust; *mm.* key, mullet to saltire ..................................................... | 500 | 1600 |

2624                          2627

|      |                                                                      | F £ | VF £ |
|------|----------------------------------------------------------------------|-----|------|
| 2624 | **Britain crown**. First bust r.; *mm*. lis to coronet .................................... | 300 | 750 |
| 2625 | Third bust; *mm*. key to cinquefoil............................................ | 300 | 750 |
| 2626 | Fifth bust; *mm*. cinquefoil to saltire...................................... | 275 | 700 |
| 2627 | **Thistle crown** (4s.). As illus.; *mm*. lis to plain cross ............................ | 275 | 700 |
| 2628 | — IR on only one side or absent both sides; *mm*. 79, 74, 71-123 .......... | 300 | 750 |
| 2629 | **Halfcrown**. I' D' G' ROSA SINE SPINA. First bust; *mm*. lis to key ...... | 225 | 500 |
| 2630 | Third bust; *mm*. key to trefoil, trefoil/tower............................................ | 225 | 500 |
| 2631 | Fifth bust; *mm*. cinquefoil to plain cross ................................................. | 225 | 500 |

## THIRD COINAGE, 1619-25

| | | | |
|------|----------------------------------------------------------------|------|-------|
| 2632 | **Rose-ryal** (30s.; 194.2 grs., 12.58 g.) (Fine gold, 23 ct.). King enthroned. R. XXX above shield; lis, lion and rose emblems around; *mm*. 24, 125, 105 | 5500 | 16500 |
| 2633 | Similar but plain back to throne; *mm*. trefoil........................................... | 5750 | 17500 |

2634

| | | | |
|------|---------------------------------------------------------------|------|-------|
| 2634 | **Spur-ryal** (15s.). As illus. R. Somewhat like 2614, but lis are also crowned. *mm*. 24-125, 46 ......................................................................... | 8500 | 27500 |

2635

| | | | |
|------|-----------------------------------------------------------|------|------|
| 2635 | **Angel** (10s.) of new type; *mm*. 24-46 ...................................................... | 2000 | 6000 |
| 2636 | — pierced for use as touch-piece........................................................... | 600 | 1850 |

2637           2638

| | F £ | VF £ |
|---|---|---|
| 2637 **Laurel** (20s.; 140.5 grs., 9.10 g.) (Crown gold, 22 ct.). First (large) laur, bust l.; *mm.* 24, 24/- | 1100 | 3500 |
| 2638 Second, medium, square headed bust, `SS' tie ends; *mm.* 24, 33 | 750 | 2250 |
| 2638A Third, small rounded head, ties wider apart; *mm.* 33, 105, 125 | 675 | 2000 |
| 2638B Fourth head, very small ties; *mm.* 105, 46 | 650 | 1850 |
| 2638C Fourth head variety, tie ends form a bracket to value; *mm.* lis | 650 | 1850 |

2639

| | | |
|---|---|---|
| 2639 Fifth, small rather crude bust; *mm.* trefoil | 2500 | 8500 |

2641A        2642A

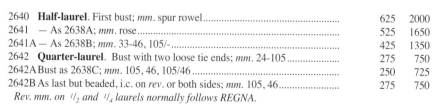

| | | |
|---|---|---|
| 2640 **Half-laurel**. First bust; *mm.* spur rowel | 625 | 2000 |
| 2641 — As 2638A; *mm.* rose | 525 | 1650 |
| 2641A — As 2638B; *mm.* 33-46, 105/- | 425 | 1350 |
| 2642 **Quarter-laurel**. Bust with two loose tie ends; *mm.* 24-105 | 275 | 750 |
| 2642A Bust as 2638C; *mm.* 105, 46, 105/46 | 250 | 725 |
| 2642B As last but beaded, i.c. on *rev.* or both sides; *mm.* 105, 46 | 275 | 750 |

*Rev. mm. on ¹/₂ and ¹/₄ laurels normally follows REGNA.*

# SILVER

2644

|  | | F | VF |
|---|---|---|---|
|  | | £ | £ |

**FIRST COINAGE, 1603-4**

| 2643 | **Crown**. King on horseback. R. EXVRGAT, etc., shield; *mm*. thistle, lis. | 1100 | 3750 |
|---|---|---|---|
| 2644 | **Halfcrown**. Similar ............................................................................. | 1250 | 5250 |

2645        2646

| 2645 | **Shilling**. First bust, square-cut beard. R. EXVRGAT, etc.; *mm*. thistle ... | 110 | 525 |
|---|---|---|---|
| 2645A | — transitional bust, nape of neck shows above broad collar, crown similar to first bust, shoulder armour as second bust, *mm*. thistle ......................... | 135 | 650 |
| 2646 | — Second bust, beard appears to merge with collar; *mm*. thistle, lis ....... | 75 | 300 |

2647        2648

| 2647 | **Sixpence**. First bust; 1603; *mm*. thistle .................................................. | 75 | 375 |
|---|---|---|---|
| 2648 | Second bust; 1603-4; *mm*. thistle, lis ...................................................... | 55 | 275 |

2649        2650        2651

| 2649 | **Halfgroat**. First bust, II behind head; *mm*. thistle, lis .............................. | 30 | 125 |
|---|---|---|---|
| 2650 | **Penny**. First bust I behind head; *mm*. thistle ............................................. | 50 | 250 |
| 2650A | — Second bust; *mm*. thistle, lis ................................................................. | 25 | 85 |
| 2651 | **Halfpenny**. As illustration; *mm*. thistle, lis ............................................. | 20 | 80 |

## SECOND COINAGE, 1604-19

2652

|      |                                                                                                                    | F £ | VF £ |
|------|--------------------------------------------------------------------------------------------------------------------|------|------|
| 2652 | **Crown**. King on horseback. ℞. QVAE DEVS, etc. *rev.* stops; *mm.* 105-84 | 950 | 3250 |
| 2653 | **Halfcrown**. Similar; *mm.* 105-79 | 1500 | 6500 |
| 2654 | **Shilling**. Third bust, beard cut square and stands out (*cf.* illus. 2657); *mm.* lis, rose | 75 | 325 |
| 2655 | — Fourth bust, armour plainer (*cf.* 2658); *mm.* 33-74, 90 over 74, or 60 over 74 | 70 | 300 |

2656

|      |                                                                                                                    |    |     |
|------|--------------------------------------------------------------------------------------------------------------------|------|------|
| 2656 | — Fifth bust, similar, but hair longer; single-arched crown, *mm.* 74; higher double-arched crown, *mm.* 74 (rare), 90-7a | 85 | 350 |

2657

2658

|       |                                                                             |    |     |
|-------|-----------------------------------------------------------------------------|------|------|
| 2657  | **Sixpence**. Third bust; 1604-6; *mm.* lis, rose, escallop | 65 | 250 |
| 2658  | — Fourth bust; 1605-16; *mm.* rose to book, 90/60, 25/60 | 65 | 250 |
| 2658A | — Fifth bust, 1618; *mm.* plain cross | 750 | 2500 |

2659

|                                                                                      | F | VF |
|--------------------------------------------------------------------------------------|-----|------|
|                                                                                      | £ | £ |
| 2659 **Halfgroat**. As illus. but larger crown on *obv.*; *mm*. lis to coronet............ | 20 | 70 |
| 2660 — — Similar, but smaller crown on *obv.*; *mm*. coronet to plain cross...... | 20 | 70 |
| 2660A As before, but TVEATVR legend both sides; *mm*. plain cross over book | 35 | 110 |
| 2661 **Penny**. As halfgroat but no crowns; *mm*. 105-32,7a and none, -/84, 32/- | 20 | 70 |
| 2662 — As before but TVEATVR legend both sides; *mm*. mullet.................... | 35 | 100 |
| 2663 **Halfpenny**. Rose, ℞ Thistle (with *mm*.) 105-25, 32; all *mm*s on rev. only | 15 | 65 |

### THIRD COINAGE, 1619-25

2664 **Crown**. As 2652, with plain or grass ground line, colon stops on *obv.*, no
stops on *rev.*; *mm*. 33-46............................................................................ 750 1850

2665

| 2665 — — plume over shield; *mm*. 125-46 ...................................................... | 1100 | 3750 |

2667

| 2666 **Halfcrown**. As 2664 with plain or grass ground line; all have bird-headed harp; *mm*. 33-46.......................................................................... | 250 | 800 |
| 2666A — — Similar but no ground line; *mm*. rose.............................................. | 675 | 2500 |

2668                              2669

|      |                                                                 | F £ | VF £ |
|------|-----------------------------------------------------------------|-----|------|
| 2667 | — — Plume over shield; groundline *mm.* 125-46...................................... | 350 | 1350 |
| 2668 | **Shilling**. Sixth (large) bust, hair longer and very curly; *mm.* 24-46......... | 80 | 350 |
| 2669 | — — plume over shield; *mm.* 125-46 ...................................................... | 225 | 900 |

2670                    2672                    2673

|      |                                                                 | F | VF |
|------|-----------------------------------------------------------------|----|----|
| 2670 | **Sixpence**. Sixth bust; 1621-4; *mm.* 33-46; 1621/0, *mm.* rose.................... | 70 | 275 |
| 2671 | **Halfgroat**. As 2660 but no stops on *rev.*; *mm.* 24-46 and none, 105 and 46, 46/- *mm.* 24 with *rev.* stops known.......................................................... | 20 | 60 |
| 2671A | Similar but no inner circles; *mm.* lis, trefoil over lis ............................... | 25 | 70 |
| 2672 | **Penny**. As illus.; *mm.* 24, 105, two pellets, none, trefoil,.......................... | 20 | 60 |
| 2672A | — Similar but without inner circles on one or both sides; *mm.* lis, two pellets............................................................................................................ | 20 | 60 |
| 2673 | **Halfpenny**. As 2663, but no *mm.* ............................................................ | 15 | 50 |

## COPPER

For further details see Tim Everson, *The Galata Guide to the Farthing Tokens of James I and Charles I*

**Farthings**

2674                              2675

|      |                                                                 | F | VF |
|------|-----------------------------------------------------------------|----|----|
| 2674 | Harington Type 1a small size, (originally tinned surface). Mintmark on cushion of crown, *Mintmarks*: A, B, C, D, F, S, Ermine, Millrind, Pellet. ............ | 40 | 100 |
| 2675 | — — 1b small size. Mintmark replaces central jewel on circlet of crown mm: Trefoil, Crescent, Mullet, or omitted (unmodified) ................................. | 30 | 50 |
| 2675A | — — 1c small size. Mintmark below crown, *mm*: :< .............................. | 40 | 100 |

2676

|  | F £ | VF £ |
|---|---|---|

2676    — — 2 normal size. Mintmark on reverse only, *mm*: Cinquefoil, Cross
        saltire, Lis, Mullet, Trefoil.....................................................    20    40
2676A  — — 3, large crown and harp, mintmark on reverse only, *mm* Martlet ...    30    70
2677    Lennox Type 1, mintmark on reverse only; *mm*: Bell, Tower ................    35    70

2678                    2679

2678    — — 2, mintmark both sides, *mm*: Flower, Fusil...............................    10    30
2679    — — 3, mintmark on obverse only, *mm*: Annulet, Coronet, Cross flory
        fitchée, Cross patée fourchée, Dagger, Eagle's head, Fusil, Key (horizontal),
        Lion passant, Quatrefoil, Rose (double), Roundel, Thistlehead, Trefoil, Tun,
        Turtle, Woolpack.................................................................    10    30
2679A  Contemporary counterfeits of Lennox Type 3, *mm*: A, Annulet, Coronet,
        Crescent, Cross (plain or patée), Dagger, Fusil, Key, Mascle, Roundel,
        Star (pierced), Stirrup, Trefoil, Triangle, Triangle with pellet below, Tun    10    25

2680

2680    — — 4, as 3 but with larger, 9 jewel, crowns, *mm*: A, Dagger, Fusil, Lion
        rampant, Lis (three), Mascle, Stirrup, Trefoil, Triangle...........................    10    30
2680A  Contemporary forgeries of Lennox Type 4, *mm* A, Annulet, Dagger, Fusil,
        Lis, Mascle, Pellets (four), Tun, ..............................................    10    25
2681    — — 5, oval flan, legend starts at bottom left, *mm* Cross patée .............    60    120

*Lennox Type 5, the oval farthings, were issued for use in Ireland*

Numismatically, this reign is one of the most interesting. Some outstanding machine-made coins were produced by Nicholas Briot, a French die-sinker, but they could not be struck at sufficient speed to supplant hand-hammering methods, and the weights often had to be adjusted by blank filing. In 1637 a branch mint was set up at Aberystwyth to coin silver extracted from the Welsh mines and dies supplied from Tower Mint. After the king's final breach with Parliament the parliamentary government continued to issue coins at London with Charles's name and portrait until the king's trial and execution. The coinage of copper farthings continued to be manufactured privately under licences held first by the Duchess of Richmond and, lastly, by Lord Maltravers. Parliament took control of the Token House in 1643, and production ceased the following year.

During the Civil War coins were struck at a number of towns to supply coinage for those areas of the country under Royalist control. Many of these coins have an abbreviated form of the 'Declaration' made at Wellington, Shropshire, Sept., 1642, in which Charles promised to uphold the Protestant Religion, the Laws of England and the Liberty of Parliament. Amongst the more spectacular pieces are the gold triple unites and the silver pounds and half-pounds struck at Shrewsbury and Oxford, and the emergency coins, some made from odd-shaped pieces of silver plate during the sieges of Newark, Scarborough, Carlisle and Pontefract.

*Mintmarks*

| 105 | 10 | 96 | 71 | 57 | 88 | 101 | 35 |
|-----|-----|-----|-----|-----|-----|-----|-----|

| 87 | 107 | 60 | 70 | 123 | 57 | 119a | 23 |
|-----|-----|-----|-----|-----|-----|-----|-----|

| 119b | 98 | 112 | 81 | 120 | 109 |
|------|-----|------|-----|------|------|

## Tower Mint under Charles I

| 1625 | Lis (105) | 1633-4 | Portcullis (107) |
|------|-----------|--------|------------------|
| 1625-6 | Cross Calvary (10) | 1634-5 | Bell (60) |
| 1626-7 | Negro's head (96) | 1635-6 | Crown (75) |
| 1627-8 | Castle (71) | 1636-8 | Tun (123) |
| 1628-9 | Anchor (57) | 1638-9 | Anchor (57) |
| 1629-30 | Heart (88) | 1639-40 | Triangle (119a) |
| 1630-1 | Plume (101) | 1640-1 | Star (23) |
| 1631-2 | Rose (35) | 1641-3 | Triangle in circle |
| 1632-3 | Harp (87) | | (119b) |

## Tower Mint under Parliament

| 1643-4 | P in brackets (98) |
|--------|---------------------|
| 1644-5 | R in brackets (112) |
| 1645 | Eye (81) |
| 1645-6 | Sun (120) |
| 1646-8 | Sceptre (109) |

Mint mark no. 57 maybe upright, inverted, or horizontal to left or right.

| 59 | B | 58var | 58 |
|-----|-----|-------|-----|

## Briot's Mint

| 1631-2 | Flower and B (59) | 1638-9 | Anchor (57) |
|--------|-------------------|--------|-------------|
| 1632 | B | | Anchor and B (58) |
| | | | (B upright or on side) |
| | | | Anchor and Mullet (58v) |

| 61 | 104 | 35 | 92 | 103 | 6 | 65b | 71 |
|----|-----|----|----|-----|---|-----|----|
| 89 | 91*var* | 131 | 84 | 94*var* | 64 | 93 | 34 |
| 102 | 67 | 127 | 128 | 129 | 25 | 83 | 100 |
| | 134 | 71 | A | B | 75 | | |

## Provincial and Civil War Mints

| | |
|---|---|
| 1638-42 | Book (61, *Aberystwyth*) |
| 1642 | Plume (104, *Shrewsbury*) |
| | Pellets or pellet (*Shrewsbury*) |
| 1642-3 | Rose (35, *Truro*) |
| | Bugle (134, *Truro*) |
| 1642-4 | Lion (92, *York*) |
| 1642-6 | Plume (103, *Oxford*) |
| | Pellet or pellets (*Oxford*) |
| | Lis (105, *Oxford*) |
| 1643 | Cross pattee (6, *Bristol*) |
| | Acorn (65b, *Bristol*) |
| | Castle (71, *Worcester* or *Shrewsbury*) |
| | Helmet (89, *Worcester* and *Shrewsbury*) |
| 1643-4 | Leopard's head (91 *var. Worcester*) |
| | Two lions (131, *Worcester*) |
| | Lis (105, *Worcs.* or *Shrews.*) |
| | Bunch of grapes (84, *Worcs.* or *Shrews.*) |
| | Bird (94 var., *Worcs.* or *Shrews.*) |

| | |
|---|---|
| 1643-4 | Boar's head (64 *Worcs.* or *Shrews.*) |
| | Lion rampant (93, *Worcs.* or *Shrews.*) |
| | Rosette (34, *Worcs.* or *Shrews.*) |
| 1643-5 | Plume (102, *Bristol*) |
| | Br. (67, *Bristol*) |
| | Pellets (*Bristol*) |
| | Rose (35, *Exeter*) |
| | Rosette (34, *Oxford*) |
| 1643-6 | Floriated cross (127, *Oxford*) |
| 1644 | Cross pattee (6, *Oxford*) |
| | Lozenge (128, *Oxford*) |
| | Billet (129, *Oxford*) |
| | Mullet (25, *Oxford*) |
| 1644-5 | Gerb (83, *Chester*) |
| | Pear (100, *Worcester*) |
| | Lis (105, *Hereford?*) |
| | Castle (71, *Exeter*) |
| 1645-6 | Plume (102, *Ashby, Bridgnorth*) |
| 1645 | A (*Ashby*) |
| 1646 | B (*Bridgnorth*) |
| 1648-9 | Crown (75, *Aberystwyth Furnace*) |

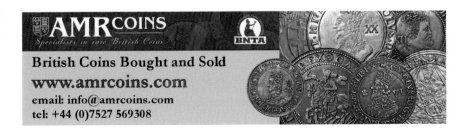

# GOLD COINAGE

**TOWER, UNDER THE KING (1625-42), AND UNDER PARLIAMENT (1642-9)**
*For bust varieties on Tower Mint Gold see H. Schneider BNJ 1955-61*
*Numbers in brackets following each entry refer to numbers employed in previous editions of this catalogue*

|  |  | F £ | VF £ |
|---|---|---|---|
| 2682 | **Angel**. St. Michael slaying dragon, no mark of value. R. Three masted ship, royal arms on mainsail; mm. lis, cross calvary | 4500 | 16500 |
| 2682A | — — — pierced for use as touch-piece (2683) | 1500 | 5500 |
| 2683 | — X in field to right of St. Michael; m.m. negro's head, castle, anchor, heart, castle and negro's head/castle, anchor and castle/anchor (2684) | 2750 | 10000 |
| 2683A | — — — pierced for use as touch-piece (2685) | 750 | 2250 |
| 2684 | — X in field to left of St. Michael; mm. negro's head, heart, rose, harp, portcullis, bell, crown, tun, anchor, triangle, star, triangle-in-circle (2686) | 2250 | 8500 |

2685

| 2684A | — — — pierced for use as touch-piece (2687) | 600 | 2000 |
|---|---|---|---|
| 2685 | **Unite**. Group A, first bust, in coronation robes, bust 1, high double-arched crown. R. Square-topped shield, plain or elaborate garnishing; mm. lis (2688, 2688A) | 800 | 2250 |
| 2686 | — — bust 1a, flatter single-arched crown; mm. lis, cross calvary (2689, 2689A) | 850 | 2500 |
| 2687 | Group B, second bust, in ruff, armour and mantle. R. Square-topped shield; m.m. cross calvary, negro's head, castle, anchor, heart (2690) | 750 | 2250 |

2688

| 2688 | — — more elongated bust, usually dividing legend, mm. anchor, heart, plume (2690A) | 800 | 2400 |
|---|---|---|---|
| 2689 | — — — anchor below bust; mm. (2691) | 1850 | 6500 |
| 2689A | Group B/C mule. R. Oval shield with CR at sides; mm. plume (2691A) | 1000 | 3500 |
| 2690 | Group C, third bust, shorter with heavier armour. R. Oval shield with CR at sides; mm. plume, rose (2692) | 900 | 2750 |
| 2691 | Group D, fourth bust, with falling lace collar, bust 4, large bust with jewelled crown.R. Oval shield with CR at sides; mm. harp, portcullis (2693) | 750 | 2250 |
| 2692 | — — bust 5, smaller bust, unjewelled crown; mm. portcullis, bell, crown, tun, anchor, triangle, star (2693A) | 750 | 2250 |

|  | F | VF |
|---|---|---|
|  | £ | £ |

2693  — — — (under Parliament); mm. (P), (P)/- (2710) ................................ 1350 4500

2694  Group F, sixth 'Briot's' bust, with stellate lace collar. R. Oval shield with
CR at sides, mm. triangle, star, triangle-in-circle (2694)......................... 900 2750

2695  — — (under Parliament); mm. (P), (R) (2711) ...................................... 1350 4500

2696

2696  Group G, (under Parliament), seventh bust, smaller collar; mm. eye, sun, sceptre
(2712)............................................................................................................. 2000 6500

2697                                    2699

2697  **Double-crown**. Group A, first bust, in coronation robes, bust 1, high double-
arched crown, both arches jewelled. R. Square-topped shield; mm. lis (2696) 525 1650

2698  — — bust 1a, flatter crown, outer arch only jewelled; m.m. lis, cross calvary
(2696A) .......................................................................................................... 475 1500

2699  Group B, second bust, in ruff, armour and mantle, bust 2. R. Square-topped
shield; mm. cross calvary, negro's head, castle, anchor (2697)............... 425 1250

2700  — — busts 3-4, more elongated bust, usually dividing legend; mm.
anchor, heart, plume (2697A) ..................................................................... 450 1350

2700A Group B/C mule, elongated bust dividing legend. R. oval shield, *mm*. plume 650 2000

2701  Group C, third bust, bust 5. R. Oval shield with CR at sides; mm. plume, rose
(2698)............................................................................................................. 525 1650

2702  Group D, fourth bust, with falling lace collar, bust 6, large bust with jewelled
crown. R. Oval shield with CR at sides; mm. harp, crown (2699) .......... 500 1500

2703  — — bust 7, smaller head, inner or both arches of crown unjewelled; mm. harp,
portcullis, bell, crown, tun, anchor (2699A-C)........................................ 475 1400

2703A — — — Group Da, (under Parliament), re-cut Group D bust punches;
m.m. eye (2713) ............................................................................................ 1350 4000

2704  Group E, fifth bust, 'Aberystwyth' bust, bust 8, double-arched crown. R. Oval
shield with CR at sides; m.m. anchor (2700)........................................... 750 2250

2705  — — bust 9, smaller 'Aberystwyth' bust, single-arched crown; m.m. anchor,
triangle (2700A)............................................................................................ 675 2100

2705A — — — Group Ea, (under Parliament), re-cut bust 9; m.m. sun, sceptre (2714) 1100 3500

2706  Group F, sixth 'Briot's' bust, with stellate lace collar, bust 10. R. Oval shield
with CR at sides; mm. triangle, star, triangle-in-circle (2701) ............... 575 1750

|      |                                                                      | *F* | *VF* |
|------|----------------------------------------------------------------------|-----|------|
|      |                                                                      | £   | £    |
| 2707 | — — (under Parliament); mm. (P), (R) (2715) ........................................ | 700 | 2250 |
| 2708 | Group H, (under Parliament), bust 11, dumpy crude bust, single flat-arched crown; mm. sun (2716).......................................................................... | 1500 | 4500 |

2710                                            2715

| 2709 | **Crown**. Group A, first bust, in coronation robes, bust 1 var, tall narrow bust, double-arched crown. ℞. Square-topped shield; mm. lis (2703) ............. | 325 | 950 |
|------|------|------|------|
| 2710 | — bust 1, broader, less angular bust; m.m. lis, cross calvary (2703A) ... | 350 | 1000 |
| 2711 | Group B, second bust, in ruff, armour and mantle, bust 2. ℞. Square-topped shield; mm. cross calvary, negro's head, castle (2704)............................. | 325 | 950 |
| 2712 | — — bust 3, narrower; more elongated bust; m.m. anchor, heart, plume (2704A)................................................................................................... | 300 | 900 |
| 2713 | — — — anchor below bust; mm. anchor (2704B)................................ | 750 | 2250 |
| 2713A | Group B/C mule. ℞. Oval shield with CR at sides; mm. plume, rose (2705) | 325 | 950 |
| 2714 | Group C, third bust, bust 4. ℞. Oval shield with CR at sides; mm. plume (2706)...................................................................................................... | 375 | 1100 |
| 2715 | Group D, fourth bust, with falling lace collar, busts 5, 7. ℞. Oval shield with CR at sides; m.m. harp, -/harp, portcullis, portcullis/bell, bell, crown, tun, anchor, triangle, star/triangle, star, triangle-in-circle (2707) ............ | 250 | 750 |
| 2716 | — — (under Parliament), bust 5, jewelled crown; m.m. (P), ( R), eye, sun (2717).................................................................................................... | 350 | 1000 |
| 2716A | — — (under Parliament), bust 6, unjewelled crown; m.m. eye, sun, sceptre (2717A)................................................................................................. | 425 | 1100 |
| 2717 | Group E, fifth bust, small 'Aberystwyth' bust, bust 8. ℞. Oval shield with CR at sides; mm. anchor (2708) ...................................................... | 450 | 1250 |
| 2721C | — Group F, sixth 'Briot's' bust, bust 9, only known as Briot/hammered mule (see 2721C below) ........................................................................... | 1250 | 4500 |

## NICHOLAS BRIOT'S COINAGES, 1631-2 and 1638-9
## MILLED ISSUES, 1631-2

| 2718 | **Angel**. Type somewhat as Tower but smaller and neater; *mm*. -/B ........ | 13500 | 35000 |
|------|------|------|------|

2719

| 2719 | **Unite**. As illustration. ℞. FLORENT etc.; *mm*. flower and B/B .............. | 4500 | 13500 |
|------|------|------|------|
| 2720 | **Double-crown**. Similar but X. ℞. CVLTORES, etc. *mm*. flower and B/B | 2500 | 7500 |

2720A Similar but King's crown unjewelled: *mm*. flower and B/B, B ..............  2750  8250
2721  **Crown**. Similar; *mm*. B ........................................................................  6500  18500

## BRIOT'S HAMMERED ISSUES, 1638-9

2721A **Unite**. Briot's (sixth) bust, large lace collar. R. FLORENT etc., Briot's
square-topped shield dividing crowned C R; *mm*. anchor ......................  7500  25000
2721B **Double-crown**. Briot's bust, similar. R. CVLTORES etc., square-topped
shield dividing crowned C R; *mm*. anchor............................................  2500  7500
2721C **Crown**. Briot's bust, similar. R. CVLTORES etc., oval shield dividing
crowned C R (a Briot hammered issue/Tower mule); *mm*. anchor ..........  1350  4500

## GOLD COINAGES

### PROVINCIAL ISSUES AND COINAGES OF THE ENGLISH CIVIL WAR, 1642-9
### CHESTER, 1644

2722  **Unite**. As Tower. Somewhat like a crude Tower sixth bust. R. Crowned,
oval shield, crowned CR, *mm*. plume .....................................................  25000  95000

### SHREWSBURY, 1642 (See also 2749)

2723  **Triple unite**, 1642. Half-length figure l holding sword and olive-branch;
*mm*.: R. EXVRGAT, etc., around RELIG PROT, etc., in two wavy lines.
III and three plumes above, date below .................................................  85000  275000

2727

|  | | F | VF |
|--|--|---|----|
|  | | £ | £ |

## OXFORD, 1642-6

| 2724 | **Triple unite**. As last, but *mm*. plume, tall narrow bust, 1642 ................. | 12500 | 35000 |
| 2725 | Similar, 1643 ........................................................................................ | 20000 | 60000 |
| 2725A | Large bust of fine style. King holds short olive branch; *mm*. small lis .... | 50000 | 175000 |
| 2726 | As last, but taller bust, with scarf behind shoulder, 1643, *mm*. plume ..... | 13500 | 37500 |
| 2727 | Similar, but without scarf, longer olive branch, 1643 ............................. | 12500 | 35000 |
| 2728 | Similar, but OXON below 1643, rosette stops ......................................... | 25000 | 75000 |
| 2729 | Smaller size, olive branch varies, bust size varies, 1644 OXON ............. | 13500 | 37500 |
| 2730 | — Obv. as 2729, 1644 / OX ................................................................. | 15000 | 42500 |
| 2731 | **Unite**. Tall thin bust. R. 'Declaration' in two wavy lines, 1642; *no mm*... | 3250 | 10500 |
| 2732 | — R. 'Declaration' in three lines on continuous scroll, 1642-3 ................ | 3500 | 11000 |
| 2733 | Tall, well-proportioned bust. R. Similar, 1643, no *mm* ........................... | 4500 | 15000 |
| 2734 | Shorter bust, king's elbow not visible. R. Similar, 1643; *mm*. plume/- .... | 3000 | 9500 |

2735

| 2735 | Similar but longer olive branch curving to l. 1644 / OX; *mm*. plume ...... | 3250 | 10500 |
| 2735A | Similar, but dumpy bust breaking lower i.c., small flan .......................... | 3250 | 10500 |
| 2736 | Tall bust to edge of coin. R. Similar, 1643 ............................................. | 7500 | 25000 |
| 2737 | As 2734. R. 'Declaration' in three straight lines, 1644 / OX (as shilling *rev*. S2971) .......................................................................................... | 5750 | 17500 |
| 2738 | Similar to 2734, but smaller size; small bust, low olive branch. 1645 ..... | 5000 | 15000 |
| 2739 | — R. Single plume above 'Declaration', 1645-6 / OX; *mm*. plume, rosette, none ........................................................................................... | 4000 | 13500 |
| 2740 | **Half-unite**. 'Declaration' in three straight lines, 1642 ............................. | 3250 | 10500 |
| 2741 | 'Declaration' on scroll; *mm*. plume; 1642-3 ............................................. | 3000 | 10000 |

2742

|  | F | VF |
|  | £ | £ |
| 2742  Bust to bottom of coin, 1643; Oxford plumes ............................................ | 2500 | 8500 |
| 2743  — 1644 / OX. Three Shrewsbury plumes (neater work) ........................ | 4000 | 12500 |

**BRISTOL, 1643-5**
2744  **Unite**. Somewhat as 2734; Two busts known. *mm*. Br. or Br/ plumelet.;
1645 .............................................................................................. 22500  75000
2745  **Half-unite**. Similar 1645 ........................................................ 13500  42500

**TRURO, 1642–3**
2745A**Half-Unite**. Crowned bust l. (similar to Tower 4th bust). R.
CVLT, etc., crowned shield.................................................... 13500  42500

**EXETER, 1643–5**
2746  **Unite**. *obv*. sim. to early Oxford bust. R. FLORENT, etc., crowned oval
shield between crowned CR, *mm*. rose ...................................... 25000  80000
2747  — R. CVLTORES, etc., similar but no CR ...................................... 25000  80000

**WORCESTER, 1643-4**
2748  **Unite**. Crude bust R. FLORENT, etc., double annulet stops, crowned oval
shield, lion's paws on either side of garniture, no *mm*........................... 22500  75000

**SALOPIA (SHREWSBURY) , 1644**
2749  **Unite**. *Obv*. bust in armour. R. Cr. shield, crowned CR. *mm*. lis/- ........... 30000  95000

**COLCHESTER BESIEGED, 1648**
2750  **Ten Shillings** Gateway of castle between CR; below OBS COL 16 S/X 48.
Uniface – now considered a later concoction ..........................................

**PONTEFRACT BESIEGED, 1648-9**. After the death of Charles I, in the name of Charles II
2751  **Unite**. DVM : SPIRO : SPERO around CR crowned. CAROLVS :
SECVИDVS : 16 48, castle, OBS on l., PC above. ........................... 85000 275000
2752  **Unite**. CAROL : II, etc., around HANC : DEVS, etc. R. POST : MORTEM,
etc.,around castle. *Octagonal*................................................ 75000 250000

## SILVER COINAGES

**TOWER, UNDER THE KING (1625-42), AND UNDER PARLIAMENT (1642-9)**
2753  **Crown**. Group I, first horseman, type 1a, king on horseback left, horse
caparisoned with plume on head and crupper. R. Square-topped shield over
long cross fourchee; mm. lis, cross calvary ...................................... 725  2400
2754  — — 1b. R. Plume above shield, no cross fourchee; mm. lis, cross
calvary, castle.......................................................... 1750  5750
2755  Group II, second horseman, type 2a, smaller horse, plume on head only,
cross on housing. R. Oval shield over cross fourchee, CR above; mm. harp  650  2000
2756  — — 2b1. R. Plume between CR above shield, no cross fourchee; mm.
plume, rose............................................................... 850  3000
2757  — — 2b2. R. Plume between CR, cross fourchee; mm. harp ............... 950  3500

2758

|      |                                                                                                                                                         | F £ | VF £ |
|------|---------------------------------------------------------------------------------------------------------------------------------------------------------|-----|------|
| 2758 | Group III, third horseman, type 3a, horse without caparisons, sword upright. R. Oval shield without CR; mm. bell, crown, tun, anchor, triangle, star.. | 750 | 2500 |
| 2759 | — — 3b. R. Plume above shield; mm. portcullis, crown, tun | 900 | 3250 |
| 2760 | 'Briot's' horseman with groundline, lozenge stops on obverse; mm. triangle in circle | 7500 | 25000 |
| 2761 | Group IV, (under Parliament), fourth horseman, type 4, foreshortened horse R. Oval shield; mm. (P), ( R), eye, sun | 750 | 2500 |
| 2762 | Group V, (under Parliament), fifth horseman, type 5, tall spirited horse; mm. sun | 950 | 3500 |

2763                                    2769

|      |                                                                                                                                                                                 | F   | VF   |
|------|---------------------------------------------------------------------------------------------------------------------------------------------------------------------------------|-----|------|
| 2763 | **Halfcrown**. Group I, first horseman, type 1a1, horse caparisoned with plume on head and crupper, rose on housings, ground-line. R. Square-topped shield over long cross fourchee; mm. lis | 450 | 1850 |
| 2764 | — — 1a2. No rose on housings, no ground-line; mm. lis, cross calvary | 225 | 950 |
| 2765 | — — — ground-line; mm. lis | 375 | 1500 |
| 2766 | — — 1a3. No rose on housings, no ground-line. R. No long cross, heavy or light garnishing to shield; mm. cross calvary*, negro's head, castle | 225 | 900 |
| 2767 | — — — 1b. R. Plume above shield, heavy or light garnishing; mm. lis, cross calvary*, negro's head, castle, anchor | 575 | 2250 |
| 2768 | Group II, second horseman, type 2/1b, plume on horse's head only, rose on housings. R. Plume over shield; mm. heart, plume | 950 | 3500 |
| 2769 | — — 2a. Smaller horse, cross on housings. R. Oval shield with CR above (CR divided by rose (very rare), lis over rose (rare), or lis); mm. plume, rose, plume/rose | 100 | 375 |
| 2770 | — — — 2b. R. Plume between CR above shield; mm. plume, rose | 250 | 1000 |

2773

|      |                                                                                                                                                                 | F £  | VF £ |
|------|-----------------------------------------------------------------------------------------------------------------------------------------------------------------|------|------|
| 2771 | — — 2c. R. Oval draped shield with CR at sides; mm. harp, portcullis, portcullis/harp                                                                            | 100  | 375  |
| 2772 | — — — 2d. R. Plume above shield; mm. harp                                                                                                                        | 1350 | 5250 |
| 2773 | Group III, third horseman, type 3a1, no caparisons on horse, scarf flying from king's waist. R. Oval garnished shield; mm. bell, bell/crown, crown, tun, triangle | 85   | 300  |
| 2774 | — — — 3b. R. Plume above shield; mm. portcullis, bell, crown, tun.....                                                                                           | 150  | 575  |
| 2775 | — — 3a2. King wears cloak flying from shoulder. R. Oval garnished shield; mm. tun, anchor, triangle, star, triangle-in-circle                                    | 80   | 275  |

2776            2779

|       |                                                                                                                                                      | F £ | VF £ |
|-------|------------------------------------------------------------------------------------------------------------------------------------------------------|-----|------|
| 2776  | — — — — rough ground under horse; mm. triangle, star                                                                                                  | 80  | 275  |
| 2777  | — — horseman of finer style, short busy tail, cloak like arrowhead behind shoulder, no ground below; mm. triangle, star                               | 110 | 450  |
| 2778  | — — 3a3, (under Parliament), no ground, cruder workmanship; mm. (P), ( R), eye, sun                                                                   | 70  | 250  |
| 2779  | Group IV, fourth horseman, type 4, foreshortened horse. R. Oval garnished shield; mm. star, triangle in circle                                        | 70  | 250  |
| 2779A | — — (under Parliament); mm. (P)                                                                                                                       | 150 | 625  |
| 2779B | — —, transitional type 4/5, mm. sun                                                                                                                   | 125 | 525  |
| 2780  | Group V, (under Parliament), fifth horseman, type 5, tall spirited horse. R. Oval garnished shield; mm. sun, sceptre                                  | 85  | 300  |

*Light weight half crowns (204 grains) exist of No. 2766 and 2767, mm. cross calvary*

2781                              2782

| | F £ | VF £ |
|---|---|---|
| 2781 **Shilling**. Group A, first bust, type 1, in coronation robes, bust 1, high double-arched crown, both arches jewelled. R. Square-topped shield over cross fourchee (Sharp A1/1); mm. lis | 95 | 475 |
| 2782 — — bust 2, larger crown, outer arch only jewelled (Sharp A2/1-2); mm. lis*, cross calvary* | 90 | 450 |
| 2783 — — — 1b1. R. Plume above shield, no cross fourchee (Sharp A2/3); mm. lis, cross calvary | 850 | 3500 |
| 2784 Group B, second bust, type 1a, in ruff, armour and mantle. R. Square-topped shield over cross fourchee (Sharp B1-5/1); mm. cross calvary*, negro's head, castle | 90 | 425 |
| 2785 — — 1b2. R. Plume above shield, no cross fourchee (Sharp B1-5/2); mm. cross calvary*, negro's head, castle, anchor, heart, plume | 200 | 800 |
| 2786 — — 1b3. R. Plume above shield, cross fourchee (Sharp B2/3); mm. negro's head | 1750 | 5750 |
| 2787 Group C, third bust, type 2a, with more visible armour. R. Oval garnished shield with CR above (Sharp C1/1, C2/1-3); mm. plume, rose | 75 | 325 |
| 2788 — — 2b. R. Plume above shield (Sharp C1/4, C2/4-6, C3/5); mm. plume, rose | 175 | 750 |
| 2789 Group D, fourth bust, type 3.1, with falling lace collar, inner circles. R. Garnished oval shield with CR at sides (Sharp D1-6/1); mm. harp, portcullis | 70 | 300 |
| 2790 — — — 3.2. R. Plume above shield (Sharp D1- 3/2); mm. harp | 750 | 2750 |

2791

| | | |
|---|---|---|
| 2791 — — 3a, no inner circles. R. Round garnished shield, no CR ( Sharp E1/1-2, E2/1-2; E3/2); mm. bell, crown, tun | 50 | 200 |
| 2792 — — — rare bust varieties, no inner circles: (a) large crude bust (Sharp E4/2); mm. tun; (b) neat 'Aberystwyth' bust (Sharp E5/2); mm. tun | 60 | 250 |
| 2793 — — 3b. R. Plume above shield (Sharp E1-2/3); mm. bell, crown, tun | 90 | 450 |

*Light weight shillings (81.75 grains) exist of No. 2782, mm. lis, cross calvary over lis; No. 2784, mm. cross calvary; and No. 2785 mm. cross calvary*
*See Sharp BNJ 1977 for shilling bust varieties including fine work coins. See also Holt, Hulett and Lyle, BNJ 2014.*

2794                                         2797

|  | | F<br>£ | VF<br>£ |
|---|---|---|---|
| 2794 | Group E, fifth "Aberystwyth' bust, type 4.2, double-arched crown, small or large XII. R. Square-topped shield over cross moline (Sharp F1/1); mm. tun, anchor ............................................................................................... | 70 | 300 |
| 2795 | — — 4.1, larger bust, single-arched crown, small or large XII (Sharp F2/1); mm. tun, anchor ..................................................................................... | 75 | 325 |
| 2796 | — — 4.3, smaller bust, single-arched crown, large XII (Sharp F3/1-2); mm. tun, anchor, triangle ........................................................................ | 60 | 250 |
| 2797 | — — 4.1var., larger bust with rounded shoulder, large XII (Sharp F5/1-2); mm. anchor, triangle ............................................................................... | 60 | 250 |
| 2798 | — — rare bust varieties : (a) small 'Aberystwyth' bust, double-arched crown (Sharp F4/1); mm. anchor (to right); (b) small 'Briot's' bust, with stellate lace collar, single-arched crown (Sharp F6/1-2); mm. triangle; (c) small 'Aberystwyth' bust, single-arched crown (Sharp F7/2); mm. triangle-in-circle ..................................................................................... | 125 | 575 |
| 2799 | Group F, sixth large 'Briot's' bust, type 4.4, with stellate lace collar, double-arched crown. R. Square-topped shield over cross moline (Sharp G 1/1-2); mm. triangle, star, triangle-in-circle ............................................ | 45 | 160 |

2800                                         2803

|  | | F<br>£ | VF<br>£ |
|---|---|---|---|
| 2800 | — — — (under Parliament) (Sharp G1-2/2); mm. (P), ( R), eye, sun ..... | 45 | 160 |
| 2801 | — — 4.4 var., (under Parliament), small thin bust, 'nick' below truncation (Sharp G3/2); mm. sun ............................................................................. | 325 | 1250 |
| 2802 | Group G, (under Parliament), seventh bust, type 4.5, tall coarse narrow bust. R. Square-topped shield over cross moline (Sharp H1/1); mm. sun, sceptre . | 80 | 350 |
| 2803 | — — 4.6, shorter slim better proportioned bust (Sharp H2/2); mm. sceptre ..................................................................................................... | 80 | 350 |
| 2804 | — — — short broad bust (Sharp H3/2); mm. sceptre ............................. | 85 | 400 |

2805                                  2810

|       |                                                                                                                                                                                                                                                                                            | F   | VF   |
|-------|--------------------------------------------------------------------------------------------------------------------------------------------------------------------------------------------------------------------------------------------------------------------------------------------|-----|------|
|       |                                                                                                                                                                                                                                                                                            | £   | £    |
| 2805  | **Sixpence**. Group A, first bust, in coronation robes, type 1, small bust, double-arched crown. R. Square-topped shield over cross fourchee, date above; 1625, mm. lis                                                                                                                      | 100 | 425  |
| 2806  | — — broader bust, larger crown; 1625, mm. lis, cross calvary*; 1626, mm. cross calvary*                                                                                                                                                                                                     | 110 | 450  |
| 2807  | Group B, second bust (several varieties), type 1a1, in ruff, armour and mantle. R. Square-topped shield over cross fourchee, date above; 1625, mm. cross calvary; 1626, mm. cross calvary*; 1627, mm. negro's head, 1627, mm. negro's head, castle; 1628, mm. castle, anchor; 1629, mm. anchor, heart | 135 | 575  |
| 2808  | — — 1a2. R. No cross fourchee; 1630, mm. heart, plume                                                                                                                                                                                                                                       | 325 | 1250 |
| 2809  | Group C, third bust, type 2a. R. Oval garnished shield with CR above; mm. plume, rose                                                                                                                                                                                                       | 85  | 325  |
| 2810  | — — 2b. R. Plume above shield; mm. plume, rose, plume/rose                                                                                                                                                                                                                                  | 125 | 500  |

2811                  2814                  2819

|       |                                                                                                                                                                                                                              | F   | VF  |
|-------|------------------------------------------------------------------------------------------------------------------------------------------------------------------------------------------------------------------------------|-----|-----|
| 2811  | Group D, fourth bust, type 3, with falling lace collar, inner circles, (medium, large and small bust). R. Oval garnished shield with CR at sides; mm. harp, portcullis                                                        | 60  | 275 |
| 2812  | — — — omits C R by shield; mm. portcullis                                                                                                                                                                                     | 135 | 525 |
| 2813  | — — 3a, no inner circles (type 3/3a mules exist); mm. bell, crown, tun.                                                                                                                                                       | 50  | 200 |
| 2814  | Group E, fifth 'Aberystwyth' bust, type 4.1, double-arched crown, small or large VI. R. Square-topped shield over cross moline; mm. tun, anchor .                                                                             | 60  | 225 |
| 2815  | — — — R. Lyre cross-ends; mm. tun                                                                                                                                                                                             | 175 | 750 |
| 2816  | — — 4.2, single-arched crown; mm. tun, anchor, triangle                                                                                                                                                                       | 50  | 200 |
| 2817  | Group F, sixth 'Briot's' bust, type 4.3, with stellate lace collar. R. Square-topped shield over cross moline; mm. triangle, star, triangle-in-circle ....                                                                    | 45  | 185 |
| 2818  | — — (under Parliament); mm. (P), ( R)                                                                                                                                                                                         | 70  | 275 |
| 2819  | Group G, (under Parliament), late 'Aberystwyth' bust with riveted shoulder, type 4.4. R. Square-topped shield over cross moline; mm. (P), ( R), eye, sun, sceptre                                                             | 60  | 250 |

*Light weight sixpences (40.85 grains) exist of No. 2806, 1625, mm. cross calvary, 1626, mm. cross calvary; and No. 2807, 1626, mm. cross calvary*

|      |                                                                 | F    | VF   |
|------|-----------------------------------------------------------------|------|------|
|      |                                                                 | £    | £    |
| 2820 | − − 4.5, squat bust of crude style; mm. eye, sun (over eye) ...............  | 125  | 475  |
| 2821 | − − 4.5 var., small 3a type bust, double-arched crown, inner circle both sides; mm. sun (over eye) ........................ | 225  | 900  |

2822                2824                2832

| 2822 | **Halfgroat**. Group A, without bust, crowned rose each side, type 1, inner circles on one or both sides;mm. lis, lis/-, cross calvary, castle, none...... | 25 | 100 |
| 2823 | − − 1a, without inner circles; mm. negro's head, castle, anchor, heart, plume .......................................................................................... | 25 | 100 |
| 2824 | Group B, second bust, type 2a, in ruff and mantle. R. Oval shield; mm. plume, rose.......................................................................................... | 25 | 110 |
| 2825 | − − 2b. R. plume above shield; mm. plume, plume/-, rose .................. | 35 | 150 |
| 2826 | Group C, third bust, more armour, crown breaks inner circle; mm. plume, rose............................................................................................ | 25 | 110 |
| 2827 | − − R. Plume above shield; mm. plume.............................................. | 35 | 150 |
| 2828 | Group D, fourth bust, type 3.1, no inner circles. R. Oval shield dividing C R; mm. harp, portcullis crown ............................... | 20 | 80 |
| 2829 | − − − − 3.2-4, inner circle on one or both sides; mm. harp, portcullis, ./harp (2811-13) ..................................................................... | 20 | 80 |
| 2830 | − − − 3.5-6. R. Oval shield, no C R, no inner circle or obv. only; mm. harp, portcullis ................................................................................... | 25 | 90 |
| 2831 | − − 3a1. R. Rounder shield, no inner circles; mm. bell, crown, tun, anchor, triangle .............................................................................................. | 20 | 80 |
| 2832 | − − 3a2-3, inner circles on obverse or both sides; mm. anchor, triangle, star, triangle-in-circle ............................................................................ | 25 | 85 |
| 2833 | − − − (under Parliament), type 3a3, inner circles both sides; mm. (P)/triangle-in-circle, (P), ( R), eye, sun, sceptre ........................ | 20 | 80 |
| 2834 | Group E, fifth 'Aberystwyth' bust, types 3a4-5, no inner circles or on reverse only; mm. anchor (2819-20) ............................................................ | 35 | 135 |
| 2835 | − − 3a6, very small bust (from penny puncheon), no inner circles; mm. anchor ................................................................................................ | 40 | 150 |
| 2836 | Group G, (under Parliament), seventh bust, type 3a7, older bust with pointed beard; mm. eye, sun, sceptre.................................................... | 25 | 85 |

2838

| 2837 | **Penny**. Group A, without bust, rose each side, type 1, inner circles; mm. lis, negro's head, one or two pellets............................................. | 20 | 80 |
| 2838 | − − 1a, no inner circles; mm. lis, anchor, one or two pellets .............. | 20 | 80 |
| 2839 | − − 1b, inner circle on reverse; mm. negro's head/two pellets ........... | 35 | 135 |
| 2840 | Group B, second bust, type 2, in ruff and mantle. R. Oval shield, inner circles; mm. plume, plume/rose, rose ..................................... | 30 | 120 |
| 2841 | − − 2.1, no inner circles; mm. plume, rose........................................ | 30 | 110 |
| 2842 | Group C, third bust, type 2a1, more armour visible, no inner circles; mm. plume, plume/rose, rose............................................... | 25 | 95 |

|  | | F £ | VF £ |
|---|---|---|---|

2843 — — 2a2-4, inner circles on obverse, both sides or reverse; mm. plume, rose ............................................................................................ 25 95

2844 Group D, fourth bust, type 3.1, with falling lace collar. R. CR by shield, no inner circles; mm. harp, one or two pellets ..................................... 20 75

2845

2845 — — — 3.2, no C R by shield, no inner circles; mm. harp, portcullis, pellets, none ........................................................................................... 20 75

2846 — — — — 3.3-4, inner circles on obverse or reverse; mm. harp, two pellets ............................................................................................. 20 80

2847 — — 3a1, shield almost round with scroll garniture, no inner circles; mm. bell, triangle, one to four pellets, none ................................... 20 70

2848 — — 3a1 var., inner circle on one or both sides; mm. triangle/two pellets ... 25 90

2849 Group E, fifth 'Aberystwyth' bust, type 3a3, inner circle on obverse or none; mm. triangle, anchor, one or two pellets, none ......................... 20 80

2850 Group G, (under Parliament), seventh bust, type 3a2, older bust, inner circle on obverse only; mm. one or two pellets .............................. 25 85

2851

2851 **Halfpenny**. Rose each side, no legend or mm ......................................... 15 60

# NICHOLAS BRIOT'S COINAGE, 1631-9

**FIRST MILLED ISSUE, 1631-2**

2852 **Crown**. King on horseback. R. Crowned shield between CR crowned; mm. flower and B / B .......................................................................... 1350 3000

2853 2855

2853 **Halfcrown**. Similar ................................................................... 650 1750

2854 **Shilling**. Briot's early bust with falling lace collar. R. Square-topped shield over long cross fourchee; R. Legend starts at top or bottom (extr. rare) mm. flower and B/B, B ................................................................ 500 1350

2855 **Sixpence**. Similar, but VI behind bust; mm. flower and B/B, flower and B/- 200 600

2856                          2856A

|  | *F* £ | *VF* £ |
|---|---|---|

2856  **Halfgroat.** Briot's bust, B below, II behind. ℞. IVSTITIA, etc., square-
topped shield over long cross fourchee .................................................... 80      250

2856A Pattern halfgroat. Uncrowned bust in ruff r. ℞. crowned, interlocked Cs.
(North 2687). (Included because of its relatively regular appearance.) ... 75      225

2857  **Penny.** Similar, but I behind bust, B below bust; position of legend may vary    80      250

**SECOND MILLED ISSUE, 1638-9**

2859

2858  **Halfcrown.** As 2853, but *mm.* anchor and B .......................................... 575     1500

2859  **Shilling.** Briot's late bust, the falling lace collar is plain with broad lace
border, no scarf. ℞. As 2854 but cross only to inner circle; *mm.* anchor and
B, anchor or muled ................................................................................... 250      675

2860  **Sixpence.** Similar, but VI; *mm.* anchor, anchor and mullet/anchor ......... 100      350

*The last two often exhibit flan reduction marks.*

**HAMMERED ISSUE, 1638-9**

2861  **Halfcrown.** King on Briot's style horse with ground line. ℞. Square-topped
shield; *mm.* anchor, triangle over anchor. Also muled with Tower *rev.* ..... 600     1750

2862  **Shilling.** Briot's first hammered issue, Sim. to 2859; ℞. Square-topped
shield over short cross fleury, contraction stops on *obv.,* pellet stops
*rev. mm.* anchor ....................................................................................... 1250     4000

2862A — Briot's second hammered issue. As 2862 but lozenge stops both sides.
*mm.* anchor, triangle over anchor or triangle ......................................... 325     1000

2862B Tower, Group E, obv. type 4.1 var. (S.2797) above ℞. as Briot's 1st or 2nd
hammered issue; mm. Δ over anchor. ...................................................... 575     1750

2862C Tower, Group F, obv. type 4.4 (S.2799 above) ℞. as Briot's 2nd hammered
issue; mm Δ/Δ over anchor. ................................................................... 375     1100

**YORK, 1643-4.** *Mm. Lion*

2867

|  | | F | VF |
|---|---|---|---|
|  | | £ | £ |
| 2863 | **Halfcrown**. 1. Ground-line below horse. ℞. Square-topped shield between CR ...................................................................................................... | 525 | 2250 |
| 2864 | — 2. — ℞. Oval shield as Tower 3a, groundline grass or dotted ............. | 475 | 2000 |
| 2865 | — 3. No ground-line. ℞. Similar ............................................................ | 475 | 2000 |
| 2866 | — 4. As last, but EBOR below horse with head held low. Base metal, often very base (*These pieces are contemporary forgeries*) ..................... | 110 | 400 |
| 2867 | — 5. Tall horse, mane in front of chest, EBOR below. ℞. Crowned square-topped shield between CR, floral spray in legend .................................... | 350 | 1200 |

2868

|  | | F £ | VF £ |
|---|---|---|---|
| 2868 | — 6. As last, but shield is oval, garnished (*rev*. detail variations)............ | 325 | 1000 |
| 2869 | — 7. Similar, but horse's tail shows between legs. R. Shield as last, but with lion's skin garniture, no CR or floral spray .............................................. | 325 | 1000 |

2870                     2872

| 2870 | **Shilling**. 1. Bust in scalloped lace collar similar to 3[1]. R. EBOR above square-topped shield over cross fleury ............................................................ | 225 | 750 |
|---|---|---|---|
| 2871 | — 2. Similar, but bust in plain armour, mantle; coarse work .................. | 275 | 950 |
| 2872 | — 3. Similar R. EBOR below oval shield ................................................ | 250 | 800 |
| 2873 | — 4. — Similar, but crowned oval shield (*obv*. finer style)..................... | 200 | 700 |
| 2874 | — 5. — As last, but lion's skin garniture ............................................... | 200 | 700 |
| 2875 | **Sixpence**. *Obv*. Sim. to 2870. Crowned oval shield ............................... | 275 | 900 |

2876                     2877

| 2876 | — — Crowned CR at sides ................................................................ | 250 | 800 |
|---|---|---|---|
| 2877 | **Threepence**. As type 1 shilling, but III behind bust. R. As 2870............ | 85 | 250 |

**ABERYSTWYTH, 1638/9-42.** *Mm.* book.
Plume 1=with coronet and band. Plume 2=with coronet only

2878

|   |   | F £ | VF £ |
|---|---|---|---|
| 2878 | **Halfcrown**. Horseman similar to 2773, but plume 2 behind. R. Oval garnished shield with large plume above. *Obv.* plume 2, *rev.* plume 1..... | 1250 | 5250 |
| 2879 | — Similar to 2774, plume 1 behind King, ground below horse. *Obv.* squat plume 1, *rev.* plume 1 ............................................................. | 1350 | 5500 |
| 2880 | As 2773 but more spirited horse, no ground. FRAN ET HIB, plume 2/1 | 1250 | 5250 |

2881

| 2881 | **Shilling**. Bust with large square lace collar, plume 2 before, small XII. R. As Tower 3b............................................................................................... | 525 | 1850 |
|---|---|---|---|
| 2882 | — inner circle on *rev.* ............................................................................ | 475 | 1650 |
| 2883 | As 2881, but large plume 1 or 2, large XII, inner circles, large or small shield | 475 | 1650 |

2884                                                              2886

| 2884 | As last, but small narrow head, square lace collar, large or square plume | 500 | 1750 |
|---|---|---|---|
| 2885 | Small Briot style face, small crown, plume 2, large shield ...................... | 750 | 2750 |
| 2885A | **Sixpence**. *Obv.* as Tower bust 3a, plume before. R. as 2889; inner circles both sides, *mm.* book (*obv.* only)............................................................ | 450 | 1500 |
| 2886 | Somewhat as 2881, but double-arched crown, small VI; no inner circles | 250 | 850 |
| 2887 | Similar to 2886, but single arched crown, plume 2, inner circle *obv.* Large VI | 275 | 900 |
| 2888 | Similar, but with inner circles both sides................................................. | 300 | 950 |
| 2889 | — — *Rev.* with small squat-shaped plume above, sometimes no *rev. mm.* | 275 | 900 |

|      |                                                                                  | F £ | VF £ |
|------|----------------------------------------------------------------------------------|-----|------|
| 2890 | Bust as the first Oxford sixpence; with crown cutting inner circle ........ | 350 | 1250 |

2891

| 2891 | **Groat**. Large bust, lace collar, no armour on shoulder. Crown breaks or touches inner circle. R. Shield, plume 1 or 2 ............................... | 75 | 225 |
| 2892 | — Similar, armour on shoulder, shorter collar. R. Similar ..................... | 80 | 240 |
| 2893 | — Smaller, neater bust well within circle. R. Similar ........................... | 75 | 225 |

2894

| 2894 | **Threepence**. Small bust, plume 2 before. R. Shield, plume 1 or 2 above, *obv.* legend variations ................................................. | 60 | 175 |
| 2895 | — Similar, but crown cuts i.c. squat pl. on *obv.*, R. Pl. 2, *obv.* legend variations ................................................................................. | 65 | 185 |
| 2900 | **Halfgroat**. Bust as Tower type 3. R. Large plume. No inner circles, *mm.* pellet/book,book ................................................................... | 110 | 450 |
| 2900A | Bust as 2886. R. As last, no inner circle .................................... | 100 | 400 |

2901                          2903

| 2901 | Bust with round lace collar; single arch crown, inner circles, colon stops | 70 | 225 |
| 2902 | After Briot's bust, square lace collar: inner circles .............................. | 65 | 200 |
| 2903 | **Penny**. As 2901; CARO; no inner circles ........................................ | 75 | 275 |
| 2904 | As 2901; CARO; inner circles ...................................................... | 70 | 250 |
| 2905 | As last but reads CAROLVS; inner circles ....................................... | 80 | 300 |
| 2906 | *Obv.* similar to 2890, tall narrow bust, crown touches inner circle ......... | 85 | 325 |

2907

| 2907 | **Halfpenny**. No legend. O. Rose. R. Plume ............................................. | 250 | 900 |

## ABERYSTWYTH-FURNACE, 1648/9. *Mm*. crown

|  |  | F<br>£ | VF<br>£ |
|---|---|---|---|
| 2908 | **Halfcrown**. King on horseback. R. Sim. to 2878 .................................. | 2000 | 7500 |
| 2909 | **Shilling**. Aberystwyth type, but *mm*. crown .......................................... | 4500 | 17500 |
| 2910 | **Sixpence**. Similar ..................................................................................... | 1500 | 4500 |

2911                                                 2913

| 2911 | **Groat**. Similar ........................................................................................ | 275 | 850 |
|---|---|---|---|
| 2912 | **Threepence**. Similar................................................................................. | 300 | 950 |
| 2913 | **Halfgroat**. Similar. R. Large plume ......................................................... | 325 | 1000 |
| 2914 | **Penny**. Similar......................................................................................... | 750 | 2500 |

## UNCERTAIN MINTS

2915

| 2915 | **Halfcrown**. As illustration, (Hereford?) dated 1645 or undated .............. | 3250 | 12000 |
|---|---|---|---|
| 2915A | **Halfcrown**. (Compton House) Scarf with long sash ends. CH (Chirk castle?)<br>below horse. R. Oval shield 1644 ............................................................... | 4000 | 15000 |
| 2915B | — — R. Crowned oval shield, lion paws ................................................. | 3750 | 13500 |

## SHREWSBURY, 1642. Plume without band used as *mm*. or in field.

| 2917 | **Pound**. King on horseback, plume behind, from the puncheon of Tower grp.<br>3 crowns. R. Declaration between two straight lines, XX and three Shrewsbury<br>plumes above, 1642 below; *mm*. pellets, pellets/- ...................................... | 4750 | 13500 |
|---|---|---|---|
| 2918 | Similar, but Shrewsbury horse walking over pile of arms; no *mm*., pellets | 3750 | 10000 |
| 2919 | As last, but cannon amongst arms and only single plume and XX above<br>Declaration, no *mm*. ................................................................................... | 5750 | 17500 |
| 2920 | **Half-pound**. As 2917, but X; *mm*. pellets ................................................ | 2250 | 6000 |
| 2921 | Similar, but only two plumes on *rev*.; *mm*., pellets.................................... | 3750 | 10500 |
| 2922 | Shrewsbury horseman with ground-line, three plumes on *rev*.; *mm*., none,<br>pellets/- ..................................................................................................... | 1750 | 5000 |
| 2923 | — with cannon and arms or arms below horse; *mm*. pellets/- ................. | 2000 | 5750 |

| | | F £ | VF £ |
|---|---|---|---|
| 2924 | — no cannon in arms, no plume in *obv.* field; *mm.* plume/pellets, plume/- | 1350 | 3500 |
| 2925 | **Crown**. Aberystwyth horseman from the puncheon of a Tower halfcrown no ground line ...................... | 17500 | 65000 |

2926

| 2926 | Shrewsbury horseman with ground-line; *mm.* -/pellets, pellets/-, none ... | 1350 | 3500 |
|---|---|---|---|
| 2927 | **Halfcrown**. *O.* From Aberystwyth die; (S2880); *mm.* book. ℞. Single plume above Declaration, 1642 ......................... | 3750 | 13500 |
| 2928 | Sim. to Aberystwyth die, fat plume behind. ℞. Three plumes above Declaration; *mm.* pellets, pellets/- ......................... | 1100 | 4000 |
| 2929 | Shrewsbury horseman, no ground line. ℞. As 2927, single plume, no *mm.* | 1350 | 4750 |
| 2929A | — — ℞. As 2933 ......................... | 1200 | 4250 |

2930

| 2930 | — ℞. 2: plume; 6, above Declaration ......................... | 3250 | 11000 |
|---|---|---|---|
| 2931 | — with ground-line. ℞. Similar ......................... | 3250 | 11000 |
| 2932 | — — ℞. As 2927, single plume ......................... | 1350 | 4750 |
| 2933 | — — ℞. Three plumes above Declaration; *mm.* none or pellets ............ | 1000 | 3750 |
| 2933A | — — ℞. Aberystwyth die, plume over shield; *mm.* -/book ......................... | 3750 | 13500 |
| 2934 | As 2933 but no plume behind king; *mm.* plume/pellets ......................... | 850 | 3250 |

2935

|       |                                                             | F | VF |
|-------|-------------------------------------------------------------|-----|------|
|       |                                                             | £ | £ |
| 2935  | **Shilling**. *O*. From Aberystwyth die; S2885 *mm*. book. Ɍ. Declaration type | 2000 | 7000 |
| 2936  | *O*. From Shrewsbury die. Ɍ. Similar ...................................................... | 4500 | 15000 |

**OXFORD, 1642-6.** *Mm*. usually plume with band, except on the smaller denominations when it is lis or pellets. There were so many dies used at this mint that we can give only a selection of the more easily identifiable varieties.

For many years Oxford Halfcrowns and Shillings have been catalogued according to Morrieson obverse die varieties. In many cases, these are very small and difficult to identify. We have, therefore, simplified the obverse classification and used the available space to expand the listing of the more interesting reverse varieties.

2943

| 2937 | **Pound**. Large horseman over arms, no exergual line, fine workmanship. Ɍ. Three Shrewsbury plumes and XX above Declaration, 1642 below; *mm*. plume/pellets........................................................................................ | 7500 | 25000 |
|------|--------------------------------------------------------------------------------------------------------------------|-------|-------|
| 2938 | — Similar, but three Oxford plumes, 1643; *mm*. as last............................ | 6750 | 22500 |
| 2939 | Shrewsbury horseman trampling on arms, exergual line. Ɍ. As last, 1642 | 3500 | 10000 |
| 2940 | — — cannon amongst arms, 1642-3; *mm*. similar .................................. | 3250 | 9500 |
| 2941 | — as last but exergue is chequered, 1642; *mm*. similar........................... | 5250 | 16500 |
| 2942 | Briot's horseman, 1643; *mm*. similar...................................................... | 7500 | 25000 |
| 2943 | *O*. As 2937. Ɍ. Declaration in cartouche, single large plume above, 1644 OX below................................................................................................ | 17500 | 52500 |

|  | F £ | VF £ |
|---|---|---|

2944 **Half-pound.** Shrewsbury horseman over arms, Oxford plume behind.
R. Shrewsbury die, 1642; mm. plume/- .................................................. 1350 4000
2945 — R. Three Oxford plumes above, 1642; mm. plume/- ......................... 1250 3750
2945A — — 1643; mm. plume/- ....................................................... 1250 3750
2946 **Crown.** Shrewsbury die with groundline. R. Three Oxford plumes,
1642; no mm. ...... 1250 3750
2946A — — 1643; no mm. ............................................................. 1250 3750
2947 Oxford horseman, grass below. R. Three Oxford plumes, 1643; mm. plume/- 1500 4500

2948

2948 Rawlins' crown. King riding over a view of the city. R. Floral scrolls
above and below Declaration, date in script, 1644 OXON; mm.
floriated cross/- *(Electrotypes and copies of this coin are common)* ........ 32500 110000
2949 **Halfcrown.** O. Shrewsbury die with groundline, plume behind. R.
Oxford die, declaration in two lines, three Oxford plumes above,
1642 below; no mm. ................................................................. 1200 3750
2950 — no plume behind. R. as last, 1642; mm. plume/- ................................ 575 2000
2951 Shrewsbury horseman with groundline, Oxford plume behind. R.
Shrewsbury die, 1642; mm. plume/- ......................................... 950 3000
2952 — R. Three Oxford plumes, 1642; mm. plume/- ................................. 375 1100
2953 — — without groundline, 1642; mm. plume/- ................................... 375 1100

2954                                          2955

2954 Oxford horseman without groundline, 1643; mm. plume/- ..................... 350 1050
2954A — — R. Shrewsbury die, 1642; mm. plume/- or no mm. ......................... 950 3000
2955 — with groundline. R. Three Oxford plumes, 1643; mm. plume/- .......... 350 1050
2956 Briot horseman, grassy, rocky or uneven ground. R. Three Oxford plumes,
1643; mm. plume/-, plume & rosette/- ....................................... 275 900
2957 — — 1643 OX; mm. plume/rosette, rosette ............................... 275 900

2961                                    2965A

|                                                                                                                              | F £ | VF £ |
|------------------------------------------------------------------------------------------------------------------------------|------|------|
| 2958 — — 1644 OX; *mm.* plume/-                                                                                              | 325  | 1000 |
| 2958A — — lozenges by OX, 1644 OX; *mm.* plume/-                                                                            | 325  | 1000 |
| 2959 — — 1645 OX; *mm.* plume/-, plume/rosette                                                                              | 300  | 950  |
| 2959A — — pellets by date, 1645 OX; *mm.* plume/-                                                                          | 425  | 1350 |
| 2960 — — 1646 OX; *mm.* plume/-                                                                                            | 275  | 900  |
| 2961 — — pellets or annulets by plumes and date, 1646 OX; *mm.* plume/- ...                                                | 325  | 1000 |
| 2962 — R. Large central plume and two Oxford plumes, 1643; *mm.* plume/-                                                    | 300  | 950  |
| 2963 — — 1643 OX; *mm.* plume/-, rosette/-, plume & rosette/rosette, plume & rosette/-                                       | 250  | 850  |
| 2964 — — rosettes by OX, 1643 OX; *mm.* rosette/-, plume & rosette/-                                                       | 350  | 1100 |
| 2965 — — plain, pellets or lozenges by plumes and/or OX, 1644 OX; *mm.* plume/- plume/rosette, rosette                       | 250  | 850  |
| 2965A — — date in script, 1644 OX; *mm.* plume/-                                                                           | 250  | 850  |
| 2966 — — rosettes by plumes and date, 1644 OX; *mm.* plume & rosette/rosette                                                | 425  | 1352 |
| 2967 — — small plumes by date, 1644 OX; *mm.* plume & rosette/-, rosette ..                                                 | 475  | 1500 |
| 2968 — R. Large central plume and two small Shrewsbury plumes, lozenges in field, date in script, 1644 OX; *mm.* plume/rosette | 475  | 1500 |
| 2969 — — small plumes by date, pellets by OX, 1644 OX; *mm.* plume/-                                                        | 525  | 1750 |

2971

|                                                                                                                              | F £  | VF £ |
|------------------------------------------------------------------------------------------------------------------------------|------|------|
| 2970 **Shilling.** *O.* Shrewsbury die. R. Declaration in three lines, three Oxford plumes above, 1642; *mm.* plume/-        | 2000 | 6500 |
| 2971 Oxford bust (small). R. Three Oxford plumes, 1642; *mm.* Oxford plume/-,                                               | 275  | 800  |
| 2972 Oxford bust (small or large). R. Three Oxford plumes, 1643; *mm.* Oxford plume/-, Oxford plume/rosette                  | 275  | 800  |
| 2972A — — pellets by date, 1644; *mm.* plume/-                                                                             | 325  | 950  |
| 2972B — — 1644 OX; mm. plume/rosette                                                                                       | 325  | 950  |
| 2973 — R. Oxford and two Shrewsbury plumes, lozenges by date, 1644 OX; *mm.* plume/-                                         | 400  | 1250 |
| 2974 — R. Three Shrewsbury plumes, 1643; *mm.* plume/-                                                                      | 300  | 925  |

|  | F £ | VF £ |
|---|---|---|

2975  Fine Oxford bust. R. Three Oxford plumes, lozenges in field, 1644
      OX; *mm.* Shrewsbury plume/- .............................................................. 325 950
2975A — — large date in script, 1644 OX; *mm.* plume/- ............................... 350 1050
2976  — 1645 OX; *mm.* plume/- ...................................................................... 2500 7500
2976A — R. Oxford and two Shrewsbury plumes, 1644 OX; *mm.* plume/- ....... 375 1200
2977  — R. Three Shrewsbury plumes, 1644 OX; *mm.* plume/- ...................... 325 950
2978  — — annulets or pellets at date, 1646; *mm.* plume/floriated cross,
      plume/- .................................................................................................. 350 1000

2979
2979  Rawlins' die. Fine bust with R. on truncation. R. Three Oxford plumes,
      rosettes or lozenges by plumes, lozenges by date, 1644 OX; *mm.*
      Shrewsbury plume/rosette, Shrewsbury plume/- .................................. 950 3500
2979A — — pellets by date, no OX, 1644; *mm.* plume/- ................................. 1000 4000
2979B — R. Oxford and two Shrewsbury plumes, 1644 OX; *mm.* plume/- ....... 1100 4250

2980A
2980  **Sixpence.** O. Aberystwyth die R. Three Oxford plumes, 1642; *mm.* book/- 275 850
2980A — — 1643; *mm.* book/- ........................................................................ 250 800
2981  — R. Three Shrewsbury plumes, 1643; *mm.* book/- ............................. 250 800
2982  — R. Shrewsbury plume and two lis, 1644 OX (groat rev. die); *mm.* book/- 525 1750
2983  **Groat.** O. Aberystwyth die. R. Shrewsbury plume and two lis, 1644 OX;
      *mm.* book/- ........................................................................................... 225 750
2984  — R. Three Shrewsbury plumes, 1644 OX; mm. book/- ......................... 275 850

2985
2985  Oxford bust within inner circle. R. As 2983, 1644 OX; mm. floriated cross/- 175 575

2988                                         2990

|                                                                                                                                    | F<br>£ | VF<br>£ |
|------------------------------------------------------------------------------------------------------------------------------------|--------|---------|
| 2985A — ℞. Three Shrewsbury plumes, 1644 OX; *mm*. floriated cross/-                                                               | 275    | 850     |
| 2985B — ℞. Single plume, 2 scrolls and OX monogram over Decl, 1645; *mm*. floriated cross/-                                       | 325    | 1000    |
| 2986 Large bust to top of coin. ℞. As 2983, 1644 OX; *mm*. lis/-                                                                   | 225    | 750     |
| 2987 Large bust to bottom of coin. ℞. As 2983, 1644 OX; no *mm*.                                                                   | 225    | 750     |
| 2988 — ℞. Single plume, 2 scrolls and OX monogram over Decl, 1645; no *mm*.                                                        | 185    | 675     |
| 2989 Rawlins' die, no inner circle, R on shoulder. ℞. As 2983, 1644 OX; no *mm*.                                                   | 375    | 1250    |
| 2990 — ℞. Single plume, Declaration in cartouche, 1645; no *mm*.                                                                   | 275    | 850     |
| 2991 — — 1646/5; no mm.                                                                                                             | 250    | 800     |
| 2992 **Threepence.** *O*. Aberystwyth die. ℞. Three lis over Declaration, 1644 OX; *mm*. book/-                                    | 250    | 750     |
| 2993 Rawlins; die, R below shoulder. ℞. Aberystwyth die, oval shield; *mm*. lis/book                                               | 250    | 750     |
| 2994 — ℞. Three lis over Declaration, 1644; *mm*. lis/-                                                                            | 125    | 375     |

2994                                         3000

| 2995 Crown breaks inner circle, no R. ℞. Three lis, 1646/4; *mm*. lis/-                                                            | 135    | 400     |
|------------------------------------------------------------------------------------------------------------------------------------|--------|---------|
| 2996 **Halfgroat.** Small bust, beaded or wireline inner circle. ℞. Large plume in field; *mm*. mullet/lis, lis, -/lis, plain cross/-, plain cross/lis | 120    | 375     |
| 2997 — ℞. Three lis over Delcaration, 1644 OX; *mm*. lis                                                                           | 125    | 425     |
| 2998 **Penny.** *O*. Aberystwyth die, CARO. ℞. Small plume in field; *mm*. book/-                                                  | 150    | 575     |
| 2999 Aberystwyth die, CAROLVS; ℞. Large plume; *mm*. book/-                                                                        | 175    | 650     |
| 3000 Rawlins' die, CARO. ℞. Small plume; *mm*. lis/mullet, lis/-                                                                   | 225    | 850     |
| 3001 Broad bust, CAROL. ℞. Small plume; *mm*. lis                                                                                  | 200    | 750     |
| 3002 — ℞. Three lis over Declaration, 1644; *mm*. lis                                                                             | 900    | 3000    |

**BRISTOL, 1643-5.** *Mm*. usually plume or Br., except on small denominations

| 3003 **Halfcrown.** *O*. Oxford die with or without ground-line. ℞. Declaration, three Bristol plumes above, 1643 below, *mm*. plume/- or plume/cross | 475    | 1650    |
|------------------------------------------------------------------------------------------------------------------------------------|--------|---------|
| 3004 — Obv. as above. ℞ as above, but *mm*. Br. 1643                                                                               | 575    | 1750    |
| 3005 King wears unusual flat crown, *obv*. *mm*. acorn? between four pellets. ℞. As 3003, 1643                                     | 500    | 1500    |
| 3006 — Obv. as above. ℞ as 3004, *mm*. Br., 1643-4                                                                                | 425    | 1250    |
| 3007 Shrewsbury plume behind king. ℞. As last                                                                                      | 350    | 950     |
| 3008 — Obv. as above. ℞ as 3004 but Br below date instead of as *mm* . 1644                                                        | 375    | 1100    |

3009

|  | | F £ | VF £ |
|---|---|---|---|
| 3009 | — Obv. as 3007 but Br below horse. ℞ as above but 1644-5 ............... | 350 | 950 |
| 3010 | — Obv. as above. ℞ as 3004, *mm*. Br. and Br. below date, 1644-5 ......... | 375 | 1100 |
| 3011 | **Shilling**. *O*. Oxford die. ℞. Declaration, 1643, 3 crude plumes above, no *mm*. | 625 | 1850 |

3012                                                    3014

|  | | F £ | VF £ |
|---|---|---|---|
| 3012 | — — ℞ Similar, but *mm*. Br., 1643-4, less crude plumes ........................ | 475 | 1500 |
| 3013 | —Obv. Coarse bust. ℞. As 3011, *mm., plume /-* 1643 ............................. | 1750 | 6000 |
| 3014 | — — Coarse bust, ℞. as 3012, *mm*. Br, but 1644 .................................... | 575 | 1750 |

3016A                                                    3017

|  | | F £ | VF £ |
|---|---|---|---|
| 3015 | Obv. Bust of good style, plumelet before face. ℞. As 3012 *mm*. Br. but 1644-5 | 425 | 1250 |
| 3016 | — — ℞.as 3012, 1644, but Br below date instead of *mm*. ....................... | 450 | 1350 |
| 3016A | — — ℞ as 3012, 1644 but plume and plumelet either side ...................... | 375 | 1100 |
| 3017 | —Obv. Taller bust with high crown, no plumelets before, *mm*. Br. on its side. ℞ As 3016 Br.below 1644-5 ............. | 650 | 2250 |
| 3018 | —Obv. As 3017 but no *mm*. ℞ as above but *mm*. Br., no Br below 1644-5 | 750 | 2500 |
| 3018A | — — ℞ as above but plume and plumelets, 1645 ................................... | 850 | 2750 |
| 3019 | **Sixpence**. Small bust, nothing before. ℞. Declaration surrounded by CHRISTO etc., 1643; *mm*. ./Br. ................................................................. | 575 | 2000 |

3020                                    3022

|                                                                                                   | F | VF |
|---|---|---|
|                                                                                                   | £ | £ |
| 3020 Fine style bust. Plumelet before face, 1644; *mm.* ./Br. (on its side) ......... | 300 | 900 |
| 3021 **Groat**. Bust l. R. Declaration, 1644 ...................................................... | 250 | 750 |
| 3022 — Plumelet before face, 1644 ................................................................ | 225 | 650 |
| 3023 — Br. below date, 1644.......................................................................... | 200 | 575 |
| 3023A — Similar, but larger bust and more spread plume before. Mm. pellet/Br; | | |
| nothing below 1644 ............................................................................... | 250 | 750 |

3024                          3026                          3027

| 3024 **Threepence**. *O*. As 2992. Aberystwyth die; *mm.* book. R. Declaration, 1644 | 275 | 850 |
|---|---|---|
| 3025 Bristol die, plume before face, no *mm.*, 1644......................................... | 375 | 1100 |
| 3026 **Halfgroat**. Br. in place of date below Declaration ................................. | 275 | 9000 |
| 3027 **Penny**. Similar bust, I behind. R. Large plume with bands..................... | 475 | 1350 |

*This penny may belong to the late declaration issue. It has the same reverse plume punch as 3044.*

## LATE 'DECLARATION' ISSUES, 1645-6

After Bristol surrendered on 11th September 1645, many of the Royalist garrison returned unsearched to Oxford and the Bristol moneyers appear to have continued work, using altered Bristol dies and others of similar type bearing the marks A, B and plume. Ashby de la Zouch was reinforced from Oxford in September 1645 and, following its fall on 28th February 1646, Royalist forces marched to Bridgnorth-on-Severn, holding out until 26th April 1646. Mr Boon suggested (cf. SCBI 33, p. xli) that Ashby and Bridgnorth are plausible mint sites and the most likely candidates for the A and B marked issues, if these do indeed represent fixed mint locations.

## ASHBY DE LA ZOUCH, 1645

| 3028 **Halfcrown**. Horseman of Bristol type, A below. R. Altered Bristol die. A | | |
|---|---|---|
| (over Br) below date, 1645; *mm.* plume/A (over Br) .............................. | 4000 | 12500 |
| 3029 - - R. A below date (new die), 1645; *mm.* plume/A ............................... | 4000 | 12500 |
| 3030 - - R. Nothing below date 1645; *mm.* plume/A........................................ | 3750 | 11000 |
| 3031 **Shilling.** Crowned bust left. R. Declaration type, A below date, 1645; mm. | | |
| plume/A .................................................................................................... | 1850 | 6500 |

3032

|  | | F £ | VF £ |
|---|---|---|---|

3032 - plumelet before face, 1645; *mm*. plume/A ............................................ 1750 6000

3033 **Sixpence.** Bust of Bristol style, plumelet before face. R. Declaration type,
1645; *mm*. A (on its side)/- .................................................................. 1500 5000

3034 **Groat.** Similar, plumelet before face, 1645; *mm*. A (on its side)/- ............ 1350 4750

3035 **Threepence.** Similar, plumelet before face. R. Single plumelet above
Declaration, 1645; no *mm*. ...................................................................... 900 3000

## BRIDGNORTH-ON-SEVERN, 1646

3036 **Halfcrown.** Horseman of Bristol type, A below (same die as 3028-30). R.
Scroll above Declaration, B below, 1646; *mm*. plume/A ...................... 4500 13500

3036A - - R. Nothing below date, 1646; *mm*. plume/- .................................... 3000 9500

3037

3037 - plumelet (over A) below horse (same die as 3028-30 recut). R. Nothing
below date, 1646; *mm*. plume, plume/- .................................................. 1750 5000

3038 - - plumelet below date, 1646; *mm*. plume ............................................ 1750 5000

3039 **Shilling.** Crowned bust left, plumelet before face (same die as 3032). R.
Scroll above Declaration, 1646; *mm*. plume/plumelet ........................... 750 2500

3039A - Bristol obverse die, nothing before face. R. Scroll above Declaration, 1646;
2000 *mm*. Br/- .......................................................................................... 1500 5000

3040 - - plume before face (altered die of 3039A), 1646; *mm*. plumelet (over
Br)/- ................................................................................................................ 850 2750

3041                          3042

|  | | F £ | VF £ |
|---|---|---|---|
| 3041 | **Sixpence.** Crowned bust left, plume before face. R. Scroll above Declaration, 1646; *mm.* B/- ............................................................................ | 275 | 950 |
| 3042 | **Groat.** Similar, plumelet before face, 1646; *mm.* plumelet, plumelet/- .......... | 250 | 750 |
| 3043 | **Threepence.** Similar, plumelet before face. R. Single plume above Declaration, 1646; *mm.* plumelet/- ..................................... | 225 | 700 |
| 3044 | **Halfgroat.** Crowned bust left, II behind. R. Large plume with bands dividing date, 1646; no *mm.* ................................................................. | 575 | 1750 |

3045                          3047

**TRURO, 1642-3.** *Mm.* rose except where stated

| 3045 | **Crown.** King on horseback, head in profile, sash flies out in two ends. R. CHRISTO, etc., round garnished shield ............................................. | 475 | 1350 |
|---|---|---|---|
| 3046 | **Halfcrown.** King on walking horse, groundline below, R. Oblong shield, CR above, *mm.* bugle/– ........................................................................ | 4000 | 13500 |
| 3047 | Galloping horse, king holds baton. R. Oblong shield, CR at sides .......... | 3500 | 12500 |
| 3048 | Walking horse, king holds sword. R. Similar ...................................... | 900 | 3250 |
| 3049 | — R. Similar, but CR above ............................................................... | 950 | 3500 |
| 3050 | Galloping horse, king holds sword. R. Similar, but CR at sides ............. | 1100 | 4500 |
| 3051 | — R. Similar, but CR above ............................................................... | 1250 | 5000 |
| 3052 | Trotting horse. R. Similar, but CR at sides ........................................... | 850 | 3000 |
| 3053 | **Shilling.** Small bust of good style. R. Oblong shield ............................ | 4500 | 13500 |

**EXETER, 1643-6.** Undated or dated 1644-5 *Mm.* rose except where stated

| 3054 | **Half-pound.** King on horseback, face towards viewer, sash in large bow. R. CHRISTO, etc., round garnished shield. Struck from crown dies of 3055 on a thick flan ........................................................................................ | 7500 | 22500 |
|---|---|---|---|
| 3055 | **Crown.** King on horseback, sash in large bow. R. Round garnished shield ........................................................................................................ | 475 | 1350 |

| | F | VF |
|---|---|---|
| | £ | £ |

3056 — Shield garnished with twelve even scrolls ............................................ 575 1750
3057 As 3055, R Date divided by *mm*. 16 rose 44 ............................................ 575 1750
3058 — R Date to l. of *mm*. 1644 ................................................................ 475 1350
3059 — *mm*: rose/Ex, 1645 ............................................................................ 550 1650
3060 King's sash flies out in two ends; *mm*. castle/rose, 1645 ......................... 600 1850
3061 — *mm*. castle/Ex, 1645 ........................................................................ 500 1500
3062 — *mm*. castle, 1645 .............................................................................. 400 1100
3063 **Halfcrown**. King on horseback, sash tied in bow. R. Oblong shield
         CR at sides ......................................................................................... 900 3250
3064 — R. Round shield with eight even scrolls ............................................... 325 950

3065

3065 — R. Round shield with five short and two long scrolls ......................... 250 750
3066 — R. Oval shield with angular garnish of triple lines ............................. 750 2500

3067

3067 Briot's horseman with lumpy ground. R. As 3064 ................................. 400 1250
3068 — R. As 3065 ........................................................................................ 350 1000
3069 — R. As 3066 ........................................................................................ 600 2250
3070 — R. As 3065, date to l. of *mm*. 1644 ................................................... 525 1750

3071

3071 King on spirited horse galloping over arms. R. Oval garnished
         shield, 1642 in cartouche below .......................................................... 4750 16000

|  |  | F | VF |
|---|---|---|---|
|  |  | £ | £ |
| 3072 | — R. As 3070, date to 1. of *mm*. 1644-5 ................................................ | 5750 | 20000 |
| 3073 | — R. *mm*. castle, 1645 ................................................................................ | 6500 | 22500 |
| 3074 | Short portly king, leaning backwards on ill-proportioned horse, | | |
|  | 1644, 16 rose 44 ........................................................................................ | 1100 | 4000 |
| 3075 | Horse with twisted tail, sash flies out in two ends R. As 3064 ................ | 575 | 1750 |

3076

| 3076 | — R. As 3070, date divided by *mm*. 16 rose 44, or date to 1. of *mm*. 1644-5 | 475 | 1500 |
|---|---|---|---|
| 3077 | — R. *mm*. castle, 1645 ............................................................................ | 525 | 1650 |
| 3078 | — R. *mm*. Ex, 1645 .................................................................................. | 475 | 1500 |
| 3079 | — R. Declaration type; *mm*. Ex. 1644-5 ................................................. | 3250 | 9500 |
| 3080 | — R. Similar, Ex also below declaration, 1644 ....................................... | 3000 | 8500 |
| 3081 | **Shilling.** Large Oxford style bust. R. Round shield with eight even scrolls | 1750 | 5250 |
| 3082 | — R. Oval shield with CR at sides ........................................................... | 2250 | 7500 |
| 3083 | Normal bust with lank hair. R. As 3081 ................................................. | 750 | 2250 |
| 3083A | — R. As 3082 ........................................................................................... | 1500 | 5000 |
| 3084 | — R. Round shield with six scrolls ......................................................... | 575 | 1750 |

3085

| 3085 | — R. Similar, date 1644, 45 to left of rose *mm*. 16 rose 44 (rare), | | |
|---|---|---|---|
|  | 1644 to right of rose (very rare)................................................................. | 375 | 1000 |
| 3086 | — R. Declaration type, 1645 ..................................................................... | 1750 | 6000 |

3087A

| 3087 | **Sixpence.** Similar to 3085, large bust and letters 1644 rose..................... | 325 | 950 |
|---|---|---|---|
| 3087A | — Smaller bust and letters from punches used on 3088, small or large | | |
|  | VI, 16 rose 44 ............................................................................................ | 325 | 950 |

|  | F £ | VF £ |
|---|---|---|
| 3088 **Groat**. Somewhat similar but 1644 at beginning of *obv*. legend............. | 150 | 450 |

3089               3092

| 3089 **Threepence**. Similar. R. Square shield, 1644 above............................... | 135 | 425 |
|---|---|---|
| 3090 **Halfgroat**. Similar, but II. R. Oval shield, 1644 ................................... | 225 | 700 |
| 3091   — R. Large rose, 1644.......................................................................... | 250 | 750 |
| 3092 **Penny**. As last but I behind head ............................................................. | 300 | 900 |

**WORCESTER, 1644-45**

| 3093 **Halfcrown**. King on horseback l., W below; *mm*. two lions. R. Declaration type 1644 altered from 1643 Bristol die; *mm*. pellets............. | 1500 | 6000 |
|---|---|---|
| 3094   — R. Square-topped shield; *mm*. helmet, castle ..................................... | 1000 | 4250 |
| 3095   — R. Oval shield; *mm*. helmet................................................................. | 1050 | 4500 |

3096

| 3096 Similar but grass indicated; *mm*. castle. R. Square-topped shield; *mm*. helmet or pellets..................................................................................... | 825 | 3500 |
|---|---|---|
| 3097   — R. Oval draped shield, lis or lions in legend...................................... | 850 | 3750 |
| 3098   — R. Oval shield CR at sides, roses in legend ...................................... | 900 | 4000 |
| 3099   — R. FLORENT etc., oval garnished shield with lion's paws each side . | 950 | 4250 |
| 3100 Tall king, no W or *mm*. R. Oval shield, lis, roses, lions or stars in legend | 800 | 3250 |
| 3101   — R. Square-topped shield; *mm*. helmet .............................................. | 825 | 3500 |
| 3102   — R. FLORENT, etc., oval shield; no *mm*............................................. | 1000 | 4500 |
| 3103 Briot type horse, sword slopes forward, ground-line. R. Oval shield, roses in legend; *mm*. 91v, 105, none (combinations)..................................... | 850 | 3750 |
| 3104   — Similar, but CR at sides, 91v/-.............................................................. | 900 | 4000 |
| 3105 Dumpy, portly king, crude horse. R. As 3100; *mm*. 91v, 105, none ........ | 800 | 3250 |

3106

|  | F £ | VF £ |
|---|---|---|
| 3106 Thin king and horse. ℞. Oval shield, stars in legend; *mm*. 91v, none | 800 | 3250 |

**WORCESTER OR SALOPIA (SHREWSBURY), 1643-4**

3107 **Shilling**. Bust of king l., adequately rendered. ℞. Square-topped shield; *mm*. castle ..... 2000 7500
3108 — ℞. CR above shield; *mm*. helmet and lion ..... 2000 7500
3109 — ℞. Oval shield; *mm*. lion, pear ..... 1750 6500
3110 — Bust a somewhat crude copy of last (two varieties); *mm*. bird, lis. ℞. Square-topped shield with lion's paws above and at sides; *mm*. boar's head, helmet ..... 1850 7000

3108

3111 — — CR above ..... 1850 7000
3112 — ℞. Oval shield, lis in legend; *mm*. lis ..... 1350 5000
3113 — ℞. Round shield; *mm*. lis, 3 lis ..... 1350 5000
3114 Bust r.; *mm*. pear/-, pear/lis. ℞. draped oval shield with or without CR. (Halfcrown reverse dies) ..... 3500 13500
3115 **Sixpence**. As 3110; *mm*. castle, castle/boar's hd ..... 1350 5000

3116          3117

3116 **Groat**. As 3112; *mm*. lis/helmet, rose/helmet ..... 575 1650
3117 **Threepence**. Similar; *mm*. lis ..... 300 900
3118 **Halfgroat**. Similar; *mm*. lis (*O*.) various (℞.) ..... 350 1000

| | F £ | VF £ |
|---|---|---|

**SALOPIA (SHREWSBURY), 1644**

3119 **Halfcrown**. King on horseback l. SA below; *mm*. lis. R. (*mm*. lis, helmet, lion rampant, none). Cr. oval shield; CHRISTO etc. *mm*. helmet ... 4750 16500
3120 — R. FLORENT, etc., crowned oval shield, no *mm*. ... 4750 16500
3121 — SA erased or replaced by large pellet or cannon ball; *mm*. lis in legend, helmet. R. As 3119 ... 2250 8000
3122 Tall horse with mane blown forward, nothing below; *mm*. lis. R. Large round shield with crude garniture; *mm*. helmet ... 950 4250
3123 — R. Uncrowned square-topped shield with lion's paw above and at sides; *mm*. helmet ... 1000 4500
3124 — R. Small crowned oval shield; *mm*. various ... 825 3500

3125

3125 — R. As 3120 ... 900 4000
3126 Finer work with little or no mane before horse. R. Cr. round or oval shield 1250 5250
3127 Grass beneath horse. R. Similar; *mm*. lis or rose ... 1250 5250
3128 Ground below horse. R. As 3120 ... 2250 7500

**HARTLEBURY CASTLE (WORCS.), 1646**

3129

3129 **Halfcrown**. O. *Mm*. pear. R. HC (Hartlebury Castle) in garniture below shield; *mm*. three pears ... 1250 4500

## CHESTER, 1644

3130

| | | F | VF |
| --- | --- | --- | --- |
| | | £ | £ |
| 3130 | **Halfcrown**. As illus. ℞. Oval shield; *mm*. three gerbs and sword ............ | 1000 | 4250 |
| 3131 | — Similar, but without plume or CHST; ℞. Cr. oval shield with lion skin; *mm*. prostrate gerb; -/cinquefoil, ⁻/: ....................................................... | 850 | 3500 |
| 3132 | — ℞. Crowned square-topped shield with CR at sides both crowned *rev*.; *mm*. cinquefoil (these dies were later crudely recut) .............................. | 1750 | 7500 |
| 3133 | As 3130, but without plume or CHST. ℞. Declaration type, 1644 *rev*.; *mm*. plume .......................................................................................................... | 1250 | 4500 |
| 3133A | **Shilling**. Bust l. ℞. Oval garnished shield; *mm*. ∴ (obv. only) ............... | 4750 | 15000 |
| 3133B | — ℞. Square-topped shield; *mm*. as last .................................................. | 3750 | 12000 |
| 3133C | — R . Shield over long cross ................................................................ | 3250 | 10000 |
| 3134 | **Threepence**. ℞. Square-topped shield; *mm*.-/ prostrate gerb .................. | 1000 | 3500 |

## WELSH MARCHES? 1644

3135

| | | | |
| --- | --- | --- | --- |
| 3135 | **Halfcrown**. Crude horseman, l. ℞. Declaration of Bristol style divided by a dotted line, 3 plumes above, 1644 below ................................................. | 1750 | 6000 |

## CARLISLE, 1644-5

3137                                    3139

|  | | F<br>£ | VF<br>£ |
|---|---|---|---|
| 3136 | **Three shillings**. Large crown above C R between rosettes III. S below. rev.<br>OBS . CARL / . 1645, rosette below ........................................................ | 12500 | 27500 |
| 3137 | Similar but :- OBS :/-: CARL :./.1645, rosette above and below ............. | 11000 | 25000 |
| 3138 | **Shilling**. Large crown above C R between trefoil of pellets, XII below.<br>*rev*. as 3137 ....................................................................................... | 6000 | 15000 |
| 3139 | R. Legend and date in two lines................................................................ | 7000 | 16500 |

**Note.** *(3136-39) Round or Octagonal pieces exist.*

## NEWARK, 1645-6

3140                                    3142

|  | | | |
|---|---|---|---|
| 3140 | **Halfcrown**. Large crown between CR ; below, XXX. *rev*. OBS / NEWARK /<br>1645 ................................................................................................. | 1000 | 2750 |
| 3140A | — Similar 1646....................................................................................... | 950 | 2500 |
| 3141 | **Shilling**. Similar but crude flat shaped crown, NEWARKE, 1645 ......... | 1000 | 2750 |
| 3142 | Similar but normal arched crown, 1645 ................................................. | 800 | 1850 |
| 3143 | — NEWARK, 1645 or 1646................................................................... | 725 | 1650 |

3144                                          3146

|      |                                                            | F £ | VF £ |
|------|------------------------------------------------------------|-----|------|
| 3144 | **Ninepence**. As halfcrown but IX, 1645 or 1646 ........... | 675 | 1600 |
| 3145 | — NEWARKE, 1645........................................ | 725 | 1750 |
| 3146 | **Sixpence**. As halfcrown but VI, 1646................... | 800 | 1850 |

**PONTEFRACT, June 1648-March 1649. Before execution of Charles I**

3147  **Two shillings** (lozenge shaped). DVM : SPIRO : SPERO around CR crowned.
R. Castle surrounded by OBS, PC, sword and 1648, weight: c.9-10g. ...   8500   30000

3148

| 3148 | **Shilling** (lozenge shaped, octagonal or round). Similar ......... | 2500 | 7000 |
|------|------------------------------------------------------|------|------|
| 3149 | — Similar but XII on r. dividing PC .................. | 2000 | 6000 |

**After the execution of Charles I (30 Jan. 1649), in the name of Charles II**

3150

3150  **Shilling** (octagonal). *O*. As last. R. CAROLVS : SECVИ DVS : 1648, castle
gateway with flag dividing PC, OBS on l., cannon protrudes on r.   2250   6500

3151  CAROL : II : etc., around HANC : DE / VS : DEDIT 1648. R. POST :
MORTEM : PATRIS : PRO : FILIO around gateway etc. as last ...........   2750   8000

**SCARBOROUGH, July 1644-July 1645\***

3152

3156

3166

| | VF |
|---|---|
| Type I. Large Castle with gateway to left, SC and value Vs below | |
| 3152 **Crown.** (various weights) ........................................................ | 65000 |
| | |
| Type II. Small Castle with gateway, no SC, value punched on flan | |
| 3153 **Five shillings and eightpence.** ............................................... | 60000 |
| 3154 **Crown.** Similar........................................................................ | 75000 |
| 3155 **Three shillings.** Similar .......................................................... | 45000 |
| 3156 **Two shillings and tenpence.** Similar ...................................... | 42500 |
| 3157 **Two shillings and sevenpence.** Similar ................................. | 42500 |
| 3158 **Halfcrown.** Similar.................................................................. | 50000 |
| 3159 **Two shillings and fourpence.** Similar .................................... | 42500 |
| 3162 **One shilling and sixpence.** Similar to 3159........................... | 37500 |
| 3163 **One shilling and fourpence.** Similar ..................................... | 37500 |
| 3164 **One shilling and threepence.** Similar..................................... | 37500 |
| 3165 **Shilling.** Similar ..................................................................... | 45000 |
| 3166 **Sixpence.** Similar ................................................................... | 35000 |
| 3167 **Groat.** Similar ........................................................................ | 27500 |

*\*No research has been done on this complicated series for many years but a detailed overview was set out in the 'Slaney' catalogue, Spink auction 229, 14th May 2015.*

*VF*

UNCERTAIN CASTLE

Type III. Castle gateway with two turrets, value punched below

| | | |
|---|---|---:|
| 3168 | **Two shillings and twopence** ................................................. | 16000 |
| 3169 | **Two shillings.** Castle punched twice...................................... | 16000 |
| 3170 | **One shilling and sixpence.** Similar to 3168 ........................... | 14000 |
| 3171 | **One shilling and fourpence.** Similar ...................................... | 14000 |
| 3172 | **One shilling and threepence.** Similar..................................... | 14000 |
| 3173 | **One shilling and twopence.** Similar ....................................... | 13000 |
| 3174 | **One shilling and one penny.** Similar...................................... | 13000 |
| 3175 | **Shilling.** Similar ................................................................... | 15000 |
| 3176 | **Elevenpence.** Similar............................................................ | 12000 |
| 3177 | **Tenpence.** Similar ................................................................ | 12000 |
| 3178 | **Ninepence.** Similar................................................................ | 12000 |
| 3178A | **Eightpence.** Similar ............................................................. | 10500 |
| 3179 | **Sevenpence.** Similar.............................................................. | 10500 |
| 3180 | **Sixpence.** Similar .................................................................. | 13000 |

## COPPER

For further details see Tim Everson, *The Galata Guide to the Farthing Tokens of James I and Charles I*

**Farthings**

3182          3183

| | | F | VF |
|---|---|---:|---:|
| | | £ | £ |
| 3181 | Richmond 1a, colon stops, CARO over IACO, five jewel crowns on obverse, mm on obverse only; *mm*: Coronet, Crescent with mullet. ...................... | 20 | 50 |
| 3182 | — — 1b, colon stops, CARO over IACO, nine jewel crowns on obverse, *mm*: Dagger, Mascle .......................................................................................... | 20 | 50 |
| 3183 | — — 2 CARO, colon stops, *mm* on obverse only, *mm*: Lombardic A, Lombardic A with pellet below, Annulet, Annulet with pellet within, Bell, Book, Castle, Cinquefoil, Crescent (large and small), Cross (pellets in angles), Cross calvary, Cross patée, Cross patée fitchée, Cross patonce, Cross patonce in saltire, Cross saltire, Dagger, Ermine, Estoile (pierced), Eye, Fish hook, Fleece, Fusil, Fusils (two), Halberd, Harp, Heart, Horseshoe, Key (vertical), Leaf, Lion passant, Lis (large), Lis (demi), Lis (three), Martlet, Mascle with pellet within, Nautilus, Pike-head, Rose (single), Shield, Star, Tower, Trefoil, Tun, Woolpack, Woolpack over Crescent. ..................................................................................................... | 10 | 30 |
| 3183A | — — CARA farthings (Contemporary forgeries manufactured from official punches. Usually F for E in REX), mm on obverse only; *mm*: Annulet, Coronet, Cross patée fourchée, Dagger, Fusil, Key, Mascle, Trefoil, Tun .............. | 150 | 300 |
| 3183B | — — Contemporary forgeries of Richmond Type 2, mm: Lombardic A, Annulet, Annulet with saltire within, Barbell and pellets, Cross (pellets in angles), Cross patée, Cross patonce, Cross patonce in saltire, Cross saltire, Dagger, Fusil, Heart, Horseshoe, Key (horizontal), Lis (large), Lis, Lis demi, Lis (three), Lis (two), Mascle, Mascle with pellet within, Rose, Star, Thistlehead, Tower, Triangle, Triangle (inverted), Tun............................................................................... | 5 | 15 |

3184                                        3185

|  | F £ | VF £ |
|---|---|---|

3184 — — 3, apostrophe stops, eagle-headed harp, mm on obverse only; *mm*: Lion rampant, Trefoil ............................... 10 24

3185 — — 4, beaded harp, *mm* Rose (double) on obverse only. ..................... 15 35

3186 — — 5, scroll-fronted harp, 5 jewels on circlet, *mm* Rose (double) on obverse only. ................... 15 35

3187 — — 6, scroll-fronted harp, 7 jewels on circlet, *mm* Rose (double) on obverse only. ................... 15 35

3187A

3187A Type 6 on an uncut square flan. ............................... 400 900
— Longer strips of two to twelve farthings also exist ........................... *Extremely Rare*

3188                3189                3193

3188 — — 7, oval flans, CARO over IACO, legend starts bottom left, *mm* Cross patée on one or both sides ...................... 50 100

3189 — — 8, CARO, colon stops, mm on obverse only, *mm* Lis (demi) ........ 50 100

3190 — — 9, mm on reverse only; *mm*: Martlet, Millrind. ................ 50 100

3195                3196

3191 — — 10a, mm on both sides; *mm*: Crescent .......................... 50 100

3192 — — 10b, upright mm both sides, *mm* Goutte ...................... 50 100

3193 — — 10c, mm both sides, between sceptre handles on obverse, *mm* 9 ... 35 75

3194 — — 11, apostrophe stops, *mm* Rose (double) on both sides. ................ 60 125

3194A — — 11/10b mule, *mm* Rose (double)/Goutte .......................... 50 150

3195 — — 12, *mm* Rose (double) on obverse only .......................... 45 90

3196 Transitional Issue Farthings, double arched crowns, mm on obverse only; *mm*: Harp, Quatrefoil. ........................... 20 50

|                                                                                          | F<br>£ | VF<br>£ |
|------------------------------------------------------------------------------------------|--------|---------|
| 3197  Maltravers Type 1, inner circles, mm on obverse only; *mm*: Rose (double), Woolpack | 50     | 100     |
| 3197A Counterfeits of Maltravers Type 1, *mm*: Bell, Lis, Tun, Woolpack                   | 15     | 35      |
| 3198  — — 2, mm both sides; *mm*: Bell, Lis (large), Lis (small), Martlet, Rose (double), Woolpack | 15 | 35 |
| 3198A Counterfeits of Maltravers Type 2, *mm*: Bell, Cross patée, Harp, Lis (small), Mascle, Star, Woolpack | 15 | 35 |

3199                                               3200

|                                                                                          | F<br>£ | VF<br>£ |
|------------------------------------------------------------------------------------------|--------|---------|
| 3199  — — 3, different mm on each side; *mm*: Woolpack/Rose (double), Martlet/Bell, Woolpack/Portcullis, Lis/Portcullis, Harp/Bell, Harp/Billet. | 15 | 35 |
| 3199A Counterfeits of Maltravers Type 3, *mm*: Bell/Cross patée fitchée, Bell/Woolpack, Cross patée fitchée/Bell, Tun/Bell, Woolpack/Lis | 15 | 35 |
| 3200  Maltravers Oval Type 4, no inner circles, legend starts bottom left, mm Lis (large) on both sides | 75 | 150 |

*Richmond Types 7 to 12 and Maltravers Type 4, 3188 to 3195 and 3200, the oval farthings, were issued for use in Ireland.*

3201                        3202                        3203

(There is frequent muling between types in the Rose Farthing sequence)

|                                                                                          | F<br>£ | VF<br>£ |
|------------------------------------------------------------------------------------------|--------|---------|
| 3201  Rose Type 1, large double-arched crowns, sceptres within inner Circle, BRIT, mm on obv. or rev. or both; *mm*: Lis, Martlet | 45 | 90 |
| 3202  — — 2, similar but small crowns and sceptres just cross inner circle, BRIT, mm on obverse only or both sides, *mm* Lis | 30 | 75 |
| 3203  — — 3, similar but crowns with pointed sides and sceptres almost to outer circle, BRIT, mm Lis, Cross patée, Mullet, Crescent | 15 | 35 |

3204                        3206                        3207

|                                                                                          | F<br>£ | VF<br>£ |
|------------------------------------------------------------------------------------------|--------|---------|
| 3204 - - Mules of Type 3 with Types 4a and 4b, mm Lis, Mullet, Crescent.                  | 15     | 35      |
| 3205 - - 4a Single arched crowns, Long legends with CAROLVS, MAG, FRAN and HIB, *mm*: Lis, Mullet, Crescent. | 10 | 25 |
| 3206  — — 4b Single arched crowns, Short legends with CAROLV, MA, FRA and HI, *mm*: Mullet, Crescent | 10 | 25 |
| 3206A Counterfeits of Rose type 4, mm Crescent                                           | 20     | 45      |
| 3207  — — 5, sceptres below crown, mm Mullet on both sides                                | 35     | 75      |

*The Rose farthings were also authorised for use in Ireland but do not seem to have reached there.*

The coins struck during the Commonwealth have inscriptions in English instead of Latin as a truer expression of Protestantism. St. George's cross and the Irish harp take the place of the royal arms. The silver halfpenny was issued for the last time. Coins with *mm.* anchor were struck during the protectorship of Richard Cromwell.

*Mintmarks*

1649-57 Sun 　　　　1658-60 Anchor

## GOLD

3208

|  | | F | VF |
|---|---|---|---|
|  | | £ | £ |
| **3208 Unite.** As illustration; *mm.* sun, | | | |
| 1649 | | 2750 | 8500 |
| 1650 | | 2500 | 6500 |
| 1651 | | 2250 | 5750 |
| 1652 | | 2500 | 6500 |
| 1653 | | 2250 | 5750 |
| 1654 | | 2400 | 6000 |
| 1655 | | 3750 | 10500 |
| 1656 | | 2750 | 7500 |
| 1657 | | 2750 | 7500 |
| 3209 Similar, *mm.* anchor, | | | |
| 1658 | | 10000 | 25000 |
| 1660 | | 9000 | 22500 |

3210

| **3210 Double-crown.** Similar; but X; *mm.* sun, | | | |
|---|---|---|---|
| 1649 | | 2250 | 7500 |
| 1650 | | 1750 | 5750 |
| 1651 | | 1650 | 5250 |

|      | F<br>£ | VF<br>£ |
|------|------|------|
| 1652 | 1850 | 6000 |
| 1653 | 1650 | 5250 |
| 1654 | 1850 | 6000 |
| 1655 | 3250 | 10500 |
| 1656 | 3000 | 10000 |
| 1657 | 3250 | 10500 |

3212

| 3211 Similar, *mm.* anchor, 1660 | 6000 | 17500 |
|------|------|------|

3212 **Crown.** Similar, but V; *mm.* sun,

|      |      |      |
|------|------|------|
| 1649 | 1600 | 4750 |
| 1650 | 1350 | 4000 |
| 1651 | 1350 | 4000 |
| 1652 | 1250 | 3750 |
| 1653 | 1250 | 3750 |
| 1654 | 1500 | 4500 |
| 1655 | 2500 | 7500 |
| 1656 | 2500 | 7500 |
| 1657 | 2250 | 6250 |

*Numerous overstruck dates exist in this series.*

3213 Similar *mm.* anchor,

|      |      |      |
|------|------|------|
| 1658 | 4500 | 13500 |
| 1660 | 5000 | 15000 |

## SILVER

3214 **Crown.** Same type; *mm.* sun,

|      |      |      |
|------|------|------|
| 1649 | 6500 | 18500 |
| 1651 | 2500 | 6500 |
| 1652 | 1350 | 3250 |
| 1653 | 1250 | 2850 |
| 1654 | 1850 | 4500 |
| 1656 | 1350 | 3000 |

3215

|  | F<br>£ | VF<br>£ |
|---|---|---|
| **3215 Halfcrown.** Similar; *mm.* sun, | | |
| 1649 | 800 | 2500 |
| 1651 | 375 | 1000 |
| 1652 | 375 | 1000 |
| 1653 | 350 | 850 |
| 1654 | 375 | 950 |
| 1655 | 1750 | 4500 |
| 1656 | 350 | 925 |
| 1657 | 1750 | 4500 |
| 3216 Similar, *mm.* anchor | | |
| 1658 | 1350 | 4250 |
| 1659 | 3750 | 10500 |
| 1660 | 1350 | 4250 |

3217 rev

| **3217 Shilling.** Similar; *mm.* sun, | | |
|---|---|---|
| 1649 | 375 | 1000 |
| 1651 | 275 | 675 |
| 1652 | 275 | 675 |
| 1653 | 250 | 625 |
| 1654 | 275 | 675 |
| 1655 | 425 | 1100 |
| 1656 | 275 | 675 |
| 1657 | 900 | 2250 |

3218 obv                              3219

3218  Similar, *mm*. anchor
|  |  |  |
|---|---|---|
| 1658 | 1000 | 2500 |
| 1659 | 3500 | 9000 |
| 1660 | 1000 | 2500 |

3219 **Sixpence.** Similar; *mm*. sun,
|  |  |  |
|---|---|---|
| 1649 | 275 | 900 |
| 1651 | 200 | 600 |
| 1652 | 200 | 600 |
| 1653 | 210 | 625 |
| 1654 | 225 | 650 |
| 1655 | 700 | 1850 |
| 1656 | 210 | 625 |
| 1657 | 750 | 2000 |

3220 Similar; *mm*. anchor,
|  |  |  |
|---|---|---|
| 1658 | 625 | 1750 |
| 1659 | 1750 | 5500 |
| 1660 | 625 | 1750 |

3221                              3222

3221 **Halfgroat.** ............................................................................................45       135
3222 **Penny.** Similar, but I above shields ....................................................40       125

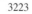

3223

3223 **Halfpenny.** ..........................................................................................35        95

Oliver Cromwell, 'the Great Emancipator' was born on 25th April 1599 in Huntingdon. He married Elizabeth Bourchier in August 1620 and had nine children, seven of whom survived infancy. The Protectorate was established on 16th December 1653, with work on the production of portrait coins authorised in 1655. Although often referred to as patterns, there is in fact nothing to suggest that the portrait coins of Oliver Cromwell were not *intended* for circulation. Authorised in 1656, the first full production came in 1657 and was followed by a second more plentiful one before Cromwell's death on 3rd September 1658. All coins were machine made, struck from dies by Thomas Simon (1618-1665) in the presses of the Frenchman, Pierre Blondeau. Later, some of Simon's puncheons were sold in the Low Countries and an imitation Crown was made there. Other Dutch dies were prepared and some found their way back to the Mint, where in 1738 it was decided to strike a set of Cromwell's coins. Shillings and Sixpences were struck from the Dutch dies, and Crowns from new dies prepared by John Tanner. Dutch and Tanner Halfbroads were also made. Oliver was succeeded as Lord Protector by his son Richard for whom no coins were struck.

## GOLD

|  | F £ | VF £ | EF £ |
|---|---|---|---|
| 3224 **Fifty shillings**. Laur. head l. R. Crowned Shield of the Protectorate, die axis ↑↓ 1656 from the same dies as the Broad....................... | 35000 | 95000 | 250000 |

Lettered edge PROTECTOR · LITERIS · LITERÆ · NUMMIS · CORONA · ET · SALUS

3225
1656 gold Broad

| 3225 **Broad**. of Twenty Shillings. Laur. head l. R. Crowned Shield of the Protectorate, but grained edge die axis ↑↓ 1656. ........................... | 8500 | 20000 | 55000 |

## SILVER

3226
1658 Crown 8 over 7 - Die flawed drapery

| 3226 | **Crown**. Dr. bust l. R. Crowned shield, 1658/7. Lettered edge ↑↓ | 2000 | 4250 | 10500 |
|---|---|---|---|---|
| 3226A | **Crown**. Dutch copy, similar with AИG legend 1658 ............... | 2400 | 6250 | 18500 |
| 3226B | **Crown**. Tanner's copy (struck 1738) dated 1658 ...................... | 2500 | 6500 | 20000 |

|  | F | VF | EF |
|---|---|---|---|
|  | £ | £ | £ |

3227   **Halfcrown.** Dr. bust l. R. Crowned shield 1656 HI type
legend, lettered edge, die axis ↑↓ .............................................    3000    7500    18500

3227A
1658 Halfcrown with HIB obverse legend

3227A **Halfcrown.** Similar,1658 HIB type legend, lettered edge, die axis ↑↓    1350    2750    6000

3228
1658 Shilling

3228   **Shilling.** Dr. bust l. R. Crowned shield, grained edge, 1658 die
axis↑↓ .........................................................................................    950    1750    4750

3229   **Sixpence.** Similar 1658 die axis↑↓ .............................................    30000    —    —

3229A Dutch copy.......................................................................................    2500    6000    12500

## COPPER

3230
Copper Farthing

3230   **Farthing.** Dr. bust l. R. CHARITIE AND CHANGE, shield ↑↓ ..    8750    18500
*There are also other reverse types for this coin, and an obverse with mullet on top.*

## CHARLES II, 1660-85

Charles II was born at St James Palace on 29th May 1630. He spent a long exile in France and returned after the fall of the Protectorate in 1660. The Restoration commenced and he married Catherine of Braganza, but he bore no legitimate successor. Charles II died on 6th February 1685.

For the first two years after the Restoration the same denominations, apart from the silver crown, were struck as were issued during the Commonwealth although the threepence and fourpence were soon added. Then, early in 1663, the ancient hand hammering process was finally superceded by the machinery of Blondeau.

For the emergency issues struck in the name of Charles II in 1648/9, see the siege pieces of Pontefract listed under Charles I, nos. 3150-1.

**HAMMERED COINAGE, 1660-2**

*Mintmark: Crown.*

### GOLD

3301

|  | F | VF |
|---|---|---|
|  | £ | £ |

**First issue.** Without mark of value; *mm.* crown on *obv.* only
3301 **Unite** (20s.). Type as illustration ....................................................................2250 | 6500

3302     3303

3302 **Double-crown**. As illustration..........................................................................1500 | 4500
3303 **Crown**. Similar ........................................................................................................1750 | 5250

3304

|  | F | VF |
|---|---|---|
|  | £ | £ |

**Second issue.** With mark of value; *mm.* crown on *obv.* only

3304 **Unite.** Type as illustration ................................................................ 2000      6000

3305

3305 **Double-crown.** As illustration ...................................................... 1500      4500

3306 **Crown.** Similar .......................................................................... 2500      7500

## SILVER

3307

**First issue.** Without inner circles or mark of value; *mm.* crown on *obv.* only

3307 **Halfcrown.** Crowned bust, as 3308 .............................................. 1500      5750

3308

|  | F<br>£ | VF<br>£ |
|---|---|---|
| 3308 **Shilling**. Similar. (Also known with smaller harp on reverse.) ...... 450 | | 1750 |

3309

| | | |
|---|---|---|
| 3309 **Sixpence**. Similar......................................................................................... 350 | | 1350 |
| 3310 **Twopence**. Similar........................................................................................ 50 | | 175 |
| 3311 **Penny**. Similar .............................................................................................. 40 | | 125 |
| 3312 As last, but without mintmark ......................................................................... 50 | | 135 |

3313

**Second issue**. Without inner circles, but with mark of value; *mm.* crown on *obv.* only

| | | |
|---|---|---|
| 3313 **Halfcrown**. Crowned bust ....................................................................... 1350 | | 5750 |
| 3314 **Shilling**. Similar ................................................................................................ 750 | | 2750 |
| 3315 **Sixpence**. Similar .............................................................................................. 1250 | | 3750 |

3316

|                                                                                         | F | VF |
|-----------------------------------------------------------------------------------------|----|-----|
|                                                                                         | £ | £ |
| 3316 **Twopence**. Similar, but mm. on obv. only ........................................90 | | 300 |
| 3317 Similar, but mm. both sides (machine made).................................20 | | 80 |
| 3318 Bust to edge of coin, legend starts at bottom l. (machine made, single arch crown) ........................................................................20 | | 75 |
| 3319 **Penny**. As 3317........................................................................25 | | 90 |
| 3320 As 3318 (single arch crown) .............................................20 | | 80 |

3321

**Third issue**. With inner circles and mark of value; *mm.* crown on both sides

| | F | VF |
|---|---|---|
| 3321 **Halfcrown**. Crowned bust to i.c. (and rarely to edge of coin) ..........................200 | | 700 |
| 3322 **Shilling**. Similar, rarely *mm.* crown on *obv.* only. (Also known with smaller harp on reverse.) ......................................................150 | | 525 |
| 3323 **Sixpence**. Similar..........................................................135 | | 475 |
| 3324 **Fourpence**. Similar...........................................................45 | | 125 |
| 3325 **Threepence**. Similar .........................................................30 | | 90 |

3326

| | F | VF |
|---|---|---|
| 3326 **Twopence**. Similar...........................................................25 | | 70 |
| 3327 **Penny**. Similar ...............................................................25 | | 75 |

# Buying and Selling Collectible Coins and Banknotes Made Easy

An authentic trading platform, tailored specifically to the needs of the Numismatic marketplace.

www.numitrading.com

01702 667420     info@numitrading.com

## Grading of Early and Later Milled Coinage

Milled coinage refers to coins that are struck by dies worked in a mechanical coining press. The early period is defined from the time of the successful installation of Peter Blondeau's hand powered machinery at the mint, initiated to strike the first portrait coins of Oliver Cromwell in 1656, continuing until the advent of Matthew Boulton's steam powered presses from 1790. The coinage of this early period is therefore cruder in its execution than the latter. When pricing coins of the early peiod, we only attribute grades as high as extremely fine, and as high as uncirculated for the latter period. Most coins that occur of the early period in superior grades than those stated, in particular copper coins retaining full original lustre, will command considerably higher prices, due to their rarity. We suggest the following definitions for grades of preservation:

## Milled Coinage Conditions

**Proof**  A very carefully struck coin from specially prepared dies, to give a superior definition to the design, with mirror-like fields. Occurs occasionally in the Early Milled Coinage, more frequently in the latter period. Some issues struck to a matt finish for Edward VII.

**FDC**  *Fleur-de-coin.* Absolutely flawless, untouched, without wear, scratches, marks or hairlines. Generally applied to proofs.

**UNC**  *Uncirculated.* A coin in as new condition as issued by the Mint, retaining full lustre or brilliance but, owing to modern mass-production methods of manufacture and storage, not necessarily perfect.

**EF**  *Extremely Fine.* A coin that exhibits very little sign of circulation, with only minimal marks or faint wear, which are only evident upon very close scrutiny.

**VF**  *Very Fine.* A coin that exhibits some wear on the raised surfaces of the design, but really has only had limited circulation.

**F**  *Fine.* A coin that exhibits considerable wear to the raised surfaces of the design, either through circulation, or damage perhaps due to faulty striking

**Fair**  *Fair.* A coin that exhibits wear, with the main features still distinguishable, and the legends, date and inscriptions still readable.

**Poor**  *Poor.* A coin that exhibits considerable wear, certainly with milled coinage of no value to a collector unless it is an extremely rare date or variety.

## Examples of Condition Grading

### Early Milled

Gold Ѵ                         Silver Ѧ                         Copper Æ

**Extremely Fine**

Gold AV          Silver AR          Copper Æ

**Very Fine**

**Fine**

*George III*          *James II*          *George II*
*Guinea*          *Crown*          *old head Halfpenny*

## Later Milled

Gold AV          Silver AR          Copper Æ

**Uncirculated**

Gold AV        Silver AR        Copper Æ

**Extremely Fine**

**Very Fine**

**Fine**

*Victoria*
*Jubilee head Sovereign*
      
*George IV*
*laureate bust Crown*
      
*Victoria*
*Young head Halfpenny*

**MILLED COINAGE, 1662-85**

Early in 1663, the ancient hand hammering process was finally superceded by the machinery of Blondeau. John and Joseph Roettier, two brothers, engraved the dies with a safeguard against clipping, the larger coins were made with the edge inscribed DECVS ET TVTAMEN and the regnal year. The medium-sized coins were given a grained edge.

The new gold coins were current for 100s., 40s., 20s. and 10s., and they came to be called 'Guineas' as the gold from which some of them were made was imported from Guinea by the Africa Company (whose badge was the Elephant and Castle). It was not until some years later that the Guinea increased in value to 21s. and more. The Africa Co. badge is also found on some silver and so is the plume symbol indicating silver from the Welsh mines. The four smallest silver denominations, though known today as 'Maundy Money', were actually issued for general circulation: at this period the silver penny was probably the only coin distributed at the Royal Maundy ceremonies. Though never part of the original agreement, smaller coins were eventually also struck by machinery.

A good regal copper coinage was issued for the first time in 1672, but later in the reign, farthings were struck in tin (with a copper plug) in order to help the Cornish tin industry.

**Engravers and designers:** John Roettier (1631-1700), Thomas Simon (1618-1665)

## GOLD

3328
1672 First bust type Five-Guineas

| | F £ | VF £ | EF £ |
|---|---|---|---|
| **3328 Five Guineas.** First laur. bust r., pointed trun., regnal year on edge in words, die axis ↑↓ (e.g. 1669=VICESIMO PRIMO), R. Crowned cruciform shields, sceptres in angles | | | |
| 1668   VICESIMO | 8250 | 20500 | 100000 |
| 1668   V. PRIMO | 8500 | 21000 | 105000 |
| 1669   V. PRIMO | 8000 | 19000 | 95000 |
| 1670   V. SECVNDO | 7250 | 17500 | 90000 |
| 1670   V. Similar proof *FDC* £240000 | | | |
| 1671   V. TERTIO | 8500 | 21000 | 100000 |
| 1672   V. QVARTO | 8500 | 21000 | 100000 |
| 1673   V. QVINTO | 8000 | 19000 | 95000 |
| 1674   V. QVINTO | 9250 | 22500 | 105000 |
| 1674   V. SEXTO | 8500 | 21500 | 100000 |
| **3328A Five Guineas.** First bust. Similar hair of different style. Shorter ties | | | |
| 1674   QVINTO | 9250 | 22500 | 105000 |
| 1675   V. SEPTIMO | 8500 | 21000 | 100000 |
| 1676   V. SEPTIMO | 8250 | 20000 | 97500 |
| 1676   V. OCTAVO | 8500 | 21000 | 100000 |
| 1677   V. NONO | 8000 | 19000 | 95000 |
| 1678/7 V. TRICESIMO | 8250 | 20000 | 97500 |

|  |  | F | VF | EF |
|---|---|---|---|---|
|  |  | £ | £ | £ |

**3329  Five Guineas.** First bust with elephant below, similar die axis ↑↓

| 1668 | VICESIMO......................................................7000 | 16500 | 85000 |
|---|---|---|---|
| 1669 | V. PRIMO..........................................................8500 | 21000 | 105000 |
| 1675 | V. SEPTIMO .....................................................8500 | 21000 | 105000 |
| 1677/5 | V. NONO ..........................................................9500 | 22500 | 110000 |

3330
1676 Five-Guineas with elephant and castle provenance mark

**3330  Five Guineas.** First bust with elephant and castle below, similar die axis ↑↓

| 1675 | V. SEPTIMO .....................................................9500 | 22500 | 110000 |
|---|---|---|---|
| 1676 | V. OCTAVO.......................................................8250 | 20000 | 97500 |
| 1677 | V. NONO ...........................................................8500 | 21000 | 105000 |
| 1678/7 | – TRICESIMO .....................................................8500 | 21000 | 105000 |

**3331  Five Guineas.** Second laur. bust r., rounded trun. similar die axis ↑↓

| 1678/7 | TRICESIMO .....................................................7500 | 18000 | 95000 |
|---|---|---|---|
| 1679 | T. PRIMO ..........................................................7250 | 17500 | 90000 |
| 1680/79 | T. SECVNDO.....................................................7500 | 18000 | 95000 |
| 1681 | T. TERTIO.........................................................7500 | 18000 | 95000 |
| 1682 | T. QVARTO .......................................................7250 | 17500 | 90000 |
| 1683 | T. QVINTO ........................................................7250 | 17500 | 90000 |
| 1683/2 | T.QVINTO .........................................................7500 | 18000 | 95000 |
| 1684 | T. SEXTO..........................................................7250 | 17500 | 90000 |

**3332  Five Guineas.** Second laur. bust r., with elephant and castle below, similar die axis ↑↓

| 1680/79 | T. SECVNDO.....................................................8500 | 21000 | 105000 |
|---|---|---|---|
| 1681 | T. TERTIO.........................................................8500 | 21000 | 105000 |
| 1682 | T. QVARTO .......................................................8250 | 20000 | 97500 |
| 1683 | T. QVINTO ........................................................8500 | 21000 | 105000 |
| 1684 | T. SEXTO..........................................................7500 | 18000 | 95000 |

3333
1664 First bust type Two Guineas

|  | F | VF | EF |
|---|---|---|---|
|  | £ | £ | £ |

**3333** **Two Guineas.** First laur. bust r., pointed trun. ℞. Crowned cruciform shields, sceptres in angles, die axis ↑↓

| 1664 | 2750 | 6750 | 27500 |
|---|---|---|---|
| 1665 | | | *Extremely rare* |
| 1669 | | | *Extremely rare* |
| 1671 | 3750 | 9000 | 37500 |
| 1673 | | | *Extremely rare* |

3334
1664 Two Guineas with elephant only below

**3334** **Two Guineas.** First bust with elephant below, similar die axis ↑↓

| 1664 | 2250 | 6250 | 20000 |
|---|---|---|---|

3335
1675 Two Guineas - second bust

**3335** **Two Guineas.** Second laur. bust r., rounded trun, similar die axis ↑↓

| 1675 | 3000 | 7250 | 32500 |
|---|---|---|---|
| 1676 | 2750 | 6500 | 30000 |
| 1677 | 2750 | 6500 | 30000 |
| 1678/7 | 2750 | 6500 | 30000 |
| 1679 | 2750 | 6500 | 30000 |
| 1680 | 3500 | 8500 | 35000 |

|      | F £ | VF £ | EF £ |
|------|-----|------|------|
| 1681 | 2750 | 6500 | 30000 |
| 1682 | 2750 | 6500 | 30000 |
| 1683 | 2750 | 6500 | 30000 |
| 1684 | 3000 | 7250 | 32500 |

**3336 Two Guineas.** Second bust with elephant and castle below, similar die axis ↑↓

| 1676 | 3000 | 7250 | 32500 |
|------|------|------|-------|
| 1677 | | | *Extremely rare* |
| 1678 | 3000 | 7250 | 32500 |
| 1682 | 3000 | 7250 | 32500 |
| 1683 | 3500 | 8500 | 35000 |
| 1684 | 3000 | 7250 | 32500 |

**3337 Two Guineas.** Second bust with elephant only below, die axis ↑↓

| 1678 | | | *Extremely rare* |
|------|------|------|-------|

**3337A Broad** of 20s. Laur. and dr. bust r. R. Crowned shield of arms
(approx. 3400 issued), die axis ↑↓

| 1662 | 3000 | 6500 | 16500 |
|------|------|------|-------|

**3338 Guinea.** First laur. bust r., R. Crowned cruciform shields, die axis ↑↓

| 1663 | 5750 | 17500 | 65000 |
|------|------|-------|-------|

3339
1663 Guinea first bust, elephant below

**3339 Guinea.** First bust with elephant below, similar die axis ↑↓

| 1663 | 4500 | 13500 | 50000 |
|------|------|-------|-------|

**3340 Guinea.** Second laur. bust r.,similar die axis ↑↓

| 1663 | 3750 | 12500 | 47500 |
|------|------|-------|-------|
| 1664 | 2250 | 8500 | 32500 |

3341                                    3342
1664 Guinea second bust elephant below    1666 Guinea - third bust

**3341 Guinea.** Second bust with elephant below, similar die axis ↑↓

| 1664 | 3750 | 12500 | 47500 |
|------|------|-------|-------|

**3342 Guinea.** Third laur. bust r. similar die axis ↑↓

| 1664 | 1350 | 3750 | 15000 |
|------|------|------|-------|
| 1665 | 1250 | 3500 | 14500 |

|      | F £ | VF £ | EF £ |
|------|-----|------|------|
| 1666 | 1250 | 3500 | 14500 |
| 1667 | 1250 | 3500 | 14500 |
| 1668 | 1100 | 3000 | 13500 |
| 1669 | 1250 | 3500 | 14500 |
| 1670 | 1250 | 3500 | 14500 |
| 1671 | 1250 | 3500 | 14500 |
| 1672 | 1400 | 4000 | 16000 |
| 1673 | 1500 | 4500 | 16500 |

**3343 Guinea.** Third laur. bust r., with elephant below, similar die axis ↑↓

| 1664 | 2250 | 6250 | 22500 |
| 1665 | 2250 | 6250 | 22500 |
| 1668 | ................Extremely rare | | |

|                | 3344 | 3345 |
|----------------|------|------|
|                | 1679 Guinea - Fourth bust | 1682 - Fourth bust - elephant below |

**3344 Guinea.** Fourth laur. bust r., rounded trun. similar die axis ↑↓

| 1672 | 1100 | 2850 | 11500 |
| 1673 | 1050 | 2750 | 11000 |
| 1674 | 1100 | 2850 | 11500 |
| 1675 | 1100 | 2850 | 11500 |
| 1675 CRAOLVS error | 2500 | 6750 | — |
| 1676 | 1050 | 2750 | 11000 |
| 1676/4 | 1200 | 3000 | 12000 |
| 1677 | 1050 | 2750 | 11000 |
| 1677 GRATIR error | 3000 | — | — |
| 1677 CAROLVS error | 1100 | 2850 | 11500 |
| 1678 | 1050 | 2750 | 11000 |
| 1679 | 1000 | 2600 | 10500 |
| 1679 'O' over 'o' on its side and R of FRA over A | 1200 | 3000 | 12000 |
| 1680 | 1100 | 2750 | 11000 |
| 1680/79 | 1250 | 3250 | 12500 |
| 1681 | 1050 | 2750 | 11000 |
| 1682 | 1050 | 2750 | 11000 |
| 1682 rev.@90° axis | 1200 | 3000 | 12000 |
| 1683 | 1050 | 2750 | 11000 |
| 1684 | 1050 | 2850 | 11500 |

**3345 Guinea.** Fourth laur. bust r., with elephant and castle below, similar die axis ↑↓

| 1674 | ................Extremely rare | | |
| 1675 | 1300 | 4250 | 14500 |
| 1676 | 1300 | 4250 | 14500 |
| 1677 | 1300 | 4250 | 14500 |
| 1677 GRATIR error | 3500 | — | — |
| 1678 | 1300 | 4250 | 14500 |

|        | F      | VF    | EF    |
|--------|--------|-------|-------|
|        | £      | £     | £     |
| 1679   | 1350   | 4500  | 15000 |
| 1680   | 1400   | 4750  | 16000 |
| 1681   | 1400   | 4750  | 16000 |
| 1682   | 1300   | 4250  | 14500 |
| 1683   | 1300   | 4250  | 14500 |
| 1684   | 1500   | 5250  | 16500 |

**3346 Guinea.** — — with elephant below bust, similar die axis ↑↓

| 1677/5 | ...................................................................................*Extremely rare* |       |
|--------|--------|-------|
| 1678   | 4000   | 13500 | — |

| 3347 | 3348 |
|------|------|
| 1669 Half-Guinea, first bust | 1684 Half-Guinea, second bust |

**3347 Half-Guinea.** First laur. bust r., pointed trun.R. Crowned cruciform shields,
sceptres in angles die axis ↑↓

| 1669   | 650    | 2200  | 7000  |
|--------|--------|-------|-------|
| 1670   | 625    | 2100  | 6750  |
| 1671   | 750    | 2500  | 7500  |
| 1672   | 675    | 2250  | 7250  |

**3348 Half-Guinea.** Second laur. bust r., rounded trun. similar die axis ↑↓

| 1672   | 575    | 1850  | 6250  |
|--------|--------|-------|-------|
| 1673   | 600    | 2000  | 6500  |
| 1674   | 625    | 2100  | 7000  |
| 1675   | 600    | 2000  | 6500  |
| 1676   | 575    | 1850  | 6250  |
| 1676/4 | 600    | 2000  | 6500  |
| 1677   | 600    | 2000  | 6500  |
| 1678   | 600    | 2000  | 6500  |
| 1678/7 | 600    | 2000  | 6500  |
| 1679   | 575    | 1850  | 6250  |
| 1680   | 575    | 1850  | 6250  |
| 1681   | 600    | 2000  | 6500  |
| 1682   | 575    | 1850  | 6250  |
| 1683   | 575    | 1850  | 6250  |
| 1684   | 550    | 1750  | 6000  |

**3349 Half-Guinea.** Second bust with elephant and castle below, similar die axis ↑↓

| 1676   | 950    | 3000  | 9500  |
|--------|--------|-------|-------|
| 1677   | 850    | 2750  | 9000  |
| 1678/7 | 850    | 2750  | 9000  |
| 1680   | 950    | 3000  | 9500  |
| 1681   | 950    | 3000  | 9500  |
| 1682   | 850    | 2750  | 9000  |
| 1683   | ...................................................................................*Extremely rare* |       |
| 1684   | 850    | 2750  | 9000  |

## SILVER

3350 - 1662 Crown, first type, rose below bust

|  | F £ | VF £ | EF £ |
|---|---|---|---|

**3350 Crown.** First dr. bust r., rose below, numerous varieties in length and style of hair ties. R. Crowned cruciform shields, interlinked C's in angles edge undated, die axis ↑↓

1662 ............200　1100　12500

**3350A Crown.** — — Similar, die axis ↑↑
1662 ............275　1350　—

**3350B Crown.** — striped cloak to drapery,
1662 similar die axis ↑↓ ............375　1750　—

**3350C Crown.** — — II of legend at 12 o'clock, similar die axis ↑↓
1662 ............2500　—　—

**3351 Crown.** — — edge dated, similar die axis ↑↓ or ↑↑
1662 ............225　1250　13500

**3352 Crown.** — legend re-arranged no rose, edge dated, similar die axis ↑↓
1662 ............250　1250　13500

**3353 Crown.** — — edge not dated, similar die axis ↑↓
1662 ............200　1100　12500

**3354 Crown.** — — shields altered, 1663, similar regnal year on edge in Roman figures
ANNO REGNI XV die axis ↑↓ ............175　1000　10000

1663 no stops on revers ............185　1100　12500

1663 edge not dated, as 3350 ............*Extremely rare*

3354A

**3354A** Pattern 'Petition' Crown, 1663 by Thomas Simon. Laur. Bust r. of fine style in high relief, *Simon* below, edge inscription of Simon's 'petition': THOMAS SIMON. MOST HVMBLY. PRAYS. YOVR MAJESTY etc., etc......40000　135000　525000

|                                                                                              | F £ | VF £ | EF £ |
|----------------------------------------------------------------------------------------------|-----|------|------|
| **3354B** Pattern 'Reddite' Crown, 1663, by Thomas Simon, struck from the same dies, edge    |     |      |      |
| inscription: REDDITE. QVAE. CESARIS etc., etc. .... | 25000 | 80000 | 375000 |

**3355  Crown.** Second dr. bust r. smaller than first bust and with curving tie to wreath. Regnal year on edge in Roman figures (e.g. 1664 = XVI), die axis ↑↓

| | | | |
|---|---|---|---|
| 1664 edge XVI | 150 | 1000 | 8750 |
| 1664 Proof *FDC* Fine work | — | — | 95000 |
| 1665 XVI | 1750 | — | — |
| 1665/4 XVII | 1600 | 4500 | — |
| 1665 XVII | 1500 | 4250 | — |
| 1666 XVIII | 275 | 1100 | 9500 |
| 1666 XVIII RE·X | 300 | 1200 | 10000 |
| 1667 XVIII | 4500 | — | — |

**3356  Crown.** Second bust elephant below, similar, die axis ↑↓

| | | | |
|---|---|---|---|
| 1666 XVIII | 950 | 3750 | 20000 |
| 1666 XVIII RE·X | 975 | 4000 | — |

3357
1668 Crown - second bust

**3357  Crown.** Second bust, similar, Regnal year on edge in words (e.g. 1667= DECIMO NONO) die axis ↑↓

| | | | |
|---|---|---|---|
| 1667 D. NONO | 200 | 800 | 9000 |
| 1667 — AN.· REG.· | 175 | 750 | 8500 |
| 1668 VICESIMO | 175 | 700 | 8500 |
| 1668 — error edge inverted | 400 | — | — |
| 1668/7 VICESIMO | 200 | 800 | 8750 |
| 1668/5 VICESIMO | 400 | — | — |
| 1669 V· PRIMO | 325 | 1350 | — |
| 1669/8 V· PRIMO | 350 | 1500 | — |
| 1670 V. SECVNDO | 175 | 700 | 8500 |
| 1670/69 V. SECVND | 250 | 900 | 9500 |
| 1671 V· TERTIO | 175 | 700 | 8500 |
| 1671 — T/R in ET | 250 | 900 | — |
| 1671 — ET over FR | 275 | 1000 | — |

3358
Third bust Crown

|                              | F        | VF       | EF       |
|                              | £        | £        | £        |

**3358  Crown.** Third dr. bust r. much larger and broader than second bust, tie nearly straight. From
end of tie to top of nose is 20mm. R.Similar die axis ↑↓

| | F | VF | EF |
|---|---|---|---|
| 1671 V. TERTIO | 175 | 650 | 7500 |
| 1671 V. QVARTO | 400 | 1350 | — |
| 1672 V. QVARTO | 175 | 650 | 7500 |
| 1673 V. QVARTO | | | *Extremely rare* |
| 1673 V. QVINTO | 175 | 650 | 7500 |
| 1673 B/R in BR | 225 | 800 | — |
| 1673/2 V. QVINTO | 185 | 700 | 8000 |
| 1674 V. SEXTO | | | *Extremely rare* |
| 1675/3 V. SEPTIMO | 700 | 2750 | — |
| 1675 — | 800 | 3250 | — |
| 1676 V. OCTAVO | 175 | 650 | 7500 |
| 1676 OCCTAVO | 185 | 700 | 8000 |
| 1677 V. NONO | 175 | 650 | 7500 |
| 1677/6 V. NONO | 175 | 650 | 7500 |
| 1678/7 TRICESIMO | 250 | 1000 | 9000 |
| 1679 T. PRIMO | 175 | 650 | 7500 |
| 1680/79 T. SECVNDO | 200 | 750 | 8250 |
| 1680 T. SECVNDO | 185 | 700 | 8000 |

3359
Fourth bust Crown

**3359  Crown.** Fourth dr. bust r. still larger, with older features and more pointed nose.
From end of tie to tip of nose is 21mm. R.Similar die axis ↑↓

| | F | VF | EF |
|---|---|---|---|
| 1679 T. PRIMO | 200 | 650 | 7500 |
| 1679 HIBR·EX | 375 | 1500 | — |

|                            |   F £ |   VF £ |   EF £ |
|----------------------------|-------|--------|--------|
| 1680 T. SECVNDO            | 200   | 650    | 7500   |
| 1680/79 T. SECVNDO         | 250   | 750    | 8250   |
| 1681 T. TERTIO             | 200   | 650    | 7500   |
| 1682/1 T. QVARTO           | 200   | 650    | 7500   |
| 1682 T. QVARTO             | 225   | 750    | 8000   |
| 1682/1 QVRRTO error        | 240   | 800    | 8250   |
| 1683 T. QVINTO             | 350   | 1250   | 9500   |
| 1684 T. SEXTO              | 275   | 900    | 8500   |

**3360  Crown.**— elephant and castle below bust, die axis ↑↓

|                 |   F £ |   VF £ |  EF £ |
|-----------------|-------|--------|-------|
| 1681 T. TERTIO  | 5500  | 15000  | —     |

3361
First bust Halfcrown

3362
Second bust Halfcrown

**3361  Halfcrown.** First dr. bust r. R. Crowned cruciform shields, interlinked C's in angles, regnal year on edge in Roman figures die axis ↑↓

|                            |   F £ |   VF £ |   EF £ |
|----------------------------|-------|--------|--------|
| 1663 XV                    | 200   | 950    | 4750   |
| 1663 XV V/S in CAROLVS     | 225   | 1000   | 5000   |
| 1663 XV A/T in GRATIA      | 250   | 1050   | 5250   |
| 1663 XV no stops on obverse| 210   | 975    | 4750   |

**3362  Halfcrown.** Second dr. bust r., similar die axis ↑↓

|           |   F £ |   VF £ |  EF £ |
|-----------|-------|--------|-------|
| 1664 XVI  | 250   | 1050   | 5250  |

**3363  Halfcrown.** Third dr. bust r., similar die axis ↑↓

|               |   F £ |   VF £ | EF £ |
|---------------|-------|--------|------|
| 1666/4 XVIII  | 1000  | 3750   | —    |

3364
Third bust, elephant below Halfcrown

**3364  Halfcrown.** Third bust elephant below, die axis ↑↓

|            |   F £ |   VF £ | EF £ |
|------------|-------|--------|------|
| 1666 XVIII | 950   | 3500   | —    |

3365 - 1670 Halfcrown, third bust

MRG for MAG var

| | F<br>£ | VF<br>£ | EF<br>£ |
|---|---|---|---|
| **3365 Halfcrown.** Third dr. bust r. regnal date on edge in words (eg. 1667=DECIMO NONO) ↑↓ | | | |
| 1667/4 D. NONO | 4000 | — | — |
| 1668/4 VICESIMO | 325 | 1350 | — |
| 1669/4 V. PRIMO | 275 | 1100 | — |
| 1669 V. PRIMO | 325 | 1350 | — |
| 1669 — R/I in PRIMO | 350 | 1450 | — |
| 1670 V. SECVNDO | 140 | 575 | 4000 |
| 1670 – MRG for MAG | 225 | 800 | — |
| 1670 V/S CAROLVS | 200 | 750 | — |
| 1670 E/R in ET | 225 | 800 | — |

3366
1671 Halfcrown third bust variety

| **3366 Halfcrown.** Third bust variety r. R. Similar die axis ↑↓ | | | |
|---|---|---|---|
| 1671 V. TERTIO | 140 | 575 | 4000 |
| 1671 A/R in MAG | 225 | 750 | — |
| 1671/0 V. TERTIO | 150 | 625 | 4250 |
| 1672 V. TERTIO | | *Extremely rare* | |
| 1672 V. QVARTO | 140 | 575 | 4000 |

3367
Fourth bust Halfcrown

|  | F £ | VF £ | EF £ |
|---|---|---|---|
| **3367 Halfcrown.** Fourth dr. bust r. R. Similar die axis ↑↓ |  |  |  |
| 1672 V. QVARTO | 150 | 550 | 3750 |
| 1673 V. QVINTO | 150 | 550 | 3750 |
| 1673 — A/R in FRA | 175 | 675 | — |
| 1673 — B/R in BR | 175 | 675 | — |
| 1673 — FR/M in FRA | 175 | 675 | — |
| 1674 V. SEXTO | 160 | 575 | 4000 |
| 1674/3 V. SEXTO | 180 | 725 | — |
| 1675 V. SEPTIMO | 150 | 550 | 3750 |
| 1675 — Retrograde 1 | 160 | 600 | 4000 |
| 1676 V. OCTAVO | 140 | 525 | 3500 |
| 1676 R/T in BR | 185 | 775 | — |
| 1676 — Retrograde 1 | 150 | 550 | 3750 |
| 1676 F/H in FRA | 180 | 675 | — |
| 1677 V. NONO | 140 | 525 | 3500 |
| 1677 F/H in FRA | 185 | 775 | — |
| 1678 TRICESIMO | 225 | 900 | 5250 |
| 1679 T. PRIMO | 140 | 525 | 3500 |
| 1679 — DECNS error | 175 | 625 | 4000 |
| 1679 — DNCVS error | 180 | 650 | — |
| 1679 — PRICESIMO | 175 | 625 | 4000 |
| 1680 T. SECVNDO | 150 | 575 | 3750 |
| 1680 T. SECVNCIO error | 175 | 625 | 4000 |
| 1681 T. TERTIO | 200 | 850 | 5000 |
| 1681/0 — | 225 | 900 | — |
| 1682 T. QVARTO | 160 | 575 | 4000 |
| 1682/79 T. QVARTO | 200 | 825 | — |
| 1683 T. QVINTO | 140 | 525 | 3500 |
| 1684/3 T. SEXTO | 350 | 1250 | — |

3369 - Plume in centre

|                                                                                      | F £ | VF £ | EF £ |
|--------------------------------------------------------------------------------------|-----|------|------|
| **3368  Halfcrown.** Fourth bust plume below, R. Similar die axis ↑↓                 |     |      |      |
| 1673 V. QVINTO.............................................................6500       | 18500 | —  |
| 1683 T. QVINTO.............................................................7500       | 22500 | —  |
| **3369  Halfcrown.**— plume below bust and in centre of *rev.*, die axis ↑↓          |     |      |      |
| 1673 V. QVINTO.............................................................8500       | 24000 | —  |

3370
Elephant and Castle below bust

|                                                                                      | F £ | VF £ | EF £ |
|--------------------------------------------------------------------------------------|-----|------|------|
| **3370      Halfcrown.**— elephant and castle below bust, die axis ↑↓                |     |      |      |
| 1681 T. TERTIO .................................................................3750 | 12500 | 32500 |

## SHILLINGS

First bust          First bust variety          Second bust          Third bust

First bust          First bust variety          First and first bust          Second bust
                                                 variety, double top leaf      single top leaf

3371 - First bust                               3372

|  | F | VF | EF |
|---|---|---|---|
|  | £ | £ | £ |

**3371 Shilling.** First dr. bust r.R. Crowned cruciform shields interlinked C's in angles edge milled,

| 1663 die axis ↑↑ (en medaille) | 135 | 600 | — |
| 1663 die axis ↑↓ as usual | 110 | 425 | 2500 |
| 1663 GARTIA error, die axis ↑↓ | 1250 | — | — |
| 1663 Transposed shields of Scotland and Ireland, die axis ↑↓ | 225 | 750 | — |
| 1663 A over G in FRA, die axis ↑↓ | 450 | — | — |

**3372 Shilling.** First bust variety r. similar die axis ↑↓

| 1663 | 110 | 425 | 2500 |
| 1666 | | | *Extremely rare* |
| 1668 | 525 | 2000 | — |
| 1669/6 | 2250 | — | — |

**3373 Shilling.** First bust variety r. elephant below bust, die axis ↑↓

| 1666 | 750 | 2500 | 10000 |

3374                               3375 - Second bust shilling

**3374 Shilling.** Guinea head, elephant below bust, die axis ↑↓

| 1666 | 3500 | 9000 | — |

**3375 Shilling.** Second dr. bust r. similar die axis ↑↓

| 1666 | 1850 | 6000 | — |
| 1668 | 110 | 425 | 2250 |
| 1668/7 | 150 | 550 | 2400 |
| 1669 | | | *Extremely rare* |
| 1670 | 175 | 700 | 2750 |
| 1671 | 175 | 700 | 2750 |
| 1672 | 175 | 700 | 2750 |
| 1673 | 175 | 700 | 2750 |
| 1673/2 | 200 | 750 | 3000 |
| 1674 | 200 | 750 | 3000 |
| 1674/3 | 175 | 700 | 2750 |
| 1675 | 240 | 800 | 3000 |
| 1675/4 | 240 | 800 | 3000 |
| 1676 | 160 | 600 | 2500 |
| 1676/4 | 200 | 700 | 2750 |
| 1676/5 | 175 | 675 | 2650 |
| 1677 | 160 | 600 | 2500 |

|        | F    | VF   | EF   |
|--------|------|------|------|
|        | £    | £    | £    |
| 1678   | 175  | 675  | 2650 |
| 1678/7 | 240  | 800  | 3000 |
| 1679   | 160  | 600  | 2500 |
| 1679/7 | 200  | 700  | 2750 |
| 1680   | 1200 | 3000 | 7000 |
| 1680/79 | 1250 | 3250 | 7500 |
| 1681   | 425  | 1250 | —    |
| 1681/0 | 450  | 1350 | —    |
| 1682/1 | 1250 | 3500 | —    |
| 1683   | 1250 | 3500 | —    |

The 1668 shilling is also known with large 6's in the date

3376 - Plume both sides shilling of 1671

**3376  Shilling.** Second Bust — plume below bust and in centre of *rev.* similar die axis ↑↓

| 1671    | 600  | 2000 | 5250 |
|---------|------|------|------|
| 1673    | 650  | 2250 | 5750 |
| 1674    | 600  | 2000 | 5250 |
| 1675    | 650  | 2250 | 5750 |
| 1676    | 650  | 2250 | 5750 |
| 1679    | 625  | 2100 | 5500 |
| 1680/79 | 1350 | 4250 | 9500 |

3378
1679 Shilling - plume on obverse only

|  | F<br>£ | VF<br>£ | EF<br>£ |
|---|---|---|---|
| **3377 Shilling.** — Plume *rev.* only, similar die axis ↑↓ | | | |
| 1674 .................................................................. 1250 | | 3750 | 9000 |
| **3378 Shilling.** — Plume *obv.* only similar die axis ↑↓ | | | |
| 1677 .................................................................. 1250 | | 3750 | 9000 |
| 1679 .................................................................. 1100 | | 3500 | 8500 |
| **3379 Shilling.** — elephant and castle below bust, die axis ↑↓ | | | |
| 1681/0 .............................................................. 4000 | | 12500 | — |

3380                              3381
Third bust Shilling          1684 Shilling - fourth bust

|  | F<br>£ | VF<br>£ | EF<br>£ |
|---|---|---|---|
| **3380 Shilling.** Third dr. (large) bust r. similar die axis ↑↓ | | | |
| 1674 .................................................................. 675 | | 2250 | 6500 |
| 1675/3 .............................................................. 450 | | 1500 | 4500 |
| **3381 Shilling.** Fourth dr. (large) bust r., older features, similar die axis ↑↓ | | | |
| 1683 .................................................................. 250 | | 900 | 3500 |
| 1684 .................................................................. 250 | | 900 | 3500 |

3382
1677 Sixpence

|  | F<br>£ | VF<br>£ | EF<br>£ |
|---|---|---|---|
| **3382 Sixpence.** Dr. bust r. R. Crowned cruciform shields, interlinked C's in angles die axis ↑↓ | | | |
| 1674 .................................................................. 75 | | 240 | 800 |
| 1675 .................................................................. 80 | | 250 | 850 |
| 1675/4 .............................................................. 80 | | 250 | 850 |
| 1676 .................................................................. 95 | | 300 | 950 |
| 1676/5 .............................................................. 90 | | 275 | 900 |

|        | F    | VF  | EF  |
|--------|------|-----|-----|
|        | £    | £   | £   |
| 1677   | 75   | 240 | 800 |
| 1678/7 | 80   | 250 | 850 |
| 1679   | 85   | 275 | 850 |
| 1680   | 85   | 275 | 900 |
| 1681   | 75   | 240 | 800 |
| 1682   | 95   | 300 | 950 |
| 1682/1 | 90   | 275 | 900 |
| 1683   | 75   | 240 | 800 |
| 1684   | 80   | 250 | 850 |

3383                                           3384 -
Undated Fourpence                       1678 Fourpence

**3383**  **Fourpence.** Undated. Crowned dr. bust l. to edge of coin, value
behind. R. Shield, die axis ↑↓ ..............................20          50          120

**3384**  **Fourpence.** Dated. Dr. bust r. R. Crowned four interlinked Cs quartered emblems die axis ↑↓

| 1670 | 20 | 45 | 125 |
|------|----|----|----|
| 1671 | 18 | 40 | 110 |
| 1672/1 | 22 | 48 | 125 |
| 1673 | 18 | 40 | 100 |
| 1674 | 18 | 40 | 100 |
| 1674/4 sideways | 20 | 40 | 150 |
| 1674 7 over 6 | 18 | 40 | 100 |
| 1675 | 18 | 40 | 100 |
| 1675/4 | 18 | 45 | 120 |
| 1676 | 18 | 40 | 100 |
| 1676 7 over 6 | 18 | 45 | 135 |
| 1676/5 | 18 | 45 | 120 |
| 1677 | 15 | 32 | 95 |
| 1678 | 18 | 45 | 120 |
| 1678/6 | 18 | 40 | 100 |
| 1678/7 | 18 | 40 | 100 |
| 1679 | 10 | 20 | 70 |
| 1680 | 12 | 22 | 80 |
| 1681 | 15 | 40 | 95 |
| 1681 B/R in HIB | 18 | 38 | 150 |
| 1681/0 | 15 | 32 | 115 |
| 1682 | 18 | 40 | 110 |
| 1682/1 | 18 | 40 | 115 |
| 1683 | 18 | 40 | 110 |
| 1684 | 20 | 40 | 120 |
| 1684/3 | 20 | 40 | 110 |

3386
1678 Threepence

|  | F | VF | EF |
|---|---|---|---|
|  | £ | £ | £ |

**3385**      **Threepence.** Undated. As 3383, die axis ↑↓ ...........14    35    110

**3386**   **Threepence.** Dated. Dr. bust r. R. Crowned three interlinked C's, die axis ↑↓

| | | | | |
|---|---|---|---|---|
| 1670 | | ...............12 | 25 | 90 |
| 1671 | | ...............10 | 22 | 80 |
| 1671 GRⱯTIA | | ...............18 | 38 | 150 |
| 1671 GRΛTIA | | ...............12 | 28 | 100 |
| 1672/1 | | ...............10 | 22 | 90 |
| 1673 | 10 | ...............22 | 80 | |
| 1674 | 12 | ...............25 | 90 | |
| 16/5 | 15 | ...............30 | 95 | |
| 1676 | 10 | ...............22 | 85 | |
| 1676/5 | 12 | ...............28 | 100 | |
| 1676 ERA for FRA | | ...............12 | 38 | 175 |
| 1677 | 15 | ...............30 | 100 | |
| 1678 | 12 | ...............25 | 100 | |
| 1678 on 4d flan | | ...............12 | 25 | 125 |
| 1679 | 10 | ...............20 | 60 | |
| 1679 O/A in CAROLVS | | ...............15 | 38 | 150 |
| 1680 | 12 | ...............25 | 85 | |
| 1681 | 14 | ...............22 | 90 | |
| 1681/0 | 12 | ...............30 | 100 | |
| 1682 | 15 | ...............30 | 105 | |
| 1682/1 | 15 | ...............32 | 95 | |
| 1683 | 15 | ...............30 | 105 | |
| 1684 | 15 | ...............30 | 105 | |
| 1684/3 | 15 | ...............32 | 95 | |

3388
1678 Twopence

**3387**   **Twopence.** Undated. As 3383 (double arch crown)

     die axis ↑↓ ...............12    30    90

**3388**   **Twopence.** Dated. Dr. bust r. R. Crowned pair of linked C's, die axis ↑↓

| | | | | |
|---|---|---|---|---|
| 1668 die axis ↑↑ | | ...............15 | 30 | 100 |
| 1670 | | ...............10 | 22 | 75 |
| 1671 | | ...............10 | 20 | 65 |
| 1672/1 | | ...............10 | 20 | 65 |
| 1672/1 GRΛTIA | | ...............13 | 38 | 165 |

|      | F<br>£ | VF<br>£ | EF<br>£ |
|------|--------|---------|---------|
| 1673 | 12 | 25 | 80 |
| 1674 | 10 | 20 | 65 |
| 1675 | 12 | 25 | 80 |
| 1676 | 10 | 20 | 75 |
| 1677 | 12 | 25 | 75 |
| 1678 | 15 | 35 | 95 |
| 1678/6 | 13 | 28 | 100 |
| 1679 | 10 | 20 | 65 |
| 1679 HIB over FRA | 13 | 38 | 150 |
| 1680 | 10 | 20 | 70 |
| 1680/79 | 13 | 28 | 85 |
| 1681 | 10 | 20 | 70 |
| 1682/1 | 13 | 28 | 80 |
| 1682/1 ERA for FRA | 13 | 38 | 150 |
| 1684 | 13 | 28 | 75 |
| 1683 | 10 | 22 | 70 |
| 1683/2 | 13 | 28 | 70 |

3390
1678 Penny

**3389 Penny.** Undated. As 3383 (double arch crown)

| | F | VF | EF |
|---|---|---|---|
| die axis ↑↓ | 12 | 35 | 110 |

**3390 Penny.** Dated. Dr. bust r. R. Crowned C die axis ↑↓

|      | F | VF | EF |
|------|---|----|----|
| 1670 | 12 | 30 | 105 |
| 1671 | 12 | 30 | 105 |
| 1672/1 | 12 | 30 | 105 |
| 1673 | 12 | 30 | 105 |
| 1674 | 14 | 35 | 120 |
| 1674 ƆRATIA error | 18 | 40 | 175 |
| 1675 | 12 | 30 | 105 |
| 1675 ƆRATIA error | 18 | 40 | 175 |
| 1676 | 22 | 50 | 145 |
| 1676 ƆRATIA error | 15 | 40 | 175 |

|        |      | F<br>£ | VF<br>£ | EF<br>£ |
|--------|------|--------|---------|---------|
| 1677   | ................12 | 30 | 105 |
| 1677 ꓛRATIA error | ................15 | 40 | 175 |
| 1678   | ................24 | 55 | 145 |
| 1678 RATIA error | ................12 | 50 | 185 |
| 1679   | ................24 | 55 | 145 |
| 1680   | ................12 | 30 | 105 |
| 1680 on 2d flan | | *Extremely rare* |
| 1681   | ................22 | 65 | 170 |
| 1682   | ................22 | 50 | 140 |
| 1682/1 | ................18 | 40 | 145 |
| 1682 ERA for FRA | ................18 | 40 | 150 |
| 1683/1 | ................13 | 35 | 110 |
| 1684   | ................24 | 50 | 145 |
| 1684/3 | ................24 | 50 | 150 |

**3391  Maundy Set.** Undated. The four coins ...........100    225    575

**3392  Maundy Set.** Dated. The four denominations. Uniform dates

|        |      | F<br>£ | VF<br>£ | EF<br>£ |
|--------|------|--------|---------|---------|
| 1670   | ................100 | 275 | 650 |
| 1671   | .................90 | 200 | 550 |
| 1672   | .................95 | 250 | 600 |
| 1673   | .................80 | 200 | 550 |
| 1674   | .................90 | 210 | 600 |
| 1675   | .................90 | 225 | 600 |
| 1676   | ................100 | 250 | 700 |
| 1677   | .................90 | 225 | 675 |
| 1678   | ................115 | 300 | 800 |
| 1679   | .................90 | 225 | 650 |
| 1680   | .................85 | 200 | 600 |
| 1681   | ................100 | 300 | 650 |
| 1682   | .................90 | 250 | 725 |
| 1683   | .................80 | 200 | 750 |
| 1684   | ................100 | 275 | 775 |

## COPPER AND TIN

3393
1675 Halfpenny

**3393  Copper Halfpenny** Cuir. bust l. R. Britannia seated l. date in ex., die axis ↑↓

| 1672 | ................60 | 350 | 1400 |
|------|------|------|------|
| 1672 CRAOLVS error | | *Extremely rare* |
| 1673 | ................50 | 330 | 1200 |
| 1673 CRAOLVS error | ...............225 | — | — |

|                                  | Fair | F   | VF            | EF   |
|----------------------------------|------|-----|---------------|------|
|                                  | £    | £   | £             | £    |
| 1673 no stops on obv.            |      |     | Extremely rare |      |
| 1673 no rev. stop                | 90   |     | 500           | —    |
| 1675                             | 60   |     | 350           | 1400 |
| 1675 no stops on obv.            | 90   |     | 500           | —    |
| 1675/3                           | 165  |     | 600           | —    |

3394
1672 Farthing

**3394** Copper **Farthing.** Cuir. bust l. R. Britannia sealed l. date in ex., die axis ↑↓

| 1672                             | 45   | 265 | 825  |
|----------------------------------|------|-----|------|
| 1672 Rev. loose drapery          | 65   | 325 | 1000 |
| 1672 no stops on obv.            | 65   | 325 | 1000 |
| 1672 RO/OL on obv.               | 90   | 450 | —    |
| 1672 die axis ↑↑                 | 65   | 325 | 1000 |
| 1673                             | 50   | 275 | 825  |
| 1673 CAROLA error                | 150  | 550 | —    |
| 1673 O/sideways O                | 75   | 325 | 1100 |
| 1673 BRITINNIA error             | 225  | —   | —    |
| 1673 no stops on obv.            | 165  | —   | —    |
| 1673 no rev. stop                | 165  | —   | —    |
| 1674                             | 55   | 300 | 900  |
| 1674 'O' for 'C' in CAROLVS      | 100  | 500 | —    |
| 1675                             | 50   | 275 | 825  |
| 1675 no stop after CAROLVS       | 165  | —   | —    |
| 1679                             | 55   | 300 | 900  |
| 1679 no rev. stop                | 65   | 325 | 1100 |

3395
Tin Farthing

Prices for tin coinage based on corrosion free examples, and in the top grades with some lustre
**3395** Tin **Farthing.** Somewhat similar, but with copper plug, edge inscribed NUMMORVM
FAMVLVS, and date on edge only die axis ↑↓

| 1684 | various varieties of edge | 55 | 250 | 900 | 3600 |
|------|---------------------------|----|-----|-----|------|
| 1685 |                           |    |     |     | Extremely rare |

James II, brother of Charles II, was born on 14th October 1633; he married Anne Hyde with whom he produced 8 children. He lost control of his subjects when the loyalist Tories moved against him over his many Catholic appointments. Parliament invited his protestant daughter Mary with husband William of Orange to be joint rulers. James II abdicated and died in exile in France.

During this reign the dies continued to be engraved by John Roettier (1631-1700), the only major difference in the silver coinage being the ommission of the interlinked C's in the angles of the shields on the reverses. The only provenance marked silver coin of this reign is the extremely rare plume on reverse 1685 Shilling. The elephant and castle provenance mark continues to appear on some of the gold coins of this reign. Tin halfpence and farthings provided the only base metal coinage during this short reign. All genuine tin coins of this period have a copper plug.

## GOLD

|  | F £ | VF £ | EF £ |
|---|---|---|---|
| **3396 Five Guineas.** First laur. bust l., R. Crowned cruciform shields sceptres misplaced in angles smaller crowns date on edge in words (e.g. 1686 = SECVNDO) die axis ↑↓ | | | |
| 1686 SECVNDO ...........................................................8000 | 18500 | 90000 |
| **3397 Five Guineas.** First laur bust l. R. similar bust sceptres normal. die axis ↑↓ | | | |
| 1687 TERTIO ..................................................8000 | 18500 | 90000 |
| 1688 QVARTO ................................................8000 | 18500 | 90000 |

3397A
1687 Five Guineas, second bust

| **3397A Five Guineas.** Second laur. bust l. R. similar die axis ↑↓ | | | |
|---|---|---|---|
| 1687    TERTIO...............................................7750 | 17500 | 85000 |
| 1688 QVARTO ...............................................7750 | 17500 | 85000 |

3398
1687 Five Guineas, first bust, elephant and castle below

|  | F | VF | EF |
|---|---|---|---|
|  | £ | £ | £ |

**3398  Five Guineas.** First laur. bust l. Elephant and castle below R. Similar die axis ↑↓
| 1687 | TERTIO | 8000 | 19500 | 95000 |
|---|---|---|---|---|
| 1688 | QVARTO | 8000 | 19500 | 95000 |

3399
Two Guineas

**3399  Two Guineas.** Laur. bust l. R. Crowned cruciform shields, sceptres in angles, edge milled, die axis ↑↓
| 1687 | 3250 | 10500 | 35000 |
|---|---|---|---|
| 1688/7 | 3500 | 11000 | 37500 |

**3400  Guinea.** First laur. bust l. R. Crowned cruciform shields, sceptres in angles, edge milled, die axis ↑↓
| 1685 | 1300 | 3750 | 12500 |
|---|---|---|---|
| 1686 | 1350 | 4000 | 13000 |
| 1686 B/I in HIB | 1400 | 4250 | 13500 |

**3401  Guinea.** First bust elephant and castle below R. similar die axis ↑↓
| 1685 | 1500 | 4500 | 15000 |
|---|---|---|---|
| 1686 | 2250 | — | — |

3402
1688 Guinea, second bust

|  | F £ | VF £ | EF £ |
|---|---|---|---|
| **3402 Guinea.** Second laur. bust l. R. similar die axis ↑↓ | | | |
| 1686 | 1300 | 3750 | 12500 |
| 1687 | 1300 | 3750 | 12500 |
| 1687/6 | 1350 | 3850 | 12750 |
| 1688 | 1300 | 3750 | 12500 |

3403

| **3403 Guinea.** Second bust elephant and castle below R. similar die axis ↑↓ | | | |
|---|---|---|---|
| 1686 | 1600 | 5000 | 14500 |
| 1687 | 1500 | 4500 | 14000 |
| 1688 | 1500 | 4500 | 14000 |

3404

| **3404 Half-Guinea.** Laur. bust l. R. Crowned cruciform shields sceptres in angles, edge milled die axis ↑↓ | | | |
|---|---|---|---|
| 1686 | 625 | 2100 | 6500 |
| 1686 OBV/BVS | 650 | 2200 | 6750 |
| 1687 | 675 | 2250 | 7000 |
| 1688 | 625 | 2100 | 6500 |
| **3405 Half-Guinea.** Laur bust with elephant and castle below, R. similar die axis ↑↓ | | | |
| 1686 | 975 | 3250 | 10000 |

## SILVER

3406
1686 Crown, first bust

| | F £ | VF £ | EF £ |
|---|---|---|---|
| **3406** **Crown**. First dr. bust, l. regnal year on edge in words (e.g. 1686 = SECVNDO) die axis ↑↓ | | | |
| 1686 SECVNDO | 300 | 1250 | 8250 |
| 1686 — No stops on obverse | 325 | 1350 | 8500 |

3407
1687 Crown, second bust

**3407 Crown.** Second dr. bust l. narrower than first bust. R. Crowned cruciform shields edge inscribed in raised letters die axis ↑↓

| | | | |
|---|---|---|---|
| 1687 TERTIO | 225 | 750 | 6750 |
| 1688 QVARTO | 250 | 800 | 7250 |
| 1688/7 QVARTO | 275 | 900 | 7500 |

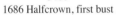

| | 3408 | 1st bust | 2nd bust |
|---|---|---|---|
| | 1686 Halfcrown, first bust | Halfcrown hair ties | |

| | F | VF | EF |
|---|---|---|---|
| | £ | £ | £ |

**3408  Halfcrown.** First laur and dr. bust, l. regnal year on edge in words
(e.g. 1685 = PRIMO) die axis ↑↓

| 1685    PRIMO | 200 | 575 | 4750 |
|---|---|---|---|
| 1686    SECVNDO | 185 | 550 | 4500 |
| 1686/5 — | 240 | 625 | 5000 |
| 1686 TERTIO V over S or B in JACOBVS | 225 | 600 | 5000 |
| 1686 TERTIO | 225 | 600 | 5000 |
| 1687 TERTIO | 200 | 575 | 4750 |
| 1687/6 — | 240 | 625 | 5000 |
| 1687 — 6 over 8 | 300 | 900 | — |
| 1687 A/R in GRATIA | 250 | 650 | 5250 |

**3409  Halfcrown.** Second laur and dr. bust l. R. Crowned cruciform shields
edge inscribed in raised letters die axis ↑↓

| 1687 TERTIO | 225 | 600 | 5000 |
|---|---|---|---|
| 1688 QVARTO | 200 | 575 | 4750 |

3410
1687 Shilling

**3410  Shilling.** Laur and Dr. bust l. R. Crowned cruciform shields die axis ↑↓

| 1685 | 240 | 650 | 3000 |
|---|---|---|---|
| 1685 no stops on rev. | 250 | 700 | 3250 |
| 1686 | 240 | 675 | 3000 |
| 1686/5 | 275 | 725 | 3400 |
| 1686 V/S in JACOBVS | 260 | 700 | 3250 |
| 1686 G/A in MAG | 260 | 700 | 3250 |
| 1687 | 260 | 700 | 3250 |
| 1687 G/A in MAG | 275 | 725 | 3400 |
| 1687/6 | 240 | 650 | 3000 |
| 1687/6 G/A in MAG | 250 | 700 | 3250 |
| 1688 | 275 | 725 | 3500 |
| 1688/7 | 260 | 700 | 3250 |

**3411  Shilling.** Similar, plume in centre of *rev.*, die axis ↑↓

| 1685 | 9000 | 20000 | — |
|---|---|---|---|

3412
1686 Sixpence, early shileds, indented tops

3413
1687 Sixpence, later shields

|  | F £ | VF £ | EF £ |
|---|---|---|---|
| **3412 Sixpence.** Laur and dr. bust l. R. Early type crowned cruciform shields die axis ↑↓ | | | |
| 1686 | 150 | 400 | 1350 |
| 1687 | 175 | 475 | 1600 |
| 1687/6 | 175 | 450 | 1500 |
| **3413 Sixpence.** Similar R. Late type shields die axis ↑↓ | | | |
| 1687 | 150 | 400 | 1400 |
| 1687/6 | 200 | 500 | 1650 |
| 1687 Later/early shields | 175 | 475 | 1600 |
| 1688 | 150 | 400 | 1400 |

| 3414 | 3415 | 3416 | 3417 |
|---|---|---|---|
| Fourpence | Threepence | Twopence | Penny |

|  | F | VF | EF |
|---|---|---|---|
| **3414 Fourpence.** Laur. head l. R. IIII Crowned die axis ↑↓ | | | |
| 1686 | 15 | 30 | 100 |
| 1686 Date over crown | 18 | 30 | 110 |
| 1687/6 | 15 | 25 | 100 |
| 1687 8 over 7 | 18 | 30 | 110 |
| 1688 | 22 | 45 | 145 |
| 1688 1 over 8 | 25 | 55 | 150 |
| 1688/7 | 22 | 45 | 140 |
| **3415 Threepence.** Laur. head l. R. III Crowned die axis-↑↓ | | | |
| 1685 | 12 | 30 | 95 |
| 1685 Groat flan | 35 | 80 | 165 |
| 1686 | 12 | 35 | 100 |
| 1686 4d obv. die | 18 | 40 | 120 |
| 1687 | 12 | 32 | 100 |
| 1687/6 | 12 | 32 | 100 |
| 1688 | 22 | 55 | 145 |
| 1688/7 | 25 | 55 | 140 |
| **3416 Twopence.** Laur. head l. R. II Crowned die axis ↑↓ | | | |
| 1686 | 15 | 35 | 90 |
| 1686 IΛCOBVS | 18 | 35 | 1150 |
| 1687 | 12 | 32 | 85 |
| 1687 ERA for FRA | 25 | 45 | 150 |
| 1688 | 18 | 40 | 13 |
| 1688/7 | 18 | 40 | 120 |

| | Fair £ | F £ | VF £ | EF £ |
|---|---|---|---|---|
| **3417  Penny.** Laur. head l. R. I Crowned die axis ↑↓ | | | | |
| 1685 | .................................................................15 | | 30 | 100 |
| 1686 | .................................................................20 | | 40 | 1100 |
| 1687 | .................................................................20 | | 40 | 1100 |
| 1687/6 | .................................................................20 | | 40 | 110 |
| 1687/8 | .................................................................25 | | 50 | 130 |
| 1688 | .................................................................25 | | 55 | 14 |
| 1688/7 | .................................................................25 | | 55 | 13 |
| **3418  Maundy Set.** As last four. Uniform dates | | | | |
| 1686 | ............................................................100 | | 300 | 575 |
| 1687 | ............................................................100 | | 300 | 575 |
| 1688 | ............................................................175 | | 350 | 750 |

## TIN

3419
Tin Halfpenny

Prices for tin coinage based on corrosion free examples, and in the top grades with some lustre

| **3419  Halfpenny.** Laur. and dr. bust r. R. Britannia seated l. date on edge die axis ↑↓ | | | | |
|---|---|---|---|---|
| 1685 | various varieties of edge.............100 | 250 | 775 | 3850 |
| 1686 | ................................................110 | 275 | 825 | 4200 |
| 1687 | ................................................90 | 300 | 775 | 3850 |

3420
Cuirassed bust Tin Farthing

| **3420  Farthing.** Laur. and Cuir. bust r. R. Britannia seated l. date on edge die axis ↑↓ | | | | |
|---|---|---|---|---|
| 1684 | ............................................................................................*Extremely rare* | | | |
| 1685 | various varieties of edge..............65 | 195 | 700 | 3000 |
| 1686 | two varieties of edge ...................80 | 225 | 775 | 3250 |
| 1687 | ............................................................................................ *Extremely rare* | | | |
| **3421  Farthing.** Dr. bust r.; date on edge, 1687 various varieties | | | | |
| of edge ↑↓ .......................................100 | 250 | 875 | 3750 | |

Mary Stuart was born on 30th April 1662, and married William of Orange as part of Charles II's foreign policy. She eventually became William's loyal servant but bore him no children. The Bill and the Claim of Rights were both passed in 1689 and curbed the Royal and Prerogative rights of Monarchs. Mary died from smallpox on 28th December 1694.

Due to the poor state of the silver coinage, much of it worn hammered coin, the Guinea, which was valued at 21s. 6d. at the beginning of the reign, circulated for as much as 30s. by 1694. The elephant and elephant and castle provenance marks continue on some gold coin. The tin Halfpennies and Farthings were replaced by copper coins in 1694. The rampant Lion of Nassau is now placed as an inescutcheon on the centre of the royal arms. The WM monogram appears in the angles of the silver coins of this reign.

**Engravers and designers:** George Bower (d.1689), Henry Harris (d.1704), John Roettier (1631-1700), James Roettier (1663-1698), Norbert Roettier (b.1665)

## GOLD

3422
Five Guineas

| | F | VF | EF |
| --- | --- | --- | --- |
| | £ | £ | £ |
| **3422   Five Guineas.** Conjoined busts r. regnal year on edge in words (e.g. 1691 = TERTIO) ↑↓ | | | |
| 1691 TERTIO | 7500 | 17500 | 110000 |
| 1692 QVARTO | 7500 | 17500 | 110000 |
| 1692 QVINTO | 9500 | 22000 | 125000 |
| 1693 QVINTO | 7500 | 17500 | 110000 |
| 1694/2 SEXTO | 8500 | 19000 | 120000 |
| 1694 SEXTO | 8250 | 18500 | 115000 |

3423
Elephant and castle below busts

**3423  Five Guineas.** Conjoined busts, elephant and castle below, R. Crowned shield of arms
die axis ↑↓
1691 TERTIO ....................................................................8000         18000         110000
1692 QVARTO ..................................................................8750         18500         115000
1693 QVINTO ...................................................................9000         19000         120000
1694/2 SEXTO .................................................................9250         20000         125000
1694 SEXTO ....................................................................9000         19000         120000

3424
1694 Two Guineas

**424  Two Guineas.** Conjoined busts r. R. Crowned shield of arms, Lion of Nassau at centre
die axis ↑↓
1693      ...........................................................................2250         7500         32500
1694/3   ...........................................................................2000         7000         30000

**3425  Two Guineas.** Conjoined busts, elephant and castle below, R. similar die axis ↑↓
1691      ..................................................................................................*Extremely rare*
1693      ...........................................................................2500         8500         37500
1694/3   ...........................................................................2250         7500         32500

<table>
<tr><td>3426</td><td>3427</td></tr>
<tr><td>1689 Guinea, later harp</td><td>1689 Elephant and castle below busts</td></tr>
</table>

|  | F | VF | EF |
|---|---|---|---|
|  | £ | £ | £ |

**3426 Guinea.** Conjoined busts r. R. Crowned shield of arms Lion of Nassau at centre die axis ↑↓

| | F | VF | EF |
|---|---|---|---|
| 1689 Early slanting harp with base of harp in line with X of REX | 1250 | 3750 | 11500 |
| 1689 Later upright harp with base of harp in line with R of REX | 1250 | 3750 | 11500 |
| 1689 MVS over EL | 1300 | 4000 | 12000 |
| 1690 | 1300 | 4000 | 12000 |
| 1690 FT for ET obv | 1350 | 4250 | 12500 |
| 1690 D/G in DEI | 1350 | 4250 | 12500 |
| 1690 GVLIFLMVS | 1350 | 4250 | 12500 |
| 1691 | 1300 | 4000 | 12000 |
| 1692 | 1300 | 4000 | 12000 |
| 1693 | 1300 | 4000 | 12000 |
| 1694 | 1300 | 4000 | 12000 |
| 1694/3 | 1350 | 4250 | 12500 |

**3427 Guinea.** Conjoined busts elephant and castle below R. Similar die axis ↑↓

| | F | VF | EF |
|---|---|---|---|
| 1689 | 1250 | 3750 | 12000 |
| 1689 G of REGINA over E | 1300 | 4000 | 12500 |
| 1690 | 1500 | 5000 | 15000 |
| 1691 | 1300 | 4000 | 12500 |
| 1692 | 1350 | 4250 | 13000 |
| 1693 | 1500 | 5000 | 15000 |
| 1694 | 1350 | 4250 | 13000 |
| 1694/3 | 1400 | 4500 | 13500 |

**3428 Guinea.** Conjoined busts elephant only below, R. Similar die axis ↑↓

| | F | VF | EF |
|---|---|---|---|
| 1692 | 1400 | 4500 | 13500 |
| 1693 | 1500 | 5000 | 15000 |

3429
1689 Half-Guniea, first busts, first shield

**3429 Half-Guinea.** First busts r. R. First Crowned shield of arms die axis ↑↓

| | F | VF | EF |
|---|---|---|---|
| 1689 | 700 | 2250 | 7250 |

3430
1690 Half-Guinea, second busts, second shield

|  | F £ | VF £ | EF £ |
|---|---|---|---|
| **3430  Half-Guinea.** Second busts r. R. Second Crowned shield of arms die axis ↑↓ | | | |
| 1690 | .....675 | 2200 | 7000 |
| 1691 | .....675 | 2200 | 7000 |
| 1692 | .....700 | 2250 | 7250 |
| 1693 | .....750 | 2500 | 8000 |
| 1693/2 | .....750 | 2400 | 7750 |
| 1694 | .....675 | 2200 | 7000 |
| **3431  Half-Guinea.** Second busts elephant and castle below, R. Second shield of arms die axis ↑↓ | | | |
| 1691 | .....750 | 2500 | 7500 |
| 1692 | .....725 | 2400 | 7250 |
| **3432  Half-Guinea.** Second busts elephant only below, R. Second shield of arms die axis ↑↓ | | | |
| 1692 | .....900 | 2750 | 8500 |

## SILVER

3433
Crown

**3433  Crown.** Conjoined busts r. regnal year on edge in words (e.g. 1691 = TERTIO)
   die axis ↑↓

| | F | VF | EF |
|---|---|---|---|
| 1691 TERTIO | .....600 | 1850 | 8500 |
| 1691 I/E in legend | .....650 | 2000 | 8750 |
| 1691 TERTTIO | .....650 | 2100 | 9000 |
| 1692 QVARTO | .....600 | 1850 | 8500 |
| 1692/ ꝝ QVARTO | .....625 | 2250 | 9000 |
| 1692/ ꝝ QVINTO | .....600 | 1850 | 8500 |

3434                                              3435
1689 Halfcrown - first reverse            1689 Halfcrown - second reverse

|  | F £ | VF £ | EF £ |
|---|---|---|---|
| **3434  Halfcrown.** First busts, r. R. First crowned shield, 1689 PRIMO Ꝛ. | | | |
| Crown with caul and interior frosted, with pearls edge inscribed | | | |
| die axis ↑↓ ..................................................................130 | 350 | 2750 | |
| 1689— 2nd L/M in GVLIELMVS ....................................135 | 375 | 3000 | |
| 1689 — 1st V/A in GVLIELMVS, only caul frosted...........135 | 375 | 3000 | |
| 1689 — — interior also frosted, no pearls ...........................135 | 375 | 3000 | |
| 1689 Caul only frosted, pearls...............................................130 | 350 | 2750 | |
| 1689 — no pearls..................................................................130 | 375 | 3000 | |
| 1689 No frosting, pearls ......................................................130 | 350 | 2750 | |
| 1689 No stops on obverse.....................................................200 | 575 | 3500 | |
| 1689 FRA for FR ..................................................................175 | 525 | 3250 | |
| **3435  Halfcrown.** First busts r. R. Second crowned shield die axis ↑↓ | | | |
| 1689 PRIMO Ꝛ. Caul and interior frosted with pearls.........120 | 350 | 2750 | |
| 1689     — — no pearls .........................................................130 | 375 | 3000 | |
| 1689 Caul only frosted pearls...............................................120 | 350 | 2750 | |
| 1689 interior frosted, no pearls.............................................130 | 350 | 2750 | |
| 1689 Caul only frosted, no pearls.........................................130 | 375 | 3000 | |
| 1689 no frosting, pearls .......................................................120 | 350 | 2750 | |
| 1689 no frosting, no pearls ...................................................120 | 350 | 2750 | |
| 1690 SECVNDO — .............................................................175 | 525 | 3250 | |
| 1690 — GRETIA error with second V of GVLIELMVS | | | |
| struck over S ....................................................325 | 850 | 4000 | |
| 1690 TERTIO ......................................................................185 | 525 | 3250 | |

3436
Halfcrown, second busts, third reverse

|  | F £ | VF £ | EF £ |
|---|---|---|---|
| **3436 Halfcrown.** Second busts r. ℞. Crowned cruciform shields, WM monogram in angles die axis ↑↓ | | | |
| 1691 TERTIO .................165 | 550 | 3500 |
| 1692 QVARTO .................175 | 600 | 3650 |
| 1692 R/G in REGINA also showing H/B in HI ...................185 | 625 | 3750 |
| 1692 QVINTO .................225 | 650 | 4000 |
| 1693 QVINTO .................150 | 4/5 | 3000 |
| 1693 3/inverted 3 .................160 | 500 | 3250 |
| 1693 inverted 3 .................325 | 900 | 4000 |

3437                               3438
Shilling                          Sixpence

|  | F | VF | EF |
|---|---|---|---|
| **3437 Shilling.** Conjoined busts r. ℞. Crowned cruciform shields, WM monogram in angles die axis ↑↓ | | | |
| 1692 .................200 | 625 | 2850 |
| 1692 inverted 1 .................225 | 675 | 3000 |
| 1692 RE/ET on R .................225 | 675 | 3000 |
| 1692 A of GRATIA over T and T over I .................250 | 750 | 3250 |
| 1693 9/0 .................225 | 675 | 3000 |
| 1693 .................200 | 625 | 2850 |
| **3438 Sixpence.** Conjoined busts r. ℞. Crowned cruciform shields, WM monogram in angles die axis ↑↓ | | | |
| 1693 .................125 | 400 | 1250 |
| 1693 inverted 3 .................225 | 550 | 1750 |
| 1694 .................145 | 450 | 1400 |

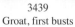

|  | 3439 | 3440 |
|---|---|---|
|  | Groat, first busts | Groat, Second busts |

|  | F | VF | EF |
|---|---|---|---|
|  | £ | £ | £ |

**3439 Fourpence.** First busts, r. no tie to wreath. R. Crowned 4 die axis ↑↓

| | F | VF | EF |
|---|---|---|---|
| 1689 GV below bust ...............15 | | 30 | 80 |
| 1689 G below bust ...............15 | | 30 | 80 |
| 1689 stop befor G ...............15 | | 30 | 80 |
| 1689 berries in wreath ...............15 | | 30 | 80 |
| 1689 GVLEELMVS ...............65 | | 200 | – |
| 1689 I over first E in GVLEELMVS corrected die for above 65 | | 200 | – |
| 1690 ...............20 | | 50 | 110 |
| 1690 6 over 5 ...............20 | | 55 | 120 |
| 1691 ...............20 | | 45 | 130 |
| 1691/0 ...............20 | | 40 | 120 |
| 1694 ...............20 | | 60 | 160 |

**3440 Fourpence.** Second busts r. tie to wreath. R. Crowned 4 die axis ↑↓

| | F | VF | EF |
|---|---|---|---|
| 1692 ...............30 | | 90 | 180 |
| 1692/1 ...............25 | | 65 | 165 |
| 1692 MAR•IA ...............*Extremely rare* | | | |
| 1693 ...............35 | | 100 | 280 |
| 1693/2 ...............35 | | 100 | 280 |
| 1694 ...............30 | | 95 | 200 |
| 1694 small lettering ...............30 | | 95 | 200 |

**3441 Threepence.** First busts, r. no tie to wreath. R. Crowned 3 die axis ↑↓

| | F | VF | EF |
|---|---|---|---|
| 1689 ...............15 | | 30 | 755 |
| 1689 No stops on rev. ...............20 | | 40 | 110 |
| 1689 LMV over MVS ...............20 | | 40 | 110 |
| 1689 Hyphen stops on rev. ...............20 | | 40 | 100 |
| 1690 ...............20 | | 50 | 105 |
| 1690 6 over 5 ...............20 | | 50 | 10 |
| 1690 Large lettering ...............20 | | 50 | 105 |
| 1690 9 over 6 ...............20 | | 50 | 105 |
| 1691 ...............100 | | 220 | 450 |

**3442 Threepence.** Second busts, r. tie to wreath R. Crowned 3 die axis ↑↓

| | F | VF | EF |
|---|---|---|---|
| 1691 ...............40 | | 130 | 220 |
| 1692 G below bust ...............25 | | 65 | 140 |
| 1692 GV below bust ...............25 | | 65 | 140 |
| 1692 GVL below bust ...............25 | | 65 | 140 |
| 1693 G below bust ...............20 | | 55 | 140 |
| 1693/2 G below bust ...............20 | | 55 | 140 |
| 1693 GV below bust ...............20 | | 55 | 140 |
| 1694 G below bust ...............20 | | 55 | 140 |
| 1694 — MΛRIΛ error ...............24 | | 60 | 170 |
| 1694 GV below bust ...............20 | | 55 | 140 |
| 1694 GVL below bust ...............20 | | 55 | 140 |

|                                    | F     | VF  | EF   |
|                                    | £     | £   | £    |
|------------------------------------|-------|-----|------|

**3443 Twopence.** Conjoined busts r. R. Crowned 2 die axis ↑↓

| | F £ | VF £ | EF £ |
|---|---|---|---|
| 1689 | 18 | 40 | 90 |
| 1691 | 18 | 45 | 110 |
| 1692 | 20 | 45 | 1205 |
| 1693 | 15 | 42 | 115 |
| 1693/2 | 18 | 42 | 1150 |
| 1693 GV below bust | 18 | 42 | 115 |
| 1694 | 20 | 45 | 120 |
| 1694/3 | 18 | 45 | 120 |
| 1694/3 no stop after DG | 18 | 45 | 120 |
| 1694 MARLA error | 35 | 65 | 27 |
| 1694 HI for HIB | 20 | 45 | 120 |
| 1694 GVLI below bust | 20 | 45 | 12 |
| 1694 GVL below bust | 20 | 45 | 120 |

3444
Penny

3445
Legend intruded

**3444 Penny.** Legend continuous over busts, R. Crowned 1 die axis ↑↓

| | | | |
|---|---|---|---|
| 1689 | 225 | 425 | 800 |
| 1689 GVIELMVS error | 250 | 525 | 1000 |
| 1689 MΛRIΛ | 250 | 450 | 850 |

**3445 Penny.** Legend broken by busts, R. Crowned 1 die axis ↑↓

| | | | |
|---|---|---|---|
| 1690 | 28 | 55 | 125 |
| 1691/0 | 35 | 60 | 135 |
| 1692 | 45 | 85 | 200 |
| 1692/1 | 35 | 80 | 180 |
| 1693 | 35 | 60 | 130 |
| 1694 date spread | 22 | 50 | 120 |
| 1694 no stops on obv. | 22 | 55 | 120 |
| 1694 HI for HIB | 28 | 60 | 190 |
| 1694 — 9/6 | 25 | 55 | 135 |

3446
Maundy Set

**3446 Maundy Set.** The four denominations. Uniform dates

| | | | |
|---|---|---|---|
| 1689 | 375 | 750 | 1500 |
| 1691 | 175 | 425 | 1000 |
| 1692 | 160 | 400 | 975 |
| 1693 | 180 | 475 | 1100 |
| 1694 | 145 | 375 | 950 |

## TIN AND COPPER

3447
Tin Halfpenny first busts

| | Fair | F | VF | EF |
|---|---|---|---|---|
| | £ | £ | £ | £ |

Prices for tin coinage based on corrosion free examples, and in the top grades with some lustre

**3447** Tin **Halfpenny.** Small dr. busts r.; date on edge ↑↓

| | | | | |
|---|---|---|---|---|
| 1689 | 925 | 1800 | — | — |
| — — — obv. with star stops 1689 | | | | *Extremely rare* |

3448
Tin Halfpenny cuirassed busts

3451
Tin Farthing

**3448** Tin **Halfpenny.** — Large cuir. busts r.; R. Britannia seated L. date only on edge, die axis ↑↓

| | | | | |
|---|---|---|---|---|
| 1690 various edge varieties | 80 | 190 | 800 | 3250 |

**3449** Tin **Halfpenny.** Similar date in ex. and on edge die axis ↑↓

| | | | | |
|---|---|---|---|---|
| 1691 various edge varieties | 70 | 175 | 700 | 2750 |
| 1691 in ex. 1692 on edge | | | | *Extremely rare* |
| 1692 | 70 | 175 | 700 | 2750 |

**3450** Tin **Farthing.** Small dr. busts r. R. Britannia seated l. die axis ↑↓

| | | | | |
|---|---|---|---|---|
| 1689 | 275 | 700 | 2250 | — |
| 1689, in ex. 1690 on edge | | | | *Extremely rare* |

**3451** Tin **Farthing.** Large cuir. busts r. R. Britannia seated l.die axis ↑↓

| | | | | |
|---|---|---|---|---|
| 1690, in ex. 1689 on edge | | | | *Extremely rare* |
| 1690 various edge varieties | 55 | 175 | 700 | 3000 |
| 1691 various edge varieties | 55 | 175 | 700 | 3000 |
| 1692 | 70 | 190 | 750 | 3000 |

3452
1694 Halfpenny

| | | F | VF | EF |
|---|---|---|---|---|
| | | £ | £ | £ |
| **3452** | Copper **Halfpenny,** Conjoined busts r. R. Britannia die axis ↑↓ | | | |
| | 1694 ..................................................................75 | | 275 | 1150 |
| | 1694 GVLIEMVS error....................................................200 | | 600 | — |
| | 1694 MVRIA error ............................................................225 | | 650 | — |
| | 1694 MΛRIΛ error ............................................................150 | | 525 | — |
| | 1694 BRITΛNNI/Λ ............................................................175 | | 550 | — |
| | 1694 no rev. stop..............................................................150 | | 525 | — |
| | 1694 GVLEELMVS .............................................................250 | | 625 | — |

3453
1694 Farthing

| | | | | |
|---|---|---|---|---|
| **3453** | Copper **Farthing**, Conjoined busts r. R. Britannia die axis ↑↓ | | | |
| | 1694 .................................................................65 | | 275 | 1000 |
| | 1694 MΛRIΛ error ............................................................175 | | 500 | — |
| | 1694 no stop after MΛRIΛ .................................................100 | | 415 | — |
| | 1694 — BRITΛNNIΛ .........................................................125 | | 415 | — |
| | 1694 no stop on rev...........................................................100 | | 350 | — |
| | 1694 no stop on obv...........................................................100 | | 350 | — |
| | 1694 GVLIELMS, BRITΛNNIΛ errors ..............................225 | | 525 | — |
| | 1694 BRITΛNNIΛ ..............................................................150 | | 475 | — |
| | 1694 Broad heavier flan 25.5mm .......................................200 | | 500 | — |

William of Orange was born on 4th November 1650. He married Mary Stuart under Charles II's foreign policy and was invited to England by Parliament, where he proceeded to supress the Jacobites. The Bank of England was founded during this reign, and William ruled alone and without issue after Mary's death until his own demise on 8th March 1702 following a serious fall from his horse.

In 1696 a great re-coinage was undertaken to replace the hammered silver that made up most of the coinage in circulation, much of it being clipped and badly worn. Branch mints were set up at Bristol, Chester, Exeter, Norwich and York to help with the re-coinage. For a short time before they were finally demonetised, unclipped hammered coins were allowed to circulate freely provided they were officially pierced in the centre. Silver coins with roses between the coats of arms were made from silver obtained from the West of England mines. The elephant and castle provenance mark continues on some guineas and half-guineas.

**Engravers and designers:** Samuel Bull (d.c.1720), John Croker (1670-1740), Henry Harris (d.1704), John Roettier (1663-1698).

## GOLD

3454
1699 Five Guineas, first bust

|  | F<br>£ | VF<br>£ | EF<br>£ |
|---|---|---|---|
| **3454  Five Guineas.** First laur. bust r. regnal year on edge in words (e.g. 1699 = UNDECIMO) ↑↓ | | | |
| 1699 UNDECIMO............................................................8500 | 20000 | 100000 |
| 1700 DVODECIMO...........................................................8500 | 20000 | 100000 |

3455
Elephant and castle below first bust

| **3455   Five Guineas.** First bust elephant and castle below | | | |
|---|---|---|---|
| 1699 UNDECIMO...........................................................9500 | 21000 | 105000 |

3456
1701 Five Guineas 'Fine Work'

|  | F<br>£ | VF<br>£ | EF<br>£ |
|---|---|---|---|

**3456  Five Guineas.** Second laur. bust r. ('fine work'), R. Crowned cruciform shields Plain or
ornamental sceptres DECIMO TERTIO die axis ↑↓

| 1701* | .....................................................................8000 | 17500 | 85000 |
|---|---|---|---|

3457
'Fine work' Two Guineas

**3457  Two Guineas.** ('fine work'), Laur. bust r. similar die axis ↑↓

| 1701 | .........................................................................2500 | 7500 | 32500 |
|---|---|---|---|

3458
1695 Guinea, first bust

**3458  Guinea.** First laur. bust r. R. Crowned cruciform shields, sceptres in angles die axis ↑↓

| 1695 | large and small lis in French arms ............................950 | 3000 | 10000 |
|---|---|---|---|
| 1696 | .........................................................................1000 | 3250 | 11000 |
| 1697 | .........................................................................1000 | 3500 | 11500 |

**3459  Guinea.** First bust elephant and castle below R. Similar die axis ↑↓

| 1695 | .........................................................................1500 | 5750 | 17500 |
|---|---|---|---|
| 1696 | ...................................................................*Extremely rare* | | |

*\* Beware of low grade counterfeits*

3460
Guinea, second bust

3463
Narrow crowns

| | F | VF | EF |
|---|---|---|---|
| | £ | £ | £ |

**3460 Guinea.** Second laur. bust r. R. Similar with human-headed harp in Irish arms. die axis ↑↓

| 1697 | ...............................................................1000 | 3250 | 11000 |
|---|---|---|---|
| 1698 | ................................................................950 | 3000 | 10000 |
| 1699 | ...............................................................1000 | 3250 | 11000 |
| 1700 large or small lions in arms | .......................................950 | 3000 | 10000 |

**3461 Guinea.** Second bust elephant and castle below. R. Similar die axis ↑↓

| 1697 | ...............................................................1750 | 6000 | — |
|---|---|---|---|
| 1698 | ...............................................................1400 | 5500 | 16000 |
| 1699 | ............................................................... *Extremely rare* | | |
| 1700 | ...............................................................1500 | 6000 | — |

**3462 Guinea.** Second laur. bust. r. R. Similar with human-headed harp.
Large lettering and large date, die axis ↑↓

| 1698 | ................................................................950 | 3000 | 10500 |
|---|---|---|---|

**3463 Guinea.** — R. Narrow crowns, plain or ornamented sceptres, axis ↑↓

| 1701 | ................................................................900 | 2750 | 9750 |
|---|---|---|---|

**3464 Guinea.** Second bust elephant and castle below, die axis ↑↓

| 1701 | ............................................................... *Extremely rare* | | |
|---|---|---|---|

**3465 Guinea.** Third laur. bust r. ('fine work'), R. Similar die axis ↑↓

| 1701 | ...............................................................1500 | 5750 | 17500 |
|---|---|---|---|

3466
1695 Half-Guinea, early harp

3468
Later harp

**3466 Half-Guinea.** Laur. bust r. R. With early harp, die axis ↑↓

| 1695 | ................................................................525 | 1400 | 5250 |
|---|---|---|---|

**3467 Half-Guinea.** Laur. bust elephant and castle below. R. With early harp, die axis ↑↓

| 1695 | ................................................................800 | 2400 | 8000 |
|---|---|---|---|
| 1696 | ................................................................600 | 1750 | 6000 |

**3468 Half-Guinea.** Laur. bust r. R. Crowned cruciform shields, sceptres in angles
with late harp, die axis ↑↓

| 1697 | ................................................................750 | 2250 | 7500 |
|---|---|---|---|
| 1698 | ................................................................525 | 1400 | 5250 |
| 1699 | ............................................................... *Extremely rare* | | |
| 1700 | ................................................................ 550 | 1500 | 5500 |
| 1701 | ................................................................525 | 1400 | 5250 |

**3469 Half-Guinea.** Laur. bust elephant and castle below, die axis ↑↓

| 1698 | ................................................................700 | 2000 | 7000 |
|---|---|---|---|

## SILVER

First harp

3470
Crown - first bust - round collar

| | F | VF | EF |
|---|---|---|---|
| | £ | £ | £ |

**3470  Crown**. First dr. bust, r. with curved breast plate or drapery. ℞.First harp, regnal year on edge in words (e.g. 1696 = OCTAVO) ↑↓

| | F | VF | EF |
|---|---|---|---|
| 1695 SEPTIMO | 110 | 375 | 3500 |
| 1695 SEPTIMO cinquefoils for crosses on edge | 175 | 525 | — |
| 1695 OCTAVO | 110 | 375 | 3250 |
| 1695 TVTA·EN error | 175 | 550 | — |
| 1695 plain edge proof *FDC* £20000 | | | |
| 1696 OCTAVO | 100 | 325 | 2750 |
| 1696 No stops on obverse | 225 | 575 | 3500 |
| 1696 G/D IN GRA | 185 | 550 | 3250 |
| 1696 — no stops | 185 | 550 | 3250 |
| 1696/5 | 185 | 550 | 3250 |
| 1696 GEI for DEI | 350 | 1250 | — |
| 1696 — no stops | 375 | 1350 | — |
| 1696 plain edge proof *FDC* £22500 | | | |

Second harp

3471
1696 Crown, second bust - hair across breast

**3471  Crown**. Second dr. bust r. with two locks of hair across the bust and no hair below the truncation. ℞. Second harp (hair across breast), 1696 (two varieties) die axis ↑↓

OCTAVO .......................................................................................................................*Each unique*

3472
Third bust, straight breastplate

| | F | VF | EF |
|---|---|---|---|
| | £ | £ | £ |

**3472  Crown.** Third dr. bust, r. Easily distinguished by the straight breast plate or drapery.
R. First harp, die axis ↑↓

| | | | |
|---|---|---|---|
| 1696 OCTAVO ....................................................................110 | 375 | 3250 |
| 1696 TRICESIMO................................................................................*Extremely rare* |
| 1696 plain edge proof *FDC* £18500 |

**3473  Crown.** Similar, R. Second harp, die axis ↑↓

| | | | |
|---|---|---|---|
| 1697 NONO...................................................................2750 | 10000 | 45000 |

Third harp

3474
1700 Crown, third bust variety

**3474  Crown.** Third bust variety r. of same general style but dies have been recut and hair
varied a little. Tie is slightly longer and thinner than normal third bust. R. Third harp with
scroll front and back, ↑↓

| | | | |
|---|---|---|---|
| 1700 DVODECIMO............................................................110 | 375 | 3250 |
| 1700 DECIMO. TERTIO ...................................................150 | 525 | 3750 |

**3475  Halfcrown.** First bust r. R. Small shields,

| | | | |
|---|---|---|---|
| 1696 die axis ↑↓OCTAVO..............................................85 | 275 | 2000 |
| — — 1696 DECVS error ............................................100 | 325 | 2250 |

**3476  Halfcrown.** B (*Bristol*) below First bust,

| | | | |
|---|---|---|---|
| die axis ↑↓ 1696 OCTAVO .........................................100 | 325 | 2250 |
| — 1696 B Similar proof *FDC* £17500 |

3477
Chester Mint

3478
Exeter Mint

|  | F<br>£ | VF<br>£ | EF<br>£ |
|---|---|---|---|
| **3477 Halfcrown.** C *(Chester)* below first bust, die axis ↑↓ | | | |
| 1696 OCTAVO ..................................................................225 | 600 | 2750 | |
| **3478 Halfcrown.** E *(Exeter)* below first bust, die axis ↑↓ | | | |
| 1696 OCTAVO ..................................................................225 | 600 | 2750 | |
| **3479 Halfcrown.** N *(Norwich)* below first bust, die axis ↑↓ | | | |
| 1696 OCTAVO ..................................................................175 | 525 | 2500 | |
| **3480 Halfcrown.** y *(York)* below first bust, die axis ↑↓ | | | |
| 1696 OCTAVO ..................................................................200 | 575 | 2600 | |

3480
1696 Halfcrown - York Mint

3481
1696 Halfcrown, large shield
reverse with early harp

| | | | |
|---|---|---|---|
| **3481 Halfcrown.** First bust r. ℞. Large shield, early harp, die axis ↑↓ | | | |
| 1696 OCTAVO ....................................................................85 | 275 | 2000 | |
| 1696 Proof plain edge *FDC* £15000 | | | |
| **3482 Halfcrown.** — B *(Bristol)* below bust, die axis ↑↓ | | | |
| 1696 OCTAVO ..................................................................100 | 325 | 2250 | |
| **3483 Halfcrown.** — C *(Chester)* below bust, die axis ↑↓ | | | |
| 1696 OCTAVO .................................................................. 200 | 600 | 2750 | |
| **3484 Halfcrown.** — E *(Exeter)* below bust, die axis ↑↓ | | | |
| 1696 OCTAVO.....................................................................175 | 525 | 2500 | |
| **3485 Halfcrown.** — N *(Norwich)* below bust, die axis ↑↓ | | | |
| 1696 OCTAVO.....................................................................375 | 1250 | — | |
| **3486 Halfcrown.** — y *(York)* below bust, die axis ↑↓ | | | |
| 1696 OCTAVO.....................................................................110 | 350 | 2400 | |
| — — die axis ↑↓ 1696 y *(York)*, Scots Arms at date .....1000 | — | — | |
| — die axis ↑↓ y over E 1696........................................250 | 850 | — | |

3487                                        3489
Large shields, ordinary harp         Chester Mint Halfcrown, large shields

|  | F | VF | EF |
|---|---|---|---|
|  | £ | £ | £ |
| **3487  Halfcrown.** First bust r. R. Large shields, ordinary harp die axis ↑↓ |  |  |  |
| 1696 OCTAVO ....................................................200 | 600 | 2750 | |
| 1697 NONO...........................................................80 | 225 | 1650 | |
| 1697 — GRR for GRA.......................................375 | — | — | |
| 1697 G/A in MAG ..............................................325 | — | — | |
| 1697/6 — .............................................................135 | 450 | 2400 | |
| 1697 Proof plain edge *FDC* £15000 |  |  |  |
| **3488  Halfcrown.** — B (*Bristol*) below first bust, die axis ↑↓ |  |  |  |
| 1697 NONO...........................................................90 | 325 | 2250 | |
| 1697 proof on thick flan *FDC* ................................................................. *Extremely rare* | | | |
| 1697 — no stops on reverse ...............................135 | 525 | 2500 | |
| **3489  Halfcrown.** — C (*Chester*) below first bust, similar die axis ↑↓ |  |  |  |
| 1696 OCTAVO ....................................................200 | 625 | 3000 | |
| 1697 NONO.........................................................150 | 525 | 2500 | |

3490
Exeter Mint Halfcrown, large shields

| **3490  Halfcrown.** — E (*Exeter*) below first bust, similar die axis ↑↓ |  |  |  |
|---|---|---|---|
| 1696    OCTAVO ..................................................150 | 525 | 2500 | |
| 1696 NONO..........................................................450 | — | — | |
| 1697 OCTAVO ....................................................475 | — | — | |
| 1697 NONO............................................................90 | 325 | 2250 | |
| 1697 E over C or B under bust ............................200 | 800 | — | |

3491
Norwich Mint Halfcrown, large shields

|  | F £ | VF £ | EF £ |
|---|---|---|---|
| **3491 Halfcrown.** — N *(Norwich)* below first bust, similar die axis ↑↓ | | | |
| 1696    OCTAVO ..................................................375 | 1350 | — |
| 1697 OCTAVO ................................................250 | 950 | — |
| 1697 NONO.......................................................125 | 525 | 2500 |
| 1697 — Scots Arms at date ............................1000 | — | — |
| **3492 Halfcrown.** — — y *(York)* below first bust, similar die axis ↑↓ | | | |
| 1697 NONO........................................................85 | 275 | 2000 |
| 1697 OCTAVO ................................................350 | — | — |
| **3493 Halfcrown.** Second dr. bust r. (hair across breast), die axis ↑↓ | | | |
| 1696 OCTAVO ...............................................................................................................*Unique* | | |

3494
1700 Halfcrown, modified large shields

| **3494 Halfcrown.** First dr. bust R. Modified large shields die axis ↑↓ | F £ | VF £ | EF £ |
|---|---|---|---|
| 1698 OCTAVO ..................................................400 | 1300 | — |
| 1698 DECIMO ...................................................85 | 225 | 1350 |
| 1698/7 — ..........................................................250 | 800 | — |
| 1698 UNDECIMO............................................350 | 1000 | — |
| 1699 UNDECIMO............................................150 | 525 | 2500 |
| 1699 — Inverted A's for V's on edge ................175 | 600 | — |
| 1699 — Scots Arms at date ...............................900 | — | — |
| 1699 — Lion of Nassau inverted.......................525 | 1500 | — |
| 1700 DVODECIMO............................................90 | 250 | 1500 |
| 1700 D. TERTIO ..............................................100 | 275 | 1600 |
| 1700 — DECⱯS error ........................................100 | 275 | 1600 |
| 1701 D. TERTIO ................................................90 | 250 | 1750 |
| 1701 — no stops on reverse ..............................125 | 375 | 2250 |

3495
1701 Halfcrown, elephant and castle below bust

|  | F<br>£ | VF<br>£ | EF<br>£ |
|---|---|---|---|
| **3495  Halfcrown.** – elephant and castle below bust, die axis ↑↓ |  |  |  |
| 1701 D. TERTIO ...............................................................3000 | | 9000 | — |

3496
1701 Halfcrown, plumes on reverse

|  | F<br>£ | VF<br>£ | EF<br>£ |
|---|---|---|---|
| **3496  Halfcrown.** – ℞. Plumes in angles, die axis ↑↓ |  |  |  |
| 1701 D. TERTIO ...................................................................325 | | 1100 | 5500 |

## SHILLINGS

**First bust**
This bust is distinctive in having the hair turned outwards above and below the crown of the head

**Third bust**
This is rather like the first bust but the hair at the back all turns downwards and inwards

**Third bust variety**
Tie thicker, more hair below bust, more aquiline profile and coarser features

|  | F £ | VF £ | EF £ |
|---|---|---|---|
| **3497  Shilling.** First dr. bust r. R. Crowned cruciform shields edge milled die axis ↑↓ | | | |
| 1695 ................................................................35 | 110 | 650 |
| 1695 E of ET over H............................................50 | 150 | 750 |
| 1696 ................................................................30 | 95 | 575 |
| 1696/5 and GVLICLMVS ...................................45 | 135 | 675 |
| 1696 no stops on reverse ...................................100 | 350 | — |
| 1696 MAB for MAG error ..................................600 | — | — |
| 1696 GVLIEMVS error........................................575 | — | — |
| 1696 GVLIELMVS error ......................................85 | 300 | — |
| 1696 GⱯLIELMVS error ....................................110 | 375 | — |
| 1696 GVLELMVS ...............................................575 | — | — |
| 1696 2nd L over M .............................................125 | 400 | — |
| 1696-1669 error date .........................................800 | 2250 | — |
| 1697 ................................................................30 | 95 | 575 |
| 1697 E/A in DEI ................................................135 | 475 | — |
| 1697 GRI for GRA error......................................225 | 650 | 2500 |
| 1697 Arms of Scot/Ireland transposed ...............650 | — | — |
| 1697 Irish Arms at date......................................750 | — | — |
| 1697 no stops on reverse ...................................110 | 375 | — |
| 1697 GVLELMVS error.......................................525 | — | — |
| 1697 GVLIELMⱯS error ....................................100 | 350 | — |
| 1697 L/M in legend ...........................................125 | 400 | — |

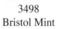

3498
Bristol Mint

3499
1696 Chester Mint Shilling

|  | F £ | VF £ | EF £ |
|---|---|---|---|
| **3498 Shilling.** Similar B (*Bristol*) below bust die axis ↑↓ | | | |
| 1696 ........................................... 65 | | 225 | 950 |
| 1696  G∀LIELMVS error and large G in MAG ................ 70 | | 240 | 1000 |
| 1696 small x in REX ........................................... *Scarce variety* | | | |
| 1697 ........................................... 65 | | 225 | 950 |
| **3499 Shilling.** Similar C (*Chester*) below bust die axis ↑↓ | | | |
| 1696 ........................................... 90 | | 275 | 1250 |
| 1696 R/V in GRA ........................................... 120 | | 350 | 1350 |
| 1696 thick flan proof *FDC* ........................................... *Extremely rare* | | | |
| 1697 ........................................... 85 | | 250 | 1250 |

3500

|  | F £ | VF £ | EF £ |
|---|---|---|---|
| **3500 Shilling.** Similar E (*Exeter*) below bust die axis ↑↓ | | | |
| 1696 ........................................... 85 | | 300 | 1100 |
| 1697 E over N ........................................... 125 | | 375 | 1350 |
| 1697 ........................................... 100 | | 350 | 1200 |
| **3501 Shilling.** Similar N (*Norwich*) below bust die axis ↑↓ | | | |
| 1696 ........................................... 110 | | 325 | 1250 |
| 1697 no stops on obv. ........................................... 125 | | 375 | 1350 |
| 1697 ........................................... 110 | | 325 | 1250 |
| **3502 Shilling.** Similar y (*York*) below bust die axis ↑↓ | | | |
| 1696 Also known with no stop after GVLIELMVS ............ 90 | | 275 | 1100 |
| 1696 ........................................... 100 | | 300 | 1200 |
| 1697 ........................................... 110 | | 325 | 1250 |
| 1697 Arms of France/Ireland transposed ........................... 1000 | | — | — |
| 1697 Arms of Scotland/Ireland transposed ....................... 1000 | | — | — |
| **3503 Shilling.** Similar Y (*York*) below bust die axis ↑↓ | | | |
| 1696 ........................................... 100 | | 325 | 1200 |
| 1697 Y over ∀ ........................................... 250 | | 900 | — |
| 1697 ........................................... 135 | | 500 | — |
| **3504 Shilling.** Second dr. bust r. (hair across breast), similar die axis ↑↓ | | | |
| 1696 ........................................... *Unique* | | | |

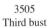

| | 3505 | 3513 |
|---|---|---|
| | Third bust | Chester Mint, Third bust variety |

|  | F | VF | EF |
|---|---|---|---|
|  | £ | £ | £ |
| **3505**  **Shilling.** Third dr. bust r., similar die axis ↑↓ 1697..40 | | 125 | 650 |
| **3506**  **Shilling.** Similar B *(Bristol)* below bust, die axis ↑↓ | | | |
| 1697 ............125 | | 375 | 1350 |
| **3507**  **Shilling.** Similar C *(Chester)* below bust die axis ↑↓ | | | |
| 1696 ............135 | | 425 | 1500 |
| 1697 small or large lettering ............90 | | 275 | 1100 |
| 1697 FR.A error............110 | | 325 | 1350 |
| 1697 no stops on reverse ............110 | | 325 | 1350 |
| 1697 Arms of Scotland at date............1000 | | — | — |
| **3508**  **Shilling.** Similar E *(Exeter)* below bust, die axis ↑↓ | | | |
| 1696 ............1750 | | — | — |
| 1697 ............125 | | 350 | 1350 |
| **3509**  **Shilling.** Similar N *(Norwich)* below bust, die axis ↑↓ | | | |
| 1697 ............135 | | 425 | 1500 |
| **3510**  **Shilling.** Similar y *(York)* below bust die axis ↑↓ | | | |
| 1696 ............750 | | — | — |
| 1697 ............85 | | 275 | 1000 |
| **3511**  **Shilling.** Third bust variety r. similar die axis ↑↓ | | | |
| 1697 GⱯLIELMVS error ............80 | | 275 | — |
| 1697 ............45 | | 135 | 700 |
| 1697 GVLIELMⱯS error ............80 | | 275 | — |
| 1698 ............110 | | 325 | 1200 |
| 1698 plain edge proof *FDC* £7500 | | | |
| **3512**  **Shilling.** Similar B *(Bristol)* below bust, die axis ↑↓ | | | |
| 1697 ............150 | | 450 | 1600 |
| **3513**  **Shilling.** Similar C *(Chester)* below bust, die axis ↑↓ | | | |
| 1697 ............160 | | 475 | 1750 |
| 1697 thick flan............*Extremely rare* | | | |
| **3514**  **Shilling.** Similar R. Plumes in angles, die axis ↑↓ | | | |
| 1698 ............250 | | 750 | 2500 |

**Third bust**        **Fourth bust**        **Fifth bust**

3515
Fourth bust

3516
Fifth bust

|  | F | VF | EF |
|---|---|---|---|
|  | £ | £ | £ |
| **3515 Shilling** Fourth dr. bust ('flaming hair') r. similar die axis ↑↓ |  |  |  |
| 1698 ................................................................200 | 675 | 2750 |
| 1698 No stops on reverse ....................................225 | 700 | 2850 |
| 1698 plain edge proof *FDC* £9000 |  |  |  |
| 1699 ................................................................175 | 625 | 2500 |
| 1699 plain edge proof *FDC* £9000 |  |  |  |
| **3516 Shilling.** Fifth dr. bust (hair high) r. similar die axis ↑↓ |  |  |  |
| 1699 ................................................................125 | 375 | 1500 |
| 1699 Plain edge proof....................................................................................*Extremely rare* |  |  |  |
| 1700 ..................................................................35 | 120 | 575 |
| 1700 no stops on rev..............................................45 | 140 | 600 |
| 1700 Circular small O's in date ...........................35 | 120 | 575 |
| 1700 no stop after DEI ...........................................50 | 150 | 675 |
| 1700 Tall O's no stops on reverse.........................45 | 140 | 625 |
| 1701 small or large lions ....................................100 | 325 | 1250 |
| 1701 DEI/GRA ......................................................300 | — | — |

3517
1701 Shilling, plumes on reverse

3518
1699 Shilling, roses on reverse

|  | F | VF | EF |
|---|---|---|---|
| **3517 Shilling.** Similar R. Plumes in angles die axis ↑↓ |  |  |  |
| 1699 ................................................................225 | 850 | 2750 |
| 1701 ................................................................225 | 850 | 2750 |
| **3518 Shilling.** Similar R. Roses in angles, die axis ↑↓ |  |  |  |
| 1699 ................................................................250 | 900 | 3000 |
| **3519 Shilling.** Similar plume below bust, die axis ↑↓ |  |  |  |
| 1700 ................................................................3250 | 11000 | — |

## SIXPENCES

**First bust**

**Third bust**

**Early harp large crown**

**Later harp small crown**

3520
First bust Sixpence, French arms at date

| | F £ | VF £ | EF £ |
|---|---|---|---|
| **3520 Sixpence.** First dr. bust r. R. Crowned cruciform shields, large crowns, edge milled, early harp, die axis ↑↓ | | | |
| 1695 ..............................................................30 | 70 | 275 |
| 1696 ..............................................................25 | 60 | 225 |
| 1696 Heavy flan ...............................................850 | — | — |
| 1696    French Arms at date...............................475 | — | — |
| 1696 GVLIELMⱯS ...........................................35 | 90 | 400 |
| 1696    Scots Arms at date ................................350 | — | — |
| 1696/5 ...........................................................30 | 90 | 375 |
| 1696 no stops on obverse .................................40 | 110 | 475 |
| 1696 DFI for DEI ..............................................75 | — | — |
| **3521 Sixpence.** Similar B *(Bristol)* below bust, die axis ↑↓ | | | |
| 1696 ..............................................................30 | 90 | 350 |
| — — 1696 B over E ........................................40 | 110 | 400 |
| **3522 Sixpence.** Similar C *(Chester)* below bust, die axis ↑↓ | | | |
| 1696 ..............................................................30 | 90 | 350 |

3523

3525
1696 York Mint sixpence, early harp, first bust

| | F £ | VF £ | EF £ |
|---|---|---|---|
| **3523 Sixpence.** Similar E *(Exeter)* below bust, die axis ↑↓ | | | |
| 1696 ..............................................................40 | 110 | 400 |
| **3524 Sixpence.** Similar N *(Norwich)* below bust, die axis ↑↓ | | | |
| 1696 ..............................................................40 | 110 | 375 |
| **3525 Sixpence.** Similar y *(York)* below bust, die axis ↑↓ | | | |
| 1696 ..............................................................30 | 90 | 350 |

|                                                                                  | F<br>£ | VF<br>£ | EF<br>£ |
|----------------------------------------------------------------------------------|--------|---------|---------|
| **3526  Sixpence.** Similar Y *(York)* below bust, die axis ↑↓                    |        |         |         |
| 1696 ...............................................................................30 | 90     | 350     |         |
| 1696 no stops on obverse .....................................................40  | 110    | 425     |         |
| **3527  Sixpence.** Similar R. Later harp, large crowns, die axis ↑↓             |        |         |         |
| 1696 ...............................................................................40 | 110    | 425     |         |
| 1696 no stops on obverse .....................................................65  | 175    | —       |         |
| **3528  Sixpence.** — — — B *(Bristol)* below bust, similar die axis ↑↓          |        |         |         |
| 1696 ...............................................................................60 | 150    | 525     |         |
| 1696 no stops on obv. ..........................................................75 | 175    | 575     |         |
| 1697 ...............................................................................40 | 110    | 400     |         |
| **3529  Sixpence.** — — — C *(Chester)* below bust, similar die axis ↑↓          |        |         |         |
| 1697 ...............................................................................90 | 225    | 650     |         |
| **3530  Sixpence.** — — — E *(Exeter)* below bust, similar die axis ↑↓           |        |         |         |
| 1697 ...............................................................................40 | 110    | 400     |         |
| **3531  Sixpence.** — — R. small crowns, similar die axis ↑↓                     |        |         |         |
| 1696 ...............................................................................40 | 110    | 425     |         |
| 1697 ...............................................................................30 | 80     | 325     |         |
| 1697 GVLIELMⱯS ...............................................................45  | 120    | —       |         |
| 1697 Arms of France/Ireland transposed...............................350          | —      | —       |         |

3532
Bristol Mint Sixpence, small crowns

|                                                                                  | F<br>£ | VF<br>£ | EF<br>£ |
|----------------------------------------------------------------------------------|--------|---------|---------|
| **3532  Sixpence.** — — — B *(Bristol)* below bust, similar die axis ↑↓          |        |         |         |
| 1696 ...............................................................................45 | 125    | 475     |         |
| 1696 no stops on O ..............................................................75 | 175    | 575     |         |
| 1697 ...............................................................................30 | 80     | 325     |         |
| 1697 B over E ......................................................................40 | 90     | 350     |         |
| **3533  Sixpence.** — — — C *(Chester)* below bust, similar die axis ↑↓          |        |         |         |
| 1696 ...............................................................................80 | 200    | 575     |         |
| 1697 ...............................................................................35 | 85     | 325     |         |
| 1697 Irish shield at date.......................................................275 | 850    | —       |         |
| 1697 Plain edge .................................................................125 | 325    | 950     |         |
| **3534  Sixpence.** — — — E *(Exeter)* below bust, similar die axis ↑↓           |        |         |         |
| 1697 ...............................................................................50 | 125    | 450     |         |
| 1697 E over B ......................................................................75 | 175    | 525     |         |
| **3535  Sixpence.** — — — N *(Norwich)* below bust, similar die axis ↑↓          |        |         |         |
| 1696 ...............................................................................80 | 185    | 550     |         |
| 1697 GVLIEMVS ...............................................................125  | 450    | —       |         |
| 1697 ...............................................................................45 | 110    | 375     |         |
| **3536  Sixpence.** — — — y *(York)* below bust, similar die axis ↑↓             |        |         |         |
| 1697 ...............................................................................45 | 110    | 425     |         |
| 1697 Irish shield at date.......................................................225 | 650    | —       |         |

3537
Second bust Sixpence

3538
Sixpence, third bust,
later harp, large crowns

| | F £ | VF £ | EF £ |
|---|---|---|---|
| **3537 Sixpence.** Second dr. bust r. R. Similar die axis ↑↓ | | | |
| 1696 | 275 | 700 | 2250 |
| 1696 hair across breast *(as 3471)* | | | *Extremely rare* |
| 1696 GVLELMVS | 300 | 750 | 2400 |
| 1697 | 175 | 650 | 2000 |
| 1697 GVLIELMⱯS | 200 | 675 | 2100 |
| 1697 G/I in GRA | 175 | 650 | 2000 |
| 1697 GVLIEMVS | 275 | 700 | 2250 |
| 1697 GR/DE in GRA | 200 | 700 | 2250 |
| **3537A Sixpence.** Third dr. bust, r. early harp, large crowns. E *(Exeter)* below bust | | | |
| 1696 | 350 | 1250 | — |
| **3537B Sixpence.** — — — Y *(York)* below bust, similar die axis ↑↓ | | | |
| 1696 | 225 | 750 | — |
| **3538 Sixpence.** Third dr. bust, r., R. Later harp, large crowns, similar die axis ↑↓ | | | |
| 1697 | 25 | 70 | 300 |
| 1697 GVLIEIMVS | 30 | 75 | 325 |
| 1697 GⱯLIELMVS | 35 | 80 | 325 |
| 1698 | 35 | 80 | 325 |
| 1699 | 90 | 225 | 650 |
| 1700 | 35 | 80 | 325 |
| 1701 | 70 | 175 | 525 |
| **3539 Sixpence.** — — B *(Bristol)* below bust, similar die axis ↑↓ | | | |
| 1697 | 50 | 135 | 475 |
| 1697 IRA for FRA | 80 | 200 | — |

3540
Chester Mint Sixpence, third bust

| | F | VF | EF |
|---|---|---|---|
| **3540 Sixpence.** — — C *(Chester)* below bust, similar die axis ↑↓ | | | |
| 1697 | 80 | 200 | 625 |
| **3541 Sixpence.** — — E *(Exeter)* below bust, similar die axis | | | |
| 1697 | 90 | 225 | 675 |

3545                                    3547
York Mint Sixpence - Y provenance mark        Sixpence, roses on reverse

|  | F | VF | EF |
|---|---|---|---|
|  | £ | £ | £ |
| **3542 Sixpence.** Third dr. bust, r. R. Small crowns, similar die axis ↑↓ | | | |
| 1697 .............................................................30 | 75 | 325 |
| 1697 D/F in DEI ........................................80 | 200 | 625 |
| 1697 G/D in GRA .......................................70 | 175 | 600 |
| **3543 Sixpence.** — — C *(Chester)* below bust, similar die axis ↑↓ | | | |
| 1697 .............................................................60 | 150 | 525 |
| **3544 Sixpence.** — — E *(Exeter)* below bust, similar die axis ↑↓ | | | |
| 1697 .............................................................60 | 150 | 525 |
| **3545 Sixpence.** — — Y *(York)* below bust, similar die axis ↑↓ | | | |
| 1697 .............................................................45 | 110 | 425 |
| **3546 Sixpence.** — — R. Plumes in angles, similar die axis ↑↓ | | | |
| 1698 .............................................................90 | 250 | 750 |
| 1699 .............................................................90 | 250 | 750 |
| **3547 Sixpence.** — R. Roses in angles, similar die axis ↑↓ | | | |
| 1699 ...........................................................100 | 275 | 850 |
| 1699 GⱯLIELMVS ......................................110 | 325 | — |

3548                                    3549
1700 Sixpence, plume below bust          1699 Groat or Fourpence

| | F | VF | EF |
|---|---|---|---|
| **3548 Sixpence.** — plume below bust, R. Similar die axis ↑↓ | | | |
| 1700 ........................................................2250 | — | — |
| **3549 Fourpence.** Laur. and dr. bust r. R. 4 Crowned die axis ↑↓ | | | |
| 1697 .................................................................................................... *Unique* |
| 1698 .............................................................28 | 60 | 190 |
| 1699 .............................................................25 | 50 | 145 |
| 1700 .............................................................25 | 50 | 165 |
| 1701 .............................................................30 | 65 | 190 |
| 1702 .............................................................20 | 45 | 90 |
| **3550 Threepence.** Laur. and dr. bust r. R. 3 Crowned die axis ↑↓ | | | |
| 1698 .............................................................20 | 40 | 110 |
| 1699 .............................................................25 | 50 | 140 |
| 1700 .............................................................22 | 45 | 130 |
| 1701 GBA for GRA ......................................24 | 45 | 150 |
| 1701 small lettering .....................................20 | 40 | 110 |
| 1701 large lettering .....................................20 | 40 | 110 |

|  | F<br>£ | VF<br>£ | EF<br>£ |
|---|---|---|---|

**3551 Twopence.** Laur. and dr. bust r. ℞. Crown to edge of coin, large figure 2 die axis ↑↓

| 1698 | 25 | 50 | 135 |

**3551A Twopence.** Laur. and dr. bust r. ℞ Crown within inner circle of legend, smaller figure 2, die axis ↑↓

| 1698 | 25 | 45 | 125 |
| 1699 | 18 | 30 | 95 |
| 1700 | 18 | 30 | 95 |
| 1701 | 18 | 30 | 95 |

**3552 Penny.** Laur. and dr. bust r. ℞. 1 Crowned die axis ↑↓

| 1698 | 25 | 45 | 135 |
| 1698 IRA for FRA error | 25 | 45 | 125 |
| 1698 HI.BREX error | 25 | 45 | 125 |
| 1699 | 40 | 80 | 225 |
| 1700 | 35 | 70 | 165 |
| 1701 | 25 | 45 | 120 |

3553 - 1701 Maundy Set

**3553 Maundy Set.** The four denominations. Uniform dates

| 1698 | 125 | 300 | 775 |
| 1699 | 175 | 400 | 9250 |
| 1700 | 165 | 375 | 825 |
| 1701 | 125 | 300 | 75 |

## COPPER

3554
Halfpenny

|  | F £ | VF £ | EF £ |
|---|---|---|---|
| **3554  Halfpenny.** First issue. Laur. and cuir. bust r. ℞. Britannia with r. hand raised die axis ↑↓ |  |  |  |
| 1695 | 45 | 210 | 1150 |
| 1695 BRITΛNNIΛ error | 200 | — | — |
| 1695 no stop on rev. | 60 | 275 | — |
| 1695 no stops on obv. | 60 | 275 | — |
| 1696 | 35 | 175 | 1000 |
| 1696    GVLIEMVS, no rev. stop | 300 | — | — |
| 1696    TERTVS error | 275 | — | — |
| 1697 | 35 | 175 | 950 |
| 1697 all stops omitted | 225 | — | — |
| 1697 I/E in TERTIVS | 225 | — | — |
| 1697 GVLILMVS, no rev. stop | 300 | — | — |
| 1697 no stop after TERTIVS | 50 | 275 | — |
| 1698 | 45 | 210 | 1150 |
| **3555  Halfpenny.** Second issue. Laur. and cuir. bust r. ℞. Britannia, date in legend die axis ↑↓ |  |  |  |
| 1698    Stop after date | 35 | 200 | 1050 |
| 1699    no stop after date | 30 | 165 | 1000 |
| 1699 BRITΛNNIΛ error | 225 | — | — |
| 1699 GVLIEMVS error | 225 | — | — |
| 1699 BRITAN  IA error | 225 | — | — |

3556

|  | F £ | VF £ | EF £ |
|---|---|---|---|
| **3556  Halfpenny.** Third issue. Laur. and cuir. bust r. ℞. Britannia, date in exergue, die axis ↑↓ |  |  |  |
| 1699 | 35 | 175 | 950 |
| 1699 stop after date | 225 | — | — |
| 1699 BRITΛNNIΛ error | 100 | 380 | — |
| 1699 GVLILELMVS error | 275 | — | — |
| 1699 TERTVS error | 275 | — | — |

|                                          | F<br>£ | VF<br>£ | EF<br>£ |
|------------------------------------------|--------|---------|---------|
| 1699 — no rev. stop                      | 150    | —       | —       |
| 1699 no stops on obv.                    | 85     | 380     | —       |
| 1699 no stop after GVLIELMVS             | 85     | 325     | —       |
| 1700                                     | 35     | 175     | 950     |
| 1700 no stops on obv.                    | 100    | 350     | —       |
| 1700 no stop after GVLIELMVS             | 100    | 350     | —       |
| 1700 BRITΛNNIΛ error                     | 40     | 175     | 950     |
| 1700 — no stop after                     | 45     | 195     | 1000    |
| 1700 GVLIELMS                            | 100    | 350     | —       |
| 1700 GVLIEEMVS                           | 65     | 250     | 1200    |
| 1700 GVLIEEMVS                           | 65     | 250     | 1200    |
| 1700 TER TIVS                            | 45     | 195     | 1000    |
| 1700 I/V in TERTIVS                      | 225    | —       | —       |
| 1701                                     | 40     | 175     | 950     |
| 1701 BRITΛNNIΛ                           | 50     | 225     | 1050    |
| 1701 — no stops on obv.                  | 225    | —       | —       |
| 1701 — inverted A's for V's              | 60     | 250     | 1050    |

3557
1696 Farthing date in exergue

3558
1699 Farthing date in legend

**3557 Farthing.** First issue Laur. and cuir. bust r. R. Britannia l. die axis ↑↓

|                                          | F<br>£ | VF<br>£ | EF<br>£ |
|------------------------------------------|--------|---------|---------|
| 1695                                     | 40     | 250     | 950     |
| 1695 GVLIELMV error                      | 200    | —       | —       |
| 1696                                     | 35     | 210     | 900     |
| 1697                                     | 30     | 175     | 825     |
| 1697 GVLIELMS error                      | 250    | —       | —       |
| 1697 TERTIV error                        | 250    | —       | —       |
| 1698                                     | 200    | 625     | —       |
| 1698 B/G on rev.                         | 325    | —       | —       |
| 1699                                     | 35     | 240     | 900     |
| 1699 GVLILEMVS•                          | 175    | 450     | —       |
| 1700                                     | 30     | 155     | 775     |
| 1700 RRITANNIA                           | 225    | —       | —       |

**3558 Farthing.** Second issue. Laur. and cuir. bust r. R̩. Britannia date at end of legend die axis ↑↓

|                                          | F<br>£ | VF<br>£ | EF<br>£ |
|------------------------------------------|--------|---------|---------|
| 1698 Stop after date                     | 45     | 275     | 1000    |
| 1699 no stop after date                  | 50     | 300     | 1050    |
| 1699 no stop after GVLIELMVS             | 125    | —       | —       |
| 1699 — No stop before or after           | *Extremely rare* | | |
| 1699 BRITΛNNIΛ                           | 225    | —       | —       |
| 1699 BRITΛNNIΛ                           | 225    | —       | —       |

Anne, the second daughter of James II, was born on 6th February 1665 and as a protestant succeeded to the throne on William III's death. Anne married Prince George of Denmark and produced 17 children, sadly none surviving to succeed to the throne. Anne died on 1st August 1714.

The Act of Union of 1707, which effected the unification of the ancient kingdoms of England and Scotland into a single realm, resulted in a change in the royal arms—on the Post-Union coinage the English lions and Scottish lion are emblazoned per pale on the top and bottom shields. After the Union the rose in the centre of the reverse of the gold coins is replaced by the Garter star.

Following a successful Anglo-Dutch expedition against Spain, bullion seized in Vigo Bay was sent to be minted into coin, and the coins made from this metal had the word VIGO placed below the Queen's bust. The elephant and castle provenance mark continues on some guineas in the Post-Union period.

**Engravers and designers:** Samuel Bull (d.c1720), Joseph Cave (d.c1760), James Clerk, John Croker (1670-1741), Godfrey Kneller (1646-1723)

# GOLD
**PRE-UNION WITH SCOTLAND 1702-07**

3560
1705 Pre-Union Five Guineas

The shields on the reverse are Pre-Union type.

|  | F<br>£ | VF<br>£ | EF<br>£ |
|---|---|---|---|
| **3560 Five Guineas.** Dr. bust l, regnal year on edge in words (e.g. 1705 = QVARTO) die axis ↑↓ | | | |
| 1705 QVARTO | 12000 | 30000 | 150000 |
| 1706 QVINTO | 11000 | 27500 | 140000 |
| **3561 Five Guineas.** Similar VIGO below bust, die axis ↑↓ | | | |
| 1703 (Three varieties) SECVNDO | 60000 | 175000 | 625000 |

| | 3562 | 3563 |
|---|---|---|
| | 1705 Pre-Union Guinea | 1703 VIGO Guinea |

| | F | VF | EF |
|---|---|---|---|
| | £ | £ | £ |

**3562  Guinea.** Dr. bust l. R. Crowned cruciform shields sceptres in angles die axis ↑↓

| | | | |
|---|---|---|---|
| 1702 | ...........................................................1400 | 6250 | 18500 |
| 1702 plain edge proof | ...........................................— | — | 27500 |
| 1705 | ...........................................................1450 | 6500 | 19000 |
| 1706 | ...........................................................1450 | 6500 | 19000 |
| 1707 | ...........................................................1500 | 6750 | 20000 |

**3563  Guinea.** Similar with VIGO below bust, die axis ↑↓

| | | | |
|---|---|---|---|
| 1703 | ......................................................22500 | 65000 | 150000 |

| | 3564 | 3565 |
|---|---|---|
| | Pre-Union Half-Guinea | VIGO Half-Guinea |

**3564  Half-Guinea.** Dr bust l. R. Crowned cruciform shields sceptres in angles die axis ↑↓

| | | | |
|---|---|---|---|
| 1702 | ...........................................................1350 | 3500 | 12500 |
| 1705 | ...........................................................1250 | 3250 | 11000 |

**3565  Half-Guinea.** Similar with VIGO below bust

| | | | |
|---|---|---|---|
| 1703 | ........................................................10000 | 32500 | 85000 |

## POST UNION WITH SCOTLAND 1707-14

3566
1706 Post-Union Five Guineas

The shields on the reverse are changed to Post-Union type die axis ↑↓

**3566  Five Guineas.** Dr. bust l., regnal year on edge in words

| | | | |
|---|---|---|---|
| 1706 QVINTO | ...........................................................8500 | 20000 | 95000 |

3567
1709 - Narrow shields

3568
1711 - Broad shields

|  | F £ | VF £ | EF £ |
|---|---|---|---|
| **3567** Five Guineas. Similar R. Narrower shields, tall narrow crowns, larger rev. lettering, die axis ↑↓ | | | |
| 1709 OCTAVO ...............9000 | | 21000 | 100000 |
| **3568** Five Guineas. New bust l. R. Broader shields edge inscribed die axis ↑↓ | | | |
| 1711 DECIMO ...............9000 | | 21000 | 100000 |
| 1713 DVODECIMO............ 9500 | | 22000 | 105000 |
| 1714/3 D. TERTIO ...............9750 | | 24000 | 110000 |
| 1714 D. TERTIO ...............9500 | | 22000 | 105000 |

3569
1713 Two Guineas

| | | | |
|---|---|---|---|
| **3569** Two Guineas. Dr. bust l.R. Crowned cruciform shields sceptres in angles edge milled die axis ↑↓ | | | |
| 1709 ...............1850 | | 5750 | 24000 |
| 1711 ...............1750 | | 5500 | 22500 |
| 1713 ...............1850 | | 5750 | 24000 |
| 1714/3 ...............2000 | | 6000 | 25000 |
| **3570** Guinea. First dr. bust l. R. Crowned cruciform shields sceptres in angles edge milled die axis↑↓ | | | |
| 1707 ...............1000 | | 3500 | 13000 |
| 1708 ...............1100 | | 3750 | 13500 |

3571
1708 Guinea, first bust,
elephant and castle below

3574
1713 Guinea, third bust

**3571 Guinea.** First dr. bust l. elephant and castle below, R. Similar die axis ↑↓

| | | | |
|---|---|---|---|
| 1707 | ...1500 | 6000 | 18500 |
| 1708 | ...Extremely rare | | |

**3572 Guinea.** Second* dr. bust l. R. Similar die axis ↑↓

| | | | |
|---|---|---|---|
| 1707 | ...1000 | 3500 | 13000 |
| 1708 | ...900 | 3000 | 11500 |
| 1709 | ...900 | 3000 | 11500 |

**3573 Guinea.** Second bust elephant and castle below R. Similar die axis ↑↓

| | | | |
|---|---|---|---|
| 1708 | ...1500 | 6000 | 18500 |
| 1709 1 | ...1350 | 5250 | 17500 |

**3574 Guinea.** Third* dr. bust l. R. Similar die axis ↑↓

| | | | |
|---|---|---|---|
| 1710 | ...750 | 2200 | 10500 |
| 1711 | ...750 | 2200 | 10500 |
| 1712 | ...800 | 2250 | 11000 |
| 1713/1 | ...725 | 2250 | 11000 |
| 1713 | ...700 | 2100 | 10000 |
| 1714 | ...700 | 2100 | 10000 |
| 1714 GRATIA | ...725 | 2200 | 10500 |

3575
1710 Half-Guinea

**3575 Half-Guinea.** Dr. bust l. R. Crowned cruciform shields, sceptres in angles, edge milled die axis ↑↓

| | | | |
|---|---|---|---|
| 1707 | ...525 | 1200 | 4750 |
| 1708 | ...550 | 1250 | 5000 |
| 1709 | ...525 | 1200 | 4750 |
| 1710 | ...500 | 1100 | 4500 |
| 1711 | ...500 | 1100 | 4500 |
| 1712 | ...525 | 1200 | 4750 |
| 1713 | ...500 | 1100 | 4500 |
| 1714 | ...500 | 1100 | 4500 |

*There is a small difference between the 2nd and 3rd busts in the facial profile and eye.*

# SILVER

**PRE UNION WITH SCOTLAND**

3576
1703 VIGO Crown

The shields on the reverse are Pre-Union type.

|  | F £ | VF £ | EF £ |
|---|---|---|---|
| **3576  Crown.** VIGO below dr. bust, l., regnal year on edge in words (e.g. 1703 = TERTIO) die axis↑↓ |  |  |  |
| 1703 TERTIO .......................................................450 | | 1500 | 12000 |

3577
1705 Crown, plumes on reverse

3578
1707 Pre-Union crown, roses and plumes

| | F £ | VF £ | EF £ |
|---|---|---|---|
| **3577  Crown.** Dr bust l. R. Plumes in angles, die axis ↑↓ | | | |
| 1705 QVINTO ......................................................575 | | 2500 | 13500 |
| **3578  Crown.** R. Similar Crowned cruciform shields Roses and plumes in angles die axis ↑↓ | | | |
| 1706 QVINTO ......................................................300 | | 800 | 4750 |
| 1707 SEXTO .......................................................275 | | 700 | 4250 |

3579
1703 Halfcrown, plain below bust

|  | F | VF | EF |
|---|---|---|---|
|  | £ | £ | £ |

**3579**   **Halfcrown** . Dr. bust l. R. Similar Regnal year on edge in words die axis ↑↓

1703 TERTIO ....................................................................750      2250      9500

3580
1703 VIGO Halfcrown

**3580**   **Halfcrown.** Similar VIGO below bust, die axis ↑↓

1703 TERTIO ....................................................................150      525      2750

3581
Halfcrown, plumes on reverse

**3581**   **Halfcrown.** Dr. bust l. R.  Plumes in angles, similar die axis ↑↓

1704 TERTIO ....................................................................200      750      4250

1705 QVINTO ....................................................................200      750      4250

3582
Halfcrown, Pre-Union,
roses and plumes

3583
Shilling

|  | F | VF | EF |
|---|---|---|---|
|  | £ | £ | £ |

**3582  Halfcrown.** Dr. bust l. R. Roses and plumes in angles, similar die axis ↑↓

| 1706    QVINTO | 135 | 400 | 2750 |
|---|---|---|---|
| 1707 SEXTO | 125 | 375 | 2500 |

**First bust**              **Second bust**

**3583  Shilling.** First dr. bust l. R. Similar die axis ↑↓

| 1702 | 110 | 375 | 1500 |
|---|---|---|---|

**3584  Shilling.** Similar R. Plumes in angles, die axis ↑↓

| 1702 | 120 | 400 | 1750 |
|---|---|---|---|

**3585  Shilling.** First dr. bust VIGO below, die axis ↑↓

| 1702 | 110 | 375 | 1500 |
|---|---|---|---|
| 1702 :ANNA | 150 | 525 | 2250 |

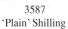

3586
1703 VIGO Shilling

3587
'Plain' Shilling

**3586  Shilling.** Second dr. bust, l. VIGO below R. Similar, die axis ↑↓

| 1703 | 100 | 325 | 1350 |
|---|---|---|---|

**3587  Shilling.** Similar R. Crowned cruciform shields, angles plain, die axis ↑↓

| 1704 | 475 | 1750 | — |
|---|---|---|---|
| 1705 | 225 | 750 | 2500 |

**3588  Shilling.** Second dr. bust l. R. Plumes in angles die axis ↑↓

| 1704 | 135 | 475 | 1850 |
|---|---|---|---|
| 1705 | 125 | 450 | 1750 |

|  | F | VF | EF |
|---|---|---|---|
|  | £ | £ | £ |

**3589 Shilling.** Second dr. bust l. R. Roses and plumes in angles die axis ↑↓

| 1705 | ............125 | 450 | 1750 |
|---|---|---|---|
| 1707 | ............135 | 475 | 1850 |

**3590 Sixpence.** Dr. bust l. VIGO below dr. bust, l. die axis ↑↓

| 1703 | ............35 | 125 | 425 |
|---|---|---|---|

**3591 Sixpence.** Dr bust l., R. Angles plain, die axis ↑↓

| 1705 | ............60 | 200 | 650 |
|---|---|---|---|

**3592 Sixpence.** Similar R. Early shields, plumes in angles, die axis ↑↓

| 1705 | ............40 | 150 | 500 |
|---|---|---|---|

3593
1705 Plumes Sixpence

Early Shield

Late Shield

**3593 Sixpence.** Similar R. Late shields, plumes in angles, die axis ↑↓

| 1705 | ............50 | 185 | 600 |
|---|---|---|---|

**3594 Sixpence.** Similar R. Crowned cruciform shields Roses and plumes in angles die axis ↑↓

| 1705 | ............45 | 175 | 575 |
|---|---|---|---|
| 1707 | ............45 | 175 | 575 |

3595
Groat or fourpence, first bust

3595C
Groat or Fourpence, second bust

**3595 Fourpence.** First dr. bust l. small face, curls at back of head point downwards.
R Small crown above the figure 4 die axis ↑↓

| 1703 | ............20 | 50 | 150 |
|---|---|---|---|
| 1704 | ............15 | 30 | 75 |

**3595A Fourpence.** Second dr. bust l. larger face, curls at back of head point upwards die axis ↑↓

| 1705 | ............40 | 95 | 200 |
|---|---|---|---|
| 1706 | ............15 | 30 | 85 |
| 1708 | ............18 | 38 | 95 |
| 1709 | ............15 | 40 | 100 |
| 1710 | ............12 | 25 | 70 |

**3595B–Fourpence.** Similar R Large crown with pearls on arch, larger serifs on the
figure 4 die axis ↑↓

| 1710 | ............12 | 25 | 75 |
|---|---|---|---|
| 1713 | ............15 | 30 | 80 |

**3595C Fourpence.** Second dr. bust l., but with re-engraved hair R. Crowned 4 die axis ↑↓

| 1710 | ............12 | 25 | 75 |
|---|---|---|---|
| 1713 | ............15 | 30 | 80 |

|  | F £ | VF £ | EF £ |
|---|---|---|---|

**3596  Threepence.** First dr. bust l., broader, tie riband pointing outwards. R. Crowned 3 die axis ↑↓

| 1703 7 above crown....18 | 45 | 130 | 1703 7 not above crown18 | 45 | 130 |
|---|---|---|---|---|---|

**3596A Threepence.** Second dr. bust l., taller and narrow, tie riband pointing inwards die axis ↑↓

| 1704 ...........................18 | 40 | 100 | 1706 ...........................15 | 35 | 105 |
|---|---|---|---|---|---|
| 1705 ...........................18 | 45 | 130 | | | |

3596B
Threepence, third bust

**3596B Threepence.** Third larger more finely engraved dr. bust l. R. Crowned 3, die axis ↑↓

| 1707 | .......................................................................15 | 30 | 75 |
|---|---|---|---|
| 1708 | .......................................................................15 | 35 | 105 |
| 1708/7 | .......................................................................15 | 35 | 105 |
| 1709 | .......................................................................15 | 35 | 105 |
| 1710 | .......................................................................12 | 28 | 85 |
| 1713 | .......................................................................15 | 35 | 100 |
| 1713 mule with 4d obv. die | .................................20 | 42 | 150 |

**3597  Twopence.** First dr. bust l., as fourpence, R. Crown to edge of coin, small figure 2 die axis ↑↓

| 1703 | .......................................................................22 | 50 | 1305 |
|---|---|---|---|
| 1704 | .......................................................................20 | 40 | 80 |
| 1704 No stops on obv. | .........................................22 | 50 | 110 |
| 1705 | .......................................................................25 | 55 | 12 |
| 1706 | .......................................................................20 | 40 | 95 |
| 1707 | .......................................................................20 | 40 | 80 |

**3597A Twopence.** Second dr. bust l., as fourpence, R Crown within inner circle of legend, large figure 2 die axis ↑↓

| 1708 | .......................................................................20 | 40 | 85 |
|---|---|---|---|
| 1709 | .......................................................................25 | 50 | 115 |
| 1710 | .......................................................................18 | 35 | 80 |
| 1713 | .......................................................................20 | 40 | 85 |

**3598  Penny.** Dr. bust l. R. Crowned 1 die axis ↑↓

| 1703 | .......................................................................25 | 50 | 125 |
|---|---|---|---|
| 1705 | .......................................................................22 | 45 | 105 |
| 1706 | .......................................................................22 | 45 | 105 |
| 1708 | .......................................................................200 | 300 | 450 |
| 1709 | .......................................................................20 | 40 | 90 |
| 1710 | .......................................................................60 | 120 | 230 |
| 1713/0 | .......................................................................30 | 55 | 135 |

3599
1713 Maundy Set

**3599 Maundy Set.** The four denominations. Uniform dates

| | | | | |
|---|---|---|---|---|
| 1703 | ...........................................................125 | 300 | 750 |
| 1705 | ...........................................................150 | 300 | 750 |
| 1706 | ...........................................................125 | 250 | 650 |
| 1708 | ...........................................................300 | 450 | 950 |
| 1709 | ...........................................................125 | 250 | 650 |
| 1710 | ...........................................................150 | 300 | 750 |
| 1713 | ...........................................................125 | 250 | 650 |

## POST UNION WITH SCOTLAND, 1707-14

The shields on the reverse are changed to the Post-Union types. The Edinburgh coins have been included here as they are now coins of Great Britain.

**3600 Crown.** Second dr. bust, l. E (Edinburgh) below, R. Crowned cruciform shields regnal
year on edge in words, die axis ↑↓ (e.g. 1708 = SEPTIMO)

| | | | |
|---|---|---|---|
| 1707 SEXTO | .......................................................200 | 575 | 4500 |
| 1707 SEPTIMO | .................................................1850 | — | — |
| 1708 SEPTIMO | .................................................210 | 600 | 4600 |
| 1708/7 SEPTIMO | .................................................225 | 650 | 4750 |

3601
Crown, second bust, plain reverse

**3601 Crown.** Second dr. bust l. R. Crowned cruciform shields, angles plain die axis ↑↓

| | | | |
|---|---|---|---|
| 1707 SEPTIMO | .................................................200 | 575 | 4500 |
| 1708 SEPTIMO | .................................................200 | 575 | 4500 |

**3602 Crown.** Similar R. Plumes in angles, die axis ↑↓

| | | | |
|---|---|---|---|
| 1708 | SEPTIMO.................................................225 | 650 | 4750 |
| 1708 — BR for BRI | ...............................................................*Extremely rare* |

3603
1713 Crown, third bust, roses and plumes

|  | F<br>£ | VF<br>£ | EF<br>£ |
|---|---|---|---|
| **3603  Crown.** Third dr. bust. l. R. Roses and plumes | | | |
| 1713 DVODECIMO............................................................250 | | 750 | 5000 |

3604
1708 Halfcrown, Post-Union

**3604  Halfcrown.** Dr. bust R. Plain, regnal year on edge in words (e.g. 1709 = OCTAVO), die axis ↑↓

| | | | |
|---|---|---|---|
| 1707 SEPTIMO .................................................................100 | | 325 | 2000 |
| 1707 no stops on reverse ......................................................150 | | 550 | — |
| 1708 SEPTIMO .................................................................100 | | 325 | 2000 |
| 1709 OCTAVO ..................................................................100 | | 325 | 2000 |
| 1713 DVODECIMO.............................................................125 | | 375 | 2250 |

3605

**3605  Halfcrown.** Dr. bust E below R. Crowned cruciform shields die axis ↑↓

| | | | |
|---|---|---|---|
| 1707     SEXTO .................................................................100 | | 325 | 2000 |
| 1707     SEPTIMO...............................................................475 | | 2250 | — |
| 1708 SEPTIMO .................................................................125 | | 375 | 2250 |
| 1709 OCTAVO ..................................................................275 | | 1000 | — |

| 3606 | 3607 |
|------|------|
| 1708 Halfcrown, plumes on reverse | 1714 Halfcrown, roses and plumes |

| | F | VF | EF |
|---|---|---|---|
| | £ | £ | £ |
| **3606  Halfcrown.** Similar R. Plumes in angles, die axis ↑↓ | | | |
| 1708 SEPTIMO ..................................................................125 | 375 | 2250 |
| **3607  Halfcrown.** Similar R. Roses and plumes in angles die axis ↑↓ | | | |
| 1710 NONO........................................................................110 | 350 | 2100 |
| 1712 UNDECIMO............................................................100 | 300 | 1850 |
| 1/13 DVODECIMO............................................................100 | 300 | 1850 |
| 1714 D. TERTIO ...............................................................110 | 350 | 2100 |
| 1714/3 D. TERTIO ............................................................125 | 375 | 2250 |

| 3608 | 3609 |
|------|------|
| 1707 Edinburgh Mint Shilling, second bust | 1708 E* Shilling |

**3608  Shilling.** Second dr. bust, l. E *(Edinburgh)* below, R. Crowned cruciform shields
      die axis ↑↓

| | | | |
|---|---|---|---|
| 1707 ..............................................................................135 | 500 | 1850 |
| 1707 no stops on reverse ...................................................250 | 900 | — |
| 1707 Plain edge proof *FDC* £12500 | | | |
| 1708 ..............................................................................225 | 675 | 2400 |

**3609  Shilling.** Similar E* *(Edinburgh)* below bust die axis ↑↓

| | | | |
|---|---|---|---|
| 1707 ..............................................................................175 | 575 | 2250 |
| 1708 ..............................................................................175 | 575 | 2250 |
| 1708/7 ............................................................................350 | — | — |
| 1708 no rays to garter star ................................................525 | — | — |

**3609A Shilling.** Similar E* *(Edinburgh)* local dies die axis ↑↓

| | | | |
|---|---|---|---|
| 1707 ..............................................................................300 | 1000 | — |
| 1708 ..............................................................................375 | 1500 | — |

**Third bust**

**Fourth bust**

3610
Shilling, third bust

3611
Shilling, plumes on reverse

|  | F £ | VF £ | EF £ |
|---|---|---|---|
| **3610  Shilling** Third dr. bust. l. R. Crowned cruciform shields, angles Plain, die axis ↑↓ | | | |
| 1707 ................................................................40 | | 135 | 650 |
| 1708 ................................................................35 | | 120 | 575 |
| 1709 ................................................................35 | | 120 | 575 |
| 1711 ................................................................100 | | 325 | 1200 |
| **3611  Shilling.** Third dr. bust. l. R. Plumes in angles die axis ↑↓ | | | |
| 1707 ................................................................80 | | 250 | 900 |
| 1708 ................................................................80 | | 250 | 900 |
| **3612  Shilling.** Third dr. bust. E below R. angles plain die axis ↑↓ | | | |
| 1707 ................................................................100 | | 325 | 1100 |
| 1708 ................................................................110 | | 350 | 1200 |
| 1708/7 ................................................................120 | | 375 | 1250 |
| **3613  Shilling.** Second dr. bust l. R. Roses and plumes, die axis ↑↓ | | | |
| 1708 ................................................................135 | | 525 | 1750 |

3614
1708 Shilling, roses and plumes

| | F £ | VF £ | EF £ |
|---|---|---|---|
| **3614  Shilling.** Third dr. bust l. R. Crowned cruciform shields Roses and plumes die axis ↑↓ | | | |
| 1708 ................................................................100 | | 325 | 1100 |
| 1710 ................................................................90 | | 300 | 1000 |

| 3615 | 3620 | 3623 |
|---|---|---|
| Edinburgh bust – E* Shilling | Edinburgh Mint Sixpence | 1707 Sixpence, plumes on reverse |

| | F £ | VF £ | EF £ |
|---|---|---|---|

**3615 Shilling.** 'Edinburgh' bust, E* below, R. Crowned cruciform shields die axis ↑↓
| 1707 | 575 | — | — |
| 1708 | 225 | 750 | 2500 |
| 1709 | 225 | 750 | 2500 |

**3616 Shilling.** — E below, R. Similar die axis ↑↓
| 1709 | 275 | 1000 | — |

**3617 Shilling.** Fourth dr. bust. l. R. Roses and plumes die axis ↑↓
| 1710 | 80 | 225 | 900 |
| 1710 plain edge proof FDC | | | Extremely rare |
| 1712 | 75 | 200 | 825 |
| 1713/2 | 90 | 225 | 900 |
| 1714 | 75 | 200 | 825 |
| 1714/3 | 95 | 275 | 950 |

**3618 Shilling.** Similar, R. angles plain, die axis ↑↓
| 1711 | 40 | 175 | 650 |
| 1711 plain edge proof FDC | | | Extremely rare |

**3619 Sixpence.** Normal dr. bust. l. R. angles plain die axis ↑↓
| 1707 | 35 | 125 | 425 |
| 1707 BR. FRA error | 450 | — | — |
| 1708 | 40 | 135 | 475 |
| 1711 | 30 | 80 | 350 |
| 1711 Large Lis | 35 | 110 | 400 |

**3620 Sixpence.** Normal dr. bust E (Edinburgh) below R. Similar die axis ↑↓
| 1707 | 45 | 150 | 525 |
| 1707 Proof FDC £6500 | | | |
| 1708/7 | 75 | 225 | 750 |
| 1708 | 60 | 185 | 650 |

**3621 Sixpence.** Normal dr. bust E* (Edinburgh) below, R. Similar die axis ↑↓
| 1708 | 70 | 225 | 700 |
| 1708/7 | 75 | 240 | 750 |

**3622 Sixpence.** 'Edinburgh' bust, l. E* below, R. Similar die axis ↑↓
| 1708 | 70 | 225 | 725 |

**3623 Sixpence.** Normal dr. bust. l. R. Plumes in angles die axis ↑↓
| 1707 | 45 | 150 | 525 |
| 1708 | 50 | 165 | 575 |

**3624 Sixpence.** Similar R. Roses and plumes in angles, die axis ↑↓
| 1710 | 60 | 185 | 650 |

# ANNE

## COPPER

3625
1714 Pattern Farthing

**3625 Farthing.** Dr. bust l. R. Britannia
1714 pattern only, die axis ↑↓ ...............................................325      650      1350

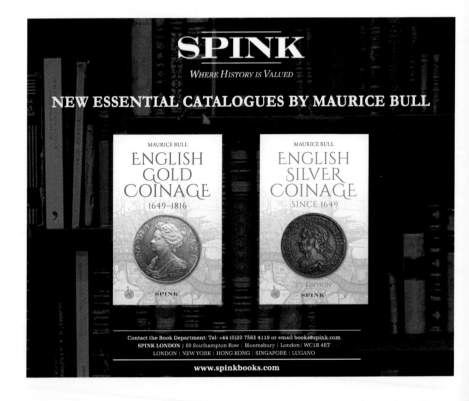

## GEORGE I, 1714-27

George I was born on 28th May 1660 son of Ernest, Elector of Hanover and Sophia, grandaughter of James I, and inherited the English Throne as Parliament considered him a better alternative than James Edward Stuart – Anne's half-brother. He was, however, thoroughly German, did not want to learn English and spent over half his reign in Germany. He brought two mistresses with him to England while his wife ironically languished in a German prison on a charge of adultery. His reign created a government that could run independently of the King. The office of Prime Minister was created in 1721. He also kept England out of war for his entire reign, and he died on 11th June 1727.

The coins of the first of the Hanoverian kings have the arms of the Duchy of Brunswick and Luneberg on one of the four shields, the object in the centre of the shield being the Crown of Charlemagne. The King's German titles also appear, in abbreviated form, and name him 'Duke of Brunswick and Luneberg. Arch-treasurer of the Holy Roman Empire, and Elector', and on the Guinea of 1714, 'Prince Elector'. A Quarter-Guinea was struck for the first time in 1718, but it was of an inconvenient size, and the issue was discontinued. The elephant and castle provenance mark continues on some guineas and half-guineas, but today are rarely seen.

Silver coined from bullion supplied to the mint by the South Sea Company in 1723 shows the Company's initials S.S.C.; similarly Welsh Copper Company bullion has the letters W.C.C. below the King's bust; and plumes and an interlinked CC in the reverse angles. Roses and plumes together on the reverse indicate silver supplied by the Company for Smelting Pit Coale and Sea Coale.

**Engravers and Designers:** Samuel Bull (d.c.1720), John Croker (1670-1741), John Rudulf Ochs Snr, (1673-c.1748), Norbert Roettier (b.1665)

**Prime Minister:** Sir Robert Walpole (1676 – 1745) –Whig, 1721-42

## GOLD

3626
1717 Five Guineas

|  | F £ | VF £ | EF £ |
|---|---|---|---|
| **3626 Five Guineas.** Laur. head r. regnal year on edge in words (e.g. 1717 = TERTIO) die axis ↑↓ | | | |
| 1716 SECVNDO ................................................................9000 | | 22500 | 110000 |
| 1717 TERTIO ...................................................................9500 | | 24000 | 120000 |
| 1717 Variety O for D on edge exits | | | |
| 1720 SEXTO .....................................................................9500 | | 24000 | 120000 |
| 1726 D. TERTIO ...............................................................9000 | | 22500 | 110000 |
| 1726 Variety И for N on edge exists | | | |

3627
Two Guineas

|  | F £ | VF £ | EF £ |
|---|---|---|---|
| **3627 Two Guineas.** Laur. head r. R. Crowned cruciform shields, sceptres in angles, edge milled, die axis ↑↓ | | | |
| 1717 | 2250 | 6250 | 24000 |
| 1720 | 2250 | 6250 | 24000 |
| 1720/17 | 2500 | 6500 | 25000 |
| 1726 | 2000 | 5750 | 22500 |

| 3628 | 3630 | 3631 |
|---|---|---|
| 1714 'Prince Elector' Guinea | Third bust | Fourth bust |

**3628 Guinea.** First laur. head r. R. Legend ends ET PR . EL (Prince Elector), die axis ↑↓

| 1714 | 2000 | 5250 | 17500 |
|---|---|---|---|

**3629 Guinea.** Second laur. head, r. tie with two ends, R. Crowned cruciform shields, sceptres in angles normal legend ↑↓

| 1715 | 950 | 2250 | 7000 |
|---|---|---|---|

**3630 Guinea.** Third laur. head, r. no hair below truncation R. Similar die axis ↑↓

| 1715 | 900 | 2200 | 6500 |
|---|---|---|---|
| 1716 | 950 | 2250 | 7000 |

|  | F £ | VF £ | EF £ |
|---|---|---|---|
| **3631 Guinea.** Fourth laur. head, r. tie with loop at one end R. Similar die axis ↑↓ | | | |
| 1716 ............................................................................. 900 | 900 | 2200 | 6500 |
| 1716 Arms of Hanover at date ................................................................... *Extremely rare* | | | |
| 1717 ............................................................................. 950 | 950 | 2250 | 6750 |
| 1718 ........................................................................................... *Extremely rare* | | | |
| 1718/7 ...................................................................................... *Extremely rare* | | | |
| 1719 ............................................................................. 900 | 900 | 2200 | 6500 |
| 1719/6 ......................................................................... 950 | 950 | 2250 | 6750 |
| 1720 large or small 20 in date ............................................ 900 | 900 | 2200 | 6500 |
| 1721 ............................................................................. 950 | 950 | 2250 | 6750 |
| 1722 ............................................................................. 900 | 900 | 2200 | 6500 |
| 1722/0 ......................................................................... 950 | 950 | 2250 | 6750 |
| 1723 ............................................................................. 950 | 950 | 2250 | 7000 |
| **3632 Guinea.** Fourth Laur. head, elephant and castle below R. Similar die axis ↑↓ | | | |
| 1721 ............................................................................... *Extremely rare* | | | |
| 1722 ............................................................................... *Extremely rare* | | | |

3633
Guinea, fifth bust

|  | F £ | VF £ | EF £ |
|---|---|---|---|
| **3633 Guinea.** Fifth (older) laur. head, r. tie with two ends R. Similar die axis ↑↓ | | | |
| 1723 ............................................................................. 900 | 900 | 2200 | 6500 |
| 1723 II for H in TH............................................................ 950 | 950 | 2250 | 6750 |
| 1724 ............................................................................. 900 | 900 | 2200 | 6500 |
| 1724 R/I in GEORGIVS..................................................... 950 | 950 | 2250 | 6750 |
| 1725 ............................................................................. 900 | 900 | 2200 | 6500 |
| 1725 large 5 in date ......................................................... 900 | 900 | 2200 | 6500 |
| 1726 ............................................................................. 800 | 800 | 2000 | 6000 |
| 1727 ............................................................................. 900 | 900 | 2750 | 8000 |
| **3634 Guinea.** Fifth laur. head, elephant and castle below, die axis ↑↓ | | | |
| 1726 ......................................................................... 2250 | 2250 | 7500 | 22500 |

**3635  Half-Guinea.** First laur. head r. R. Crowned cruciform shields, sceptres in angles die axis ↑↓

| | | | |
|---|---|---|---|
| 1715 | 750 | 1750 | 6500 |
| 1717 | 500 | 1150 | 4500 |
| 1718 | 475 | 1100 | 4250 |
| 1718/7 | 500 | 1150 | 4500 |
| 1719 | 475 | 1100 | 4250 |
| 1720 | 500 | 1150 | 4500 |
| 1721 | | | *Extremely rare* |
| 1722 | 500 | 1100 | 4250 |
| 1722/0 | 525 | 1150 | 4500 |
| 1723 | 525 | 1200 | 4750 |
| 1724 | 575 | 1350 | 5500 |

**3636  Half-Guinea.** First laur. head elephant and castle below, die axis ↑↓

| | |
|---|---|
| 1721 | *Extremely rare* |

3637
Half-Guinea, second bust

3638
Quarter Guinea

**3637  Half-Guinea.** Second (older) laur. head r. R. Crowned cruciform shields, sceptres in angles die axis ↑↓

| | | | |
|---|---|---|---|
| 1725 | 425 | 1000 | 4000 |
| 1726 | 475 | 1100 | 4250 |
| 1727 | 475 | 1100 | 4250 |

**3638  Quarter-Guinea.** Laur. head R. Similar die axis ↑↓

| | | | |
|---|---|---|---|
| 1718 | 250 | 450 | 1100 |

# SILVER

3639A
1726 Crown - small roses and plumes

|  | F £ | VF £ | EF £ |
|---|---|---|---|
| **3639** **Crown.** Laur and dr. bust r. R. Roses and plumes in angles, regnal year on edge in words (e.g. 1716 – SECVNDO) die axis ↑↓ | | | |
| 1716 SECVNDO | 600 | 1750 | 6750 |
| 1718/6 QUINTO | 750 | 2000 | 7500 |
| 1720/18 SEXTO | 650 | 1850 | 7000 |
| **3639A Crown.** Similar R. small roses and plumes in angles | | | |
| 1720 SEXTO | 800 | 2250 | 8500 |
| 1726 D. TERTIO | 600 | 1750 | 6750 |
| **3640** **Crown.** Similar R. SSC (South Sea Company) in angles, die axis ↑↓ | | | |
| 1723 DECIMO | 575 | 1650 | 6500 |

3641
1715 Pattern Halfcrown

**3641** **Halfcrown.** Laur and dr. bust r. R. Angles plain (pattern only), die axis ↑↓
1715 *FDC* £16500

3642
Halfcrown, roses and plumes

|  | F | VF | EF |
|---|---|---|---|
|  | £ | £ | £ |

**3642 Halfcrown.** — R. Roses and plumes in angles, regnal year on edge in words
(e.g. 1717 = TIRTIO)

| | F | VF | EF |
|---|---|---|---|
| 1715 SECVNDO | 350 | 950 | 4250 |
| 1715 Edge wording out of order | 450 | 1250 | 4750 |
| 1715 Plain edge | 575 | 1750 | — |
| 1717 TIRTIO | 350 | 950 | 4250 |
| 1720/17 SEXTO | 350 | 950 | 4250 |
| 1720 SEXTO | 425 | 1100 | 4500 |

3643
1723 SSC Halfcrown

**3643 Halfcrown.** Similar R. SSC in angles, die axis ↑↓

| | F | VF | EF |
|---|---|---|---|
| 1723 DECIMO | 325 | 850 | 4000 |

3644
1726 Halfcrown small roses and plumes

**3644 Halfcrown.** — R. Small roses and plumes, die axis ↑↓

| | F | VF | EF |
|---|---|---|---|
| 1726 D. TERTIO | 3750 | 12500 | 27500 |

|       | 3645 | 3646 |
|-------|------|------|
| Shilling, roses and plumes | | 1721 Shilling, plain reverse |

|       | *F* | *VF* | *EF* |
|-------|-----|------|------|
|       | £ | £ | £ |

**3645  Shilling.** First laur. and dr. bust. r. ℞. Roses and plumes in angles, die axis ↑↓

| 1715 | ..............85 | 275 | 1000 |
|------|------|------|------|
| 1716 | ............135 | 450 | 1500 |
| 1717 | ............125 | 375 | 1350 |
| 1718 | ..............80 | 250 | 950 |
| 1719 | ............135 | 450 | 1500 |
| 1720 | ............110 | 350 | 1350 |
| 1720/18 | ............150 | 500 | 1650 |
| 1721 | ............135 | 450 | 1500 |
| 1721/0 | ............110 | 350 | 1350 |
| 1721/19 | ............135 | 450 | 1500 |
| 1721/18  plumes and roses error | ............375 | 1500 | — |
| 1722 | ............110 | 350 | 1350 |
| 1723 | ............125 | 375 | 1350 |

**3646  Shilling.** First laur. and dr. bust r. ℞. angles plain (i.e. no marks either side) die axis ↑↓

| 1720 | ..............50 | 160 | 725 |
|------|------|------|------|
| 1720 large O | ..............60 | 175 | 750 |
| 1721 | ............200 | 675 | 2000 |
| 1721 O of GEORGIVS over zero | | | |

LETTERING ERRORS:

**3645** 1716 V of GEORGIVS over L

1720 Large O in date

1717 Large lettering on obverse

3647

1723 SSC Shilling, first bust

**3647  Shilling.** First laur. and dr. bust r. ℞. SSC in angles, die axis ↑↓

| 1723 | ..............30 | 85 | 350 |
|------|------|------|------|
| 1723 | French Arms at date | ............110 | 375 | 1100 |
| 1723 C/SS in 3rd quarter | ..............35 | 95 | 375 |

LETTERING VARIETIES:

B·RVN on Rev., Large N in BRVN and stop between E.T. after BRVN.

3649
1727 Shilling, second bust

3650
1726 WCC Shilling

|  | F | VF | EF |
|---|---|---|---|
|  | £ | £ | £ |

**3648  Shilling**. Second dr. bust, r. bow to tie. R. Similar, die axis ↑↓

| 1723 | 50 | 150 | 525 |
|---|---|---|---|

**3649  Shilling**. Similar R. Roses and plumes in angles die axis ↑↓

| 1723 | 110 | 350 | 1350 |
|---|---|---|---|
| 1724 | 120 | 375 | 1500 |
| 1725 | 110 | 350 | 1350 |
| 1725 no stops on obv | 120 | 375 | 1500 |
| 1725 no stops on rev | 135 | 450 | 1650 |
| 1726 no stops on obv | 750 | 2500 | — |
| 1727 | 575 | 1850 | — |
| 1727 no stops on obv | 500 | 1750 | 4500 |
| 1727 no stops on rev | 600 | 2000 | — |

**3650  Shilling**. Second laur. and dr. bust r. W.C.C. (Welsh Copper Company) below bust die axis ↑↓

| 1723 | 750 | 2500 | 8500 |
|---|---|---|---|
| 1724 | 750 | 2500 | 8500 |
| 1725 | 800 | 2750 | 9000 |
| 1726 | 800 | 2750 | 9000 |

**3651  Sixpence.** Laur. and dr. bust r. R. Roses and plumes in angles, die axis ↑↓

| 1717 | 110 | 350 | 1000 |
|---|---|---|---|
| 1717     Plain edge | | | *Extremely rare* |
| 1720/17 | 100 | 300 | 850 |

3652
1723 SSC Sixpence

3653
1726 Sixpence, small roses and plumes

**3652  Sixpence.** Laur. and dr. bust r. R. SSC in angles, die axis ↑↓

| 1723 | 25 | 95 | 400 |
|---|---|---|---|
| 1723 larger lettering | 30 | 110 | 425 |

**3653  Sixpence.** Similar R. Small roses and plumes, die axis ↑↓

| 1726 | 85 | 275 | 800 |
|---|---|---|---|

| | F £ | VF £ | EF £ |
|---|---|---|---|
| **3654 Fourpence.** Laur. and dr. bust r. R. Crowned 4, die axis ↑↓ | | | |
| 1717 ................................................15 | | 40 | 100 |
| 1721 ................................................15 | | 40 | 100 |
| 1723 ................................................20 | | 50 | 160 |
| 1727 ................................................22 | | 55 | 160 |
| **3655 Threepence.** Laur. and dr. bust r. R. Crowned 3, die axis ↑↓ | | | |
| 1717 ................................................20 | | 45 | 95 |
| 1721 ................................................25 | | 48 | 95 |
| 1723 ................................................20 | | 55 | 160 |
| 1727 small lettering ................................20 | | 50 | 150 |
| **3656 Twopence.** Laur. and dr. bust r. R. Crowned 2, die axis ↑↓ | | | |
| 1717 ................................................12 | | 32 | 65 |
| 1721 ................................................12 | | 25 | 60 |
| 1723 ................................................15 | | 40 | 110 |
| 1726 ................................................12 | | 25 | 60 |
| 1727 small lettering ................................15 | | 32 | 85 |
| **3657 Penny.** Laur. and dr. bust r. R. Crowned 1, die axis ↑↓ | | | |
| 1716 ................................................12 | | 32 | 65 |
| 1718 ................................................12 | | 32 | 65 |
| 1720 ................................................12 | | 32 | 65 |
| 1720 HIPEX error................................20 | | 85 | 150 |
| 1723 ................................................15 | | 30 | 80 |
| 1725 ................................................12 | | 32 | 65 |
| 1726 ................................................15 | | 40 | 70 |
| 1727 BRI·FR ................................20 | | 50 | 110 |

3658

| **3658 Maundy Set.** As last four. Uniform dates | | | |
|---|---|---|---|
| 1723 ................................................150 | | 275 | 800 |
| 1727 ................................................125 | | 250 | 700 |

# COPPER

3659

|  | F £ | VF £ | EF £ |
|---|---|---|---|
| **3659** **Halfpenny.** 'Dump' issue obv. legend continuous over bust, plain edge, die axis ↑↓ | | | |
| 1717 ...........................................................................................40 | | 250 | 800 |
| 1717 no stops on obv. ...........................................................100 | | 525 | — |
| 1718 ...........................................................................................30 | | 225 | 725 |
| 1718 R/B on rev.....................................................................50 | | 250 | 900 |
| 1718 no stops on obv. ...........................................................150 | | 500 | — |
| 1719 ......................................................................................1000 | | — | — |
| 1719 grained edge................................................................1000 | | — | — |

*(1719 is an extremely rare date, perhaps only 2 or 3 known to exist of each type)*

3660

| | F | VF | EF |
|---|---|---|---|
| **3660** **Halfpenny.** Second issue, second obverse, plain left shoulder strap, less hair to the right of tie knot, R. Britannia plain edge, die axis ↑↓ | | | |
| 1719 ...........................................................................................40 | | 210 | 900 |
| 1719 grained edge................................................................1000 | | — | — |
| 1720 ...........................................................................................30 | | 175 | 825 |
| 1721 ...........................................................................................30 | | 165 | 725e |
| 1721 stop after date ..............................................................40 | | 200 | 800 |
| 1721/0 ......................................................................................40 | | 200 | 8000 |
| 1722 ...........................................................................................30 | | 155 | 700 |
| 1722 Ɐ for V on obv. ...........................................................100 | | 500 | — |
| 1723 ...........................................................................................30 | | 155 | 750 |
| 1723 Thin Flan.............................................................................................*Extremely rar* | | | |
| 1723 no stop on rev...............................................................100 | | 525 | — |
| 1724 ...........................................................................................30 | | 155 | 70 |
| **3660A Halfpenny.** Second issue, second obverse, ornate shoulder straps, die axis ↑↓ | | | |
| 1719 . ........................................................................................40 | | 195 | 900 |

3661

|  | F<br>£ | VF<br>£ | EF<br>£ |
|---|---|---|---|
| **3661** Farthing. 'Dump' issue, Similar die axis ↑↓ | | | |
| 1717 ...................................................................200 | | 675 | 1250 |
| 1718 ...................................................................................... Unique | | | |

3662

| **3662** Farthing. Second issue laur. and cuir. bust r. R. Britannia, date in ex. die axis ↑↓ | | | |
|---|---|---|---|
| 1719 small letters.............................................60 | | 330 | 775 |
| 1719 no stop on rev...........................................70 | | 380 | — |
| 1719 large lettering on obv. ...............................30 | | 165 | 650 |
| 1719 — no stops on obv. ...................................70 | | 410 | — |
| 1719 — no stops on rev ....................................90 | | 450 | — |
| 1719 last A/I on rev..........................................80 | | 350 | — |
| 1720 .................................................................30 | | 165 | 600 |
| 1720 milled edge .............................................150 | | 500 | 1150 |
| 1720 obv. large letters.......................................80 | | 350 | — |
| 1721 .................................................................25 | | 135 | 650 |
| 1721/0 ..............................................................40 | | 165 | 675 |
| 1721 stop after date ..........................................35 | | 165 | 625 |
| 1722 .................................................................30 | | 155 | 625 |
| 1722 obv. large letters.......................................40 | | 210 | 725 |
| 1723 R/≈ in REX...............................................100 | | 330 | 900 |
| 1723 .................................................................30 | | 165 | 600 |
| 1724 .................................................................30 | | 165 | 625 |

George II was born on 30th October 1683 and was raised in Hanover, but upon his succession to the throne as George I's only son, he adapted himself to English society. His passions were the military, music and his wife – Caroline of Anspach, though he despised his eldest son Frederick as his own father despised him. George declared war on Spain in 1739 and he was the last King to have personally led his troops at the battle of Dettingen on 17th June 1743. Upon his death on 25th October 1760 the throne passed to his grandson George as Frederick had already died.

Silver was coined only spasmodically by the Mint during this reign; and no copper was struck after 1754. Gold coins made from bullion supplied by the East India Company bear the Company's E.I.C. initials. Some of the treasure seized by Admiral Anson during his circumnavigation of the globe, 1740-4, and by other privateers, was made into coin, which had the word LIMA below the king's bust to celebrate the expedition's successful harassment of the Spanish Colonies in the New World. Hammered gold was finally demonetized in 1733.

**Engravers and designers:** John Croker (1670-1741), John Rudolf Ochs Snr (1673-1748) and jnr (1704-88), Johann Sigismund Tanner (c.1706-75)

**Prime Ministers:** Sir Robert Walpole (1676-1745) Whig, 1721-43; Spencer Compton (1673-1743) Whig 1742-3; Henry Pelham (c.1695-1754) Whig 1743-54; William Cavendish (1720-1764) Whig 1756-7; Thomas Pelham-Holles (1693-1768) Whig 1754-6; 1757-62

## GOLD

3663A
1741 Five Guineas - revised shield

|  | F | VF | EF |
|---|---|---|---|
|  | £ | £ | £ |
| **3663 Five Guineas.** Young laur. head l. R. Crowned shield of arms, die axis ↑↓ regnal year on edge in words (e.g. 1729 = TERTIO) | | | |
| 1729 TERTIO ................8250 | 18500 | | 95000 |
| 1729 Plain edge proof *FDC* £225000 | | | |
| **3663A Five Guineas.** Similar R. Revised shield garnish die axis ↑↓ | | | |
| 1731 QVARTO ................9500 | 21500 | | 110000 |
| 1731 QVARTO proof *FDC* £225000 | | | |
| 1735 NONO................9500 | 21500 | | 110000 |
| 1738 DVODECIMO................8500 | 19000 | | 100000 |
| 1741/38 D. QVARTO ................8250 | 18500 | | 95000 |
| 1741 D. QVARTO ................8000 | 18000 | | 90000 |
| **3664 Five Guineas.** Young laur. head, E.I.C. (East India Company) below, die axis ↑↓ | | | |
| 1729 TERTIO ................7500 | 17500 | | 85000 |

3665
1746 LIMA Five Guineas

| | F | VF | EF |
|---|---|---|---|
| | £ | £ | £ |
| **3665** **Five Guineas.** Old laur. head, l. LIMA below, ↑↓ | | | |
| 1746 D. NONO | 8000 | 18000 | 90000 |
| **3666** **Five Guineas.** Old laur. head plain below, R. Crowned shield, edge inscribed die axis ↑↓ | | | |
| 1748 V. SECVNDO | 8000 | 18000 | 90000 |
| 1753 V. SEXTO | 8000 | 18000 | 90000 |
| **3667** **Two Guineas.** Young laur. head l. R Crowned shield with rounded arches, die axis ↑↓ | | | |
| 1733 Proof *FDC* £67500 | | | |
| 1734/3 | 3000 | 8500 | 30000 |

3667A
1735 Two Guineas - new reverse

| | | | |
|---|---|---|---|
| **3667A Two Guineas.** – R. Crown with pointed arches, new type of shield garnishing die axis ↑↓ | | | |
| 1735 | 1850 | 5250 | 17500 |
| **3667B Two Guineas.** Repositioned legend on obverse R. Similar | | | |
| 1738* | 950 | 2500 | 7500 |
| 1739 | 1000 | 2750 | 8000 |

*\*Beware recent forgeries.*

3668
1740 Two Guineas - Intermediate head

|  | F | VF | EF |
|---|---|---|---|
|  | £ | £ | £ |

**3668  Two Guineas.** Intermediate laur. head l. R. Crowned shield of arms die axis ↑↓

| 1739* | ...............950 | 2500 | 7500 |
|---|---|---|---|
| 1740/39 | ...........1000 | 2750 | 8000 |
| 1740 | ...........1000 | 2750 | 8000 |

**3669     Two Guineas.** Old laur. head l. R. Crowned shield of arms die axis ↑↓

| 1748 | ...........1250 | 3750 | 12500 |
|---|---|---|---|
| 1753 | ...........1350 | 4500 | 15000 |

**3670  Guinea.** First young laur. head, l. small lettering, die axis ↑↓

| 1727 | ...........1500 | 5000 | 16500 |
|---|---|---|---|

3671
1727 Guinea - small reverse shield

**3671  Guinea**. Similar larger lettering, smaller shield, die axis ↑↓

| 1727 | ...........1750 | 5500 | 17500 |
|---|---|---|---|
| 1728 | ...........1750 | 5500 | 17500 |

**3672  Guinea.** Second (narrower) young laur. head l. die axis ↑↓
1729 Proof *FDC* £27500

| 1730 | ...............950 | 3000 | 10000 |
|---|---|---|---|
| 1731 | ...............850 | 2500 | 9000 |
| 1732 | ...............900 | 2750 | 9500 |

**3673  Guinea.** Second young laur. head, E.I.C. below R. Crowned shield of arms die axis ↑↓

| 1729 | ...........1650 | 5500 | 17500 |
|---|---|---|---|
| 1731 | ...........1500 | 5250 | 16000 |
| 1732 | ...........1350 | 4750 | 15000 |

*\*Beware recent forgeries.*

|  | F | VF | EF |
|---|---|---|---|
|  | £ | £ | £ |

**3674 Guinea.** Second young laur. head l. larger lettering R. Crowned shield of arms die axis ↑↓

| 1732 | 750 | 2250 | 7500 |
|---|---|---|---|
| 1733 | 650 | 1750 | 6500 |
| 1734 | 650 | 1750 | 6500 |
| 1735 | 650 | 1750 | 6500 |
| 1736 | 650 | 1750 | 6500 |
| 1737 | 675 | 1850 | 6750 |
| 1738 | 675 | 1850 | 6750 |

**3675 Guinea.** — — E.I.C. below, die axis ↑↓

| 1732 | 1500 | 5250 | 16000 |
|---|---|---|---|

3676

*Note: All 1739-45 Guineas read GEORGIUS*

**3676 Guinea.** Intermediate laur. head l. r. Crowned shield of arms die axis ↑↓

| 1739 | 800 | 2000 | 8500 |
|---|---|---|---|
| 1740 | 850 | 2250 | 9000 |
| 1741/39 | 950 | 2750 | 10000 |
| 1743 | 950 | 2750 | 10000 |

**3677 Guinea.** Similar E.I.C. below, R. Similar die axis ↑↓

| 1739 | 1500 | 5250 | 16000 |
|---|---|---|---|

**3678 Guinea.** Similar larger lettering on *obv.*, GEORGIUS die axis ↑↓

| 1745 (also exists with small S in date) | 650 | 1600 | 6750 |
|---|---|---|---|

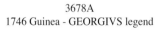

3678A
1746 Guinea - GEORGIVS legend

3679
LIMA below bust Guinea

**3678A Guinea.** Similar as last but reads GEORGIVS die axis ↑↓

| 1746 | 700 | 1750 | 7250 |
|---|---|---|---|

**3679 Guinea.** Intermediate laur. head LIMA below, GEORGIUS die .axis ↑↓

| 1745 | 2500 | 7500 | 25000 |
|---|---|---|---|

3680
Old head Guinea

| | F | VF | EF |
|---|---|---|---|
| | £ | £ | £ |

**3680 Guinea**. Old laur. head l. R. Crowned shield of arms die axis ↑↓

| | | F | VF | EF |
|---|---|---|---|---|
| 1747 | ......600 | 1500 | 6250 |
| 1748 | ......600 | 1500 | 6250 |
| 1749 | ......600 | 1500 | 6250 |
| 1750 | ......600 | 1500 | 6250 |
| 1751 | ......575 | 1500 | 6250 |
| 1752 | ......575 | 1500 | 6250 |
| 1753 | ......600 | 1600 | 6500 |
| 1755 | ......600 | 1600 | 6500 |
| 1756 | ......600 | 1500 | 6250 |
| 1758 | ......550 | 1350 | 5750 |
| 1759 | ......525 | 1300 | 5500 |
| 1760 | ......550 | 1350 | 5750 |

**3681 Half-Guinea**. Young laur. head. l. R First shield of arms, die axis ↑↓

| | F | VF | EF |
|---|---|---|---|
| 1728 | ......750 | 1750 | 7500 |
| 1728 Proof *FDC* £15000 | | | |
| 1729 | ......700 | 1600 | 7000 |

3681A
1731 Half-Guinea - modified shield

**3681A Half-Guinea**. Young laur. head l. R. Modified garnished shield die axis ↑↓

| | F | VF | EF |
|---|---|---|---|
| 1730 | ......650 | 1500 | 6500 |
| 1731 | ......475 | 1000 | 4750 |
| 1732 | ......525 | 1100 | 5000 |
| 1734 | ......475 | 1000 | 4750 |
| 1736 | ......525 | 1100 | 5000 |
| 1737 | ......625 | 1350 | 6000 |
| 1738 | ......475 | 1000 | 4750 |
| 1739 | ......475 | 1000 | 4750 |

**3682 Half-Guinea**. Young laur. head l. E.I.C. below R. Similar die axis ↑↓

| | F | VF | EF |
|---|---|---|---|
| 1729 | ......750 | 1750 | 7000 |
| 1730 | ......950 | 2250 | 8500 |
| 1731 | ...............*Extremely rare* | | |
| 1732 | ...............*Extremely rare* | | |
| 1739 | ...............*Extremely rare* | | |

3683A
Half-guinea - GEORGIVS legend

|  | F | VF | EF |
|---|---|---|---|
|  | £ | £ | £ |
| **3683 Half-Guinea**. Intermediate laur. head l. R. Similar die axis ↑↓ | | | |
| 1740 | ...............475 | 1000 | 4750 |
| 1743 | ................................................................................*Extremely rare* | | |
| 1745 | ...............575 | 1250 | 5750 |
| **3683A Half-Guinea**. Similar, but reads GEORGIVS, die axis ↑↓ | | | |
| 1746 | ...............400 | 850 | 3750 |

3684
LIMA Half-Guinea

3685
Half-Guinea, old head

| | F | VF | EF |
|---|---|---|---|
| **3684 Half-Guinea**. Intermediate laur. head LIMA below, die axis ↑↓ | | | |
| 1745 | ...............1250 | 4000 | 12500 |
| **3685 Half-Guinea**. Old laur. head l. R. Similar die axis ↑↓ | | | |
| 1747 | ...............575 | 1250 | 5500 |
| 1748 | ...............450 | 950 | 4250 |
| 1749 | ...............650 | 1500 | 6500 |
| 1750 | ...............575 | 1250 | 5500 |
| 1751 | ...............450 | 950 | 4250 |
| 1751/0 | ...............475 | 1000 | 4500 |
| 1752 | ...............375 | 800 | 3250 |
| 1753 | ...............375 | 800 | 3250 |
| 1755 | ...............375 | 800 | 3250 |
| 1756 | ...............350 | 725 | 3000 |
| 1758 | ...............400 | 850 | 3750 |
| 1759 | ...............325 | 700 | 2750 |
| 1759/8 | ...............350 | 725 | 3000 |
| 1760 | ...............350 | 725 | 3000 |

# SILVER

3686
Crown, young head

| | F | VF | EF |
|---|---|---|---|
| | £ | £ | £ |

**3686 Crown.** Young laur. and dr. bust. l. R. Crowned cruciform shields Roses and plumes in angles, regnal year on edge in words (e.g. 1736 = NONO), die axis ↑↓

| | | F | VF | EF |
|---|---|---|---|---|
| 1732 | SEXTO | 375 | 1100 | 5000 |
| 1732 Proof, plain edge *FDC* £25000 | | | | |
| 1734 | SEPTIMO | 375 | 1100 | 5000 |
| 1735 | OCTAVO | 350 | 1000 | 4500 |
| 1736 | NONO | 350 | 1000 | 4500 |

3687

**3687 Crown.** Similar R. Roses in angles die axis ↑↓

| | | F | VF | EF |
|---|---|---|---|---|
| 1739 | DVODECIMO | 350 | 950 | 4000 |
| 1741 | D. QVARTO | 350 | 950 | 4000 |

3688
Crown, old head

|  | F £ | VF £ | EF £ |
|---|---|---|---|
| **3688 Crown.** Old laur. and dr. bust l. R. Crowned cruciform shields Roses in angles, die axis ↑↓ | | | |
| 1743 D. SEPTIMO | 325 | 850 | 3500 |
| **3689 Crown.** — LIMA below, die axis ↑↓ | | | |
| 1746 D. NONO | 325 | 900 | 3750 |

3690
Plain reverse

3691
1731 Pattern Halfcrown

**3690 Crown.** Old laur. and dr. bust l. R. angles Plain (i.e. no marks either side) die axis ↑↓
1746 Proof only, VICESIMO *FDC* £14000

| 1750 V. QVARTO | 350 | 1000 | 4500 |
|---|---|---|---|
| 1751 V. QVARTO | 375 | 1100 | 5000 |

**3691 Halfcrown.** Young dr. bust l. R. angles plain (pattern only)

1731 *FDC* £11000

3692
1736 Halfcrown, roses and plumes

3693
1741 Halfcrown, roses on reverse

|  | F | VF | EF |
|---|---|---|---|
|  | £ | £ | £ |

**3692  Halfcrown.** Young laur. and dr. bust l. R. Roses and plumes, regnal year on edge in words
(e.g. 1732 = SEXTO), die axis ↑↓

| 1731 QVINTO | 150 | 450 | 2500 |
|---|---|---|---|
| 1732 SEXTO | 150 | 450 | 2500 |
| 1734 SEPTIMO | 175 | 500 | 2850 |
| 1735 OCTAVO | 165 | 475 | 2750 |
| 1736 NONO | 165 | 475 | 2750 |

**3693   Halfcrown.** Young laur. and dr. bust l. R. Roses in angles die axis ↑↓

| 1739 DVODECIMO | 135 | 400 | 2250 |
|---|---|---|---|
| 1741 D. QVARTO | 140 | 425 | 2400 |
| 1741 Large *obv.* letters | 150 | 450 | 2500 |
| 1741/39 D. QVARTO | 150 | 450 | 2500 |

**3694   Halfcrown.** Old dr. bust. l. GEORGIUS R. Roses in angles die axis ↑↓

| 1743 D. SEPTIMO | 135 | 400 | 2250 |
|---|---|---|---|
| 1745 D. NONO | 125 | 350 | 2100 |
| 1745/3 D. NONO | 135 | 400 | 2250 |

**3695   Halfcrown.** Old laur. and dr. bust LIMA below die axis ↑↓

| 1745 D. NONO | 70 | 180 | 850 |
|---|---|---|---|
| 1745/3 | 90 | 225 | 1100 |

**3695A Halfcrown.** Old laur. and dr. bust as last LIMA below but reads GEORGIVS die axis ↑↓

| 1746 D. NONO | 65 | 175 | 750 |
|---|---|---|---|
| 1746/5 D. NONO | 80 | 200 | 900 |

3696
1751 Halfcrown

**3696   Halfcrown.** Old laur. and dr. bust l. R. Plain angles die axis ↑↓
1746 proof only  VICESIMO *FDC* £5250

| 1750 V. QVARTO | 200 | 525 | 3000 |
|---|---|---|---|
| 1751 V. QVARTO | 225 | 575 | 3250 |

3697
1727 Plumes reverse

3698
Shilling, young bust,
small letters

3699
Plain reverse

|  | F £ | VF £ | EF £ |
|---|---|---|---|
| **3697  Shilling.** Young laur. dr. bust. l. R. Plumes in angles, die axis ↑↓ | | | |
| 1727 | 150 | 550 | 2500 |
| 1731 | 175 | 650 | 2750 |
| **3698  Shilling.** Young laur. and dr. bust l. R. Roses and plumes in angles, die axis ↑↓ | | | |
| 1727 | 110 | 325 | 1650 |
| 1728 | 135 | 450 | 1850 |
| 1729 | 135 | 450 | 1850 |
| 1731 | 110 | 325 | 1650 |
| 1732 | 120 | 375 | 1750 |
| **3699  Shilling.** Young laur. and dr. bust l. R. Plain, die axis ↑↓ | | | |
| 1728 | 110 | 300 | 1500 |

3700 - Shilling, larger lettering

3701 - Shilling, roses reverse

| | | | |
|---|---|---|---|
| **3700  Shilling.** Similar larger lettering. R. Roses and plumes in angles die axis ↑↓ | | | |
| 1734 | 65 | 250 | 950 |
| 1735 | 70 | 275 | 1000 |
| 1736 | 65 | 250 | 950 |
| 1736/5 | 70 | 275 | 1000 |
| 1737 | 65 | 250 | 950 |
| 1737 known with GR ΛTIΛ error | | | |
| 1737 with 3/5 exists | | | |
| **3701  Shilling.** Young laur. and dr. bust l. R. Roses in angles die axis ↑↓ | | | |
| 1739  normal garter star | 50 | 200 | 750 |
| 1739/7 | 100 | 300 | 1250 |
| 1739 smaller garter star | 65 | 250 | 900 |
| 1741 | 50 | 200 | 750 |
| 1741/39 | 100 | 300 | 1250 |

3702
Shilling, old bust, roses

3703
LIMA Shilling

|  | F | VF | EF |
|---|---|---|---|
|  | £ | £ | £ |

**3702 Shilling.** Old laur. and dr. bust, l. R. Roses in angles die axis ↑↓

| 1743 | 35 | 130 | 575 |
|---|---|---|---|
| 1743/1 | 50 | 150 | 700 |
| 1745 | 60 | 165 | 725 |
| 1745/3 | 65 | 175 | 750 |
| 1747 only known with GEORGIVS on obv | 40 | 135 | 650 |

**3703 Shilling.** Old laur. and dr. bust LIMA below die axis ↑↓

| 1745 | 35 | 130 | 575 |
|---|---|---|---|
| 1746 | 90 | 275 | 1050 |
| 1746/5 | 90 | 275 | 1050 |

*N.B. In and after 1746 the 'U' was changed to 'V' on old Head Shillings.*

3704
1758 Shilling

**3704 Shilling.** Old laur. and dr. bust R. plain angles die axis ↑↓

1746 Proof only *FDC* £2750

| 1750 | 45 | 150 | 750 |
|---|---|---|---|
| 1750/46 | 50 | 160 | 775 |
| 1750 Wide O | 50 | 160 | 775 |
| 1751 | 110 | 350 | 1350 |
| 1758 also known with small 58 in date | 20 | 50 | 240 |

3705
1728 Sixpence, young bust

3706
1728 Sixpence, plumes on reverse

|  | F £ | VF £ | EF £ |
|---|---|---|---|
| **3705 Sixpence.** Young laur. and dr. bust. l. ℞. Angles plain, die axis ↑↓ | | | |
| 1728 | 50 | 150 | 575 |
| 1728 Proof *FDC* £3500 | | | |
| **3706 Sixpence.** Similar ℞. Plumes in angles  die axis ↑↓ | | | |
| 1728 | 45 | 140 | 550 |

3707
1728 Sixpence, roses and plumes

| **3707 Sixpence.** Young laur. and dr. bust l. ℞. Roses and plumes in angles die axis ↑↓ | | | |
|---|---|---|---|
| 1728 | 35 | 125 | 425 |
| 1731 | 35 | 130 | 475 |
| 1732 | 35 | 130 | 475 |
| 1734 | 40 | 135 | 500 |
| 1735 | 40 | 135 | 500 |
| 1735/4 | 45 | 150 | 525 |
| 1736 | 50 | 175 | 550 |

3708
Sixpence, roses

3709
Sixpence, old bust, roses

| **3708 Sixpence.** Young laur. and dr. bust l., ℞. Roses in angles, die axis ↑↓ | | | |
|---|---|---|---|
| 1739 | 35 | 125 | 450 |
| 1739 O/R in legend | 40 | 135 | 500 |
| 1741 | 35 | 125 | 450 |
| **3709 Sixpence.** Old laur. and dr. bust. l. ℞. Roses in angles die axis ↑↓ | | | |
| 1743 | 25 | 75 | 325 |
| 1745 | 25 | 75 | 325 |
| 1745/3 | 30 | 80 | 350 |

|                                                                                 | F<br>£ | VF<br>£ | EF<br>£ |
|---------------------------------------------------------------------------------|--------|---------|---------|

**3710  Sixpence.** Old laur. and dr. bust LIMA below bust R. angle plain die axis ↑↓

| 1745 | ............................................................... 25 | 80 | 350 |

**3710A Sixpence.** Similar as last but reads GEORGIVS die axis ↑↓

| 1746 | ............................................................... 20 | 75 | 325 |
| 1746/5 | ............................................................... 30 | 100 | 375 |

3711
Proof Sixpence

**3711  Sixpence.** Old laur. and dr. bust l. R. angles plain die axis ↑↓

1746 *proof only FDC* £1500

| 1750 | ............................................................... 30 | 75 | 350 |
| 1751 | ............................................................... 35 | 90 | 400 |
| 1757 | ............................................................... 10 | 30 | 135 |
| 1758 | ............................................................... 10 | 30 | 135 |
| 1758 ÐEI error | ............................................................... 20 | 40 | 175 |
| 1758/7 | ............................................................... 15 | 35 | 160 |

**3712  Fourpence.** Young laur. and dr. bust l. R. Small dome-shaped crown without pearls on arch, figure 4

| 1729 | ............................................................... 22 | 48 | 120 |
| 1731 | ............................................................... 20 | 45 | 110 |

**3712A Fourpence.** Similar R. Double arched crown with pearls, large figure 4, die axis ↑↓

| 1732 | ............................................................... 22 | 48 | 120 |
| 1735 | ............................................................... 22 | 48 | 125 |
| 1737 | ............................................................... 22 | 48 | 125 |
| 1739 | ............................................................... 20 | 45 | 110 |
| 1740 | ............................................................... 18 | 35 | 100 |
| 1743 | ............................................................... 35 | 80 | 250 |
| 1743/0 | ............................................................... 35 | 80 | 250 |
| 1746 | ............................................................... 15 | 30 | 85 |
| 1760 | ............................................................... 22 | 45 | 130 |

**3713  Threepence.** Young laur. and dr. bust l. R. Crowned 3, pearls on arch, die axis ↑↓

| 1729 | ............................................................... 18 | 38 | 90 |

**3713A Threepence.** Similar R. Ornate arch die axis ↑↓

| 1731 Smaller lettering | ............................................................... 18 | 38 | 90 |
| 1731 | ............................................................... 18 | 38 | 90 |

**3713B Threepence.** Similar R. Double arched crown with pearls, die axis ↑↓

| 1732 | ............................................................... 18 | 38 | 85 |
| 1732 with stop over head | ............................................................... 18 | 38 | 85 |
| 1735 | ............................................................... 18 | 38 | 90 |
| 1737 | ............................................................... 15 | 35 | 80 |
| 1739 | ............................................................... 15 | 30 | 80 |
| 1740 | ............................................................... 15 | 30 | 80 |
| 1743 Large lettering | ............................................................... 15 | 30 | 80 |
| 1743 Small lettering | ............................................................... 15 | 30 | 80 |

|  | F<br>£ | VF<br>£ | EF<br>£ |
|---|---|---|---|
| 1743 — stop over head | 18 | 35 | 85 |
| 1746 | 12 | 25 | 75 |
| 1746/3 | 14 | 30 | 75 |
| 1760 | 18 | 38 | 85 |

**3714 Twopence.** Young laur. and dr. bust l. R. Small crown and figure 2, die axis ↑↓

| 1729 | 15 | 25 | 70 |
|---|---|---|---|
| 1731 | 15 | 25 | 65 |

**3714A Twopence.** Young laur. and dr. bust l. R. Large crown and figure 2 die axis ↑↓

| 1732 | 15 | 25 | 70 |
|---|---|---|---|
| 1735 | 15 | 25 | 65 |
| 1737 | 15 | 25 | 70 |
| 1739 | 15 | 25 | 70 |
| 1740 | 22 | 35 | 90 |
| 1743 | 15 | 28 | 70 |
| 1743/0 | 15 | 28 | 70 |
| 1746 | 12 | 22 | 60 |
| 1756 | 12 | 25 | 50 |
| 1759 | 12 | 25 | 45 |
| 1760 | 18 | 30 | 75 |

**3715 Penny.** Young laur. and dr. bust l. head. R. Date over small crown and figure 1, die axis ↑↓

| 1729 | 12 | 25 | 70 |
|---|---|---|---|
| 1731 | 12 | 25 | 70 |

**3715A Penny.** Young laur. and dr. bust l. R. Large crown dividing date die axis ↑↓

| 1732 | 12 | 25 | 65 |
|---|---|---|---|
| 1735 | 15 | 30 | 60 |
| 1737 | 15 | 30 | 65 |
| 1739 | 12 | 25 | 60 |
| 1740 | 12 | 25 | 60 |
| 1743 | 10 | 22 | 60 |
| 1746 | 10 | 20 | 60 |
| 1746/3 | 12 | 32 | 65 |
| 1750 | 10 | 20 | 40 |
| 1752 | 10 | 20 | 40 |
| 1752/0 | 10 | 30 | 60 |
| 1753/2 | 10 | 25 | 45 |
| 1753 | 10 | 20 | 40 |
| 1754 | 10 | 25 | 45 |
| 1755 | 10 | 20 | 45 |
| 1756 | 10 | 20 | 45 |
| 1757 | 10 | 20 | 50 |
| 1757 GRATIA: | 12 | 35 | 70 |
| 1758 | 10 | 20 | 45 |
| 1759 | 10 | 20 | 50 |
| 1760 | 18 | 30 | 75 |

3716

| | F £ | VF £ | EF £ |
|---|---|---|---|
| **3716 Maundy Set.** The four denominations. Uniform dates | | | |
| 1729 | 80 | 225 | 500 |
| 1731 | 80 | 225 | 500 |
| 1732 | 80 | 200 | 450 |
| 1735 | 80 | 200 | 450 |
| 1737 | 80 | 200 | 450 |
| 1739 | 75 | 165 | 425 |
| 1740 | 75 | 165 | 425 |
| 1743 | 100 | 250 | 550 |
| 1746 | 70 | 150 | 400 |
| 1760 | 85 | 225 | 500 |

## COPPER

3717

**3717 Halfpenny.** Young laur. and cuir. bust l. R. Britannia, date in ex. die axis ↑↓

| | F | VF | EF |
|---|---|---|---|
| 1729 | 15 | 100 | 380 |
| 1729 rev. no stop | 20 | 110 | 410 |
| 1730 | 10 | 100 | 360 |
| 1730 GEOGIVS error | 20 | 150 | 470 |
| 1730 stop after date | 20 | 110 | 380 |
| 1730 no stop after REX on obv. | 25 | 160 | 470 |
| 1731 | 10 | 90 | 360 |
| 1731 rev. no stop | 20 | 150 | 440 |
| 1732 | 10 | 100 | 360 |
| 1732 rev. no stop | 20 | 150 | 440 |
| 1733 | 10 | 90 | 370 |
| 1734 | 10 | 90 | 370 |
| 1734 R/O on obv | 20 | 145 | 450 |
| 1734/3 | 30 | 210 | — |
| 1734 no stops on obv. | 30 | 210 | — |
| 1735 | 10 | 90 | 370 |
| 1736 | 15 | 110 | 400 |

|  | F £ | VF £ | EF £ |
|---|---|---|---|
| 1736/0 | 20 | 130 | 450 |
| 1737 | 15 | 100 | 400 |
| 1738 | 10 | 75 | 370 |
| 1738 V/S on obv. | 20 | 145 | 450 |
| 1739 | 10 | 75 | 370 |

**3718  Halfpenny.** Old laur. and cuir. bust l., GEORGIUS R. Britannia, date in ex. die axis ↑↓

| 1740 | 10 | 70 | 300 |
|---|---|---|---|
| 1742 | 10 | 70 | 300 |
| 1742/0 | 20 | 130 | 425 |
| 1743 | 10 | 70 | 300 |
| 1744 | 10 | 70 | 300 |
| 1745 | 10 | 70 | 300 |

3719
1746 Halfpenny

**3719  Halfpenny.** Old laur. and cuir. bust l. GEORGIVS, R. Britannia, date in ex. die axis ↑↓

| 1746 | 10 | 65 | 300 |
|---|---|---|---|
| 1747 | 10 | 70 | 320 |
| 1748 | 10 | 70 | 320 |
| 1749 | 10 | 70 | 300 |
| 1750 | 10 | 70 | 320 |
| 1751 | 10 | 65 | 300 |
| 1752 | 10 | 65 | 300 |
| 1753 | 10 | 65 | 300 |
| 1754 | 10 | 70 | 320 |

3720

**3720 Farthing.** Young laur. and cuir. bust l. R. Britannia, date in ex. die axis ↑↓

| | | | |
|---|---|---|---|
| 1730 | 10 | 70 | 330 |
| 1731 | 10 | 70 | 330 |
| 1732 | 15 | 75 | 365 |
| 1732/1 | 20 | 110 | 385 |
| 1733 | 10 | 70 | 330 |
| 1734 | 15 | 75 | 365 |
| 1734 no stop on obv. | 30 | 120 | 385 |
| 1735 | 10 | 65 | 300 |
| 1735 3 over 5 | 20 | 130 | 425 |
| 1736 | 10 | 70 | 330 |
| 1736 triple tie ribands | 30 | 130 | 425 |
| 1737 small date | 10 | 65 | 300 |
| 1737 large date | 15 | 80 | 375 |
| 1739 | 10 | 65 | 300 |
| 1739/5 | 25 | 100 | 300 |

**3721 Farthing.** Old laur. and cuir. bust. GEORGIUS R. Britannia, date in ex. die axis ↑↓

| | | | |
|---|---|---|---|
| 1741 | 15 | 80 | 300 |
| 1744 | 10 | 65 | 275 |

**3722 Farthing.** Similar R. Britannia, date in ex. die axis ↑↓

| | | | |
|---|---|---|---|
| 1746 | 8 | 65 | 240 |
| 1746 V over U | 90 | 250 | — |
| 1749 | 15 | 75 | 275 |
| 1750 | 15 | 75 | 275 |
| 1754 | 5 | 45 | 135 |
| 1754/0 | 25 | 130 | 300 |

George III, grandson of George II, was born on 4th June 1738. He married Charlotte of Mecklenburg and they had nine sons and six daughters. The French Revolution and the American War of Independence both happened in his long reign, the longest yet of any King. The naval battle of Trafalgar and the Battle of Waterloo also took place during his reign. Later in his reign, he was affected by what seems to be the mental disease porphyria, and the future George IV was appointed as regent. George III died at Windsor Castle on 29th January 1820.

During the second half of the 18th century very little silver or copper was minted. In 1797 Matthew Boulton's 'cartwheels', the first copper Pennies and Twopences, demonstrated the improvement gleaned from the application of steam power to the coining press.

During the Napoleonic Wars bank notes came into general use when the issue of Guineas was stopped between 1799 and 1813, but gold 7s. pieces, Third-Guineas; were minted to relieve the shortage of smaller money. As an emergency measure Spanish 'Dollars' were put into circulation for a short period after being countermarked, and in 1804 Spanish Eight Reales were overstruck and issued as Bank of England Dollars.

The transition to a 'token' silver coinage began in 1811 when the Bank of England had 3s and 1s. 6d. tokens made for general circulation. Private issues of token money in the years 1788-95 and 1811-15 helped to alleviate the shortage of regal coinage. A change over to a gold standard and a regular 'token' silver coinage came in 1816 when the Mint, which was moved from its old quarters in the Tower of London to a new site on Tower Hill, began a complete re-coinage. The Guinea was replaced by a 20s. Sovereign, and silver coins were made which had an intrinsic value lower than their face value. The St. George design used on the Sovereign and Crown was the work of Benedetto Pistrucci.

**Engravers and Designers:–** Conrad Heinrich Kuchler (c.1740-1810), Nathaniel Marchant (1739-1816), John Rudulf Ochs Jnr. (1704-88), Lewis Pingo (1743-1830), Thomas Pingo (d.1776) Benedetto Pistrucci (1784-1855), Johann Sigismond Tanner (c.1706-75), Thomas Wyon (1792-1817), William Wyon (1795-1851), Richard Yeo (d.1779)

## GOLD

**EARLY COINAGES**

3723
1770 Pattern Five Guineas

**3723 Five Guineas.** Pattern only, young long haired bust r. R. crowned shield of arms, die axis ↑↑ (en medaille)
1770 *FDC* £450000
1773 *FDC* £450000
**3723A Five Guineas.** Pattern only, young bust right, hair extends under bust similar
1777 *FDC* £435000

3724
1768 Pattern Two Guineas

3724A
1777 Pattern Two Guineas

|  | F | VF | EF |
|---|---|---|---|
|  | £ | £ | £ |

**3724  Two Guineas.** Pattern only, young long haired bust r. R. crowned shield of arms,
  die axis ↑↑ (en medaille)
  1768 *FDC* £140000
  1773 *FDC* £140000

**3724ATwo Guineas.** Pattern only, thinner young bust right, hair extends under bust similar
  1777 *FDC* £100000

*There are six different bust varieties for 3723 and 3724, for further details see Wilson & Rasmussen*

3725                                        3726
1761 Guinea first head, two leaf wreath          1763 Guinea second head

**3725  Guinea.**  First laur. head r., 1761 (varieties with two or three leaves at top of wreath).
    R. Crowned shield of arms die axis ↑↓ .....................2250      6500      15000

**3726  Guinea.**  Second laur. head r. R. Crowned shield of arms die axis ↑↓
    1763 ............................................................................1300      4500      11500
    1764 ............................................................................1300      4000      11000
    1764  no stop over head....................................................2250      5250      11500

*Plain edge patterns exist of 1761 Guinea by John Tanner and 1763 by Richard Yeo. Both are
extremely rare and trade too infrequently to price.*

| 3727 | 3728 | 3729 |
|---|---|---|
| Guinea, third head | Guinea, fourth head | Guinea, fifth head, 'spade' type |

| | F | VF | EF |
|---|---|---|---|
| | £ | £ | £ |

**3727 Guinea.** Third laur. head r. R. Crowned shield of arms die axis ↑↓

| | | F | VF | EF |
|---|---|---|---|---|
| 1765 | | 500 | 950 | 2350 |
| 1766 | | 500 | 975 | 2500 |
| 1767 | | 600 | 1200 | 3200 |
| 1768 | | 525 | 950 | 2350 |
| 1769 | | 650 | 900 | 2750 |
| 1770 | | 1400 | 2850 | 8000 |
| 1771 | | 525 | 850 | 2250 |
| 1772 | | 525 | 850 | 2350 |
| 1773 | | 525 | 850 | 1950 |
| 1773 first 7 over 1 | | 600 | 1250 | — |

**3728 Guinea.** Fourth laur. head r. Crowned shield of arms die axis ↑↓

| | | F | VF | EF |
|---|---|---|---|---|
| 1774 | | 425 | 700 | 1350 |
| 1774 Proof *FDC* £15000 | | | | |
| 1775 | | 465 | 700 | 1350 |
| 1776 | | 465 | 875 | 1750 |
| 1777 | | 465 | 700 | 1550 |
| 1778 | | 485 | 1100 | 2750 |
| 1778 E over C in REX *exists* | | | | |
| 1779 | | 465 | 850 | 1750 |
| 1779 9/7 error *exists* | | | | |
| 1781 | | 465 | 700 | 1500 |
| 1782 | | 465 | 700 | 1500 |
| 1783 | | 465 | 750 | 1500 |
| 1784 | | 465 | 700 | 1450 |
| 1785 | | 465 | 700 | 1450 |
| 1786 | | 465 | 700 | 1450 |

**3729 Guinea.** Fifth laur. head r. R. 'Spade'-shaped shield, die axis ↑↑

| | | F | VF | EF |
|---|---|---|---|---|
| 1787 | | 385 | 500 | 1100 |
| 1787 Proof *FDC* £14000 | | | | |
| 1788 | | 385 | 525 | 1100 |
| 1788 second 8/7 *exists* | | | | |
| 1789 | | 385 | 525 | 1100 |
| 1790 | | 385 | 525 | 1250 |
| 1791 | | 385 | 495 | 1100 |
| 1792 | | 385 | 495 | 1100 |
| 1793 | | 385 | 525 | 1100 |
| 1794 | | 385 | 495 | 1000 |
| 1795 | | 385 | 495 | 1000 |
| 1796 | | 385 | 600 | 1300 |
| 1797 | | 385 | 575 | 1350 |

|        | F      | VF   | EF   |
|--------|--------|------|------|
|        | £      | £    | £    |
| 1798*  | 385    | 475  | 975  |
| 1798/2 error *exists* |  |  |  |
| 1798/7 | 385    | 700  | 1700 |
| 1799   | 400    | 750  | 1950 |

3730
1813 Guinea "Military type"

3731
Half-Guinea, first head

**3730**   **Guinea.** Sixth laur. head. r. Ɍ. Shield in Garter, known as the Military guinea, die axis ↑↑

| 1813 | 1350 | 2650 | 6000 |
|------|------|------|------|

**3731  Half-Guinea.** First laur. head r. R. Crowned shield of arms die axis ↑↓

| 1762 | 750 | 2000 | 5500 |
|------|-----|------|------|
| 1763 | 850 | 2650 | 6500 |

3732
1764 Half-Guinea, second head

3733
Half-Guinea, third head

**3732  Half-Guinea.** Second laur. head r. R. Crowned shield of arms die axis ↑↓

| 1764 | 400 | 700  | 1800 |
|------|-----|------|------|
| 1765 | 600 | 1600 | 4000 |
| 1766 | 400 | 800  | 2000 |
| 1768 | 400 | 800  | 2000 |
| 1769 | 425 | 850  | 2100 |
| 1772 | *Extremely rare* |  |  |
| 1773 | 450 | 850  | 2250 |
| 1774 | 500 | 900  | 2500 |
| 1775 | 500 | 1100 | 3500 |

**3733  Half-Guinea** Third laur. head (less fine style) r. R. Crowned shield of arms die axis ↑↓

| 1774 | 1950 | 4000 | 11000 |
|------|------|------|-------|
| 1775 | 1375 | 3000 | 8500  |

*\* Beware counterfeits*
*Note: All figure 1's are Roman style I's for Guineas from 1781-1799.*

3734
Half-Guinea, fourth head

3735
Half-Guinea, fifth head

|  | F | VF | EF |
|---|---|---|---|
|  | £ | £ | £ |

**3734  Half-Guinea** Fourth laur. head r. R. Crowned shield of arms die axis ↑↓

| 1775 | ......................................................................300 | 525 | 1300 |
|---|---|---|---|
| 1775 Proof *FDC* £12500 | | | |
| 1776 | ......................................................................375 | 600 | 1700 |
| 1777 | ......................................................................300 | 500 | 1250 |
| 1778 | ......................................................................300 | 550 | 1350 |
| 1779 | ......................................................................300 | 550 | 1350 |
| 1781 | ......................................................................300 | 550 | 1350 |
| 1783 | ......................................................................500 | 1750 | 3750 |
| 1784 | ......................................................................300 | 550 | 1350 |
| 1785 | ......................................................................300 | 485 | 1250 |
| 1786 | ......................................................................300 | 450 | 1250 |

**3735  Half-Guinea** Fifth laur. head. r. R. 'Spade' shaped shield, date below, die axis ↑↑

| 1787 | ......................................................................200 | 400 | 950 |
|---|---|---|---|
| 1787 Proof *FDC* £8500 | | | |
| 1788 | ......................................................................225 | 425 | 1050 |
| 1789 | ......................................................................225 | 500 | 1100 |
| 1790 | ......................................................................225 | 475 | 1050 |
| 1791 | ......................................................................225 | 475 | 1050 |
| 1792 | ....................................................................1500 | 4000 | — |
| 1793 | ......................................................................225 | 425 | 1000 |
| 1794 | ......................................................................225 | 500 | 1100 |
| 1795 | ......................................................................225 | 525 | 1150 |
| 1796 | ......................................................................225 | 475 | 1050 |
| 1797 | ......................................................................225 | 475 | 1050 |
| 1798 | ......................................................................225 | 425 | 950 |
| 1798/7 | ..................................................................275 | 550 | 1250 |
| 1800 | ......................................................................350 | 1000 | 2500 |

3736
Half-Guinea, sixth head

**3736  Half-Guinea** Sixth laur. head. r. R. Shield in Garter, date below die axis ↑↑

| 1801 | ......................................................................225 | 365 | 850 |
|---|---|---|---|
| 1802 | ......................................................................250 | 385 | 900 |
| 1803 | ......................................................................275 | 425 | 950 |

3737

1813 Half-Guinea, seventh head

|  | F | VF | EF |
|---|---|---|---|
|  | £ | £ | £ |

**3737  Half-Guinea** Seventh laur. head. r. with short hair. R. Shield in garter,
date below die axis ↑↑

| 1804 | ............................................225 | 325 | 700 |
|---|---|---|---|
| 1805 | ...............................................................Extremely rare | | |
| 1806 | ............................................225 | 425 | 900 |
| 1808 | ............................................225 | 400 | 850 |
| 1809 | ............................................225 | 400 | 850 |
| 1810 | ............................................225 | 350 | 750 |
| 1811 | ............................................400 | 600 | 1500 |
| 1813 | ............................................265 | 500 | 1150 |

1813 Proof *FDC* £5500

3738                                          3739

Third-Guinea, first reverse            Third-Guinea, second reverse

**3738  Third-Guinea.** First laur. head r. R. Crown, date in legend, die axis ↑↑

| 1797 | ............................................150 | 300 | 725 |
|---|---|---|---|
| 1798 | ............................................135 | 275 | 700 |
| 1799 | ............................................475 | 1000 | 2000 |
| 1800 | ............................................165 | 350 | 800 |

**3739  Third-Guinea.** First laur. head r. R. Similar but date below crown, die axis ↑↑

| 1801 | ............................................175 | 400 | 900 |
|---|---|---|---|
| 1802 | ............................................165 | 350 | 775 |
| 1803 | ............................................165 | 350 | 775 |

3740
1804 Third Guinea, second head

3741
1762 Quarter Guinea

**3740  Third-Guinea.** Second laur. head r. with short hair, R. Similar, die axis ↑↑

| | | | |
|---|---|---|---|
| 1804 | ......150 | 275 | 625 |
| 1806 | ......150 | 325 | 725 |
| 1808 | ......150 | 325 | 725 |
| 1809 | ......150 | 325 | 725 |
| 1810 | ......150 | 275 | 625 |
| 1811 | ......550 | 1350 | 3000 |
| 1813 | ......300 | 625 | 1350 |

**3741 Quarter-Guinea.** Laur. head r. R. Crowned shield die axis ↑↓

| | | | |
|---|---|---|---|
| 1762 | ......250 | 525 | 900 |

*For gold of the 'new coinage', 1816-20, see page 419.*

# SILVER

**EARLY COINAGES**

3742
1763 'Northumberland shilling'

**3742  Shilling.** Young laur. and dr. bust, r. known as the 'Northumberland' shilling, die axis ↑↓

| | | | |
|---|---|---|---|
| 1763* | ......300 | 575 | 1350 |

*Plain edge patterns exist for 1764 and 1778. Both are extremely rare.*

**3743  Shilling.** Older laur. and dr. bust, R. No semée of hearts in Hanoverian shield, die axis ↑↑

| | | | |
|---|---|---|---|
| 1787 | ......25 | 50 | 150 |
| 1787 Proof *FDC* | ...... | *Extremely rare* | |

1787 plain edge proof *FDC* £2750
1787 plain edge pattern by Pingo, border of dots at perimeter *FDC* £1250

**3744  Shilling.** — No stop over head, die axis ↑↑ 1787 ......40    85    300

*\*Beware, low grade counterfeits exist*

3745
1781 No stops at date Shilling

|  | F £ | VF £ | EF £ |
|---|---|---|---|
| **3745 Shilling.** — No stops at date, die axis ↑↑ |  |  |  |
| 1787 ............65 | | 125 | 475 |
| **3745A Shilling.** — No stops on *obv.*, die axis ↑↑ |  |  |  |
| 1787 ............450 | | 1000 | 2750 |
| **3746 Shilling.** — R. With semée of hearts, die axis ↑↑ |  |  |  |
| 1787 ............20 | | 55 | 135 |
| 1787 1/1 retrograde............55 | | 150 | 400 |
| 1787 plain edge proof *FDC (Also known on large 27mm flan.)* £2500 | | | |

Hanoverian Arms

No semée of hearts　　With semée of hearts　　　3747 - 1798 Shilling

**3747 Shilling.** No stop over head, 1798: known as the 'Dorrien and Magens' shilling *UNC* £30000

**3748 Sixpence.** Laur. and dr. bust r. R. Without semée of hearts, die axis ↑↑

| 1787 ............15 | | 45 | 115 |
|---|---|---|---|
| 1787 Proof *FDC* ............*Extremely rare* | | | |

3749
1787 Sixpence, with hearts

**3749 Sixpence.** Similar R. With semée of hearts, die axis ↑↑

| 1787 ............15 | | 45 | 115 |
|---|---|---|---|

3750
1772 Fourpence

|  | F £ | VF £ | EF £ |
|---|---|---|---|
| **3750 Fourpence.** Young laur. and dr. bust r. R. Crowned 4, die axis ↑↓ | | | |
| 1763 | 12 | 25 | 75 |
| 1763 Proof *FDC of highest rarity* | | | |
| 1765 | 250 | 500 | 1250 |
| 1766 | 12 | 25 | 75 |
| 1770 | 10 | 25 | 55 |
| 1772 | 15 | 30 | 80 |
| 1772/0 | 8 | 25 | 95 |
| 1776 | 12 | 25 | 75 |
| 1780 | 12 | 25 | 75 |
| 1784 | 15 | 30 | 90 |
| 1786 | 18 | 35 | 95 |

| 3751 | 3753 | 3755 |
|---|---|---|
| 'Wire Money' Fourpence | Young bust Threepence | Older bust Threepence |

| | F £ | VF £ | EF £ |
|---|---|---|---|
| **3751 Fourpence.** Older laur. and dr. bust. R. Thin 4 ('Wire Money'), die axis ↑↑ | | | |
| 1792 | 18 | 50 | 125 |
| **3752 Fourpence.** Older laur. and dr. bust r. R. Normal Crowned 4, die axis ↑↑ | | | |
| 1795 | 8 | 25 | 75 |
| 1800 | 10 | 20 | 65 |
| **3753 Threepence.** Young laur. dr. bust r. R. Crowned 3, die axis ↑↓ | | | |
| 1762 | 5 | 15 | 50 |
| 1763 | 5 | 15 | 50 |
| 1763 Proof *FDC of highest rarity* | | | |
| 1765 | 300 | 550 | 1250 |
| 1766 | 10 | 30 | 70 |
| 1770 | 10 | 25 | 65 |
| 1772 small III | 10 | 25 | 70 |
| 1772 very large III | 8 | 20 | 70 |
| 1780 | 10 | 20 | 70 |
| 1784 | 12 | 30 | 75 |
| 1786 | 10 | 20 | 65 |
| **3754 Threepence.** Older laur. dr. bust. r. R. Thin 3 ('Wire Money'), die axis ↑↑ | | | |
| 1792 | 18 | 55 | 150 |
| **3755 Threepence.** Older laur. and dr. bust r. R. Normal Crowned 3, die axis ↑↑ | | | |
| 1795 | 10 | 25 | 65 |
| 1800 | 8 | 20 | 45 |

3756
Young bust Twopence

|  | F | VF | EF |
|---|---|---|---|
|  | £ | £ | £ |

**3756  Twopence.** Young laur. and dr. bust r. ℞. Crowned 2, die axis ↑↓

| 1763 | ...............15 | 30 | 60 |
|---|---|---|---|
| 1763 Proof *FDC of highest rarity* | | | |
| 1765 | ...............200 | 400 | 700 |
| 1766 | ...............8 | 20 | 45 |
| 1772 | ...............8 | 20 | 45 |
| 1772 second 7/6 | ...............6 | 25 | 70 |
| 1776 | ...............10 | 20 | 60 |
| 1780 | ...............12 | 20 | 60 |
| 1784 | ...............8 | 20 | 60 |
| 1786 | ...............8 | 20 | 60 |
| 1786 large obv. lettering | 5 | 20 | 60 |

**3757  Twopence.** Older laur. and dr. bust. r. ℞. Thin 2 ('Wire Money'), die axis ↑↑

| 1792 | ...............18 | 50 | 115 |
|---|---|---|---|

**3758  Twopence.** Older laur. and dr. bust r. ℞. Normal Crowned 2, die axis ↑↑

| 1795 | ...............6 | 15 | 45 |
|---|---|---|---|
| 1800 | ...............6 | 15 | 45 |

**3759  Penny.** Young laur. and dr. bust r. ℞. Crowned 1, die axis ↑↓

| 1763 | ...............15 | 25 | 60 |
|---|---|---|---|
| 1763 Proof *FDC* | .....................*Extremely rare* | | |
| 1766 | ...............10 | 20 | 60 |
| 1770 | ...............8 | 15 | 60 |
| 1772 | ...............8 | 20 | 60 |
| 1776 | ...............8 | 15 | 60 |
| 1779 | ...............8 | 15 | 60 |
| 1780 | ...............10 | 20 | 60 |
| 1781 | ...............10 | 18 | 60 |
| 1784 | ...............10 | 18 | 55 |
| 1786 | ...............8 | 15 | 45 |

**3760  Penny.** Older laur. and dr. bust. r. ℞. Thin 1 ('Wire Money'), die axis ↑↑

| 1792 | ...............10 | 30 | 95 |
|---|---|---|---|

**3761  Penny.** Older laur. and dr. bust r. ℞. Normal Crowned 1, die axis ↑↑

| 1795 | ...............8 | 18 | 50 |
|---|---|---|---|
| 1800 | ...............6 | 18 | 50 |

**3762  Maundy Set.** Young laur. and dr. bust. r. Uniform dates

| 1763 | ...............115 | 200 | 425 |
|---|---|---|---|
| 1763 Proof set *FDC* £11500 | | | |
| 1766 | ...............115 | 200 | 425 |
| 1772 | ...............115 | 200 | 425 |
| 1780 | ...............115 | 200 | 425 |
| 1784 | ...............115 | 200 | 425 |
| 1786 | ...............115 | 200 | 425 |

|        | F   | VF  | EF  |
|--------|-----|-----|-----|
|        | £   | £   | £   |

**3763  Maundy Set.** — Older laur. and dr. bust. r. ℞. Thin numerals ('Wire Money'),

1792 ............................................................175        350        850

**3764  Maundy Set.** Older laur. and dr. bust r. ℞. Normal numerals. Uniform dates

1795 ............................................................60        150        400

1800 ............................................................60        130        375

*N.B. Set prices are for matched sets, condition, toning etc.*

**EMERGENCY ISSUES,** die axis ↑↑

**3765  Dollar.** Pillar type (current for 4s 9d). Spanish American 8 Reales, oval countermark with head of George III.

Mexico City Mint — m mint mark in reverse legend ........1350        3500        —

Bolivia, Potosi Mint – PTS monogram in reverse legend ...... 1650        4250        —

Peru, Lima Mint – LIMÆ monogram in reverse legend ....1750        4500        —

two initials of mint master

denomination

mint mark

3765A

Peru Mint Portrait type Dollar with oval countermark

**3765A Dollar.** Portrait type, oval countermark.

Mexico City Mint — m mint mark in reverse legend .........125        375        900

Bolivia, Potosi Mint — PTS monogram in reverse legend .......175        650        1400

Chile, Santiago Mint — s mint mark in reverse legend .....725        1950        —

Guatemala Mint — NG mint mark in reverse legend ..........900        2500        —

Spain, Madrid Mint mint mark in reverse left field...............400        1600        3500

Spain, Seville Mint mint mark in reverse left field ..............400        1500        3000

Peru, Lima Mint — LIMÆ monogram in reverse legend ....250        800        1650

**3765B Dollar.** — Oval countermark on silver French Ecu of

crown size .......................................................3950        12000        —

**3765C Dollar.** — Oval countermark on USA Dollar.............................................*Of highest rarity*

**3765D Dollar.** — Oval countermark on silver Italian crown size coins ..................*Of highest rarity*

mint mark S                    Mint Master
                               Initials

3766                                      3766B

Seville Mint Portrait Dollar
with octagonal countermark

|  | F | VF | EF |
|---|---|---|---|
|  | £ | £ | £ |
| **3766** **Dollar** octagonal countermarks with head of George III |  |  |  |
| Mexico City Mint — m̥.......................................................425 | | 975 | 2500 |
| Bolivia, Potosi Mint — PTS monogram ...........................850 | | 2150 | 4500 |
| Guatamala Mint — NG ....................................................1250 | | 3500 | — |
| Peru, Lima Mint — LIME monogram ...............................575 | | 1650 | 4000 |
| Spain, Madrid Mint M to left of reverse shield ..................1100 | | 2750 | — |
| Spain, Seville Mint S to left of reverse shield ....................1250 | | 3250 | — |
| **3766A Dollar.** — Octagonal countermark on French Ecu |  |  |  |
| or Italian Scudi ..............................................................................................*Of highest rarity* | | | |
| **3766B Dollar.** — Octagonal countermark on USA Dollar ........................................*Of highest rarity* | | | |

3767
Half-Dollar with oval countermark, Madrid Mint

| **3767** **Half-Dollar.** With similar oval countermark of George III, |  |  |  |
|---|---|---|---|
| Bolivia, Potosi Mint — PTS monogram ...........................325 | | 650 | 1500 |
| Chile, Santiago Mint — s° mint mark ...........................475 | | 1250 | — |
| Spain, Madrid Mint — Crowned M to left of shield...........175 | | 450 | 1000 |
| Spain, Seville Mint — Crowned S to left of shield..............175 | | 450 | 1000 |
| **3767A Half Dollar.** With Octagonal countermark. |  |  |  |
| Similar | *from*...850 | 1750 | — |

**BANK OF ENGLAND ISSUE, 1804-16**

3768

|  | F £ | VF £ | EF £ |
|---|---|---|---|
| **3768 Dollar.** (current for 5s. until 1811, revalued at 5s. 6d. until withdrawn from circulation in 1817). laur. and dr. bust of king. r. ℞. Britannia seated l., several varieties occur, die axis ↑↑ | | | |
| 1804 O. Top leaf to left side of E, R. Upright K to left of shield ...............125 | 300 | 500 |
| 1804 — —no stops in CHK on truncation ...........175 | 400 | 950 |
| 1804 O. Top leaf to centre of E R. Similar ...........150 | 350 | 850 |
| 1804 — —no stop after REX ...............125 | 300 | 800 |
| 1804 —R. K inverted and incuse ...............175 | 475 | 1100 |
| 1804 O. Top leaf to right side of E, R. normal K .........................*Extremely rare* | | |
| 1804 —R. K inverted to left of shield ...............175 | 450 | 1000 |
| Various 1804 Proof strikings of varieties above *FDC from* £1950 to £4750 | | | |

*These dollars were re-struck from Spanish-American 8-Reales until at least 1811. Dollars that still show dates and Mint marks of original coin beneath are worth up to 25% more.*

3769
1811 Three Shillings, first bust

| **3769 Three Shillings.** Dr and laur. bust in armour r. ℞. BANK / TOKEN / 3 SHILL. / date (in oak wreath), die axis ↑↑ | | |
|---|---|---|
| 1811 ...............20 | 75 | 275 |
| 1811 Proof *FDC* £1950 | | |
| 1812 ...............20 | 75 | 300 |

3770
Three Shillings, second head

| | F | VF | EF |
|---|---|---|---|
| | £ | £ | £ |

**3770  Three Shillings.** — Laureate head r. Top leaf between I/G R. As before
but wreath of oak and olive, die axis ↑↑

| | | | |
|---|---|---|---|
| 1812 | ....................20 | 75 | 275 |
| 1812 Proof *FDC* £2000 | | | |
| 1812 Proof in gold *FDC* | | | *Extremely rare* |
| 1812 Proof in platinum *FDC* | | | *Of the highest rarity* |
| 1813 | ....................20 | 75 | 325 |
| 1814 | ....................20 | 75 | 325 |
| 1815 | ....................20 | 75 | 325 |
| 1816* | ....................375 | 800 | 2750 |

| 3771 | 3772 |
|---|---|
| Eighteenpence, first bust | Eighteenpence, second head |

**3771  Eighteenpence.** Dr. and laur. bust r. in armour R BANK/TOKEN/Is. 6D./date
(in oak wreath) ↑↑

| | | | |
|---|---|---|---|
| 1811 | ....................12 | 40 | 225 |
| 1811 Proof *FDC* £1500 | | | |
| 1812 | ....................15 | 45 | 250 |

**3772  Eighteenpence.** Laureate head r. die axis ↑↑

| | | | |
|---|---|---|---|
| 1812 | ....................12 | 40 | 225 |
| 1812 Proof *FDC* £1500 | | | |
| 1812 Platinum proof | | | *Of the highest rarity* |
| 1812 Proof R. Small letters *FDC* £3750 | | | |
| 1813 | ....................12 | 45 | 250 |
| 1813 Platinum proof *FDC* | | | *Of the highest rarity* |
| 1814 | ....................12 | 45 | 275 |
| 1815 | ....................12 | 45 | 275 |
| 1816 | ....................12 | 45 | 275 |

*\*Beware of counterfeits*

3773
1812 Pattern Ninepence, 9D type

|  | F | VF | EF |
|---|---|---|---|
|  | £ | £ | £ |

**3773  Ninepence.** Similar, Laur. head 1812, ℞. 9D type (pattern only) die axis ↑↑ *FDC* £3000
**3773ANinepence.** — — 1812, ℞. 9 pence type (pattern only) die axis ↑↑ FDC £5000

# COPPER

**First Issue** — Tower Mint, London

3774

**3774  Halfpenny.** Laur. and Cuir. bust r. ℞. Britannia l. date in ex., die axis ↑↓

| | | | |
|---|---|---|---|
| 1770 ................................................................10 | 60 | 300 |
| 1770 Proof die axis ↑↑ *FDC* £2500 ......................................... | | |
| 1770 Proof in silver *FDC* ................................................................*Extremely rare* |
| 1770 no stop on rev.................................................15 | 65 | 250 |
| 1771 ................................................................10 | 50 | 200 |
| 1771 no stop on rev.................................................15 | 65 | 250 |
| 1771 ball below spear blade ...................................10 | 50 | 200 |
| 1772 incuse hair coil on rev. ..................................10 | 55 | 200 |
| 1772 GEORIVS error .............................................50 | 150 | 400 |
| 1772 ball below spear blade ...................................10 | 50 | 200 |
| 1772 no incuse hair coil..........................................10 | 55 | 200 |
| 1772 — no stop on rev.............................................15 | 65 | 225 |
| 1773 ................................................................12 | 55 | 200 |
| 1773 no stop after REX ...........................................20 | 65 | 250 |
| 1773 no stop on rev.................................................20 | 65 | 250 |
| 1774 different obv. profile .......................................20 | 80 | 300 |
| 1775 — ................................................................12 | 75 | 300 |

3775
Rev. C, leaves point between A and N

|  | F | VF | EF |
|---|---|---|---|
|  | £ | £ | £ |

**3775   Farthing.** Laur. and cuir. bust r. R. Britannia l. date in ex., die axis ↑↓

| | F | VF | EF |
|---|---|---|---|
| 1771 Proof *FDC* £1750 | | | |
| 1771 Rev A. leaf to r.of N......................................15 | 55 | 225 | |
| 1771 Rev B. leaf to N ...........................................15 | 50 | 225 | |
| 1771 Rev C................................................................15 | 50 | 220 | |
| 1771 1st 7/1 .........................................................20 | 165 | 400 | |
| 1773      ..............................................................10 | 40 | 175 | |
| 1773 no stop on rev..............................................10 | 55 | 250 | |
| 1773 no stop after REX .........................................20 | 65 | 275 | |
| 1774      ..............................................................10 | 40 | 225 | |
| 1775      ..............................................................10 | 40 | 225 | |
| 1775 struck en medaille ↑↑  ..............................20 | 65 | 255 | |
| 1775 GEORGI Ⅴ S.................................................30 | 225 | 575 | |

*Note: 1771 varieties refer to the direction the top leaf of olive branch points in Britannia's hand*

**Second Issue**—Soho Mint. Birmingham 'Cartwheel' coinage, die axis ↑↓

3776

**3776   Twopence.** Legends incuse on raised rim

1797 Copper proof *FDC* £2750
1797 Bronzed proof *FDC* £2500
1797 Silver proof *FDC* ............................................................................*Extremely rare*
1797      ..............................................................30         75         375
1797 Gold proof *FDC*  ............................................................................*Extremely rare*
1797 Gilt copper *FDC* £3750

Prices for UNCIRCULATED copper coins are no longer quoted. Truly uncirculated copper coins of this period are too seldom traded on the market to fix a meaningful price. As a guide a truly uncirculated coin with full lustre or bloom should fetch 3-4 times the EF price.

3777

| | F | VF | EF |
|---|---|---|---|
| | £ | £ | £ |

**3777  Penny.**

| | | | |
|---|---|---|---|
| 1797 Similar, 10 leaves in wreath on obv. | 10 | 50 | 165 |
| 1797 11 leaves in wreath on obv. | 12 | 75 | 225 |
| 1797 Gilt copper proof *FDC* £2250 | | | |
| 1797 Copper proof *FDC* £1500 | | | |
| 1797 Bronzed proof *FDC* £1250 | | | |
| 1797 Silver proof *FDC* | | | *Extremely rare* |
| 1797 Gold proof *FDC* | | | *Extremely rare* |

*Halfpence and Farthings of this issue are patterns.*

**Third Issue**—Soho Mint, Birmingham, die axis ↑↓

3778

**3778  Halfpenny.** Laur. and dr. bust r., R. Britannia l. date below

| | | |
|---|---|---|
| 1799 Ship on rev. with 5 incuse gunports | 10 | 50 |
| 1799 Ship with 6 relief gunports | 10 | 100 |
| 1799 Ship with 9 relief gunports | 15 | 125 |
| 1799 Ship with plain hull | 12 | 125 |
| 1799 — raised line on hull | 15 | 125 |
| 1799 Copper proof *FDC* £750 | | |
| 1799 Bronzed proof *FDC* £700 | | |
| 1799 Gilt copper proof *FDC* £1250 | | |

3779

|  | VF | EF |
|---|---|---|
|  | £ | £ |

**3779   Farthing.** Laur. and dr. bust r. date below R. Britannia l.

1799     Obv. with 3 berries in wreath ................................................................5          50
1799 Copper *FDC* £550
1799 Bronzed proof *FDC* £500
1799 Copper gilt proof *FDC* £975
1799 Obv. with 4 berries in wreath................................................................5          75
1799 Gold proof *FDC* ...................................................................................*Of the highest rarity*
1799 Silver proof *FDC* ..............................................................................................*Extremely rare*

**Fourth Issue** — Soho Mint, Birmingham, die axis ↑↓

3780

**3780   Penny.** Shorter haired, laur. and dr. bust r. date below. R. Britannia l. date below

1806 incuse hair curl by tie knot ........................................................................12          65
1806 no incuse hair curl ....................................................................................12          95
1806 Copper proof *FDC*  £650
1806 Bronzed proof *FDC*  £550
1806 Gilt copper proof *FDC* £1350
1806 Silver proof *FDC*  £6500
1807     ..............................................................................................20          80
1807 Copper proof *FDC* £750
1807 Bronzed proof *FDC* £650
1807 Gilt copper proof *FDC* £2000
1807 Silver proof *FDC* ................................................................................................*Extremely rare*
1807 Gold proof *FDC*  ...............................................................................................*Extremely rare*
1807 Platinum proof *FDC*  .........................................................................................*Extremely rare*
1808 Proof *FDC* .................................................................................................................*Unique*

3781                              3782

|   | VF<br>£ | EF<br>£ |
|---|---|---|
| **3781 Halfpenny.** Shorter haired laur. and dr. bust r. date below, R. Britannia l. | | |
| 1806 rev. no berries | 7 | 30 |
| 1806 rev. 3 berries | 7 | 65 |
| 1806 Copper proof *FDC* £550 | | |
| 1806 Bronzed proof *FDC* £500 | | |
| 1806 Gilt proof *FDC* £950 | | |
| 1806 Silver proof *FDC* | | *Extremely rare* |
| 1807 | 8 | 50 |
| 1807 Copper proof *FDC* £550 | | |
| 1807 Bronzed proof *FDC* £500 | | |
| 1807 Silver proof *FDC* £4500 | | |
| 1807 Gold proof *FDC* | | *Extremely rare* |
| **3782 Farthing.** Shorter haired laur. and dr. bust r. date below, R. Britannia l. | | |
| 1806 K. on tr. | 8 | 45 |
| 1806 incuse dot on tr | 25 | 110 |
| 1806 Copper proof *FDC* £550 | | |
| 1806 Bronzed proof *FDC* £500 | | |
| 1806 Gilt copper proof *FDC* £950 | | |
| 1806 Silver proof *FDC* | | *Extremely rare* |
| 1806 Gold proof *FDC* | | *Extremely rare* |
| 1807 | 8 | 75 |
| 1807 Copper proof *FDC* £600 | | |
| 1807 Bronzed proof *FDC* £550 | | |
| 1807 Silver proof *FDC* | | *Extremely rare* |
| 1807 Gold proof *FDC* | | *Extremely rare* |

Prices for UNCIRCULATED copper coins are no longer quoted. Truly uncirculated copper coins of this period are too seldom traded on the market to fix a meaningful price. As a guide a truly uncirculated coin with full lustre or bloom should fetch 3-4 times the EF price.

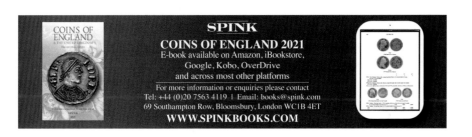

## LAST OR NEW COINAGE, 1816-20

The year 1816 is a landmark in the history of our coinage. For some years at the beginning of the 19th century Mint production was virtually confined to small gold denominations, regular full production being resumed only after the Mint had been moved from the Tower of London to a new site on Tower Hill. Steam powered minting machinery made by Boulton and Watt replaced the old hand-operated presses and these produced coins which were technically much superior to the older milled coins.

In 1816 for the first time British silver coins were produced with an intrinsic value somewhat below their face value, the first official token coinage. The old Guinea was replaced by a Sovereign of twenty shillings in 1817, the standard of 22 carat (0.916) fineness still being retained.

**Mint Master or Engraver's and/or designer's initials:**

B.P. (Benedetto Pistrucci 1784-1855)     WWP (William Wellesley Pole)

## GOLD

3783

**3783   Five Pounds.** 1820 LX (Pattern only) laur. head r. date below R. St George and dragon, edge inscribed die axis ↑↓ *FDC* £475000

1820 Similar plain edge proof *FDC* (only two struck) ......................................... *Of highest rarity*

3784

**3784   Two Pounds.** 1820 LX (Pattern only) laur. head r. date below R. St George and dragon, edge inscribed die axis ↑↓ *FDC* £75000

1820 Similar plain edge proof *FDC* ............................................................... *Extremely rare*

|       |     3785 |      |     3785A |        |      |
|-------|---------|------|----------|--------|------|
|       | F       | VF   |          | EF     | UNC  |
|       | £       | £    |          | £      | £    |

**3785 Sovereign.** laur. head r. coarse hair, legend type A (Descending colon after BRITANNIAR, no space between REX and F:D:). R. St. George and dragon, die axis ↑↓

| | F | VF | EF | UNC |
|---|---|---|---|---|
| 1817 .....................................................600 | | 1000 | 1950 | 5000 |
| 1817 Proof *FDC* £27500 | | | | |
| 1817 ↑↑ die axis .......................................1250 | | — | — | — |
| 1818 .....................................................850 | | 1650 | 4500 | 8750 |
| 1819 .....................................................45000 | | 75000 | 250000 | — |

**3785A Sovereign.** Similar legend type B (Ascending colon after BRITANNIAR, space between REX and F:D:) ↑↓

| | F | VF | EF | UNC |
|---|---|---|---|---|
| 1818 .....................................................750 | | 1500 | 4000 | 7500 |
| 1818 Proof *FDC* £37500 | | | | |

**3785B Sovereign.** laur head r. hair with tighter curls, legend type A. R. Similar die axis ↑↓

| | |
|---|---|
| 1818 ...........................................................................*Extremely rare* | |

3785C
Large date, open 2 variety

3786
1817 Half-Sovereign

**3785C Sovereign.** Similar legend type B. (as above) die axis ↑↓

| | F | VF | EF | UNC |
|---|---|---|---|---|
| 1818 ...........................................................................*Extremely rare* | | | | |
| 1820 Roman I in date ....................................................*Extremely rare* | | | | |
| 1820 open 2, alignment of date varies .........................500 | | 800 | 1300 | 4750 |
| 1820 thin date, smaller 0 Proof *FDC* £21500 | | | | |
| 1820 short date height, alignment varies .....................550 | | 950 | 2000 | 4750 |
| 1820 closed 2 alignment of date varies .........................475 | | 800 | 1600 | 4500 |

The above 1820 entries are the main variations, there do exist other subtle differences which are merely sub-varieties and therefore are not included.

**3786 Half-Sovereign.** laur head r. date below R. Crowned shield, edge milled die axis ↑↓

| | F | VF | EF | UNC |
|---|---|---|---|---|
| 1817 .....................................................250 | | 350 | 750 | 2050 |
| 1817 Proof *FDC* £12500 | | | | |
| 1818/7* .................................................450 | | 1250 | — | — |
| 1818 Proof *FDC* £15000 | | | | |
| 1818 .....................................................265 | | 400 | 950 | 2500 |
| 1820 .....................................................250 | | 375 | 800 | 2250 |
| 1820 Letter O for zero .................................350 | | 500 | 950 | 2750 |

*Note: 7 under 8 clearly visible at top right of 8*

## SILVER

3787 - 1818 George III Crown

| | F £ | VF £ | EF £ | UNC £ |
|---|---|---|---|---|
| **3787 Crown.** Laur. head r. ℞. Pistrucci's St. George and dragon within Garter edge inscribed, die axis ↑↓ | | | | |
| 1818 LVIII, edge ................................................45 | 100 | 600 | 1750 |
| 1818 LVIII error edge inscription ...........................................*Extremely rare* |
| 1818 LVIII Proof *FDC* ...........................................................*Extremely rare* |
| 1818 LIX ...........................................................45 | 110 | 625 | 2000 |
| 1818 LIX TUTΛMEN error ...........................................80 | 350 | — | — |
| 1819 LIX ...........................................................40 | 100 | 525 | 1750 |
| 1819 LIX no stops on edge ...............................65 | 200 | 775 | 2250 |
| 1819 LIX ℞. Thicker ruled garter .....................60 | 135 | 850 | — |
| 1819/8 LIX ..........................................................70 | 250 | 900 | — |
| 1819 LX ..............................................................50 | 120 | 550 | 1850 |
| 1819 LX no stop after TUTAMEN ....................60 | 150 | 750 | — |
| 1820 LX ..............................................................45 | 110 | 575 | 1900 |
| 1820 LX ℞. S/T in SOIT ...................................65 | 225 | 850 | — |
| 1820/19 LX .........................................................80 | 275 | 975 | — |

3788 - 1817 Halfcrown, large bust

| | F £ | VF £ | EF £ | UNC £ |
|---|---|---|---|---|
| **3788 Halfcrown.** Large laur. bust or 'bull' head r. date below ℞. Crowned garter and shield die axis ↑↑ | | | | |
| 1816 ...........................................................30 | 75 | 350 | 700 |
| 1816 Proof *FDC* £5250 |
| 1816 Plain edge proof *FDC* £6750 |
| 1817 ...........................................................25 | 75 | 325 | 675 |
| 1817 D/T in DEI ...............................................75 | 300 | 800 | — |
| 1817 E/R in DEI ....................................................................*Extremely rare* |
| 1817 S/I in PENSE ............................................55 | 225 | 725 | — |
| 1817 Proof *FDC* £5250 |
| 1817 Plain edge proof *FDC* £6250 |

3789
1817 Halfcrown, small head

3790
1819 Shilling

| | F | VF | EF | UNC |
|---|---|---|---|---|
| | £ | £ | £ | £ |

**3789 Halfcrown.** Small laur. head r. date below, R. Crowned garter and shield die axis ↑↑

| | | | | |
|---|---|---|---|---|
| 1817* ...................30 | 75 | 300 | 675 |
| 1817 Proof *FDC* £5250 | | | | |
| 1817 Plain edge proof *FDC* £5500 | | | | |
| 1817 Reversed s's in garter........................*Extremely rare* | | | | |
| 1818 Reversed s's in garter........................*Extremely rare* | | | | |
| 1818** ...................40 | 100 | 400 | 775 |
| 1818 Proof *FDC* £5750 | | | | |
| 1819 Proof *FDC* £5500 | | | | |
| 1819 ...................30 | 75 | 350 | 700 |
| 1819/8 ...................*Extremely rare* | | | | |
| 1820 ...................40 | 100 | 425 | 725 |
| 1820 Proof *FDC* £5250 | | | | |
| 1820 Plain edge proof *FDC* £5750 | | | | |

**3790 Shilling.** laur. head r. date below R. Crowned Shield in Garter edge milled, die axis ↑↑

| | | | | |
|---|---|---|---|---|
| 1816 ...................10 | 18 | 75 | 200 |
| 1816 Proof *FDC* £1650 | | | | |
| 1816 Plain edge proof *FDC* £1850 | | | | |
| 1816 Proof in gold *FDC* ........................*Extremely rare* | | | | |
| 1817 ...................10 | 18 | 75 | 225 |
| 1817 RRITT flaw...................20 | 30 | 150 | 375 |
| 1817 Plain edge proof *FDC* £1750 | | | | |
| 1817 GEOE error...................65 | 225 | 525 | 1000 |
| 1817 E over R in GEOR ...................85 | 125 | 425 | 650 |
| 1818 ...................25 | 50 | 190 | 500 |
| 1818 High 8 ...................30 | 65 | 225 | 475 |
| 1819/8 ...................15 | 30 | 135 | 375 |
| 1819 ...................15 | 25 | 100 | 275 |
| 1819 9/6 *exists* | | | | |
| 1820 ...................15 | 25 | 100 | 250 |
| 1820 I/S in HONI ...................35 | 65 | 250 | 525 |
| 1820 Proof *FDC* £1750 | | | | |

*\* Beware recent low grade forgeries*
*\*\* Beware of silvered base metal contemporary forgeries*

3791
1817 Sixpence

|  | F £ | VF £ | EF £ | UNC £ |
|---|---|---|---|---|

**3791  Sixpence.** laur head r. date below R̶. Crowned Shield in Garter edge milled, die axis ↑↑

| | F | VF | EF | UNC |
|---|---|---|---|---|
| 1816 ............................................................................7 | 14 | 65 | 150 |
| 1816 Proof plain edge *FDC* £1350 | | | |
| 1816 Proof in gold *FDC* ...........................................................................*Extremely rare* | | | |
| 1817 ............................................................................9 | 16 | 75 | 165 |
| 1817 Proof plain edge *FDC* £1350 | | | |
| 1817 Proof milled edge *FDC* £1650 | | | |
| 1818 ...........................................................................11 | 18 | 80 | 165 |
| 1818 Proof milled edge *FDC* £1800 | | | |
| 1819/8 ........................................................................14 | 23 | 90 | 200 |
| 1819 ...........................................................................11 | 18 | 85 | 165 |
| 1819 small 8 ..............................................................11 | 18 | 78 | 165 |
| 1820 ...........................................................................11 | 18 | 78 | 150 |
| 1820 inverted 1 ..✶.....................................................70 | 300 | 575 | — |
| 1820 I/S in HONI ......................................................70 | 275 | 525 | — |
| 1820 obv. no colons .................................................115 | 350 | 675 | — |
| 1820 milled edge Proof *FDC* £1650 | | | |

3792

**3792  Maundy Set.** (4d., 3d., 2d. and 1d.) laur. head, date below die axis ↑↑

| | | EF | UNC |
|---|---|---|---|
| 1817 ...........................................................................80 | 175 | 400 |
| 1818 ...........................................................................75 | 150 | 375 |
| 1820 ...........................................................................75 | 150 | 375 |
| **3793** — **Fourpence.** 1817, 1818, 1820 .................*from* 12 | 25 | 65 | 100 |
| **3794** — **Threepence.** 1817, 1818, 1820,.................*from* 10 | 20 | 55 | 80 |
| **3795** — **Twopence.** 1817, 1818, 1820......................*from* 10 | 18 | 35 | 65 |
| **3796** — **Penny.** 1817, 1818, 1820 ...........................*from*  8 | 15 | 35 | 65 |

Maundy pennies are always the most requested oddment, it is the smallest coin in the set and is therefore the easiest to lose. Penny collectors also dictate supply and demand for this coin.

George IV, eldest son of George III, was born on 12th August 1762 and was almost the complete opposite to his father. He was very extravagant and lived in the height of luxury. He especially influenced fashion of the time which became known as the 'Regency' style. He had numerous mistresses, and had an arranged marriage with Caroline of Brunswick. She later left England and travelled Southern Europe, North Africa and the Holy Land, basing herself in Naples, but returned to claim her place as Queen upon George's accession. George banned her from ever being crowned, and he died without ever conceiving a son on 26th June 1830, when his younger brother William ascended the throne.

The Mint resumed the coinage of copper farthings in 1821, and pennies and halfpennies in 1825. A gold Two Pound piece was first issued for general circulation in 1823. A full cased proof set of the new bare head coinage was issued in limited quantities in 1826.

**Engraver's and/or designer's initials on the coins:**

B. P. (Benedetto Pistrucci)  W.W. P. (William Wellesley Pole) – Master of the Mint
J. B. M. (Jean Baptiste Merlen)

**Engravers and Designers:**– Francis Legett Chantrey (1781-1842) Jean Baptiste Merlen (1769-c.1850) Benedetto Pistrucci (1784-1855) William Wyon (1795-1851)

## GOLD

3797

**3797 Five Pounds.** 1826 Bare head l. date below Ŗ. Crowned shield and mantle, inscribed edge, die axis ↑↓ Proof *FDC* £70000
1826 Piedfort proof *FDC*..........................................................................................*Extremely rare*

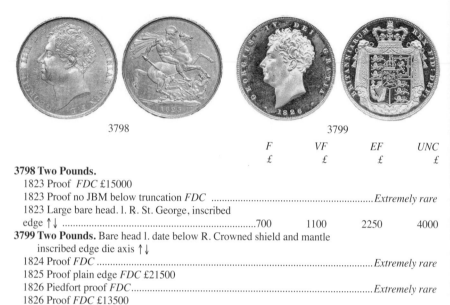

3798          3799

|  | F | VF | EF | UNC |
|---|---|---|---|---|
|  | £ | £ | £ | £ |

**3798 Two Pounds.**
 1823 Proof *FDC* £15000
 1823 Proof no JBM below truncation *FDC* ............................................................*Extremely rare*
 1823 Large bare head. l. R. St. George, inscribed
 edge ↑↓ ..........................................700          1100          2250          4000
**3799 Two Pounds.** Bare head l. date below R. Crowned shield and mantle
  inscribed edge die axis ↑↓
 1824 Proof *FDC* ....................................................................................................*Extremely rare*
 1825 Proof plain edge *FDC* £21500
 1826 Piedfort proof *FDC*..........................................................................................*Extremely rare*
 1826 Proof *FDC* £13500

3801
Sovereign, second type

**3800   Sovereign.** Laur. head. l. R. St. George and dragon date in ex., die axis ↑↓
 1821          ...............................................................400          700          1850          3750
 1821 Proof *FDC* £11500
 1822*          ...............................................................400          750          1850          4250
 1823          ...............................................................1100          2750          8000          —
 1824          ...............................................................500          900          2250          4250
 1825          ...............................................................750          2000          5750          9250
**3801   Sovereign.** Bare head. date below l. R. Crowned shield, die axis ↑↓
 1825          ...............................................................400          750          1600          3500
 1825 Proof 8 heart semée *FDC* £13500
 1825 Plain edge proof 7 heart semée *FDC* £14500
 1826          ...............................................................400          700          1500          3750
 1826 Proof *FDC* £9500
 1827*          ...............................................................425          750          1600          4000
 1828          ...............................................................6000          15000          29500          —
 1829          ...............................................................500          800          2000          4250
 1830          ...............................................................500          800          2000          4250
 1830 die axis ↑↑ ..................................................................................... *Extremely rare*
 1830 Milled edge proof ..............................................................................*Extremely rare*
**3802 Half-Sovereign.** Laur. head. l. R. Ornately garnished Crowned shield. die axis ↑↓
 1821          ...............................................................800          1650          2950          4750
 1821 Proof *FDC* £7500

*Beware counterfeits

3803
Half-Sovereign, second reverse

3804
1825 Half Sovereign, bare head

| | F £ | VF £ | EF £ | UNC £ |
|---|---|---|---|---|
| **3803 Half-Sovereign.** Laur. head l. R. Plain Crowned shield die axis ↑↓ | | | | |
| 1823 | 265 | 485 | 1100 | 2350 |
| 1824 | 250 | 450 | 875 | 2000 |
| 1825 | 250 | 400 | 750 | 1800 |
| **3804 Half-Sovereign.** Bare head. date below l. R. Crowned garnished shield die axis ↑↓ | | | | |
| 1826 | 250 | 385 | 950 | 1850 |
| 1826 Proof *FDC* £6000 | | | | |
| 1827 | 250 | 400 | 1000 | 2100 |
| 1828 | 250 | 350 | 950 | 2000 |
| **3804A Half-Sovereign.** Similar with extra tuft of hair to l. ear, much heavier border, die axis ↑↓ | | | | |
| 1826 | 250 | 350 | 900 | 1850 |
| 1826 Proof *FDC* £6000 | | | | |
| 1827 | 250 | 400 | 950 | 2100 |
| 1828 | 250 | 375 | 900 | 2000 |

## SILVER

3805
1821 Laureate bust Crown

**3805 Crown.** Laur. head. l. R. St. George, date in exergue, B.P. to upper right, tiny italic WWP under lance, die axis ↑↓

| | | | | |
|---|---|---|---|---|
| 1821* edge SECUNDO | 50 | 150 | 700 | 2250 |
| 1821 SECUNDO WWP inverted under lance | 75 | 350 | 900 | 2500 |
| 1821 SECUNDO L - very clearly defined WWP Proof *FDC* £6750 | | | | |
| 1821 SECUNDO Proof in copper | | | | *Extremely rare* |
| 1821 TERTIO Proof *FDC* £10000 | | | | |
| 1822 SECUNDO | 60 | 200 | 975 | 2850 |
| 1822 TERTIO | 55 | 200 | 900 | 2350 |

*\* Beware of recent counterfeits in high grade*

3806
1826 Proof Crown, bare head

| | F | VF | EF | UNC |
|---|---|---|---|---|
| | £ | £ | £ | £ |

**3806 Crown.** Bare head. l. R. Shield with crest inscribed edge, die axis ↑↓
    1825   Proof *FDC* £25000
    1826   Proof *FDC* £18500

| 3807 | 3807 |
|---|---|
| Halfcrown, lightly garnished shield, right thistle leaf further from stem | Heavy garnishing, right thistle leaf closer, more parallel to its stem |

**3807 Halfcrown.** Laur. head. l. R. Crowned Garnished shield, die axis ↑↓

| | | F | VF | EF | UNC |
|---|---|---|---|---|---|
| 1820 | ..................................................................... | 25 | 85 | 300 | 750 |
| 1820 Proof *FDC* £3500 | | | | | |
| 1820 Plain edge proof *FDC* £4500 | | | | | |
| 1821 | ..................................................................... | 25 | 85 | 300 | 750 |
| 1821 Heavier shield garnishing | ..................................... | 40 | 90 | 425 | 1000 |
| 1823 — | ..................................................................... | 1250 | 4500 | 14850 | — |
| 1821 Proof *FDC* £3000 | | | | | |

3808
Halfcrown, second reverse

3809
1826 Halfcrown, bare head, third reverse

|  | F | VF | EF | UNC |
|---|---|---|---|---|
|  | £ | £ | £ | £ |

**3808 Halfcrown.** Laur. head l. R. Crowned Shield in garter and collar die axis ↑↓

| 1823 | ..............30 | 90 | 385 | 950 |
|---|---|---|---|---|
| 1823 Proof *FDC* £7000 | | | | |
| 1824 | ..............40 | 110 | 425 | 1000 |
| 1824 Proof *FDC* £7000 | | | | |

**3809 Halfcrown.** Bare head. date below l. R. Crowned Shield with crest die axis ↑↓

| 1824 | ..............*Extremely rare* | | | |
|---|---|---|---|---|
| 1824 Proof *FDC* £12500 | | | | |
| 1825 | ..............30 | 80 | 350 | 750 |
| 1825 Proof *FDC* £3750 | | | | |
| 1825 Plain edge proof *FDC* £3750 | | | | |
| 1826 | ..............35 | 85 | 375 | 800 |
| 1826 Proof *FDC* £2500 | | | | |
| 1828 | ..............110 | 300 | 1000 | 2750 |
| 1829 | ..............75 | 150 | 550 | 1100 |

3810 - First reverse

3811 - Second reverse

**3810 Shilling.** Laur. head. l. R. Crowned garnished shield, die axis ↑↓

| 1821 | ..............10 | 48 | 200 | 450 |
|---|---|---|---|---|
| 1821 Milled edge Proof *FDC* £1950 | | | | |

**3811 Shilling.** Laur. head l. R. Crowned shield in Garter die axis ↑↓

| 1823 | ..............55 | 90 | 295 | 795 |
|---|---|---|---|---|
| 1823 Proof *FDC* £3750 | | | | |
| 1824 | ..............8 | 50 | 225 | 575 |
| 1824 Milled edge Proof *FDC* £3750 | | | | |
| 1825 | ..............15 | 55 | 250 | 575 |
| 1825 Milled edge Proof *FDC* £3500 | | | | |
| 1825/3 | ..............*Extremely rare* | | | |

3812
Third reverse

|  | F £ | VF £ | EF £ | UNC £ |
|---|---|---|---|---|
| **3812 Shilling.** Bare head l. date below R. Lion on crown die axis ↑↓ | | | | |
| 1825 ................................ | 8 | 45 | 165 | 425 |
| 1825 Roman I ................................ | 125 | 375 | 1100 | 2750 |
| 1825 Milled edge Proof *FDC* £1500 | | | | |
| 1826 ................................ | 5 | 35 | 110 | 400 |
| 1826 Proof *FDC* £1100 | | | | |
| 1826/2 ................................ | — | — | — | 2000 |
| 1827 ................................ | 45 | 110 | 395 | 875 |
| 1829 ................................ | 25 | 65 | 250 | 700 |
| 1829 Milled edge Proof *FDC* £4750 | | | | |

| 3813 | 3814 | 3815 |
|---|---|---|
| First reverse | Second reverse | Third reverse |

| | F £ | VF £ | EF £ | UNC £ |
|---|---|---|---|---|
| **3813 Sixpence.** Laur. head. l. R. Crowned Garnished shield, die axis ↑↓ | | | | |
| 1821 ................................ | 8 | 25 | 150 | 450 |
| 1821 Proof *FDC* £1150 | | | | |
| 1821 BBITANNIAR ................................ | 100 | 325 | 900 | — |
| **3814 Sixpence.** Laur. head l. R. Crowned Shield in Garter die axis ↑↓ | | | | |
| 1824 ................................ | 8 | 25 | 175 | 450 |
| 1824 Proof *FDC* £1750 | | | | |
| 1825 ................................ | 8 | 20 | 175 | 425 |
| 1825 Proof *FDC* £1750 | | | | |
| 1826 ................................ | 30 | 85 | 300 | 650 |
| 1826 Proof *FDC* £2650 | | | | |
| **3815 Sixpence.** Bare head. l. with or without tuft of hair to l. of ear date below R. Lion on crown die axis ↑↓ | | | | |
| 1826 ................................ | 8 | 30 | 100 | 385 |
| 1826 Proof *FDC* £1250 | | | | |
| 1827 ................................ | 40 | 125 | 325 | 695 |
| 1828 ................................ | 12 | 60 | 250 | 550 |
| 1829 ................................ | 12 | 35 | 160 | 450 |
| 1829 Proof *FDC* £1950 | | | | |

3816
1822 Maundy Set

| | EF £ | FDC £ |
|---|---|---|
| **3816 Maundy Set.** (4d., 3d., 2d. and 1d.) laur head l. die axis ↑↓ | | |
| 1822 | 250 | 450 |
| 1822 Proof set *FDC* | *Extremely rare* | |
| 1823 | 175 | 400 |
| 1824 | 200 | 450 |
| 1825 | 175 | 400 |
| 1826 | 175 | 400 |
| 1827 | 175 | 400 |
| 1828 | 175 | 400 |
| 1828 Proof set *FDC* | *Extremely rare* | |
| 1829 | 175 | 400 |
| 1830 | 165 | 400 |
| **3817 Maundy Fourpence.** 1822-30 | *from* 18 | 55 |
| **3818 — Threepence.** small head, 1822 | 35 | 85 |
| **3819 — Threepence.** normal head, 1823-30 | *from* 15 | 50 |
| **3820 — Twopence.** 1822-30 | *from* 15 | 45 |
| **3821 — Penny.** 1822-30 | *from* 22 | 60 |

*See note under 3796.*

# COPPER

3822
First Issue Farthing

| | F £ | VF £ | EF £ | BU £ |
|---|---|---|---|---|
| **First Issue, 1821-6. Obv. reads GEORGIUS IIII** | | | | |
| **3822 Farthing.** Laur. and dr. bust l. R. Britannia r. date in ex. die axis ↑↓ | | | | |
| 1821 Proof *FDC* £1100 | | | | |
| 1821 | 3 | 12 | 55 | 175 |
| 1822 leaf ribs incuse | 2 | 10 | 45 | 150 |
| 1822 — inv. A's legend | 30 | 95 | 340 | — |
| 1822 leaf ribs raised | 2 | 10 | 45 | 150 |
| 1822 Proof *FDC* £1250 | | | | |
| 1822 Proof die axis ↑↑ *FDC* £1400 | | | | |
| 1823 — | 3 | 12 | 55 | 175 |
| 1823 — I for 1 in date | 25 | 85 | 270 | — |

|                              | F   | VF  | EF   | BU  |
|------------------------------|-----|-----|------|-----|
|                              | £   | £   | £    | £   |
| 1825 —                       | 3   | 12  | 55   | 175 |
| 1825 — D/U in DEI            | 20  | 85  | 295  | —   |
| 1825 leaf ribs raised        | 5   | 15  | 60   | 200 |
| 1825 gold proof *FDC* | | | | *Extremely rare* |
| 1826 —                       | 5   | 18  | 70   | 225 |
| 1826 R/E in GRATIA           | 20  | 80  | 270  | —   |

*See 3825 for Second Issue farthings of 1826 which have die axis ↑↑*

3823
1826 Penny - plain saltire

## Second issue, 1825-30. Obv. reads GEORGIUS IV

**3823  Penny.** Laur. head. l. R. Britannia, with shield bearing saltire of arms die axis ↑↑

| | | | | |
|---|---|---|---|---|
| 1825 | 10 | 50 | 375 | 750 |
| 1825 Proof *FDC* £1750 | | | | |
| 1826 plain saltire on rev. | 8 | 45 | 225 | 675 |
| 1826 Proof *FDC* £1200 | | | | |
| 1826 thin line on saltire | 8 | 50 | 375 | 750 |
| 1826-Proof *FDC* £975 | | | | |
| 1826 thick line on saltire | 12 | 70 | 300 | 825 |
| 1826-Proof *FDC* £1100 | | | | |
| 1827 plain saltire | 225 | 950 | 6000 | — |

3824
1827 Halfpenny

**3824  Halfpenny**.die axis ↑↑ Laur. head. l. R. Britannia, with shield bearing saltire of arms

| | | | | |
|---|---|---|---|---|
| 1825 | 10 | 40 | 160 | 400 |
| 1826 rev. two incuse lines on saltire | 5 | 15 | 100 | 350 |
| 1826 Proof *FDC* £825 | | | | |
| 1826 rev. raised line on saltire | 8 | 30 | 175 | 350 |
| 1827 rev. two incuse lines on saltire | 8 | 20 | 150 | 350 |

3825
1830 Farthing

|  | F £ | VF £ | EF £ | BU £ |
|---|---|---|---|---|

**3825  Farthing.** die axis ↑↑ Laur. head. l. ℞. Britannia, with shield bearing saltire of arms

| 1826 | 2 | 8 | 60 | 175 |
|---|---|---|---|---|
| 1826 Proof *FDC* £750 | | | | |
| 1826 Roman I | 15 | 55 | 350 | 675 |
| 1827 | 3 | 8 | 70 | 200 |
| 1828 | 2 | 8 | 75 | 185 |
| 1829 | 3 | 12 | 80 | 250 |
| 1830 | 2 | 8 | 75 | 185 |

3826                         3827
1828 Half-Farthing          1827 Third-Farthing

**3826  Half-Farthing.** (for use in Ceylon). Laur. head. l. date below ℞.Britannia die axis ↑↑

| 1828 rev. helmet intrudes legend | 10 | 25 | 125 | 350 |
|---|---|---|---|---|
| 1828 rev. helmet to base of legend | 10 | 30 | 160 | 450 |
| 1830 rev. helmet to base of legend 22 | 70 | 300 | — | |
| 1830 rev. helmet intrudes legend | 10 | 30 | 150 | 425 |

**3827  Third-Farthing.** (for use in Malta). Laur. head. l. date below ℞.Britannia die axis ↑↑

| 1827 | — | 12 | 50 | 225 |
|---|---|---|---|---|
| 1827 Proof *FDC* £900 | | | | |

*Copper coins graded in this catalogue as BU have full mint lustre.*

**PROOF SET**
**PS1** new issue, 1826. Five pounds to Farthing (11 coins) *FDC* £135000

William IV was born on 21st August 1765, and ascended the throne on his elder brother's death. From c.1791-1811 while Duke of Clarence, he was cohabiting with the actress Dorothea Jordan (1762-1816) who bore him ten illegitimate children. After the death of George IV's daughter, William was coerced into a legitimate marriage with Adelaide of Saxe-Coburg and Saxe-Meinigen. She bore him two daughters who both died in childhood. His reign was most notable for the introduction of the Reform bill and abolition of slavery. William was the last Hanoverian King of Britain. On his death on 20th June 1837 the throne passed to his niece Victoria.

In order to prevent confusion between the Sixpence and Half-Sovereign the size of the latter was reduced in 1834, although the weight remained the same. The smaller gold piece was not acceptable to the public and in the following year it was made to the normal size. In 1836 the silver Groat was again issued for general circulation: it is the only British silver coin which has a seated Britannia as the type and was revised upon the suggestion of Mr Joseph Hume thus rendering the nickname "Joey". Crowns were not struck during this reign for general circulation; but proofs or patterns of this denomination were made and are greatly sought after. Silver Threepences and Three-Halfpence were minted for use in the Colonies.

**Engraver's and/or designer's initials on the coins:**
W. W. (William Wyon)
**Engravers and Designers:–** Francis Legett Chantrey (1781-1842) Jean Baptiste Merlen (1769-c.1850) William Wyon (1795-1851).

## GOLD

3828
1831 Proof Two Pounds

| | F | VF | EF | BU |
|---|---|---|---|---|
| | £ | £ | £ | £ |
| **3828 Two Pounds.** bare head r. R. crowned shield and mantle, date below, edge plain. die axis ↑↓ | | | | |
| 1831 (proof only) *FDC* £20000 | | | | |
| **3829 Sovereign.** First bust. r. top of ear narrow and rounded, nose to 2nd N of BRITANNIAR, fine obv. beading. R. Crowned shield. Die axis ↑↓ | | | | |
| 1830 Proof plain edge *FDC* £25000 | | | | |
| 1831 ...........550 | 1000 | 2750 | 5500 |
| 1832 ...........700 | 1500 | 3750 | 7500 |
| 1832 Proof *FDC* £26500 | | | | |
| **3829A Sovereign.** Similar, WW without stops die axis ↑↓ | | | | |
| 1831 ...........750 | 1750 | 3750 | 8000 |

3829B
Second bust with broad ear top

|  | F £ | VF £ | EF £ | BU £ |
|---|---|---|---|---|
| **3829B Sovereign.** Second bust. r. top of ear broad and flat, nose to 2nd I in BRITANNIAR, coarser obv. beading.↑↓ | | | | |
| 1830 plain edge proof *FDC* 21500 | | | | |
| 1831 ........................................................................6000 | 12500 | — | — | |
| 1831 Proof plain edge *FDC* £12500 | | | | |
| 1832* ........................................................................475 | 800 | 2000 | 4000 | |
| 1833 ........................................................................550 | 950 | 2250 | 4500 | |
| 1835 ........................................................................550 | 950 | 2250 | 5000 | |
| 1836 ........................................................................450 | 850 | 1850 | 4250 | |
| 1836 N of ANNO struck in shield ..............................5000 | 8500 | 17500 | — | |
| 1837 ........................................................................500 | 900 | 2000 | 4500 | |
| 1837 Tailed 8 ............................................................550 | 1000 | 2750 | — | |

3830                              3831
1834 Half-sovereign           Large size Half-Sovereign

**3830 Half-Sovereign.** Small size (17.9mm), bare head r.R. Crowned shield and mantle. Die axis ↑↓

| 1831 Proof plain edge *FDC* £6000 | | | | |
|---|---|---|---|---|
| 1831 Proof milled edge *FDC* £12500 | | | | |
| 1834 ........................................................................350 | 750 | 1750 | 3250 | |

**3831 Half-Sovereign.** Large size (19.4mm), bare head r.R. Crowned shield and mantle. Die axis ↑↓

| 1835 ........................................................................325 | 700 | 1500 | 2650 | |
|---|---|---|---|---|
| 1836 ........................................................................500 | 1200 | — | — | |
| 1837 ........................................................................400 | 700 | 1700 | 3000 | |

**3832 Half-Sovereign.** *Obv.* struck from Sixpence die (19.4mm) in error,

| 1836 ........................................................................3000 | 6000 | 12000 | — | |
|---|---|---|---|---|

* *Beware of counterfeits*

## SILVER

3833
1831 Crown. W.W. on truncation

| | F | VF | EF | BU |
|---|---|---|---|---|
| | £ | £ | £ | £ |

**3833 Crown.** R̃. Shield on mantle
1831 Proof only incuse W.W. on trun. struck ↑↓ *FDC* £35000
1831 Proof struck in gold of five pounds weight *FDC* £350000
1831 Bare head r. raised W. WYON on trun. struck ↑↑ en medaille
   (medal die axis) *FDC* £45000
1831 Bare head r. similar die axis ↑↓ *FDC* £40000
1831 Bare head r. incuse WW over W. WYON on trun. *FDC* ........................................*Extremely rare*
1834 Bare head r.  W.W. on trun. struck die axis ↑↓ *FDC* £60000

WW script

3834

**3834 Halfcrown.** Bare head.WW in script on trun. R̃. Shield on mantle, die axis ↑↓
1831 Plain edge proof *FDC* £3750
1831 Milled edge proof *FDC* £4000

| | F | VF | EF | BU |
|---|---|---|---|---|
| 1834 | 25 | 75 | 475 | 1100 |
| 1834 Plain edge proof *FDC* £4750 | | | | |
| 1834 Milled edge proof *FDC* £3750 | | | | |
| 1835 | 35 | 125 | 575 | 1400 |
| 1836/5 | 45 | 125 | 775 | 1500 |
| 1836 | 25 | 75 | 450 | 1100 |
| 1836 Proof *FDC* £4750 | | | | |
| 1837 | 45 | 175 | 550 | 1600 |

WW block

3834A

|  | F £ | VF £ | EF £ | BU £ |
|---|---|---|---|---|

**3834A Halfcrown.** Bare head r. block WW on trun. R. Similar. die axis ↑↓

| | | | | |
|---|---|---|---|---|
| 1831 Proof *FDC* £3750 | | | | |
| 1834 ..................................................45 | 165 | 675 | 1500 | |

3835
1831 Shilling

3836
1834 Sixpence

**3835 Shilling.** Bare head r. R. Value in wreath, date below. die axis ↑↓

| | F | VF | EF | BU |
|---|---|---|---|---|
| 1831 Plain edge Proof *FDC* £1500 | | | | |
| 1831 Milled edge proof *FDC* £3500 | | | | |
| 1834 ..................................................12 | 45 | 250 | 600 | |
| 1834 Milled edge Proof *FDC* £3500 | | | | |
| 1835 ..................................................18 | 50 | 250 | 550 | |
| 1835 Proof *FDC* £4000 | | | | |
| 1836 ..................................................18 | 45 | 250 | 550 | |
| 1836 Proof *FDC* £4000 | | | | |
| 1837 ..................................................25 | 75 | 325 | 725 | |
| 1837 Proof *FDC* £3500 | | | | |

**3836 Sixpence.** Bare head r. R. Value in wreath, date below. die axis ↑↓

| | F | VF | EF | BU |
|---|---|---|---|---|
| 1831 ..................................................12 | 25 | 135 | 325 | |
| — Proof *FDC* die axis ↑↓ or ↑↑ £1000 | | | | |
| 1831 Proof milled edge *FDC* £1250 | | | | |
| 1834 ..................................................12 | 25 | 145 | 350 | |
| 1834 large date..................................18 | 35 | 200 | 450 | |
| 1834 Proof *FDC* £1500 | | | | |
| 1835 ..................................................12 | 25 | 135 | 375 | |
| 1835 Proof *FDC* .....................................*Extremely rare* | | | | |
| 1836 ..................................................20 | 45 | 275 | 500 | |
| 1836 Proof *FDC* .....................................*Extremely rare* | | | | |
| 1837 ..................................................25 | 60 | 275 | 500 | |
| 1837 Proof *FDC* .....................................*Extremely rare* | | | | |
| 1837 B/RRITANNIAR .....................................*Extremely rare* | | | | |

3837 - 1836 Groat

3839 - 1835 Three-Halfpence

| | F £ | VF £ | EF £ | BU £ |
|---|---|---|---|---|
| **3837 Groat.** Bare head r. R. Britannia seated, date in ex. die axis ↑↑ | | | | |
| 1836 .................................................................5 | | 18 | 70 | 150 |
| 1836 Proof *FDC* £1250 | | | | |
| 1836 Plain edge proof *FDC* £1150 | | | | |
| 1836 Proof in gold *FDC* £17500 | | | | |
| 1837 .................................................................8 | | 22 | 90 | 200 |
| 1837 Type 2 obv. 'more wiry hair' *values as above* | | | | |
| 1837 Proof *FDC* £1425 | | | | |
| 1837 Plain edge proof *FDC* £1750 | | | | |
| **3838 Threepence.** Obverse 1, small head, low hair (for use in the West Indies). As Maundy threepence but with a dull surface, ↑↓ | | | | |
| 1834 ...............................................................12 | | 25 | 110 | 250 |
| 1835 .................................................................5 | | 18 | 85 | 225 |
| 1836 .................................................................5 | | 18 | 95 | 250 |
| 1837 ...............................................................12 | | 25 | 115 | 265 |
| **3838A** — Obverse 2, large head, high hair | | | | |
| 1834 .................................................................8 | | 20 | 95 | 225 |
| 1835 .................................................................7 | | 15 | 80 | 185 |
| 1836 .................................................................5 | | 12 | 65 | 150 |
| 1837 ...............................................................75 | | 150 | 250 | 575 |
| **3839 Three-Halfpence** (for Colonial use). Bare head r. R. Value, Crowned in wreath, die axis ↑↓ | | | | |
| 1834 .................................................................4 | | 10 | 50 | 110 |
| 1835/4 .............................................................5 | | 15 | 55 | 130 |
| 1835 unconfirmed without 5/4 | | | | |
| 1836 .................................................................5 | | 15 | 55 | 130 |
| 1837 ...............................................................12 | | 40 | 150 | 375 |
| 1837 Proof *FDC* £1500 | | | | |

3840 - 1831 Maundy Set

| | EF £ | FDC £ |
|---|---|---|
| **3840 Maundy Set** (4d., 3d., 2d. and 1d.). Bare head r. Die axis ↑↓ | | |
| 1831 ...............................................................200 | | 475 |
| — Proof *FDC* £1000 | | |
| 1831 Proof struck in gold *FDC* £35000 | | |
| 1832 ...............................................................175 | | 450 |
| 1833 ...............................................................165 | | 425 |
| 1834 ...............................................................165 | | 425 |
| 1835 ...............................................................165 | | 425 |
| 1836 ...............................................................200 | | 450 |
| 1837 ...............................................................200 | | 450 |

|  |  |  | EF | FDC |
|---|---|---|---|---|
|  |  |  | £ | £ |
| **3841** | — **Fourpence,** 1831-7 | *from* | 15 | 40 |
| **3842** | — **Threepence,** 1831-7 | *from* | 25 | 60 |
| **3843** | — **Twopence,** 1831-7 | *from* | 12 | 40 |
| **3844** | — **Penny,** 1831-7 | *from* | 22 | 50 |

*See note on under 3796.*

# COPPER

3845

| | F | VF | EF | BU |
|---|---|---|---|---|
| | £ | £ | £ | £ |
| **3845   Penny.** Bare head r. No initials on trun. date below. R. Britannia r. die axis ↑↑ | | | | |
| 1831 | 15 | 65 | 300 | 1250 |
| 1831 Proof *FDC* ↑↓ £1250 | | | | |
| 1831 Proof *FDC* ↑↑ £1400 | | | | |
| 1834 | 18 | 80 | 425 | 1500 |
| 1837 | 55 | 175 | 825 | 2000 |
| **3846   Penny.** Bare head r. date below. incuse initials on trun. R. Britannia r. die axis ↑↑ | | | | |
| 1831   W.W on trun | 110 | 475 | — | — |
| 1831 .W.W on trun | 30 | 115 | 475 | 1100 |

3847
1831 Halfpenny

| | F | VF | EF | BU |
|---|---|---|---|---|
| **3847   Halfpenny.** Bare head r. date below. R. Britannia r. die axis ↑↑ | | | | |
| 1831 | 10 | 30 | 150 | 325 |
| 1831 Proof  *FDC* ↑↓ £825 | | | | |
| 1831 Proof  *FDC* ↑↑ £925 | | | | |
| 1834 | 12 | 35 | 165 | 375 |
| 1837 | 8 | 25 | 135 | 325 |

3848
1831 Farthing

| | F | VF | EF | BU |
|---|---|---|---|---|
| | £ | £ | £ | £ |

**3848   Farthing.** Bare head r. date below. R. Britannia r. die axis ↑↑

| | F | VF | EF | BU |
|---|---|---|---|---|
| 1831 rev. incuse line on saltire ........................................2 | 12 | 65 | 150 |
| 1831 Proof  *FDC* ↑↓ £800 | | | |
| 1831 Proof *FDC* ↑↑ £850 | | | |
| 1834 incuse saltire ...............................................2 | 12 | 70 | 165 |
| 1834 rev. raised line on saltire ............................................4 | 15 | 85 | 200 |
| 1835 die axis ↑↓ ................................................................8 | 25 | 135 | 325 |
| 1835 die axis ↑↑ ................................................................2 | 12 | 90 | 250 |
| 1835 rev. incuse line on saltire ...............................2 | 15 | 85 | 200 |
| 1836 rev. raised line on saltire ............................................2 | 12 | 85 | 200 |
| 1837 — ...........................................................................2 | 15 | 85 | 200 |

3849                              3850
1837 Half-Farthing              1835 Third-Farthing

**3849   Half-Farthing** (for use in Ceylon). Bare head r. date below. R. Britannia r. die axis ↑↑

| | F | VF | EF | BU |
|---|---|---|---|---|
| 1837      ..........................................................................60 | 225 | 495 | — |

**3850   Third-Farthing** (for use in Malta). Bare head r. date below. R. Britannia r. die axis ↑↑

| | F | VF | EF | BU |
|---|---|---|---|---|
| 1835      ...........................................................................8 | 30 | 120 | 175 |
| 1835 Proof *FDC* £1100 | | | |

Copper coins graded in this catalogue as UNC have full mint lustre

**PROOF SET.**
**PS2** Coronation, 1831. Two pounds to farthing (14 coins). *FDC* £100000

# VICTORIA, 1837-1901

Victoria was born on 24th May 1819, the only child of Prince Edward, Duke of Kent and Princess Victoria of Saxe-Coburg-Saalfeld, and ascended to the throne in 1837. In 1840 she married her cousin Prince Albert of Saxe-Coburg and Gotha, with whom she enjoyed 21 years of marriage producing nine children. Upon Albert's untimely death in 1861 she descended into a lengthy period of mourning, her excessive melancholy leading her to be nick-named 'the widow of Windsor'. She skilfully avoided conflict with other European powers, and produced connections with many Royal houses all over Europe. Victoria died on 22nd January 1901 at the age of 81, and was the last British monarch of the House of Hanover.

In 1849, as a first step towards decimalisation, a silver Florin (1/10th pound) was introduced, but the coins of 1849 omitted the usual *Dei Gratia* and these so-called 'Godless' Florins were replaced in 1851 by the 'Gothic' issue. The Halfcrown was temporarily discontinued but was minted again from 1874 onwards. Between 1863 and 1880 reverse dies of the gold and silver coins were numbered in the course of Mint experiments into the wear of dies. The exception was the Florin where the die number is on the obverse below the bust.

The gold and silver coins were redesigned for the Queen's Golden Jubilee in 1887. The Double-Florin which was then issued was abandoned after only four years; the Jubilee Sixpence of 1887, known as the 'withdrawn' type, was changed to avoid confusion with the Half-Sovereign. Gold and silver were again redesigned in 1893 with an older portrait of the Queen, but the 'old head' was not used on the bronze coinage until 1895. The heavy copper Penny had been replaced by the lighter bronze 'bun' Penny in 1860. In 1874-6 and 1881-2 some of the bronze was made by Heaton in Birmingham, and these have a letter H below the date. From 1897 Farthings were issued with a dark surface.

Early Sovereigns had a shield-type reverse, but Pistrucci's St. George design was used again from 1871. In order to increase the output of gold coinage, branches of the Royal Mint were set up in Australia at Sydney and Melbourne and, later, at Perth for coining gold of imperial type.

**Engraver's and/or designer's initials on the coins:**
W. W. (William Wyon 1795-1851)          T. B. (Thomas Brock 1847-1922)
L. C. W. (Leonard Charles Wyon 1826-91)     B. P. (Benedetto Pistrucci, 1784-1855)
J. E. B. (Joseph Edgar Boehm 1834-90)

**Engravers and Designers:** George William De Saulle, (1862-1903) William Dyce (1806-64), Jean Baptiste Merlen (1769-c.1850) Edward Poynter (1836-1919)

## GOLD
**YOUNG HEAD COINAGE, 1838-87**

3851
1839 Five Pounds - DIRIGIT reverse

**3851 Five Pounds.** 1839. Young filleted bust l. plain rear fillet R. 'Una and the lion' (proof only)
DIRIGIT legend, inscribed edge, die axis ↑↑ *FDC* ..................................................... *Extremely rare*
– 1839 Similar – DIRIGIT legend, struck on thick flan .............................................. *Extremely rare*
– 1839 Similar – DIRIGIT legend, plain edge die axis ↑↑ ........................................ *Extremely rare*
– 1839 –13 leaves to rear fillet, R. DIRIGE legend–proof *FDC* £250000
– 1839 Similar – DIRIGE legend edge plain proof ..................................................... *Extremely rare*
– 1839 –9 leaves to rear fillet, DIRIGE legend *FDC* £250000
– 1839 Similar – DIRIGE legend edge plain ................................................................. *Extremely rare*
– 1839 Similar – DIRIGIT legend edge plain proof ..................................................... *Extremely rare*
*Truly FDC 1839 Five Pound coins are hardly ever encountered.*

3852
Sovereign - first smaller young head

| | F | VF | EF | BU |
|---|---|---|---|---|
| | £ | £ | £ | £ |

**3852 Sovereign.** First (small) young head. l. date below. ℞. First shield. London mint, die axis ↑↓

| | F | VF | EF | BU |
|---|---|---|---|---|
| 1838 | 875 | 1500 | 3500 | 6750 |
| 1838 Proof *FDC* | | | | *Extremely rare* |
| 1838 Plain edge proof *FDC* £27500 | | | | |
| 1839 | 1250 | 2500 | 4000 | 9500 |
| 1839 die axis ↑↓ Proof *FDC* £13500 | | | | |
| 1839 die axis ↑↑ Proof *FDC* £13500 | | | | |
| 1839 Milled edge proof *FDC* £25000 | | | | |
| 1841 | 5000 | 10000 | 22500 | — |
| 1841 GRATIΛ | 4500 | 9500 | 21000 | — |
| 1842 | 375 | 550 | 975 | 2000 |
| 1842 Open 2 | 600 | 1000 | — | |
| 1842 GRATIΛ | 550 | 950 | — | — |
| 1843 | BV | 450 | 925 | 2000 |
| 1843 Roman I | 675 | 1250 | — | — |
| 1843/2 or Ɀ | 450 | 700 | 1400 | 2900 |
| 1844 wider date | BV | 450 | 900 | 2000 |
| 1844 closer date | BV | 450 | 950 | 2000 |
| 1844 first 4/ ƀ | 750 | 1500 | 2250 | — |
| 1845 wider date | BV | 450 | 900 | 2000 |
| 1845 closer date | BV | 475 | 925 | 2000 |
| 1845 4/ ƀ | 750 | 1500 | 2250 | — |
| 1845 Roman I | 725 | 1400 | — | — |
| 1846 | BV | 500 | 950 | 2000 |
| 1846 4/ ƀ | 750 | 1500 | — | — |
| 1846 Roman I | 675 | 1250 | — | — |
| 1847 | BV | 500 | 950 | 2000 |
| 1847 Roman I | 700 | 1450 | — | — |
| 1848 | 1000 | 2250 | 7000 | — |

**3852A Sovereign.** Similar ℞ similar but leaves of the wreath arranged differently with tops of leaves closer to crown.

| | F | VF | EF | BU |
|---|---|---|---|---|
| 1838 | 5000 | 9500 | 23000 | — |

| | F £ | VF £ | EF £ | BU £ |
|---|---|---|---|---|

**3852BSovereign.** Similar narrower shield. Considerably modified floral emblems, different leaf arrangement ↑↓

| | | | | |
|---|---|---|---|---|
| 1843 | .............................................................5000 | 10000 | 21000 | — |

3852C
Second large head

**3852CSovereign.** Second (large) head. l. W W still in relief. date below R. Shield with repositioned legend die axis ↑↓

| | | | | |
|---|---|---|---|---|
| 1848 | ........................................................BV | 425 | 900 | 2500 |
| 1849 | ........................................................BV | 425 | 900 | 2600 |
| 1849 Roman I | ........................................675 | 1250 | — | — |
| 1850 | ........................................................BV | 500 | 950 | 2400 |
| 1850 Roman I | ........................................675 | 1250 | — | — |
| 1850    ∀ICTORIA | ................................1250 | — | — | — |
| 1850 8/5 | ........................................................................Extremely rare | | | |
| 1851 | ........................................................BV | 375 | 675 | 1750 |
| 1852 Roman I | ........................................675 | 1250 | — | — |
| 1852 | ........................................................BV | 365 | 775 | 2250 |
| 1853 | ........................................................BV | 365 | 700 | 1950 |
| 1853 F over E in DEF | ................................750 | 1650 | — | — |
| 1853∀ICTORIA | ................................1250 | — | — | — |
| 1854 | ........................................................BV | 475 | 1350 | 3100 |
| 1855 | ........................................................BV | 375 | 1000 | — |

| 3852D | 3852E |
|---|---|
| WW Incuse on truncation | Extra line in ribbon - 'Ansell' named after Royal Mint Chemist G.F. Ansell |

**3852D Sovereign.** Similar — WW incuse on trun. die axis ↑↓

| | | | | |
|---|---|---|---|---|
| 1853 | ........................................................BV | 575 | 1000 | 2300 |
| 1853 Roman I | ........................................675 | 1250 | — | — |
| 1853 Proof *FDC* £22500 | | | | |
| 1854 | ........................................................BV | 375 | 725 | 1500 |
| 1854 C over rotated C | ................................750 | 1650 | — | — |
| 1855 Roman I | ........................................650 | 1450 | — | — |
| 1855 | ........................................................BV | 375 | 725 | 1500 |
| 1856 | ........................................................BV | 375 | 725 | 1500 |

*BV= Bullion value only (if gold price over £1400 an ounce)*
*NB Truly BU Victorian sovereigns without any surface marks or hairlines are very rarely encountered.*

| | F | VF | EF | BU |
|---|---|---|---|---|
| | £ | £ | £ | £ |
| 1857 ........................................................................BV | | 375 | 725 | 1500 |
| 1857 ⱯICTORIA.................................................1250 | | — | — | — |
| 1857/5 ...................................................................................................*Variety exists* | | | | |
| 1858 small date..................................................BV | | 375 | 725 | 1600 |
| 1858 large date ..................................................BV | | 400 | 775 | 1600 |
| 1858 8/7...............................................................750 | | — | — | — |
| 1859 ....................................................................BV | | 375 | 725 | 1500 |
| 1860 O over C in obv. leg...................................450 | | 1100 | — | — |
| 1860 Roman I......................................................650 | | 1450 | — | — |
| 1860 ⱯICTORIA.................................................1250 | | 2750 | — | — |
| 1860 DEI GRⱯ ...................................................650 | | 1500 | — | — |
| 1860 ....................................................................BV | | 375 | 500 | 1150 |
| 1860 large 0 .......................................................BV | | 375 | 625 | 1300 |
| 1861 ....................................................................BV | | 300 | 575 | 1200 |
| 1861 Roman I......................................................500 | | 750 | 3250 | 3250 |
| 1861 C over rotated C in obv. leg........................750 | | 1650 | — | — |
| 1861 T over V in VICTORIA................................400 | | 750 | — | — |
| 1861 F/V in DEF narrow date ..............................500 | | 1250 | — | — |
| 1861 E over rotated E..........................................750 | | 1650 | — | — |
| 1862 R/E in BRIT................................................750 | | 1650 | — | — |
| 1862 Roman I......................................................500 | | 975 | — | — |
| 1862 wide date ...................................................BV | | 365 | 550 | 1300 |
| 1862 R/Я in VICTORIA.......................................1000 | | 2500 | — | — |
| 1862 F/Ɐ in DEF ................................................500 | | 1250 | — | — |
| 1862 narrow date ................................................BV | | 365 | 550 | 1300 |
| 1863 ....................................................................BV | | 365 | 550 | 1300 |
| 1863 Roman I .....................................................500 | | 975 | — | — |

**3852E Sovereign.** Similar — As 3852D 'Ansell' ribbon. Additional raised line on the lower part of the ribbon ↑↓

| 1859 ....................................................................750 | | 1850 | 8000 | 14500 |

**3852F Sovereign.** Similar — As 3852D with die number 827 on trun. die axis ↑↓

| 1863 ....................................................................4750 | | 10000 | 18500 | — |

3853
Die number location

**3853 Sovereign.** Similar As 3852D R. die number in space below wreath, above floral emblem, die axis ↑↓

| 1863 ...................................................................BV | BV | 495 | 1100 |
|---|---|---|---|
| 1864 ...................................................................BV | BV | 495 | 1100 |
| 1865 ...................................................................BV | BV | 500 | 1200 |
| 1866 ...................................................................BV | BV | 495 | 1100 |
| 1866/5 DIE 17 only ............................................375 | 450 | 675 | 1350 |
| 1868 ...................................................................BV | BV | 495 | 1100 |
| 1869 ...................................................................BV | BV | 495 | 110 |
| 1870 ...................................................................BV | BV | 495 | 1100 |

*BV= Bullion value only (if gold price over £1400 an ounce)*

|  | F | VF | EF | BU |
|---|---|---|---|---|
|  | £ | £ | £ | £ |

**3853A Sovereign.** Similar — As 3853 with die number 827 on trun. R. die number is always
no. 22 die axis ↑↓

| 1863 | ............................................................4500 | 7000 | 13500 | — |

**3853B Sovereign.** Similar — WW in relief on trun. R. die number below wreath, above floral
emblem die axis ↑↓

| 1870 | ............................................................BV | BV | 450 | 1000 |
| 1871 | ............................................................BV | BV | 425 | 900 |
| 1872 | ............................................................BV | BV | 495 | 1100 |
| 1872 no die number | ............................................BV | BV | 450 | 950 |
| 1873 | ............................................................BV | 365 | 525 | 1000 |
| 1874 | ............................................................1925 | 4050 | 9000 | — |

|  |  |
|---|---|
| 3854 | 3855 |
| 'M' Melbourne Mint mark | 'S' Sydney Mint mark |

**3854 Sovereign.** Second (large) head. l. WW in relief date below R. M below wreath for
Melbourne Mint, Australia ↑↓

| 1872 M | ............................................................BV | BV | 400 | 775 |
| 1872/1 M | ........................................................BV | 365 | 750 | 2250 |
| 1874 M | ............................................................BV | BV | 400 | 975 |
| 1880 M | ............................................................450 | 1250 | 3000 | 7000 |

**3854A Sovereign.** Third young head. Similar but different hair arrangement.

| 1881 M | ............................................................BV | BV | 400 | 2000 |
| 1882 M | ............................................................BV | BV | 400 | 850 |
| 1883 M | ............................................................BV | 300 | 500 | 2500 |
| 1884 M | ............................................................BV | BV | 400 | 850 |
| 1885 M | ............................................................BV | BV | 400 | 950 |
| 1886 M | ............................................................1500 | 4000 | 6000 | 13500 |
| 1887 M | ............................................................600 | 1100 | 3000 | 9000 |

**3855 Sovereign.** Similar — As 3854. R. with S below wreath for Sydney Mint, Australia
die axis ↑↓

| 1871 S | ............................................................BV | BV | 400 | 775 |
| 1872 S | ............................................................BV | BV | 400 | 975 |
| 1873 S | ............................................................BV | BV | 400 | 975 |
| 1875 S | ............................................................BV | BV | 400 | 975 |
| 1877 S | ............................................................BV | BV | 400 | 775 |
| 1878 S | ............................................................BV | BV | 400 | 775 |
| 1879 S | ............................................................BV | BV | 400 | 775 |
| 1880 S | ............................................................BV | BV | 400 | 975 |
| 1880 S VICTORIA | ..............................................450 | 1500 | 2700 | 7500 |

**3855A Sovereign.** Second (large) head WW incuse on trun. date below R. with S below wreath
for Sydney Mint die axis ↑↓

| 1871 S | ............................................................BV | BV | 400 | 1400 |

*BV= Bullion value only. At the time of going to press the spot price for gold was £1400 per oz.*

|  | F<br>£ | VF<br>£ | EF<br>£ | BU<br>£ |
|---|---|---|---|---|

**3855B** (Previously listed under 3855) as 3854A. Third head with different hair arrangements

| | | F | VF | EF | BU |
|---|---|---|---|---|---|
| 1881 S | ................................................BV | BV | 400 | 900 |
| 1882 S | ................................................BV | BV | 400 | 900 |
| 1883 S | ................................................BV | BV | 400 | 900 |
| 1884 S | ................................................BV | BV | 400 | 900 |
| 1885 S | ................................................BV | BV | 400 | 900 |
| 1886 S | ................................................BV | BV | 400 | 900 |
| 1887 S | ................................................BV | BV | 400 | 1250 |

*: The prices for Australian mint sovereigns are led by current trends in the Australian numismatic market place (which moved sharply downwards in 2014) and this trend has continued, although stabilising in 2017-2018. Being very condition conscious, it is truly UNC coins which command the highest price, any detraction from a true UNC coin should be taken at the EF guide price. The exchange rate of the Pound Sterling versus Australian Dollar also has an influence on price.*

| 3856A | 3857 |
|---|---|
| Horse with long tail, small BP in exergue | Melbourne Mint, WW buried in truncation |

**3856 Sovereign.** First young head. l. WW buried in narrow trun. ℞. St. George. London mint. Horse with short tail. Large BP and date in ex. die axis ↑↓

| | | F | VF | EF | BU |
|---|---|---|---|---|---|
| 1871 | ................................................— | BV | 400 | 850 |

1871 Proof milled edge*FDC* £18500
1871 Plain edge proof *FDC* £12500

**3856A Sovereign.** — — As 3856 ℞. Horse with long tail. Small BP and date in ex.die axis ↑↓

| | | F | VF | EF | BU |
|---|---|---|---|---|---|
| 1871 | ................................................— | BV | 400 | 850 |

1871 Proof *FDC* plain edge £11000

| | | F | VF | EF | BU |
|---|---|---|---|---|---|
| 1872 | ................................................— | BV | 400 | 850 |
| 1873 | ................................................— | BV | 400 | 850 |
| 1874 | ................................................— | BV | 400 | 850 |
| 1876 | ................................................— | BV | 400 | 850 |
| 1878 | ................................................— | BV | 400 | 850 |
| 1879 | ................................................600 | 1350 | 4750 | — |
| 1880 | ................................................— | BV | 400 | 850 |

**Horse tails** - three variations in tail length exist across Melbourne and Sydney, all are defined more accurately by the number of spurs of extra hair, or not, at tail indent on left side.
**Short tail** - two spurs of hair in left indent.
**Medium tail** - no spurs of hair in left indent.
**Long tail** - one spur of hair in left indent.

**3856B Sovereign.** — — As 3856 ℞. Horse with short tail, small BP and date in ex.die axis ↑↓

| | | F | VF | EF | BU |
|---|---|---|---|---|---|
| 1880 | ................................................— | BV | 400 | 850 |
| 1880 Second 8/7 | ................................................BV | BV | 485 | 1100 |
| 1884 | ................................................— | BV | 400 | 850 |
| 1885 | ................................................— | BV | 400 | 850 |

**3856C Sovereign.** — — As 3856 ℞. Horse with short tail, date but no BP in ex.die axis ↑↓

| | | F | VF | EF | BU |
|---|---|---|---|---|---|
| 1880 | ................................................BV | BV | 450 | 775 |
| 1880 Second 8/7 | ................................................BV | BV | 485 | 850 |

*BV= Bullion value only. At the time of going to press the spot price for gold was £1400 per oz.*

|  | F £ | VF £ | EF £ | BU £ |
|---|---|---|---|---|

**3856D Sovereign.** Second head. l. WW complete, on broad trun. Ṛ. Horse with long tail, small BP and date in ex.die axis ↑↓

| 1880 Second 8/7 | BV | BV | 400 | 950 |
| 1880 | BV | BV | 365 | 775 |

**3856E Sovereign.** — — As 3856D Ṛ. Horse with short tail. Date but no BP in ex. die axis ↑↓

| 1880 BV | BV | BV | 775 | |

**3856F Sovereign.** — — As 3856E Ṛ. Horse with short tail, small BP and date in ex. die axis ↑↓

| 1880 BV | BV | BV | 850 | |
| 1884 BV | BV | BV | 850 | |
| 1885 BV | BV | BV | 850 | |
| 1887 Proof *FDC* £29500 | | | | |

**3857 Sovereign.** — — First head. l. WW buried in trun. M below head for Melbourne Mint, Australia. Ṛ. Horse with long tail, small BP and date in ex. die axis ↑↓

| 1872 M | BV | BV | 475 | 2250 |
| 1873 M | BV | BV | 395 | 725 |
| 1874 M | BV | BV | 395 | 725 |
| 1875 M | BV | BV | 395 | 725 |
| 1876 M | BV | BV | 395 | 725 |
| 1877 M | BV | BV | 395 | 600 |
| 1878 M | BV | BV | 395 | 600 |
| 1879 M | BV | BV | 395 | 465 |
| 1880 M | BV | BV | 395 | 550 |
| 1881 M | BV | BV | 395 | 550 |

**3857A Sovereign.** — — As 3857 Ṛ. horse with short tail, date but no BP in ex die axis ↑↓

| 1881 M | BV | BV | 365 | 550 |
| 1882 M | BV | BV | 365 | 465 |
| 1883 M | BV | BV | 365 | 1000 |
| 1885 M | BV | BV | 365 | 700 |

**3857B Sovereign.** First head l. WW buried in trun. M below head for Melbourne Mint, Australia Ṛ. Horse with short tail, small BP and date in ex. die axis ↑↓

| 1882 M | BV | BV | 365 | 450 |
| 1883 M | BV | BV | 365 | 450 |
| 1884 M | BV | BV | 365 | 450 |
| 1885 M | BV | BV | 365 | 595 |

**3857C Sovereign.** — — Second head. l. WW complete on broad truncation. Ṛ. Horse with short tail, small BP in ex.

| 1882 M | BV | BV | 365 | 675 |
| 1883 M | BV | BV | 365 | 450 |
| 1884 M | BV | 200 | 365 | 400 |
| 1885 M | BV | BV | 365 | 450 |
| 1886 M | BV | BV | 365 | 450 |
| 1887 M | BV | BV | 365 | 725 |

**3857D Sovereign.** First head. l. WW buried in trun. M below Ṛ. Horse with medium tail, small BP

| 1879 M | BV | BV | 365 | 725 |
| 1880 M | BV | BV | 365 | 725 |
| 1881 M | BV | BV | 365 | 900 |
| 1882 M | BV | BV | 365 | 900 |

**3857E Sovereign.** Second head. l. WW complete on trun. M below Ṛ. Horse with short tail, no BP in ex.

| 1884 M | | | | *Extremely rare* |
| 1885 M | BV | BV | 395 | 600 |

*BV= Bullion value only. At the time of going to press the spot price for gold was £1400 per oz.*

|  | F<br>£ | VF<br>£ | EF<br>£ | BU<br>£ |
|---|---|---|---|---|

**3858 Sovereign** First head. l. WW buried in narrow trun. S below head for Sydney Mint, Australia, R. Horse with short tail, large BP and date in ex. die axis ↑↓

| 1871 S | BV | BV | 500 | 1800 |
|---|---|---|---|---|

**3858A Sovereign.** — — As 3858 R. Horse with long tail, small BP and date in ex. die axis ↑↓

| 1871 S | BV | BV | 425 | 2250 |
|---|---|---|---|---|
| 1872 S | BV | BV | 395 | 900 |
| 1873 S | BV | BV | 395 | 1550 |
| 1874 S | BV | BV | 395 | 1100 |
| 1875 S | BV | BV | 395 | 450 |
| 1876 S | BV | BV | 395 | 450 |
| 1879 S | BV | BV | 850 | 2250 |
| 1880 S | BV | BV | 395 | 725 |

**3858B Sovereign.** First head. As 3858 R. Horse with short tail, date but no BP in ex. die axis ↑↓

| 1880 S | BV | BV | 395 | 975 |
|---|---|---|---|---|
| 1881 S | BV | BV | 395 | 675 |

**3858C Sovereign.** Second head. l. WW complete on broad trun. R. Horse with long tail, small BP and date in ex. die axis ↑↓

| 1880 S | BV | BV | 395 | 725 |
|---|---|---|---|---|

**3858D Sovereign.** — — As 3858C R. Horse with short tail, date but no BP in ex. die axis ↑↓

| 1881 S | BV | BV | 395 | 585 |
|---|---|---|---|---|
| 1882 S | BV | BV | 395 | 475 |

**3858E Sovereign.** — — As 3858D R. Horse with short tail small BP and date in ex. die axis ↑↓

| 1882 S | BV | BV | 395 | 475 |
|---|---|---|---|---|
| 1883 S | BV | BV | 395 | 1100 |
| 1884 S | BV | BV | 395 | 500 |
| 1885 S | BV | BV | 395 | 475 |
| 1886 S | BV | BV | 395 | 475 |
| 1887 S | BV | BV | 395 | 475 |

**3858F Sovereign.** Second head. Horse with long tail, no BP in ex.

| 1880 S | BV | 365 | 425 | 775 |
|---|---|---|---|---|

3859                 3859A
Type A1          Type A2

**3859 Half-Sovereign.** Type A1. First (smallest) young head. date below l. R. First shield, die axis ↑↓

| 1838 | 200 | 325 | 1100 | 2000 |
|---|---|---|---|---|

1839 die axis ↑↓ or ↑↑ Proof only *FDC* £6500

1839 Milled edge proof *FDC* ..............................................................*Extremely rare*

| 1841 | 250 | 350 | 1350 | 3250 |
|---|---|---|---|---|
| 1842 | 200 | 300 | 800 | 1750 |
| 1843 | 200 | 325 | 850 | 2000 |
| 1844 | 200 | 325 | 800 | 1900 |
| 1845 | 300 | 800 | 3000 | — |
| 1846 | 200 | 325 | 800 | 1900 |
| 1847 | 200 | 325 | 800 | 1900 |

*BV= Bullion value only. At the time of going to press the spot price for gold was £1400 per oz.*

| | F £ | VF £ | EF £ | BU £ |
|---|---|---|---|---|
| 1848 Close date | 185 | 325 | 800 | 1900 |
| 1848/7 | 250 | 500 | 1100 | 2350 |
| 1848 Wide date | 200 | 325 | 1000 | 2000 |
| 1849 | 185 | 300 | 850 | 1900 |
| 1850 | 250 | 600 | 2250 | — |
| 1851 | 185 | 300 | 700 | 1600 |
| 1852 | 185 | 300 | 800 | 1750 |
| 1853 | 185 | 300 | 750 | 1600 |
| 1853 Proof small date *FDC* £12000 | | | | |
| 1853 Proof large date *FDC* £15000 | | | | |
| 1855 | 185 | 300 | 750 | 1700 |
| 1856 | 185 | 300 | 725 | 1750 |
| 1856/5 | 225 | 350 | 850 | 1850 |
| 1857 | 185 | 300 | 750 | 1600 |
| 1858 | 185 | 300 | 750 | 1600 |

**3859A Half-Sovereign**. Type A2, Second (larger) young head. date below. R. First shield die axis ↑↓

| | F £ | VF £ | EF £ | BU £ |
|---|---|---|---|---|
| 1858 | 185 | 300 | 625 | 1400 |
| 1859 | 185 | 300 | 625 | 1400 |
| 1860 | 185 | 300 | 600 | 1350 |
| 1861 | 185 | 300 | 700 | 1350 |
| 1862 | 850 | 2500 | 9000 | — |
| 1863 | 185 | 300 | 575 | 1350 |

| 3860 | 3860D | 3860E | 3860F |
|---|---|---|---|
| Die number location | Type A3 | Type A4 | Type A5 |

**3860 Half-Sovereign.** Type A2, second head, date below R. die number below shield, die axis ↑↓

| | F £ | VF £ | EF £ | BU £ |
|---|---|---|---|---|
| 1863 | 185 | 250 | 700 | 1500 |
| 1864 | BV | 200 | 600 | 1250 |
| 1865 | BV | 200 | 600 | 1250 |
| 1866 | BV | 200 | 600 | 1250 |
| 1867 | BV | 200 | 600 | 1250 |
| 1869 | BV | 200 | 600 | 1250 |
| 1870 | BV | 175 | 575 | 1100 |
| 1871 | BV | 175 | 575 | 1150 |

**3860A Half-Sovereign.** Second head, date below R. Re-engraved shield legend and rosettes closer to border, coarse boarder teeth both sides, with die number below shield die axis ↑↓

| | F £ | VF £ | EF £ | BU £ |
|---|---|---|---|---|
| 1870 | 275 | 675 | 1500 | — |
| 1871 | 225 | 575 | 1350 | — |

**3860B Half-Sovereign.** Second head, date below R. As last but with normal border teeth and no die number below shield die axis ↑↓

| | F £ | VF £ | EF £ | BU £ |
|---|---|---|---|---|
| 1871 | 300 | 750 | 1900 | — |

**3860C Half-Sovereign.** Second head, date below obv. with repositioned legend, nose now points to T in VICTORIA. R Similar to last but with die number below shield die axis ↑↓

| | F £ | VF £ | EF £ | BU £ |
|---|---|---|---|---|
| 1871 | 300 | 875 | 1800 | — |
| 1872 | 225 | 575 | 1350 | — |

*BV= Bullion value only. At the time of going to press the spot price for gold was £1400 per oz.*

|         | F    | VF   | EF   | BU   |
|---------|------|------|------|------|
|         | £    | £    | £    | £    |

**3860DHalf-Sovereign.** Type A3, Third (larger still) young head l, date below. ℞. As 3860A, with die number below shield die axis ↑↓

| 1872 | ..................................................BV | 185 | 500 | 1200 |
| 1873 | ..................................................BV | 185 | 500 | 1200 |
| 1874 | ..................................................BV | 200 | 525 | 1200 |
| 1875 | ..................................................BV | 175 | 475 | 1100 |
| 1876 | ..................................................BV | 175 | 475 | 1100 |
| 1877 | ..................................................BV | 175 | 475 | 1100 |

3860E
Half Sovereign

3861
Type A5

**3860E Half-Sovereign.** Type A4. Fourth young head l. hair ribbon now narrow, date below. ℞. As last with die number below shield die axis ↑↓

| 1876 | ..................................................BV | 175 | 475 | 1100 |
| 1877 | ..................................................BV | 175 | 475 | 1100 |
| 1878 | ..................................................BV | 175 | 475 | 1100 |
| 1879 | ..................................................500 | 895 | — | — |

**3860F Half-Sovereign.** Type A5. Fifth young head l. in very low relief, date below. ℞. As last with die number below shield die axis ↑↓

| 1880 | ..................................................185 | 235 | 675 | 1475 |

**3860G Half-Sovereign.** Type A4. Fourth young head, without die number below shield.

| 1876 | ..................................................*Extremely rare* |

**3861 Half-Sovereign.** Fifth head, date below. ℞. Cross on crown buried in border. Legend and rosettes very close to heavy border, no die number below shield die axis ↑↓

| 1880 | ..................................................BV | 185 | 500 | 1200 |
| 1883 | ..................................................BV | 175 | 450 | 1000 |
| 1884 | ..................................................BV | 175 | 450 | 1000 |
| 1885 | ..................................................BV | 175 | 450 | 900 |
| 1885/3 | ..................................................200 | 300 | 850 | 1650 |

**3862 Half-Sovereign.** Type A2, Second (larger) young head l. nose points between T and O. Date below ℞. First crowned shield cross clear of border with S below shield for Sydney Mint, Australia, die axis ↑↓

| 1871 S | ..................................................BV | 200 | 800 | 8000 |
| 1871 S Proof | ..................................................*Extremely rare* |

**3862A Half-Sovereign.** Similar obv. with repositioned legend, nose now points to T in VICTORIA. Date below ℞ Re-engraved shield cross touches border, S below shield die axis ↑↓

| 1872 S | ..................................................BV | 200 | 800 | 8000 |

**3862B Half-Sovereign.** Type A3. Third (larger still) young head l. I of DEI points to rear fillet. Date below ℞. As last die axis ↑↓

| 1875 S | ..................................................BV | 200 | 800 | 8000 |

**3862C Half-Sovereign.** Type A4. Fourth young head l. front hair fillet now narrow. ℞. As last, die axis ↑↓

| 1879 S | ..................................................BV | 200 | 850 | 7500 |

*\* Beware recent forgeries*
*BV= Bullion value only. At the time of going to press the spot price for gold was £1400 per oz.*

|  | F £ | VF £ | EF £ | BU £ |
|---|---|---|---|---|

**3862E Half-Sovereign.** Fifth head, date below Ŗ. Cross on crown buried in border. Legend
and rosettes very close to heavy border, S below shield die axis ↑↓

| | | | | |
|---|---|---|---|---|
| 1880 S | BV | 200 | 500 | 11500 |
| 1881 S | BV | 225 | 900 | 10000 |
| 1882 S | BV | 600 | 2250 | 14000 |
| 1883 S | BV | 200 | 650 | 4500 |
| 1883 S Proof | | | | *Extremely rare* |
| 1886 S | BV | 200 | 650 | 4750 |
| 1887 S | BV | 200 | 550 | 3750 |

**3863 Half-Sovereign.** Type A3. Third (larger still) young head l. Date below Ŗ. Re-engraved
shield with M below shield for Melbourne Mint, Australia die axis ↑↓

| | | | | |
|---|---|---|---|---|
| 1873 M | BV | 200 | 1100 | 8000 |
| 1877 M | BV | 250 | 2750 | 9500 |

**3863A Half-Sovereign.** Type A4, fourth young head l. hair ribbon now narrow. Ŗ.
As last die axis ↑↓

| | | | | |
|---|---|---|---|---|
| 1877 M | BV | 200 | 850 | 8000 |
| 1882 M | BV | 200 | 2250 | 9500 |

**3863B Half-Sovereign.** Type A5. Fifth young head l. in low relief.Date below Ŗ.
As last die axis ↑↓

| | | | | |
|---|---|---|---|---|
| 1881 M | BV | 600 | 4000 | 12000 |
| 1882 M | BV | 200 | 750 | 4500 |
| 1884 M | BV | 250 | 2750 | 10000 |
| 1884 M Proof | | | | *Extremely rare* |
| 1885 M | 175 | 550 | 5000 | 11000 |
| 1886 M | BV | 400 | 7000 | 12000 |
| 1886 M Proof | | | | *Extremely rare* |
| 1887 M | BV | 1250 | 10000 | 16500 |

## JUBILEE COINAGE, 1887-93, die axis ↑↑

3864
1887 Five Pounds

**3864\* Five Pounds.** Jubilee bust l. Ŗ. St. George date in ex.

| | | | | |
|---|---|---|---|---|
| 1887 | 1600 | 2000 | 2750 | 3500 |

— Proof *FDC* £13500
— Proof no B.P. in exergue £20000

**3864A\* Five Pounds.** Jubilee bust l. Ŗ. St George, S on ground for Sydney Mint, Australia

| | |
|---|---|
| 1887 S | *Extremely rare* |

*\* Beware recent forgeries*
*BV= Bullion value only. At the time of going to press the spot price for gold was £1400 per oz.*
*(See note on page 449 re. horse tails.)*
*For a detailed variety synopsis of Jubilee Head Sovereigns and their rarity see publication 'The Jubilee*
*Head Gold Sovereign' by David Iverson. (DISH)*

| | F | VF | EF | BU |
|---|---|---|---|---|
| | £ | £ | £ | £ |

**3865\* Two Pounds.** Jubilee bust 1. R. St George die axis ↑↑

1887 ..................................................................685 875 1150 1600

1887 Proof *FDC* £3250

1887 Proof no BP in exergue FDC *Extremely rare*

**3865A\* Two Pounds.** R. St George, S on ground for Sydney Mint, Australia ↑↑

1887 S ............................................................................................*Extremely rare*

3866

1887 Sovereign

**3866\* Sovereign.** Normal JEB (angled J) designer's initials fully on trun. R. St. George.
die axis ↑↑ (*DISH L7, L8*)

| 1887 | .......................................................................— | BV | 275 | 425 |
|---|---|---|---|---|
| 1888 | ................................................................365 | 750 | 1250 | 2000 |
| 1889 | ...................................................................................... *Exists?* |
| 1890 | ...................................................................................... *Exists?* |

**3866A Sovereign.** Similar with tiny JEB (hooked J) closer designer's initials at base of truncation;
stops in an arc, die axis ↑↑ (*DISH L1, L4*)

| 1887 | ................................................................365 | 750 | 1250 | 2000 |
|---|---|---|---|---|

**3866B Sovereign.** Similar repositioned legend. G: of D:G: now closer to crown. Normal JEB
(angled J) designer's initials at base of trun. ↑↑ (*DISH L9, L11, L13, L14*))

1887 Proof *FDC* £3000

| 1888 | ..............................................................— | BV | 350 | 500 |
|---|---|---|---|---|
| 1889 | ..............................................................— | BV | 350 | 450 |
| 1890 | ..............................................................— | BV | 350 | 450 |
| 1891 | ................................................................600 | 1200 | 2000 —? | — |

**3866C Sovereign.** Similar obv. as last. R. Horse with longer tail, two variations of hair strands
die axis ↑↑ (*DISH L15, L16*)

| 1891 | ..............................................................— | BV | 350 | 450 |
|---|---|---|---|---|

1891 Proof *FDC* £19500

| 1892 | ..............................................................— | BV | 350 | 450 |
|---|---|---|---|---|

**3866D Sovereign.** First legend with tiny JEB (hooked J) with initials more spread across truncation;
stops all in line ↑↑ (*DISH L2, L3*)

| 1887 | ................................................................350 | 750 | 1250 | 2000 |
|---|---|---|---|---|

3867

"M' Melbourne Mint on groundline above 8's in date

**3867 Sovereign.** Similar with small spread JEB (hooked J) designer's initials fully on trun. R.
M on ground for Melbourne Mint, Australia, die axis ↑↑ (*DISH M1-M4*)

1887 M ...................................................................................BV 650 1000 1850

*\* Beware recent forgeries*

*BV= Bullion value only. At the time of going to press the spot price for gold was £1400 per oz.*

| | F £ | VF £ | EF £ | BU £ |
|---|---|---|---|---|

**3867A Sovereign.** Similar with normal JEB designer's initials on trun. (angled J) die axis ↑↑ (*DISH M7, M9, M11*)

| | | | | |
|---|---|---|---|---|
| 1887 M | — | BV | 350 | 500 |
| 1888 M | BV | 600 | 1100 | 2000 |
| 1889 M | — | BV | 600 | 1850 |
| 1890 M | | | | *Exists?* |

**3867B Sovereign.** Similar repositioned legend. G: of D: G: now closer to crown. Normal JEB (angled J) initials at base of trun. die axis ↑↑ (*DISH M8, M10, M12, M14, M15*)

| | | | | |
|---|---|---|---|---|
| 1887 M | — | BV | 450 | 725 |
| 1888 M | — | BV | 350 | 500 |
| 1888 Proof *FDC* | | | | *Extremely rare* |
| 1889 M | — | BV | 350 | 500 |
| 1890 M | — | BV | 350 | 500 |
| 1891 M | BV | 600 | 1100 | 2000 |

**3867C Sovereign.** Similar obv. as last. Ŗ. Horse with longer tail, two variations of hair strands die axis ↑↑ (*DISH M16-M18*)

| | | | | |
|---|---|---|---|---|
| 1891 M | — | BV | 375 | 575 |
| 1892 M | — | BV | 350 | 450 |
| 1893 M | — | BV | 350 | 550 |

**3868 Sovereign.** First legend with closer JEB (angled J) stops in arc on trun. Ŗ. S on ground for Sydney Mint, Australia die axis ↑↑ (*DISH S9, S11, S13*)

| | | | | |
|---|---|---|---|---|
| 1888 S | — | BV | 375 | 600 |
| 1889S | — | BV | 375 | 625 |
| 1890S | — | BV | 600 | 1350 |

**3868A Sovereign.** Similar with spread JEB designer's initials stop level on left side of trun. (hooked J) die axis ↑↑ (*DISH S1-S8*)

| | | | | |
|---|---|---|---|---|
| 1887 S | 400 | 750 | 1500 | 3000 |
| 1887 S Proof | | | | |

*Extremely rare*

| | | | | |
|---|---|---|---|---|
| 1888 S | BV | 600 | 1100 | 2000 |

**3868B Sovereign.** Similar repositioned legend. G: of D:G: now closer to crown. Normal JEB (angled J) initials on trun. die axis ↑↑ (*DISH S10, S12, S14*)

| | | | | |
|---|---|---|---|---|
| 1888 S | — | BV | 350 | 500 |
| 1889 S | — | BV | 350 | 550 |
| 1890 S | — | BV | 350 | 550 |

*BV= Bullion value only. At the time of going to press the spot price for gold was £1400 per oz.*

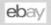

| | F<br>£ | VF<br>£ | EF<br>£ | BU<br>£ |
|---|---|---|---|---|

**3868C Sovereign.** Similar obv. as last. R. Horse with longer tail die axis ↑↑ (*DISH S15-S17*)

| | | | | |
|---|---|---|---|---|
| 1891 S | — | BV | 350 | 465 |
| 1892 S | — | BV | 350 | 550 |
| 1893 S | — | BV | 375 | 575 |

**3868D Sovereign.** First legend with spread JEB initials ending at right side of trun. (hooked J) ↑↑ (*DISH S2*)

| | | | | |
|---|---|---|---|---|
| 1887 S | 400 | 800 | 1500 | 3000 |

3869 ✳            3869D
higher shield, cross blends into border        Plain trun., lower shield, cross clear of border

**3869 Half-Sovereign.** Similar obv. normal JEB designer's initials. on trun. R. High shield die axis ↑↑

| | | | | |
|---|---|---|---|---|
| 1887 | BV | BV | 225 | 350 |
| — Proof *FDC* £2250 | | | | |
| 1890 | BV | 185 | 500 | — |

**3869A Half-Sovereign.** Similar small close JEB intitials. on trun. R. High shield die axis ↑↑

| | | | | |
|---|---|---|---|---|
| 1887 | BV | 165 | 450 ✳ | — |

**3869B Half-Sovereign.** Similar normal JEB initials. on trun. R. Lower shield, date therefore spread apart, complete cross at top, die axis ↑↑

| | | | | |
|---|---|---|---|---|
| 1890 | BV | 165 | 475 | — |
| 1892 | BV | 165 | 475 | — |

**3869C Half-Sovereign.** Similar no JEB initials on trun. R. High Shield die axis ↑↑

| | | | | |
|---|---|---|---|---|
| 1887 | BV | 165 | 450 . | — |
| 1890 | BV | 165 | 240 | 400 |
| 1891 | BV | 165 | 450 | — |
| 1892 | BV | 165 | 450 ✓ | — |

**3869D Half-Sovereign.** Jubilee bust 1. R. Lower shield, date therefore spread apart die axis ↑↑

| | | | | |
|---|---|---|---|---|
| 1890 | — | 165 | 225 | 350 |
| 1891 | — | 165 | 250 | 375 |
| 1892 | — | 165 | 225 | 350 |
| 1893 | — | 165 | 250 | 375 |

3870

**3870 Half-Sovereign.** Similar small very spread JEB initials on trun. R. High shield, M below for Melbourne Mint, Australia, die axis ↑↑

| | | | | |
|---|---|---|---|---|
| 1887 M | BV | 200 | 400 | 1600 |
| 1887 M Proof | | | | *Extremely rare* |

*BV= Bullion value only. At the time of going to press the spot price for gold was £1400 per oz.*

|  | F | VF | EF | BU |
|---|---|---|---|---|
|  | £ | £ | £ | £ |

**3870A Half-Sovereign.** Similar small close JEB initials on trun. ℞. As last die axis ↑↑

1887 M ........................................................................ BV   200   350   1400

1887 M Proof........................................................................................*Extremely rare*

**3870B Half-Sovereign.** Similar normal JEB initials on trun. ℞. Lower shield, date therefore
   spread part die axis ↑↑

1893 M ........................................................................ BV   250   500   2250

**3871 Half-Sovereign.** Similar small very spread JEB initials on trun. (hooked J) ℞. High shield S
   below for Sydney Mint, Australia ↑↑

1887 S ........................................................................ BV   200   400   1200

**3871A Half-Sovereign.** Similar small close JEB initials on trun. ℞ As last. die axis ↑↑

1887 S ........................................................................ BV   200   325   1100

1887 S Proof ........................................................................................*Extremely rare*

**3871B Half-Sovereign.** Jubilee bust 1. Normal JEB initials on trun. ℞. Lower shield,
   date therefore spread apart, S below for Sydney Mint, Australia die axis ↑↑

1889 S ........................................................................ BV   250   1400   4500

**3871C Half-Sovereign.** Jubilee bust 1. Normal JEB initials on trun. ℞. High shield,
   S below for Sydney Mint, Australia die axis ↑↑

1891 S ........................................................................ BV   300   1100   3750

**3871D Half-Sovereign.** Jubilee bust 1. No JEB initials on trun. ℞. As last die axis ↑↑

1891 S ........................................................................ BV   250   700   3000

## OLD HEAD COINAGE, 1893-1901, die axis ↑↑

3872
1893 Five Pounds

**3872\* Five Pounds.** Old veiled bust 1. ℞. St. George and dragon, date and BP in ex.

1893   ....................................................................1750   2500   4000   6500

1893 Proof  *FDC* £17500

3873
1893 Two Pounds

**3873\* Two Pounds.** Old veiled bust 1. ℞. St. George and dragon, date and BP in ex. die axis ↑↑

1893..................................................................................................750   1000   1950   2750

1893 Proof  *FDC* £5250

*\* Beware recent forgeries*

*BV= Bullion value only. At the time of going to press the spot price for gold was £1400 per oz.*

3874 - 1893 Sovereign

|  | F £ | VF £ | EF £ | BU £ |
|---|---|---|---|---|
| **3874 Sovereign.** Old veiled bust 1. R. St. George, London Mint die axis ↑↑ | | | | |
| 1893 | — | — | BV | 375 |
| 1893 Proof *FDC* £3500 | | | | |
| 1894 | — | — | BV | 375 |
| 1895 | — | — | BV | 375 |
| 1896 | — | — | BV | 375 |
| 1898 | — | — | BV | 375 |
| 1899 | — | — | BV | 375 |
| 1900 | — | — | BV | 375 |
| 1901 | — | — | BV | 375 |
| **3875 Sovereign.** Similar R. St. George. M on ground for Melbourne Mint, Australia die axis ↑↑ | | | | |
| 1893 M | — | — | BV | 475 |
| 1894 M | — | — | BV | 425 |
| 1895 M | — | — | BV | 425 |
| 1896 M | — | — | BV | 400 |
| 1897 M | — | — | BV | 400 |
| 1898 M | — | — | BV | 425 |
| 1899 M | — | — | BV | 400 |
| 1900 M | — | — | BV | 400 |
| 1901 M | — | — | BV | 400 |

3876 - Perth Mint mark

3878 - 1893 Half -Sovereign

| | F | VF | EF | BU |
|---|---|---|---|---|
| **3876 Sovereign.** Similar — P on ground for Perth Mint, Australia die axis ↑↑ | | | | |
| 1899 P | BV | BV | 475 | 2250 |
| 1900 P | — | BV | BV | 475 |
| 1901 P | — | BV | BV | 475 |
| **3877 Sovereign.** Similar — S on ground for Sydney Mint, Australia die axis ↑↑ | | | | |
| 1893 S | — | — | BV | 425 |
| 1894 S | — | — | BV | 425 |
| 1895 S | — | — | BV | 425 |
| 1896 S | — | BV | BV | 475 |
| 1897 S | — | BV | BV | 475 |
| 1898 S | — | BV | BV | 475 |
| 1899 S | — | — | BV | 425 |
| 1900 S | — | — | BV | 425 |
| 1901 S | — | — | BV | 425 |

*BV= Bullion value only. At the time of going to press the spot price for gold was £1400 per oz.*
*NB Truly BU old bust sovereigns are very scarce. Any surface defects will cause the value to drop*
*significantly.*

|  | F £ | VF £ | EF £ | BU £ |
|---|---|---|---|---|

**3878 Half-Sovereign**. Old veiled bust 1.R. St. George. Date in ex. (no B.P. on this issue in exergue) London Mint die axis ↑↑

| | F | VF | EF | BU |
|---|---|---|---|---|
| 1893 | — | BV | 175 | 325 |
| — Proof *FDC* £2650 | | | | |
| 1894 | — | BV | 175 | 325 |
| 1895 | — | BV | 175 | 325 |
| 1896 | — | BV | 175 | 325 |
| 1897 | — | BV | 175 | 325 |
| 1898 | — | BV | 175 | 325 |
| 1899 | — | BV | 175 | 325 |
| 1900 | — | BV | 175 | 325 |
| 1901 | — | BV | 175 | 325 |

**3879 Half-Sovereign**. Similar — M on ground for Melbourne Mint, Australia die axis ↑↑

| | F | VF | EF | BU |
|---|---|---|---|---|
| 1893 M | | | *Extremely rare* | |
| 1896 M | BV | 250 | 400 | 2250 |
| 1899 M | BV | 250 | 600 | 2500 |
| 1899 M Proof | | | *Extremely rare* | |
| 1900 M | BV | 250 | 650 | 2000 |
| 1900 M Proof | | | *Extremely rare* | |
| 1896 M Proof | | | *Extremely rare* | |

**3880 Half-Sovereign**. Similar — P on ground for Perth Mint, Australia die axis ↑↑

| | F | VF | EF | BU |
|---|---|---|---|---|
| 1899 P Proof only | | | *unique* | |
| 1900 P | 150 | 300 | 750 | 4000 |

**3881 Half-Sovereign**. Similar — S on ground for Sydney Mint, Australia die axis ↑↑

| | F | VF | EF | BU |
|---|---|---|---|---|
| 1893 S | BV | 250 | 500 | 1650 |
| 1893 S Proof | | | *Extremely rare* | |
| 1897 S | BV | 250 | 425 | 2000 |
| 1900 S | BV | 300 | 375 | 1200 |

*BV= Bullion value only. At the time of going to press the spot price for gold was £1400 per oz.*
*NB Truly BU old bust sovereigns are very scarce. Any surface defects will cause the value to drop*
*significantly.*

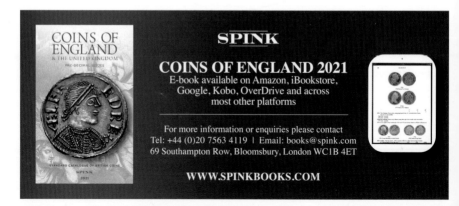

# VICTORIA

## SILVER

**YOUNG HEAD COINAGE, 1838-87,** die axis ↑↓

**Edge Stops**

Cinquefoil

3882
1844 Crown

Star

| | F | VF | EF | BU |
|---|---|---|---|---|
| | £ | £ | £ | £ |

†**3882 Crown.** Young head. l. ℞. Crowned shield, regnal year on edge in Roman figures
(eg 1847 = XI)

| | | | | |
|---|---|---|---|---|
| 1839 Proof only *FDC* £27500 | | | | |
| 1844 Star stops, extra square of metal at tip of ponytail  150 | 350 | 1500 | 4500 |
| 1844 Star stops ................................................60 | 200 | 1450 | 4000 |
| 1844 Cinquefoil stops....................................125 | 400 | 1750 | 4250 |
| 1844 Mistruck edge lettering.........................145 | 475 | 3500 | – |
| 1845 Cinquefoil stops......................................65 | 250 | 1500 | 4000 |
| 1847 XI Cinquefoil stops...............................125 | 375 | 2000 | 5000 |

3883 - 1847 Gothic Crown

**3883*Crown.** 'Gothic' type, bust 1. ℞. Crowned cruciform Shields, emblems in angles.
inscribed edge, mdcccxlvii=

1847 Undecimo on edge die axis ↑↓ ............................800 | 1350 | 2650 | 6500

1847 Septimo on edge of highest rarity.

1847 Proof in gold plain edge *FDC* ......................................................... *Of highest rarity*

1847 Proof, Plain edge die axis ↑↑ *FDC* £11000

1847 Proof in white metal plain edge *FDC*

**3884 Crown.** Similar mdccliii=

1853. Septimo on edge die axis ↑↑ Proof *FDC* £32000

1853 plain edge proof *FDC* £42000

†*The Victorian young head Crowns are notoriously hard to grade. A truly BU coin must show all design elements clearly expecially on hair fillets and the reverse shield. All facial features and hair must also be present.*

\**Beware of recent forgeries.*

|                                          | F    | VF   | EF    | BU   |
|                                          | £    | £    | £     | £    |

**3885 Halfcrown.** Type A[1]. Young head l. with one ornate and one plain fillet binding hair. WW in relief on trun. R. Crowned shield of arms, edge milled. Die axis ↑↓
  1839 Milled edge Proof *FDC Extremely rare*
  1839 Proof plain edge *FDC* £5000

**3886 Halfcrown.** Type A[2] Similar, but two ornate fillets binding hair.die axis ↑↓
  1839 Proof only *FDC* £6750

**3886A Halfcrown.** Type A[2/3] Similar, Two plain fillets, WW relief, die axis ↑↓ plain edge
  1839 Proof *FDC* £7750

**3887 Halfcrown.** Type A[3]. Similar two plain fillets. WW incuse on trun. die axis ↑↓

| 1839 | 1250 | 3500 | 10000 | — |
| 1839 Milled edge Proof *FDC* £6750 | | | | |
| 1839 Plain edge Proof *FDC* £6750 | | | | |
| 1840 | 60 | 200 | 1100 | 2750 |

**3888 Halfcrown.** Type A[4]. Similar but no initials on trun. die axis ↑↓

| 1841 | 1000 | 2000 | 4850 | 8000 |
| 1842 | 40 | 135 | 700 | 1250 |
| 1843 | 125 | 450 | 1850 | 4250 |
| 1844 | 40 | 125 | 585 | 1475 |
| 1844 not in edge collar | | | | *Extremely rare* |
| 1845 | 40 | 125 | 585 | 1475 |
| 1845 5/3 | | | | *Extremely rare* |
| 1846 | 40 | 125 | 585 | 1475 |
| 1848/6 | 185 | 525 | 1500 | 3500 |
| 1848/7 | | | | *Extremely rare* |
| 1848 | 200 | 575 | 2000 | 4250 |
| 1849 large date | 65 | 200 | 975 | 2250 |
| 1849/7 | | | | *Extremely rare* |
| 1849 small date | 100 | 350 | 1100 | 2650 |
| 1850 | 65 | 275 | 900 | 2350 |
| 1850 Proof *FDC* £14500 | | | | |
| 1853 Proof *FDC* £7500 | | | | |
| 1862 Proof *FDC* £13500 | | | | |
| 1862 Plain edge Proof *FDC* £12500 | | | | |
| 1864 Proof *FDC* £13500 | | | | |
| 1864 Plain edge Proof *FDC* £12500 | | | | |

3889
Type A5 Halfcrown

3890
1849 'Godless' Florin

**3889 Halfcrown.** Similar Type A[5]. As last but design of inferior workmanship R. Crowned shield die axis ↑↓

| 1874 | 20 | 65 | 250 | 650 |
| 1874 Proof *FDC* £8000 | | | | |

| | F | VF | EF | BU |
|---|---|---|---|---|
| | £ | £ | £ | £ |
| 1875 .................................................................20 | | 55 | 225 | 625 |
| 1875 Proof *FDC* £9500 | | | | |
| 1876 .................................................................20 | | 65 | 265 | 650 |
| 1876/5 ..............................................................30 | | 75 | 355 | 900 |
| 1877 .................................................................20 | | 65 | 265 | 600 |
| 1878 .................................................................25 | | 65 | 265 | 650 |
| 1878 Proof *FDC* £8500 | | | | |
| 1879 .................................................................25 | | 65 | 325 | 700 |
| 1879 Proof *FDC* £8500 | | | | |
| 1880 .................................................................18 | | 45 | 200 | 500 |
| 1880 Proof *FDC* £8500 | | | | |
| 1881 .................................................................18 | | 45 | 200 | 500 |
| 1881 Proof *FDC* £8500 | | | | |
| 1881 Plain edge proof *FDC* £9750 | | | | |
| 1882 .................................................................20 | | 65 | 325 | 600 |
| 1883 .................................................................12 | | 45 | 225 | 525 |
| 1883 Plain edge proof *FDC* £9750 | | | | |
| 1884 .................................................................15 | | 45 | 225 | 525 |
| 1885 .................................................................15 | | 45 | 225 | 525 |
| 1885 Proof *FDC* £8500 | | | | |
| 1886 .................................................................15 | | 45 | 225 | 525 |
| 1886 Plain edge proof *FDC* £9000 | | | | |
| 1887 .................................................................20 | | 60 | 250 | 550 |
| 1887 Proof *FDC* £9000 | | | | |

**3890 Florin.** 'Godless' type A (i.e. without D.G.), WW behind bust within linear circle, die axis ↑↓

1848 Plain edge (Pattern) *FDC* £3750
1848 Milled edge ↑↑ or ↑↓ Proof *FDC* £5500

| | F | VF | EF | BU |
|---|---|---|---|---|
| 1849 WW obliterated..................................................45 | | 75 | 400 | 800 |
| 1849 .................................................................20 | | 55 | 275 | 575 |

**3891 Florin.** 'Gothic' type B[1]. Reads brit:, WW below bust, date at end of obverse legend in gothic numerals (1851 to 1863) Crowned cruciform Shields, emblems in angles, edge milled. die axis ↑↓

| | F | VF | EF | BU |
|---|---|---|---|---|
| mdcccli Proof only *FDC* £32500 | | | | |
| mdccclii ..........................................................15 | | 45 | 250 | 600 |
| mdccclii Proof *FDC* £5750 | | | | |
| mdccclii, ii/i ..................................................20 | | 55 | 375 | 760 |
| mdcccliii .........................................................15 | | 45 | 300 | 675 |
| mdcccliii Proof *FDC* £6500 | | | | |
| mdcccliv ........................................................850 | | 1950 | 7000 | — |
| mdccclv...........................................................25 | | 75 | 325 | 760 |
| mdccclvi .........................................................25 | | 75 | 325 | 760 |
| mdccclvii ........................................................20 | | 55 | 325 | 750 |
| mdccclvii Proof *FDC* £6500 | | | | |
| mdccclviii .......................................................15 | | 45 | 325 | 750 |
| mdccclviii Proof *FDC* £6500 | | | | |
| mdccclix .........................................................15 | | 45 | 325 | 750 |
| mdccclx...........................................................20 | | 50 | 400 | 875 |
| mdccclxii ......................................................250 | | 685 | 1850 | 5000 |
| mdccclxii Plain edge Proof *FDC* £8000 | | | | |
| mdccclxiii .....................................................900 | | 2250 | 7000 | 14250 |
| mdccclxiii Plain edge Proof *FDC* £10000 | | | | |

3891          3893

1853 Florin Type B¹

|  | F | VF | EF | BU |
|---|---|---|---|---|
|  | £ | £ | £ | £ |

**3892 Florin.** Type B². Similar as last but die number below bust (1864 to 1867) die axis ↑↓

| mdccclxiv | 20 | 60 | 325 | 675 |
|---|---|---|---|---|
| mdccclxiv heavy flan | 350 | 800 | 2500 | 5250 |

mdccclxiv heavy flan Proof *FDC* £9500

mdccclxvii Proof *FDC* £6500

| mdccclxv | 40 | 100 | 485 | 825 |
|---|---|---|---|---|
| mdccclxvi | 35 | 80 | 400 | 750 |
| mdccclxvii | 35 | 85 | 450 | 850 |

**3893 Florin.** Type B³. Similar reads britt:, die number below bust (1868 to 1879) die axis

| mdccclxviii | 30 | 90 | 485 | 900 |
|---|---|---|---|---|
| mdccclxix | 30 | 90 | 500 | 950 |

mdccclxix Proof *FDC* £6750

| mdccclxx | 20 | 55 | 350 | 900 |
|---|---|---|---|---|

mdccclxx Proof *FDC* £6750

| mdccclxxi | 20 | 55 | 325 | 685 |
|---|---|---|---|---|

mdccclxxi Proof *FDC* £6000

| mdccclxxii | 15 | 40 | 250 | 775 |
|---|---|---|---|---|
| mdccclxxiii | 20 | 55 | 250 | 775 |

mdccclxxiii Proof *FDC* £5500

| mdccclxxiv | 25 | 65 | 300 | 800 |
|---|---|---|---|---|
| mdccclxxiv iv/iii | 35 | 80 | 325 | 950 |
| mdccclxxv | 20 | 50 | 300 | 725 |
| mdccclxxvi | 20 | 50 | 285 | 675 |
| mdccclxxvii | 25 | 50 | 300 | 850 |
| mdccclxxix | | | | *Extremely rare* |

**3894 Florin.** Type B⁴. Similar as last but with border of 48 arcs and no WW below bust die axis ↑↓

| mdccclxxvii | | | | *Extremely rare* |
|---|---|---|---|---|

**3895 Florin.** Type B⁵. Similar but border of 42 arcs (1867, 1877 and 1878) die axis ↑↓

| mdccclxxvii | 2850 | — | — | — |
|---|---|---|---|---|
| mdccclxxvii | 25 | 60 | 350 | 900 |
| mdccclxxviii | 20 | 50 | 300 | 775 |
| mdccclxxviii Proof *FDC* | | | | *Extremely rare* |

**3896 Florin.** Type B⁵/⁶. Similar as last but no die number below bust (1877, 1879) die axis ↑↓

| mdccclxxvii | 125 | 275 | 600 | 1400 |
|---|---|---|---|---|
| mdccclxxix | 110 | 275 | 725 | 1625 |

3897
1878 - Florin Type B⁶

|  | F £ | VF £ | EF £ | BU £ |
|---|---|---|---|---|

**3897 Florin.** Type B⁶. Similar reads britt:, WW; Border of 48 arcs (1879) die axis ↑↓
mdccclxxviii .......................................................................................*Extremely rare*
mdccclxxix ......................................................20      50      295      725
**3898 Florin.** Type B⁷. Similar as last but no WW, Border of 38 arcs (1879) die axis ↑↓
mdccclxxix ......................................................20      50      295      725
mdccclxxix Proof *FDC* £6000
**3899 Florin.** Type B³/₈. Similar as next but younger portrait (1880) die axis ↑↓
mdccclxxx...........................................................................................*Extremely rare*
**3900 Florin.** Type B⁸. Similar but border of 34 arcs (1880 to 1887) die axis ↑↓
mdccclxxx......................................................15      40      350      575
mdccclxxx Proof *FDC* £6000
mdccclxxxi .....................................................15      40      275      625
mdccclxxxi Proof *FDC* £5750
mdccclxxxi/xxri.............................................30      80      385      795
mdccclxxxiii ..................................................15      40      285      625
mdccclxxxiii Proof *FDC* £5000
mdccclxxxiv ..................................................15      50      285      625
mdccclxxxv ...................................................20      60      285      625
mdccclxxxv Proof *FDC* £6000
mdccclxxxvi ..................................................15      50      285      625
mdccclxxxvi Proof *FDC* £6250
**3901 Florin.** Type B⁹. Similar but border of 46 arcs die axis ↑↓
1887 mdccclxxxvii .......................................30      75      365      825
mdccclxxxvii Proof *FDC* .............................................*Extremely rare*
**3902 Shilling.** Type A¹. First head l., WW on trun.R. crowned mark of value within wreath,
date below, die axis ↑↓
1838  ......................................................15      35      195      450
1838 Proof *FDC* £4000
1839  ......................................................35      90      275      800
1839 Proof *FDC* £3650
**3903 Shilling** Type A². Second head, l. WW on trun. (proof only), 1839 die axis ↑↑ *FDC* £2000

3904 - Type A³ Shilling

|  | F £ | VF £ | EF £ | BU £ |
|---|---|---|---|---|
| **3904 Shilling** Type A³. Second head, l. no initials on trun. R. Similar die axis ↑↓ | | | | |
| 1839 ..............................................................18 | 35 | 185 | 450 |
| 1839 Proof plain edge *FDC* £1750 | | | | |
| 1839 Proof plain edge en medaille ↑↑ *FDC* £3000 | | | | |
| 1839 Proof milled edge *FDC* £4000 | | | | |
| 1840 ..............................................................18 | 35 | 225 | 525 |
| 1840 Proof *FDC* £4250 | | | | |
| 1841 ..............................................................25 | 60 | 250 | 525 |
| 1842 ..............................................................18 | 45 | 225 | 500 |
| 1842 Proof *FDC* £4250 | | | | |
| 1843 ..............................................................25 | 60 | 265 | 600 |
| 1844 ..............................................................18 | 35 | 195 | 485 |
| 1845 ..............................................................25 | 45 | 225 | 525 |
| 1846 ..............................................................20 | 40 | 200 | 450 |
| 1848 over 6 ......................................................65 | 225 | 825 | 1750 |
| 1849 ..............................................................25 | 45 | 250 | 600 |
| 1850 ............................................................800 | 1750 | 5000 | — |
| 1850/49 ..........................................................875 | 2000 | 5250 | — |
| 1851 ..............................................................50 | 125 | 575 | 1250 |
| 1851 Proof *FDC* £5500 | | | | |
| 1852 ..............................................................10 | 25 | 180 | 425 |
| 1853 ..............................................................10 | 20 | 165 | 425 |
| 1853 Milled edge Proof *FDC* £3000 | | | | |
| 1854 ............................................................250 | 600 | 2000 | 5000 |
| 1854/1 ..........................................................300 | 875 | 3500 | — |
| 1855 ..............................................................10 | 25 | 165 | 425 |
| 1856 ..............................................................10 | 25 | 165 | 425 |
| 1857 ..............................................................10 | 25 | 165 | 425 |
| 1857 REG F: Ɔ:error ........................................250 | 600 | 1950 | — |
| 1858 ..............................................................10 | 25 | 165 | 425 |
| 1859 ..............................................................10 | 25 | 165 | 425 |
| 1859 9/8 ..........................................................25 | 65 | 375 | 800 |
| 1859 Proof *FDC* £4500 | | | | |
| 1860 ..............................................................12 | 35 | 225 | 525 |
| 1861 ..............................................................12 | 35 | 225 | 500 |
| 1861 D/B in FD ..............................................150 | 400 | 1000 | — |
| 1862 ..............................................................40 | 85 | 325 | 675 |
| 1863 ..............................................................50 | 185 | 550 | 1350 |
| 1863/1 ............................................................90 | 275 | 900 | — |

| | F | VF | EF | BU |
|---|---|---|---|---|
| | £ | £ | £ | £ |

**3905 Shilling** Type A⁴. Similar as last, R. Die number above date die axis ↑↓

| | F | VF | EF | BU |
|---|---|---|---|---|
| 1864 | 10 | 25 | 145 | 425 |
| 1865 | 10 | 25 | 145 | 425 |
| 1866 | 10 | 25 | 145 | 425 |
| 1866 BBITANNIAR | 60 | 300 | 1100 | 1750 |
| 1867 | 15 | 30 | 145 | 425 |

**3906 Shilling** Type A⁵. Third head, l. R. Similar no die number above date die axis ↑↓
1867 Proof £4500
1867 Proof plain edge £4750

| | F | VF | EF | BU |
|---|---|---|---|---|
| 1879 | 225 | 500 | 1250 | 2200 |

1879 Proof, milled edge, *FDC* £4500

3906A - Type A⁶ Shilling

Die number location above date

**3906A Shilling** Type A⁶. Third head, l. R. Similar die number above date die axis ↑↓

| | F | VF | EF | BU |
|---|---|---|---|---|
| 1867 | 200 | 500 | 1500 | 2750 |
| 1868 | 10 | 25 | 145 | 425 |
| 1869 | 20 | 40 | 190 | 425 |
| 1870 | 15 | 35 | 195 | 425 |
| 1871 | 10 | 20 | 135 | 425 |

1871 Plain edge proof *FDC* £4250
1871 Milled edge proof *FDC* £4000

| | F | VF | EF | BU |
|---|---|---|---|---|
| 1872 | 10 | 20 | 145 | 425 |
| 1873 | 10 | 20 | 145 | 425 |
| 1874 | 10 | 20 | 145 | 425 |
| 1875 | 10 | 20 | 145 | 395 |
| 1876 | 15 | 30 | 150 | 425 |
| 1877 | 10 | 20 | 145 | 420 |
| 1878 | 20 | 40 | 200 | 480 |

1878 Milled edge Proof *FDC* £4250
1879 uncertain to exist as normal coin or proof?

**3907 Shilling** Type A⁷. Fourth head, l. R. Similar no die number above date die axis ↑↓

| | F | VF | EF | BU |
|---|---|---|---|---|
| 1879 | 10 | 18 | 130 | 395 |
| 1879 B over R in GBATIA | 350 | — | — | — |

1879 Proof *FDC* £4250

| | F | VF | EF | BU |
|---|---|---|---|---|
| 1880 | 10 | 18 | 125 | 295 |

1880 Proof plain edge £4000
1880 Proof milled edge £3500

| | F | VF | EF | BU |
|---|---|---|---|---|
| 1881 | 10 | 18 | 100 | 225 |

1881 Proof plain edge £4250
1881 Proof milled edge £3250

| | F | VF | EF | BU |
|---|---|---|---|---|
| 1882 | 10 | 28 | 165 | 385 |
| 1883 | 10 | 18 | 135 | 325 |

1883 plain edge Proof *FDC* £4750

| | F | VF | EF | BU |
|---|---|---|---|---|
| 1884 | 10 | 18 | 110 | 300 |

1884 Proof *FDC* £3750

| | F | VF | EF | BU |
|---|---|---|---|---|
| 1885 | 10 | 15 | 100 | 295 |

| | F | VF | EF | BU |
|---|---|---|---|---|
| | £ | £ | £ | £ |
| 1885 Proof *FDC* £3750 | | | | |
| 1886 ..................................................10 | 15 | 110 | 285 |
| 1886 Proof *FDC* £3750 | | | | |
| 1887 ..................................................10 | 20 | 125 | 325 |
| 1887 Proof *FDC* £3250 | | | | |

**3907A Shilling.** Type A$^7$. Fourth head, R. Similar die number above date die axis ↑↓

| 1878 ..................................................15 | 25 | 100 | 300 |
|---|---|---|---|
| 1878 Milled edge Proof *FDC* £4000 | | | | |
| 1879 ..................................................10 | 30 | 145 | 400 |

3908
Type A$^1$ Sixpence

**3908 Sixpence.** Type A$^1$. First head l. R. Crowned mark of value within wreath, date below
die axis ↑↓

| 1838 ..................................................8 | 22 | 130 | 325 |
|---|---|---|---|
| 1838 Proof *FDC* £2750 | | | | |
| 1839 ..................................................8 | 22 | 130 | 350 |
| 1839 Proof  *FDC* £1200 | | | | |
| 1840 ..................................................8 | 22 | 130 | 375 |
| 1841 ..................................................10 | 25 | 150 | 400 |
| 1842 ..................................................8 | 22 | 120 | 325 |
| 1843 ..................................................8 | 22 | 120 | 325 |
| 1844 Small 44..................................8 | 17 | 130 | 375 |
| 1844 Large 44..................................12 | 25 | 150 | 400 |
| 1845 ..................................................8 | 17 | 120 | 350 |
| 1846 ..................................................8 | 17 | 115 | 400 |
| 1847 An example in fair condition sold at DNW, 29/9/10, lot 1773 for £850 + premium | | | | |
| 1848 ..................................................90 | 275 | 950 | 3250 |
| 1848/6 or 7........................................90 | 275 | 950 | 3250 |
| 1850 ..................................................8 | 17 | 110 | 300 |
| 1850/3 ..............................................12 | 25 | 150 | 350 |
| 1851 ..................................................8 | 17 | 150 | 350 |
| 1852 ..................................................7 | 17 | 130 | 350 |
| 1853 ..................................................7 | 17 | 120 | 395 |
| 1853 Proof  *FDC* £1650 | | | | |
| 1854 ..................................................200 | 450 | 1500 | 3250 |
| 1855 ..................................................7 | 17 | 110 | 350 |
| 1855/3 ..............................................10 | 22 | 150 | 400 |
| 1855 Proof *FDC* .......................................................................*Extremely rare* | | | | |
| 1856 ..................................................7 | 17 | 130 | 375 |
| 1857 ..................................................7 | 17 | 130 | 375 |
| 1858 ..................................................7 | 17 | 130 | 375 |
| 1858 Proof *FDC* .......................................................................*Extremely rare* | | | | |
| 1859 ..................................................7 | 17 | 130 | 375 |
| 1859/8 ..............................................8 | 17 | 130 | 375 |
| 1860 ..................................................8 | 17 | 130 | 375 |
| 1862 ..................................................110 | 285 | 750 | 1500 |
| 1863 ..................................................75 | 175 | 525 | 1100 |
| 1866 ...............................................................................................*Extremely rare* | | | | |

| | 3909 | | 3912 |
|---|---|---|---|

Die number location above date

Type A⁵ Sixpence

| | F £ | VF £ | EF £ | BU £ |
|---|---|---|---|---|

**3909 Sixpence.** Type A². First head, R. Similar die number above date die axis ↑↓

| 1864 | 7 | 17 | 130 | 385 |
|---|---|---|---|---|
| 1865 | 7 | 20 | 150 | 365 |
| 1866 | 7 | 12 | 130 | 385 |
| 1867 | 8 | 20 | 150 | 395 |

| | 3910 | | 3911 |
|---|---|---|---|

**3910 Sixpence.** Type A³. Second head, l. R. Similar die number above date, die axis ↑↓

| 1867 | 8 | 17 | 120 | 300 |
|---|---|---|---|---|
| 1867 Proof *FDC* £2750 | | | | |
| 1868 | 8 | 17 | 120 | 300 |
| 1869 | 8 | 17 | 150 | 425 |
| 1869 Proof *FDC* £3000 | | | | |
| 1870 | 8 | 17 | 150 | 425 |
| 1870 plain edge Proof *FDC* £3000 | | | | |
| 1871 | 8 | 15 | 110 | 325 |
| 1871 plain edge Proof *FDC* £3000 | | | | |
| 1872 | 8 | 15 | 110 | 325 |
| 1873 | 10 | 18 | 125 | 325 |
| 1874 | 7 | 12 | 90 | 250 |
| 1875 | 8 | 15 | 110 | 300 |
| 1876 | 9 | 18 | 160 | 425 |
| 1877 | 8 | 15 | 110 | 300 |
| 1878 | 8 | 15 | 110 | 300 |
| 1878 DRITANNIAR | 150 | 420 | 1250 | — |
| 1878 Proof *FDC* £2750 | | | | |
| 1878/7 | 35 | 175 | 800 | — |
| 1879 | 8 | 17 | 125 | 325 |

**3911 Sixpence.** Type A⁴. Second head, l. R. Similar No die number, die axis ↑↓

| 1871 | 8 | 15 | 125 | 325 |
|---|---|---|---|---|
| 1871 Proof *FDC* £22500 | | | | |
| 1877 | 8 | 15 | 125 | 325 |
| 1879 | 8 | 15 | 125 | 325 |
| 1879 milled edge Proof *FDC* £2750 | | | | |
| 1879 plain edge Proof *FDC* £3000 | | | | |
| 1880 | 5 | 10 | 95 | 275 |

3912              3913

| | F | VF | EF | BU |
|---|---|---|---|---|
| | £ | £ | £ | £ |

**3912 Sixpence.** Type A[5]. Third head l. R. Similar, die axis ↑↓

| | F | VF | EF | BU |
|---|---|---|---|---|
| 1880 ........8 | | 15 | 80 | 200 |
| 1880 Proof *FDC* £2750 | | | | |
| 1881 ........8 | | 15 | 70 | 185 |
| 1881 plain edge Proof *FDC* ........................................................................*Extremely rare* | | | | |
| 1881 milled edge Proof *FDC* .....................................................................*Extremely rare* | | | | |
| 1882 ........10 | | 25 | 110 | 350 |
| 1883 ........8 | | 15 | 70 | 185 |
| 1883 Small R legend ........15 | | 40 | 150 | 400 |
| 1883 plain edge Proof *FDC Extremely rare* | | | | |
| 1884 ........8 | | 15 | 75 | 200 |
| 1885 ........8 | | 15 | 75 | 200 |
| 1885 Proof *FDC* £2500 | | | | |
| 1886 ........8 | | 15 | 75 | 200 |
| 1886 Proof *FDC* £2500 | | | | |
| 1887 ........8 | | 12 | 75 | 200 |
| 1887 Proof *FDC* £2250 | | | | |

**3913 Groat** (4d.). Young head 1.R. Britannia seated r. date in ex, edge milled, die axis ↑↑

| | F | VF | EF | BU |
|---|---|---|---|---|
| 1837 Plain edge Proof £13500 | | | | |
| 1837 Milled edge Proof £12500 | | | | |
| 1838 ........5 | | 12 | 60 | 135 |
| 1838 plain edge Proof *FDC* £1500 | | | | |
| 1838 Milled edge Proof £1350 | | | | |
| 1838/∞ 8 ........20 | | 80 | 175 | |
| 1839 ........7 | | 15 | 70 | 175 |
| 1839 die axis ↑↑ Proof plain edge *FDC* £750 | | | | |
| 1839 die axis ↑↓ Proof plain edge *FDC* £800 | | | | |
| 1840 ........7 | | 15 | 65 | 150 |
| 1840 small round o ........10 | | 20 | 65 | 175 |
| 1841 ........10 | | 25 | 100 | 250 |
| 1842 ........8 | | 15 | 65 | 175 |
| 1842 Proof *FDC* £1500 | | | | |
| 1842/1 ........10 | | 20 | 70 | 225 |
| 1843 ........8 | | 15 | 65 | 150 |
| 1843 4 over 5 ........10 | | 25 | 75 | 250 |
| 1844 ........7 | | 15 | 70 | 150 |
| 1845 ........8 | | 15 | 65 | 150 |
| 1846 ........8 | | 15 | 65 | 150 |
| 1847/6 (or 8) ........30 | | 125 | 360 | 700 |
| 1848/6 ........10 | | 35 | 90 | 200 |
| 1848 ........6 | | 15 | 65 | 150 |
| 1848/7/6 ........10 | | 30 | 110 | 325 |
| 1849 ........5 | | 15 | 65 | 150 |
| 1849/8 ........8 | | 15 | 75 | 150 |
| 1851 ........20 | | 80 | 350 | 725 |
| 1852 ........50 | | 165 | 600 | 1000 |

| | F | VF | EF | BU |
|---|---|---|---|---|
| | £ | £ | £ | £ |
| 1853 .................................................................................125 | 400 | 900 | — |
| 1853 Proof *FDC* milled edge £1600 | | | | |
| 1853 Proof *FDC* plain edge £1700 | | | | |
| 1854 .................................................................................5 | 15 | 60 | 150 |
| 1855 .................................................................................5 | 15 | 60 | 150 |
| 1855/3 ............................................................................10 | 25 | 75 | 175 |
| 1857 Milled or plain edge proof *FDC* £2250 | | | | |
| 1857 Plain edge pattern £2750 | | | | |
| 1862 Plain or milled edge Proof *FDC* £2750 | | | | |
| 1862 Plain edge pattern *FDC* £3500 | | | | |

**3914 Threepence.** Type A¹. First bust, young head, high relief, ear fully visible, die axis ↑↓
Ｒ Crowned 3; as Maundy threepence but with a less prooflike surface.

| | F | VF | EF | BU |
|---|---|---|---|---|
| 1838* .............................................................................6 | 18 | 75 | 200 |
| 1838 BRITANNIAB .....................................................*Extremely rare* | | | |
| 1839* .............................................................................8 | 28 | 100 | 250 |
| 1839 Proof (see Maundy) | | | | |
| 1840* .............................................................................8 | 25 | 90 | 250 |
| 1841* .............................................................................8 | 28 | 100 | 250 |
| 1842* .............................................................................8 | 28 | 125 | 275 |
| 1843* .............................................................................6 | 18 | 75 | 200 |
| 1844* .............................................................................8 | 25 | 100 | 200 |
| 1845 .............................................................................6 | 12 | 70 | 175 |
| 1846 .............................................................................27 | 75 | 275 | 550 |
| 1847* .............................................................................40 | 135 | 350 | 800 |
| 1848* .............................................................................50 | 165 | 650 | — |
| 1849 .............................................................................8 | 30 | 100 | 250 |
| 1850 .............................................................................8 | 25 | 90 | 350 |
| 1851 .............................................................................6 | 18 | 75 | 225 |
| 1851 reads 1551 .............................................................650 | — | — | — |
| 1851 5 over 8 ................................................................15 | 35 | 175 | 325 |
| 1852* .............................................................................90 | 225 | 650 | 1100 |
| 1853 .............................................................................23 | 80 | 275 | 500 |
| 1854 .............................................................................6 | 15 | 90 | 225 |
| 1855 .............................................................................8 | 25 | 100 | 250 |
| 1856 .............................................................................6 | 15 | 90 | 200 |
| 1857 .............................................................................6 | 22 | 100 | 250 |
| 1858 .............................................................................6 | 12 | 75 | 200 |
| 1858 BRITANNIAB .....................................................*Extremely rare* | | | |
| 1858/6 ............................................................................15 | 28 | 200 | — |
| 1858/5 ............................................................................10 | 25 | 150 | — |
| 1859 .............................................................................6 | 12 | 75 | 200 |
| 1860 .............................................................................6 | 22 | 100 | 250 |
| 1861 .............................................................................6 | 12 | 75 | 20 |

*\*Issued for Colonial use only.*

3914A - Type A²        3914C - Type A⁴        3914D - Type A⁵

| | F £ | VF £ | EF £ | BU £ |
|---|---|---|---|---|
| **3914A Threepence.** Type A². First bust variety, slightly older portrait with aquiline nose ↑↓ | | | | |
| 1859 | 6 | 12 | 75 | 175 |
| 1860 | 6 | 12 | 75 | 175 |
| 1861 | 6 | 12 | 75 | 175 |
| 1862 | 9 | 20 | 75 | 175 |
| 1863 | 14 | 27 | 100 | 200 |
| 1864 | 6 | 12 | 75 | 175 |
| 1865 | 6 | 15 | 100 | 200 |
| 1866 | 6 | 12 | 75 | 175 |
| 1867 | 6 | 12 | 75 | 175 |
| 1868 | 6 | 12 | 75 | 175 |
| 1868 RRITANNIAR | | | | *Extremely rare* |
| **3914B Threepence.** Type A³. Second Bust, slightly larger, lower relief, mouth fuller, nose more pronounced, rounded truncation, die axis ↑↓ | | | | |
| 1867 | 6 | 23 | 100 | 225 |
| **3914C Threepence.** Type A⁴. Obv. as last. ℞. Tie ribbon further from tooth border, cross on crown nearer to tooth border die axis ↑↓ | | | | |
| 1866 | | | | *Extremely rare* |
| 1867 | 6 | 22 | 80 | 200 |
| 1868 | 6 | 22 | 80 | 200 |
| 1869 | 9 | 22 | 100 | 275 |
| 1870 | 4 | 12 | 70 | 150 |
| 1871 | 6 | 16 | 75 | 175 |
| 1872 | 6 | 16 | 75 | 175 |
| 1873 | 4 | 12 | 55 | 125 |
| 1874 | 4 | 12 | 55 | 100 |
| 1875 | 4 | 12 | 55 | 100 |
| 1876 | 4 | 12 | 55 | 100 |
| 1877 | 4 | 12 | 65 | 125 |
| 1878 | 4 | 12 | 65 | 125 |
| 1879 | 4 | 12 | 65 | 125 |
| 1879 Proof *FDC* | | | | *Extremely rare* |
| 1884 | 4 | 7 | 55 | 100 |
| **3914D Threepence.** Type A⁵. Third bust, older features, mouth closed, hair strands leading from 'bun' vary, die axis ↑↓ | | | | |
| 1880 | 4 | 9 | 60 | 115 |
| 1881 | 4 | 9 | 45 | 100 |
| 1882 | 4 | 9 | 65 | 175 |
| 1883 | 4 | 9 | 45 | 100 |
| 1885 | 5 | 8 | 45 | 100 |
| 1885 Proof *FDC* | | | | *Extremely rare* |
| 1886 | 5 | 8 | 45 | 100 |
| 1887 | 5 | 10 | 60 | 115 |
| **3914E Twopence.** Young head 1. ℞ Date divided by a crowned 2 within a wreath, die axis ↑↓ | | | | |
| 1838 | 4 | 9 | 30 | 75 |
| 1848 | 4 | 9 | 40 | 80 |

3915 - Three-Halfpence

| | F £ | VF £ | EF £ | BU £ |
|---|---|---|---|---|

**3915 Three-Halfpence.** (for Colonial use).Young head 1. R. Crowned value and date, die axis ↑↓

| | F | VF | EF | BU |
|---|---|---|---|---|
| 1838 | 4 | 9 | 45 | 115 |
| 1838 Proof *FDC* £1000 | | | | |
| 1839 | 4 | 9 | 40 | 100 |
| 1840 | 7 | 23 | 85 | 200 |
| 1841 | 4 | 14 | 50 | 125 |
| 1842 | 4 | 14 | 50 | 125 |
| 1843 | 4 | 7 | 35 | 115 |
| 1843 Proof *FDC* £1200 | | | | |
| 1843/34 | 4 | 18 | 75 | 150 |
| 1843/34 Proof *FDC* £1000 | | | | |
| 1860 | 4 | 18 | 70 | 175 |
| 1862 | 4 | 18 | 70 | 175 |
| 1862 Proof *FDC* £1500 | | | | |
| 1870 Proof only £1750 | | | | |

3916 - 1880 Maundy Set

**3916 Maundy Set.** (4d., 3d., 2d. and 1.) Young head 1., die axis ↑↓

| | F | VF | EF | BU |
|---|---|---|---|---|
| 1838 | — | — | 200 | 500 |
| 1838 Proof *FDC* £2250 | | | | |
| 1838 Proof in gold *FDC* £35000 | | | | |
| 1839 | — | — | 175 | 475 |
| 1839 Proof die axis ↑↑ *FDC* £1650 | | | | |
| 1840 | — | — | 225 | 500 |
| 1841 | — | — | 275 | 585 |
| 1842 | — | — | 225 | 475 |
| 1843 | — | — | 175 | 485 |
| 1844 | — | — | 200 | 500 |
| 1845 | — | — | 175 | 450 |
| 1846 | — | — | 275 | 625 |
| 1847 | — | — | 275 | 575 |
| 1848 | — | — | 275 | 575 |
| 1849 | — | — | 225 | 500 |
| 1850 | — | — | 175 | 485 |
| 1851 | — | — | 175 | 465 |
| 1852 | — | — | 325 | 675 |
| 1853 | — | — | 250 | 625 |
| 1853 Proof *FDC* £1850 | | | | |
| 1854 | — | — | 150 | 485 |
| 1855 | — | — | 175 | 485 |
| 1856 | — | — | 125 | 400 |
| 1857 | — | — | 175 | 485 |

| | F £ | VF £ | EF £ | BU £ |
|---|---|---|---|---|
| 1858 | — | — | 125 | 365 |
| 1859 | — | — | 125 | 365 |
| 1860 | — | — | 125 | 365 |
| 1861 | — | — | 150 | 365 |
| 1862 | — | — | 175 | 400 |
| 1863 | — | — | 175 | 400 |
| 1864 | — | — | 125 | 375 |
| 1865 | — | — | 125 | 375 |
| 1866 | — | — | 125 | 365 |
| 1867 | — | — | 125 | 365 |
| 1867 Proof set *FDC* £2250 | | | | |
| 1868 | — | — | 125 | 375 |
| 1869 | — | — | 125 | 400 |
| 1870 | — | — | 125 | 375 |
| 1871 | — | — | 100 | 365 |
| 1871 Proof set *FDC* £2250 | | | | |
| 1872 | — | — | 100 | 365 |
| 1873 | — | — | 100 | 365 |
| 1874 | — | — | 100 | 365 |
| 1875 | — | — | 100 | 365 |
| 1876 | — | — | 100 | 365 |
| 1877 | — | — | 100 | 365 |
| 1878 | — | — | 125 | 375 |
| 1878 Proof set *FDC* £2250 | | | | |
| 1879 | — | — | 100 | 365 |
| 1880 | — | — | 100 | 365 |
| 1881 | — | — | 100 | 365 |
| 1881 Proof set *FDC* £2250 | | | | |
| 1882 | — | — | 100 | 365 |
| 1882 Proof set *FDC* £2250 | | | | |
| 1883 | — | — | 100 | 365 |
| 1884 | — | — | 100 | 365 |
| 1885 | — | — | 100 | 365 |
| 1886 | — | — | 100 | 365 |
| 1887 | — | — | 125 | 375 |
| **3917 — Fourpence,** 1838-87 | | | *from* 10 | 35 |
| **3918 — Threepence**, 1838-87 | | | *from* 15 | 55 |
| **3919 — Twopence**, 1838-87 | | | *from* 10 | 35 |
| **3920 — Penny**, 1838-87 | | | *from* 15 | 50 |

*Maundy Sets in good quality original cases are worth approximately £40 more than the prices quoted.*

*Refer to footnote after 3796.*

**JUBILEE COINAGE 1887-93,** die axis ↑↑

3921
1887 Crown

| | F | VF | EF | BU |
|---|---|---|---|---|
| | £ | £ | £ | £ |

**3921 Crown.** Jubilee bust 1. ℞. St. George and dragon, date in ex, edge milled, die axis ↑↑

| | | | | |
|---|---|---|---|---|
| 1887 ........................................................................25 | 40 | 120 | 250 |
| 1887 Proof *FDC* £3250 | | | |
| 1888 narrow date..................................................25 | 50 | 185 | 425 |
| 1888 wide date.............................................100 | 250 | 575 | 1100 |
| 1889 ........................................................................25 | 40 | 135 | 350 |
| 1890 ........................................................................25 | 50 | 165 | 425 |
| 1891 ........................................................................25 | 50 | 200 | 475 |
| 1892 ........................................................................35 | 65 | 250 | 600 |

**3922 Double-Florin** (4s.).Jubilee bust 1. ℞. (As Florin) Crowned cruciform shields. Sceptre in angles. Roman I in date, die axis ↑↑

| | | | | |
|---|---|---|---|---|
| 1887 ........................................................................20 | 40 | 95 | 200 |
| 1887 Proof *FDC* £1250 | | | |

3923
1887 Double-Florin, Arabic 1 in date

**3923 Double-Florin** Jubilee bust l. ℞. Similar but Arabic 1 in date, die axis ↑↑

| | | | | |
|---|---|---|---|---|
| 1887 ........................................................................20 | 35 | 75 | 175 |
| 1887 Proof *FDC* £1200 | | | |
| 1888 ........................................................................20 | 40 | 100 | 250 |
| 1888 inverted 1 for I in VICTORIA ...............40 | 90 | 200 | 550 |
| 1889 ........................................................................20 | 40 | 100 | 250 |
| 1889 inverted 1 for I in VICTORIA ...............45 | 85 | 275 | 575 |
| 1890 ........................................................................20 | 50 | 125 | 300 |

3924
1887 Halfcrown

3925
1890 Florin reverse

| | F<br>£ | VF<br>£ | EF<br>£ | BU<br>£ |
|---|---|---|---|---|
| **3924 Halfcrown.** Jubilee bust l. R. Crowned shield in garter and collar, die axis ↑↑ | | | | |
| 1887 | 15 | 20 | 40 | 100 |
| 1887 Proof *FDC* £675 | | | | |
| 1888 | 15 | 25 | 80 | 225 |
| 1889 | 15 | 30 | 80 | 250 |
| 1890 | 15 | 30 | 110 | 250 |
| 1891 | 15 | 30 | 120 | 350 |
| 1892 | 15 | 35 | 135 | 300 |
| **3925 Florin.** Jubilee bust l. R. Crowned cruciform shields, sceptres in angles, die axis ↑↑ | | | | |
| 1887 | 8 | 12 | 35 | 75 |
| 1887 Proof *FDC* £500 | | | | |
| 1888 obverse die of 1887 | 15 | 45 | 110 | 225 |
| 1888 | 12 | 30 | 70 | 185 |
| 1889 | 12 | 35 | 95 | 215 |
| 1890 | 15 | 45 | 185 | 450 |
| 1891 | 25 | 70 | 300 | 600 |
| 1892 | 35 | 110 | 350 | 700 |
| 1892 Proof *FDC* £10000 | | | | |

3926
small head Shilling

| | F<br>£ | VF<br>£ | EF<br>£ | BU<br>£ |
|---|---|---|---|---|
| **3926 Shilling**. Small Jubilee head. R. Crowned shield in Garter, die axis ↑↑ | | | | |
| 1887 | 4 | 10 | 18 | 40 |
| 1887 Proof *FDC* £425 | | | | |
| 1888 | 35 | 80 | 175 | 325 |
| 1888/7 | 6 | 12 | 55 | 125 |
| ⋆ 1889 | 50 | 150 | 500 | 875 |
| **3927 Shilling**. Large Jubilee head. R. Similar as before, die axis ↑↑ | | | | |
| 1889 | 6 | 15 | 55 | 125 |
| 1889 Proof *FDC* £2250 | | | | |
| 1890 | 8 | 16 | 65 | 150 |
| 1891 | 10 | 16 | 75 | 175 |
| 1891 Proof *FDC* £2250 | | | | |
| 1892 | 10 | 16 | 75 | 175 |

3928
1887 'withdrawn type' Sixpence

|  | F £ | VF £ | EF £ | BU £ |
|---|---|---|---|---|
| **3928 Sixpence**. JEB designer's initials below trun. R̲. Shield in Garter (withdrawn type), die axis ↑↑ |  |  |  |  |
| 1887 ............................................................2 | | 5 | 12 | 28 |
| 1887 Proof *FDC* £300 | | | | |
| 1887 JEB on trun..........................................18 | | 55 | (125) | (350) |
| 1887 R/V in VICTORIA...............................15 | | 40 | 110 | 250 |

| 3929 | 3930 |
|---|---|
| Crowned value Sixpence | 1888 Groat |

| **3929 Sixpence**. R̲. Jubilee bust 1. Crowned, value in wreath, die axis ↑↑ |  |  |  |  |
|---|---|---|---|---|
| 1887 ............................................................2 | | 7 | 15 | (35) |
| 1887 Proof *FDC* £1200 | | | | |
| 1888 ............................................................5 | | 10 | 30 | 85 |
| 1888 Proof *FDC* £1850 | | | | |
| 1889 ............................................................5 | | 10 | 30 | 85 |
| 1890 ............................................................6 | | 12 | 40 | 100 |
| 1890 Proof *FDC* ................................ | | *Extremely rare* | | |
| 1891 ............................................................9 | | 18 | 50 | 125 |
| 1892 ............................................................8 | | 20 | 45 | 120 |
| 1893 ........................................................550 | | 1100 | 3250 | 6500 |

**3930 Groat** (for use in British Guiana). Jubilee Bust 1. R̲. Britannia seated r. date in axis, die axis ↑↑

| 1888 Milled edge Proof *FDC* £1250 | | | | |
|---|---|---|---|---|
| 1888 ..........................................................10 | | 25 | 65 | 135 |

**3931 Threepence**. As Maundy but less prooflike surface, die axis ↑↑

| 1887 ............................................................— | | 2 | 11 | 25 |
|---|---|---|---|---|
| 1887 Proof *FDC* £225 | | | | |
| 1888 ............................................................3 | | 5 | 18 | 55 |
| 1889 ............................................................2 | | 4 | 13 | 45 |
| 1890 ............................................................2 | | 4 | 13 | 45 |
| 1891 ............................................................2 | | 4 | 16 | 50 |
| 1892 ............................................................3 | | 5 | 18 | 55 |
| 1893 ..........................................................18 | | 60 | 185 | 450 |

3932
1889 Maundy Set

|  | EF £ | FDC £ |
|---|---|---|
| **3932 Maundy Set.** (4d., 3d., 2d. and 1d.) Jubilee bust 1. die axis ↑↑ | | |
| 1888 ................................................. | 110 | 200 |
| 1888 Proof set *FDC* ................................................. | *Extremely rare* | |
| 1889 ................................................. | 110 | 200 |
| 1890 ................................................. | 110 | 200 |
| 1891 ................................................. | 110 | 200 |
| 1892 ................................................. | 110 | 200 |
| **3933 — Fourpence**, 1888-92 ................................................. *from* | 12 | 35 |
| **3934 — Threepence**, 1888-92 ................................................. *from* | 18 | 40 |
| **3935 — Twopence**, 1888-92 ................................................. *from* | 10 | 30 |
| **3936 — Penny**, 1888-92 ................................................. *from* | 15 | 40 |

*Maundy Sets in the original undamaged cases are worth approximately £25 more than the prices quoted. Also see footnote after 3796.*

## OLD HEAD COINAGE 1893-1901, die axis ↑↑

3937
1893 Old Head Crown

|  | F £ | VF £ | EF £ | BU £ |
|---|---|---|---|---|
| **3937 Crown.** Old veiled bust l. R. St. George. date in ex. Regnal date on edge, die axis ↑↑ | | | | |
| 1893 edge LVI ................................................. 17 | 25 | 175 | 425 | |
| 1893 Proof *FDC* £3250 | | | | |
| 1893 LVII ................................................. 26 | 75 | 325 | 650 | |
| 1894 LVII ................................................. 17 | 40 | 265 | 550 | |
| 1894 LVIII ................................................. 17 | 40 | 265 | 550 | |
| 1895 LVIII ................................................. 17 | 35 | 225 | 525 | |
| 1895 LIX ................................................. 17 | 35 | 200 | 500 | |
| 1896 LIX ................................................. 19 | 60 | 375 | 625 | |
| 1896 LX ................................................. 17 | 40 | 225 | 550 | |
| 1897 LX ................................................. 17 | 35 | 200 | 475 | |
| 1897 LXI ................................................. 17 | 35 | 200 | 475 | |
| 1898 LXI ................................................. 26 | 75 | 400 | 700 | |
| 1898 LXII ................................................. 17 | 35 | 275 | 550 | |

| | F | VF | EF | BU |
|---|---|---|---|---|
| | £ | £ | £ | £ |
| 1899 LXII | 17 | 35 | 200 | 525 |
| 1899 LXIII | 17 | 35 | 225 | 575 |
| 1900 LXIII | 17 | 35 | 200 | 575 |
| 1900 LXIV | 17 | 35 | 200 | 550 |

3938
Halfcrown

**3938 Halfcrown.** Old veiled bust l. R. Shield in collar, edge milled, die axis ↑↑

| | | | | |
|---|---|---|---|---|
| 1893 | 10 | 26 | 65 | 165 |
| 1893 Proof  *FDC* £950 | | | | |
| 1894 | 13 | 40 | 135 | 375 |
| 1895 | 10 | 35 | 100  - | 275 |
| 1896 | 10 | 35 | 100 | 275 |
| 1897 | 10 | 26 | 65 | 200 |
| 1898 | 15 | 40 | 100 | 300 |
| 1899 | 13 | 30 | 75 | 250 |
| 1900 | 13 | 26 | 65 | 200 |
| 1901 | 13 | 26 | 70 | 225 |

**3938A** Small reverse design with long border teeth

| | | | | |
|---|---|---|---|---|
| 1896 | 15 | 35 | 150 | 300 |

3939
Old Head Florin

**3939 Florin.** Old veiled bust l. R. Three shields within garter, die axis ↑↑

| | | | | |
|---|---|---|---|---|
| 1893 | 10 | 20 | 75 | 150 |
| 1893 Proof  *FDC* £650 | | | | |
| 1894 | 12 | 30 | 110 | 275 |
| 1895 | 10 | 25 | 100 | 225 |
| 1896 | 10 | 25 | 100 | 225 |
| 1897 | 10 | 20 | 80 | 175 |
| 1898 | 10 | 25 | 95 | 225 |
| 1899 | 10 | 20 | 90 | 200 |
| 1900 | 10 | 20 | 80 | 165 |
| 1901 | 10 | 20 | 85 | 175 |

3940A
1901 Shilling

3941
1897 Sixpence

| | F | VF | EF | BU |
|---|---|---|---|---|
| | £ | £ | £ | £ |

**3940 Shilling**. Old veiled bust l. R. Three shields within Garter, small rose, die axis ↑↑

| | | | | |
|---|---|---|---|---|
| 1893 | 8 | 15 | 55 | 110 |
| 1893 small lettering | 8 | 12 | 50 | 100 |
| 1893 Proof *FDC* £400 | | | | |
| 1894 | 8 | 15 | 60 | 145 |
| 1895 | 10 | 20 | 65 | 160 |
| 1896 | 8 | 15 | 60 | 150 |

**3940A Shilling**. Old veiled bust l. R. Second reverse, larger rose, die axis ↑↑

| | | | | |
|---|---|---|---|---|
| 1895 | 8 | 15 | 60 | 140 |
| 1896 | 8 | 12 | 55 | 140 |
| 1897 | 8 | 12 | 48 | 120 |
| 1898 | 8 | 12 | 55 | 140 |
| 1899 | 8 | 15 | 60 | 140 |
| 1900 | 8 | 12 | 50 | 120 |
| 1901 | 8 | 12 | 50 | 120 |

**3941 Sixpence.** Old veiled bust l. R. Value in wreath, die axis ↑↑

| | | | | |
|---|---|---|---|---|
| 1893 | 5 | 12 | 40 | 95 |
| 1893 Proof *FDC* £375 | | | | |
| 1894 | 8 | 12 | 55 | 135 |
| 1895 | 7 | 12 | 50 | 120 |
| 1896 | 7 | 12 | 45 | 95 |
| 1897 | 7 | 12 | 40 | 85 |
| 1898 | 7 | 12 | 45 | 95 |
| 1899 | 7 | 12 | 45 | 95 |
| 1900 | 7 | 12 | 45 | 95 |
| 1901 | 6 | 10 | 40 | 85 |

**3942 Threepence**. Old veiled bust l. R. Crowned 3. As Maundy but less prooflike surface, die axis ↑↑

| | | | | |
|---|---|---|---|---|
| 1893 | 3 | 5 | 15 | 60 |
| 1893 Proof *FDC* £225 | | | | |
| 1894 | 3 | 6 | 22 | 70 |
| 1895 | 3 | 6 | 20 | 60 |
| 1896 | 3 | 6 | 20 | 60 |
| 1897 | 3 | 5 | 15 | 45 |
| 1898 | 3 | 4 | 15 | 50 |
| 1899 | 3 | 4 | 15 | 50 |
| 1900 | 3 | 4 | 12 | 45 |
| 1901 | 3 | 4 | 15 | 45 |

3943
1901 Maundy Set

|  | EF<br>£ | FDC<br>£ |
|---|---|---|
| **3943 Maundy Set.** (4d., 3d., 2d. and 1d.) Old veiled bust l., die axis ↑↑ | | |
| 1893 | 90 | 175 |
| 1894 | 90 | 190 |
| 1895 | 90 | 190 |
| 1896 | 90 | 190 |
| 1897 | 90 | 190 |
| 1898 | 90 | 190 |
| 1899 | 90 | 190 |
| 1900 | 90 | 190 |
| 1901 | 90 | 180 |
| **3944 — Fourpence.** 1893-1901 *from* | 8 | 30 |
| **3945 — Threepence.** 1893-1901 *from* | 15 | 40 |
| **3946 — Twopence.** 1893-1901 *from* | 8 | 30 |
| **3947 — Penny.** 1893-1901 *from* | 15 | 40 |

*Maundy Sets in the original undamaged cases are worth approximately £25 more than the prices quoted.*
*See footnote after 3796.*

## COPPER AND BRONZE

**YOUNG HEAD COPPER COINAGE, 1838-60,** die axis ↑↑

3948
Penny
Rev. with ornamental trident prongs (OT)

|  | F<br>£ | VF<br>£ | EF<br>£ | BU<br>£ |
|---|---|---|---|---|
| **3948 Penny.** Young head l. date below ℞. Britannia seated r. | | | | |
| 1839 Bronzed proof *FDC* £2250 | | | | |
| 1841 Rev. OT | 90 | 150 | 350 | 1000 |
| 1841 Proof *FDC* £3500 | | | | |
| 1841 Silver Proof *FDC* £9000 | | | | |
| 1841 OT. no colon after REG | 5 | 20 | 120 | 425 |
| 1843 OT. — | 70 | 275 | 1650 | 4000 |

| | F | VF | EF | BU |
|---|---|---|---|---|
| | £ | £ | £ | £ |
| 1843 OT REG:...........................................80 | 400 | 1850 | 4250 |
| 1844 OT....................................................10 | 20 | 200 | 625 |
| 1844 Proof *FDC* ....................................................................*Extremely rare* |
| 1845 OT....................................................12 | 35 | 300 | 825 |
| 1846 OT....................................................10 | 25 | 275 | 600 |
| 1846 OT colon close to DEF .................12 | 30 | 300 | 775 |
| 1847 – – ..................................................7 | 20 | 165 | 500 |
| 1847 OT DEF–: .......................................7 | 20 | 190 | 500 |
| 1848/7 OT................................................5 | 20 | 160 | 575 |
| 1848 OT....................................................5 | 20 | 190 | 575 |
| 1848/6 OT................................................20 | 125 | 600 | — |
| 1849 OT....................................................225 | 600 | 2250 | 4250 |
| 1851 OT....................................................15 | 30 | 250 | 700 |
| 1851 OT DEF:..........................................10 | 25 | 190 | 625 |
| 1853 OT DEF–: ........................................5 | 15 | 110 | 475 |
| 1853 Proof *FDC* £3500 |
| 1853 Plain trident, (PT) DEF: ..............15 | 30 | 170 | 585 |
| 1854 PT....................................................5 | 15 | 135 | 475 |
| 1854/3 PT ................................................10 | 65 | 250 | 725 |
| 1854 OT DEF–: ........................................7 | 20 | 120 | 500 |
| 1855 OT – ................................................5 | 15 | 120 | 425 |
| 1855 PT DEF:...........................................5 | 15 | 130 | 425 |
| 1856 PT DEF:...........................................90 | 250 | 575 | 2450 |
| 1856 Proof *FDC* £4500 |
| 1856 OT DEF–: ........................................100 | 350 | 900 | 3250 |
| 1857 OT DEF–: ........................................7 | 20 | 100 | 400 |
| 1857 PT DEF:...........................................5 | 15 | 95 | 395 |
| 1858 OT DEF–: ........................................5 | 12 | 95 | 375 |
| 1858/7 – – ...............................................5 | 15 | 95 | 400 |
| 1858/3 ....................................................7 | 30 | 135 | 575 |
| 1858 no ww on trun ...............................5 | 18 | 95 | 400 |
| 1859 ....................................................5 | 20 | 110 | 475 |
| 1859 Proof *FDC* £4500 |
| 1860/59 ...................................................800 | 1750 | 3250 | 6250 |

*Copper coins graded in this catalogue as BU have full mint lustre.*

3949
1845 Halfpenny

**3949 Halfpenny.** Young head l. date below R. Britannia seated r., die axis ↑↑ 1853 Rev. incuse dots

| 1838 ....................................................4 | 12 | 75 | 250 |
|---|---|---|---|
| 1839 Bronzed proof FDC £1100 |
| 1841 ....................................................4 | 12 | 75 | 300 |
| 1841 – Proof FDC £1650 |

| | F £ | VF £ | EF £ | BU £ |
|---|---|---|---|---|
| 1841 Silver proof FDC | | | | *Extremely rare* |
| 1843 | 25 | 50 | 250 | 800 |
| 1844 | 12 | 35 | 165 | 375 |
| 1845 | 250 | 500 | 2000 | — |
| 1846 | 12 | 35 | 175 | 400 |
| 1847 | 12 | 35 | 160 | 360 |
| 1848 | 25 | 70 | 200 | 600 |
| 1848/7 | 10 | 30 | 190 | 400 |
| 1851 | 5 | 15 | 90 | 325 |
| 1851 Rev. incuse dots on shield | 5 | 15 | 100 | 350 |
| 1852 Similar | 7 | 15 | 95 | 325 |
| 1852 Rev. normal shield | 10 | 20 | 110 | 350 |
| 1853 dots on shield | 3 | 7 | 55 | 175 |
| 1853 — Proof FDC £900 | | | | |
| 1853/2 — | 15 | 40 | 165 | 400 |
| 1854 — | 4 | 7 | 45 | 175 |
| 1855 — | 4 | 7 | 45 | 185 |
| 1856 — | 5 | 12 | 80 | 275 |
| 1857 — | 4 | 10 | 60 | 215 |
| 1857 Rev. normal shield | 4 | 10 | 55 | 200 |
| 1858 — | 5 | 10 | 55 | 225 |
| 1858/7 — | 5 | 10 | 55 | 225 |
| 1858/6 — | 5 | 10 | 70 | 225 |
| 1859 — | 5 | 10 | 70 | 225 |
| 1859/8 — | 10 | 20 | 100 | 300 |
| 1860* — | 1850 | 3500 | 7000 | 12500 |

*Overstruck dates are listed only if commoner than normal date, or if no normal date is known.*

*\*These 1860 large copper pieces are not to be confused with the smaller and commoner bronze issue with date on reverse (nos. 3954, 3956 and 3958).*

*Copper coins graded in this catalogue as UNC have full mint lustre.*

3950
1849 Farthing

3950
1864 Proof

**3950 Farthing.** Young head l. date below R. Britannia seated r. die axis ↑↑

| | F | VF | EF | BU |
|---|---|---|---|---|
| 1838 WW raised on trun. | 4 | 9 | 60 | 200 |
| 1839 | 3 | 6 | 55 | 150 |
| 1839 Bronzed Proof *FDC* £825 | | | | |
| 1839 Silver Proof *FDC* | | | | *Extremely rare* |
| 1839 Copper Proof *FDC* £1250 | | | | |
| 1840 | 4 | 7 | 60 | 170 |
| 1841 | 4 | 7 | 60 | 170 |
| 1841 Proof *FDC* | | | | *Extremely rare* |
| 1842 | 10 | 40 | 150 | 395 |

| | F | VF | EF | BU |
|---|---|---|---|---|
| | £ | £ | £ | £ |
| 1843/2 ..........................................................10 | 25 | 110 | 350 |
| 1843 ................................................2 | 5 | 35 | 125 |
| 1843 I for 1 in date .......................................75 | 325 | 700 | 1850 |
| 1844 ..............................................65 | 220 | 750 | 1950 |
| 1845 ................................................5 | 8 | 58 | 165 |
| 1846 ................................................5 | 12 | 75 | 200 |
| 1847 ................................................4 | 8 | 58 | 165 |
| 1848 ................................................4 | 8 | 58 | 165 |
| 1849 ..............................................35 | 95 | 375 | 775 |
| 1850 ................................................4 | 8 | 58 | 165 |
| 1850 5/4 ..........................................8 | 25 | 100 | 325 |
| 1851 ................................................8 | 20 | 80 | 250 |
| 1851 D/ ◙ in DEI .........................................80 | 275 | 650 | 1100 |
| 1852 ................................................8 | 18 | 80 | 250 |
| 1853 ................................................4 | 8 | 40 | 165 |
| 1853 WW incuse on trun ...............................8 | 25 | 140 | 395 |
| 1853 Proof *FDC* £1100 | | | |
| 1854 ................................................4 | 8 | 45 | 150 |
| 1855 ................................................4 | 10 | 75 | 185 |
| 1855 WW raised ...........................................5 | 10 | 75 | 185 |
| 1856 WW incuse ..........................................5 | 18 | 80 | 250 |
| 1856 R/E in VICTORIA ...............................12 | 50 | 325 | 600 |
| 1857 ................................................4 | 8 | 50 | 165 |
| 1858 ................................................4 | 8 | 50 | 165 |
| 1859 ................................................8 | 15 | 80 | 295 |
| 1860* ..........................................1600 | 3500 | 6250 | 12500 |
| 1864 IWW on truncation proof *FDC* £25000 | | | |

3951

Half-Farthing

**3951 Half-Farthing.** Young head l. R. Crowned Value and date, die axis ↑↑

| | F | VF | EF | BU |
|---|---|---|---|---|
| 1839 ................................................4 | 8 | 50 | 165 |
| 1839 Bronzed proof *FDC* £750 | | | |
| 1842 ................................................4 | 8 | 50 | 145 |
| 1843 ................................................— | 5 | 28 | 100 |
| 1844 ................................................— | 3 | 25 | 90 |
| 1844 E/N in REGINA....................................8 | 17 | 85 | 295 |
| 1847 ................................................2 | 6 | 40 | 145 |
| 1851 5/0 ..........................................8 | 17 | 100 | 275 |
| 1851 ................................................4 | 8 | 60 | 150 |
| 1852 ................................................2 | 8 | 60 | 150 |
| 1853 ................................................4 | 12 | 60 | 175 |
| 1853 Proof *FDC* £750 | | | |
| 1854 ................................................6 | 25 | 100 | 300 |
| 1856 ................................................6 | 25 | 100 | 300 |
| 1856 Large date .......................................45 | 135 | 350 | 825 |
| 1868 Proof *FDC* £850 | | | |
| 1868 Cupro nickel Proof *FDC* £1250 | | | |

3952
Third-Farthing

|  | F | VF | EF | BU |
|---|---|---|---|---|
|  | £ | £ | £ | £ |

**3952 Third-Farthing** (for use in Malta). Young head l. date below R. Britannia seated r.
die axis ↑↑

| 1844 | ........................................................................20 | 35 | 110 | 350 |
| 1844 RE for REG | ........................................................30 | 65 | 375 | 800 |

3953
Quarter-Farthing

**3953 Quarter-Farthing** (for use in Ceylon). Young head l. R. Crowned Value and date,
die axis ↑↑

| 1839 | ........................................................................20 | 30 | 90 | 250 |
| 1851 | ........................................................................15 | 25 | 85 | 275 |
| 1852 | ........................................................................15 | 25 | 80 | 225 |
| 1852 Proof *FDC* £1500 |  |  |  |  |
| 1853 | ........................................................................25 | 45 | 125 | 375 |
| 1853 Proof *FDC* £1100 |  |  |  |  |
| 1868 Proof *FDC* £800 |  |  |  |  |
| 1868 Cupro-nickel Proof *FDC* £1100 |  |  |  |  |

*Copper coins graded in this catalogue as BU have full mint lustre.*

*\*These 1860 large copper pieces are not to be confused with the smaller and commoner bronze
issue with date on reverse (nos. 3954, 3956 and 3958).*

**BRONZE COINAGE, "BUN HEAD" ISSUE, 1860-95,** die axis ↑↑

When studying an example of the bronze coinage, if the minutiae of the variety is not evident due to wear from circulation, then the coin will not be of any individual significance. Proofs exist of most years and are generally extremely rare for all denominations.

**3954 The Bronze Penny.** The bronze coinage is the most complicated of the milled series from the point of view of the large number of different varieties of obverse and reverse and their combinations. Below are set out illustrations with explanations of all the varieties. The obverse and reverse types listed below reflect those as listed originally by C W Peck in his British Museum Catalogue of Copper, Tin and Bronze Coinage 1558-1958, and later in "The Bronze Coinage of Great Britain" by Michael J Freeman which gives much fuller and detailed explanations of the types. Reference can also be compared to "The British Bronze Penny" by Michael Gouby.

**OBVERSES**

**Obverse 1 (1860)** - laureate and draped bust facing left, hair tied in bun, wreath of 15 leaves and 4 berries, L C WYON raised on base of bust, **beaded border** and thin linear circle.

**Obverse 1\* (1860)** - laureate and draped bust facing left, hair tied in bun, **more bulging lowered eye with more rounded forehead**, wreath of **15 leaves and 4 berries**, which are weaker in part, L C WYON raised on base of bust, **beaded border** and thin linear circle.

**Obverse 3 (1860-61)** - laureate and draped bust facing left, hair tied in bun, **complete rose to drapery**, wreath of 15 leaves and 4 berries, **two leaves have incuse outlines, L C WYON** raised on base of bust **nearly touches border**, toothed border and thin linear circle both sides.

**Obverse 2 (1860-62)** - laureate and draped bust facing left, hair tied in bun, wreath of 15 leaves and 4 berries, **L C WYON** raised **lower on base of bust** and clear of border, **toothed border** and thin linear circle both sides.

**Obverse 4 (1860-61)** - laureate and draped bust facing left, hair tied in bun, **finer hair strands at nape of neck**, wreath of 15 leaves and 4 berries, two leaves have incuse outlines, **L C WYON below bust, nearly touches border, toothed border of shorter teeth**, and thin linear circle both sides.

**OBVERSES** (*continued*)

**Obverse 7 (1874)** - laureate and draped bust facing left, hair tied in bun, finer hair strands at nape of neck, **wreath of 17 leaves**, **leaf veins raised**, **6 berries**, no signature, toothed border and thin linear circle both sides.

**Obverse 5 (1860-61)** - laureate and draped bust facing left, hair tied in bun, **finer hair strands at nape of neck**, wreath of 15 leaves and 4 berries, **leaf veins incuse**, two leaves have incuse outlines, **no signature below bust**, toothed border and thin linear circle both sides.

**Obverse 8 (1874-79)** - laureate and draped bust facing left, hair tied in bun, with **close thicker ties to ribbons**, wreath of 17 leaves, leaf veins raised, 6 berries, no signature, toothed border and thin linear circle both sides.

**Obverse 6 (1860-74)** - laureate and draped bust facing left, hair tied in bun, finer hair strands at nape of neck, **wreath of 16 leaves, leaf veins raised**, **no signature**, toothed border and thin linear circle both sides. There is a **prominent flaw** on the **top stop of the colon after D at the end of the legend.**

**Obverse 9 (1879-81)** - laureate and draped bust facing left, hair tied in bun, with close thicker ties, wreath of 17 leaves, **double leaf veins incuse**, 6 berries, no signature, toothed border and thin linear circle both sides.

**OBVERSES** *(continued)*

**Obverse 10 (1880-81)** - laureate and draped bust facing left, hair tied in bun, with close thicker ties, **wreath of 15 leaves, leaf veins raised and recessed, 4 berries**, no signature, toothed border and thin linear circle both sides.

**Obverse 12 (1881-94)** - laureate and draped bust facing left, hair tied in bun, with close thicker ties, **no curls at nape of neck**, nose more hooked, wreath of 15 leaves, leaf veins raised, 4 berries, no signature, **toothed border, more numerous teeth**, and thin linear circle both sides, weak on obverse, **larger lettering**.

**Obverse 11 (1881-83)** - laureate and draped bust facing left, more **hooked nose**, hair tied in bun, with close thicker ties, nose more hooked, wreath of 15 leaves, **leaf veins raised**, 4 berries, no signature, toothed border and thin linear circle both sides, **weak circle on obverse**.

**Obverse 13 (1889)** - laureate and draped bust facing left, hair tied in bun, with close thicker ties, no curls at nape of neck, nose more hooked, **wreath of 14 leaves, leaf veins raised**, no signature, toothed border and thin linear circle both sides, larger lettering.

**REVERSES**

**Reverse A (1860)** - Britannia seated right on rocks with shield and trident, **crosses on shield outlined with double raised lines**, L.C.W. incuse below shield, date below in exergue, lighthouse with 4 windows to left, ship sailing to right, **beaded border** and linear circle.

**Reverse C (1860)** - Britannia seated right on rocks with shield and trident, **crosses on shield outlined with wider spaced thinner double raised lines, thumb touches St. George Cross**, L.C.W. incuse below shield, date below in exergue, lighthouse with 4 windows to left, rocks touch linear circle, ship sailing to right, **beaded border** and linear circle.

**Reverse B (1860)** - Britannia with **one incuse hemline**, seated right on rocks with shield and trident, **crosses on shield outlined with treble incuse lines**, L.C.W. incuse below shield, date below in exergue, lighthouse with 4 windows to left, ship sailing to right, **beaded border** and linear circle.

**Reverse D (1860-61)** - Britannia seated right on rocks with shield and trident, crosses on shield outlined with wider spaced thinner double raised lines, thumb touches St. George Cross, L.C.W. incuse below shield, date below in exergue, lighthouse with 4 windows to left, rocks touch linear circle, ship sailing to right, **toothed border**.

**REVERSES** *(continued)*

**Reverse E (1860)** - Britannia seated right on rocks with **thick rimmed shield and trident**, crosses on shield outlined with wider spaced thinner double raised lines, thumb touches St. George Cross, **L.C.W. incuse below foot**, date below in exergue, lighthouse with **sharper masonry** to left, **rocks touch linear circle**, ship sailing to right, toothed border.

**Reverse G (1861-75)** - Britannia seated right on rocks with **convex shield and trident**, no signature, date below in exergue, bell-topped lighthouse to left, **lamp area depicted with five vertical lines**, **no rocks to left, sea crosses linear circle**, ship sailing to right, toothed border.

**Reverse F (1861)** - Britannia seated right on rocks with thick rimmed shield and trident, **incuse lines on breastplate**, crosses on shield outlined with wider spaced thinner double raised lines, thumb touches St. George Cross, **no L.C.W. extra rocks**, date below in exergue, **lighthouse with rounded top** and sharp masonry, **three horizontal lines** between masonry and top, rocks touch linear circle, ship sailing to right, toothed border.

**Reverse H (1874-75, 1877)** - Britannia seated right on rocks, **smaller head, thinner neck**, with convex shield and trident, no signature, **narrow date** below in exergue, **tall thin lighthouse** to left with **6 windows**, **lamp area of four vertical lines**, close date numerals, **tiny rock to left, sea touches linear circle**, ship sailing to right, toothed border.

**REVERSES** *(continued)*

**Reverse I (1874)** - Britannia seated right on rocks with convex shield and trident, **thick trident shaft**, no signature, **narrow date** below in exergue, **thicker lighthouse** to left with **4 windows**, lamp area of four vertical lines, close date numerals, tiny rock to left, sea touches linear circle, ship sailing to right, toothed border.

**Reverse L (1880)** - Britannia seated right on rocks with shield and trident, **extra feather to helmet plume, trident with three rings above hand**, date below in exergue, lighthouse with **cluster of rocks to left**, ship sailing to right, toothed border.

**Reverse J (1875-81)** - **larger Britannia** seated right on rocks with shield and trident, **left leg more visible, wider date** below in deeper exergue, lighthouse to left, ship sailing to right, **sea does not meet linear circle either side**, toothed border.

**Reverse M (1881-82)** - larger Britannia seated right on rocks with shield and trident, **flatter shield heraldically coloured**, date and **H below in exergue**, lighthouse to left with faint masonry, ship sailing to right, **sea does not meet linear circle**, toothed border.

**Reverse K (1876, 1879)** - Britannia with **larger head** seated right on rocks with convex shield and trident, **thicker helmet**, no signature, **narrow date** and in exergue, **tall thin lighthouse** to left, tiny rock to left, **sea touches linear circle**, ship sailing to right, toothed border.

**REVERSES** (*continued*)

Reverse O (1882 - proof only) – larger
**Britannia** seated right on rocks with shield
and trident, flatter shield heraldically coloured,
date and **H in exergue**, lighthouse to left with
faint masonry, ship sailing to right, **sea meets
linear circle**, toothed border with more teeth.

**Reverse N (1881-94)** - **thinner Britannia**
seated right on rocks with shield and thinner
trident, **helmet plume ends in a single strand**,
shield heraldically coloured with different
thickness crosses, date in exergue, thinner
lighthouse to left, ship sailing to right, sea
meets linear circle, toothed border with more
teeth.

Beaded border

Toothed border

Shield outlined
with double raised
lines

Shield outlined
with treble incuse
lines

Normal nose

More hooked nose

3954

|  | F | VF | EF | BU |
|---|---|---|---|---|
|  | £ | £ | £ | £ |

**3954 Penny.** Laur. bust l. R. Britannia seated r. date in ex. lighthouse l. ship to r., die axis ↑↑

| | F | VF | EF | BU |
|---|---|---|---|---|
| 1860 obv 1, rev A | 60 | 125 | 625 | 1750 |
| 1860 obv 1, rev B | 12 | 50 | 300 | 900 |
| 1860 obv 1*, rev A | 350 | 1200 | 2000 | — |
| 1860 obv 1, rev C | 60 | 165 | 700 | 2500 |
| 1860 obv 1*, rev C | 200 | 700 | 2000 | — |
| 1860 obv 1, rev D | 600 | 950 | 2700 | 5500 |
| 1860 obv 2, rev B | 525 | 975 | 3000 | 5750 |
| 1860 obv 2, rev D | 3 | 15 | 75 | 325 |
| 1860 — heavy flan | 2750 | — | — | — |
| 1860 N/Z in ONE, 2+D | 80 | 275 | 575 | 1250 |
| 1860 obv 3, rev D | 3 | 12 | 90 | 385 |
| 1860 obv 3, rev E | 110 | 325 | 875 | 2500 |
| 1860 obv 4, rev D | 2 | 10 | 90 | 400 |
| 1860 obv 5, rev D | 7 | 40 | 225 | 750 |
| 1860 obv 6, rev D | 30 | 125 | 400 | 900 |
| 1861 obv 2, rev D | 65 | 165 | 500 | 1350 |
| 1861 obv 2, rev F | | | | *Extremely rare* |
| 1861 obv 2, rev G | 25 | 100 | 425 | 1100 |
| 1861 obv 3, rev D | 225 | 550 | 1500 | 2850 |
| 1861 obv 4, rev D | 2 | 15 | 95 | 385 |
| 1861 — — heavy flan | 2750 | — | — | — |
| 1861 obv 4, rev F | 200 | 425 | 1750 | — |
| 1861 obv 4, rev G | 50 | 200 | 750 | 2250 |
| 1861 obv 5, rev D | 2 | 10 | 95 | 400 |
| 1861 obv 5, rev F | 950 | — | — | — |
| 1861 obv 5, rev G | 100 | 375 | 1250 | 2500 |
| 1861 obv 6, rev D | 2 | 10 | 85 | 300 |
| 1861 — — — 6 over 8 | 450 | 2150 | — | — |
| 1861 obv 6, rev F | 150 | 550 | 1500 | — |
| 1861 obv 6, rev G | 2 | 10 | 90 | 350 |
| 1861 — 8 over 6 | 450 | 2150 | — | — |
| 1862 obv 2, rev G | 475 | 1250 | 2950 | 4000 |
| 1862 obv 6, rev G | 2 | 10 | 70 | 265 |
| 1862 — 8 over 6 | 300 | 500 | 800 | — |
| 1862 — Halfpenny numerals | 900 | 2750 | 4250 | — |
| 1863 obv 6, rev G | 2 | 10 | 70 | 245 |
| 1863 Die number 2 | *from* 1500 | — | — | — |
| 1863 Die number 3 | *from* 1500 | — | — | — |
| 1863 Die number 4 | *from* 1500 | — | — | — |
| 1863 Die number 5 | | | | *Extremely rare* |
| 1863 slender 3 | | | | *Extremely rare* |
| 1863/1 obv 6, rev G | | | | *Extremely rare* |

|  | F | VF | EF | BU |
|---|---|---|---|---|
|  | £ | £ | £ | £ |
| 1864 Upper serif | 20 | 110 | 1000 | 3500 |
| 1864 Crosslet 4 | 25 | 150 | 1200 | 4000 |
| 1865 obv 6, rev G | 6 | 18 | 200 | 695 |
| 1865/3 obv 6, rev G | 45 | 125 | 450 | 1650 |
| 1866 obv 6, rev G | 2 | 12 | 100 | 400 |
| 1867 obv 6, rev G | 6 | 30 | 250 | 1000 |
| 1868 obv 6, rev G | 8 | 40 | 300 | 1000 |
| 1869 obv 6, rev G | 95 | 450 | 1650 | 4000 |
| 1870 obv 6, rev G | 8 | 20 | 200 | 550 |
| 1871 obv 6, rev G | 35 | 120 | 650 | 1950 |
| 1872 obv 6, rev G | 2 | 12 | 95 | 300 |
| 1873 obv 6, rev G | 2 | 12 | 95 | 350 |
| 1874 obv 6, rev G | 2 | 12 | 135 | 650 |
| 1874 obv 7, rev G | 5 | 30 | 125 | 400 |
| 1874 obv 8, rev G | 18 | 45 | 250 | 900 |
| 1874 obv 8 rev H | 12 | 40 | 185 | 750 |
| 1874 obv 6, rev H | 30 | 85 | 385 | 850 |
| 1874 obv 7, rev H | 5 | 30 | 150 | 425 |
| 1875 obv 8, rev G | 12 | 50 | 275 | 675 |
| 1875 obv 8, rev H | 2 | 10 | 80 | 300 |
| 1875 obv 8, rev J | 3 | 2 | 85 | 325 |
| 1877 obv 8, rev J | 2 | 10 | 90 | 325 |
| 1877 obv 8, rev H | 3250 | — | — | — |
| 1878 obv 8, rev J | 2 | 12 | 120 | 500 |
| 1879 obv 8, rev J | 7 | 20 | 185 | 825 |
| 1879 obv 9, rev J | 1 | 6 | 85 | 275 |
| 1879 obv 9, rev K | 20 | 80 | 325 | 1250 |
| 1880 obv 9, rev J | 2 | 12 | 135 | 500 |
| 1880 obv 9, rev L | 2 | 10 | 120 | 475 |
| 1881 obv 9, rev J | 2 | 12 | 125 | 600 |
| 1881 obv 10, rev J | 20 | 80 | 295 | 875 |
| 1881 obv 11, rev J | 50 | 135 | 500 | 1100 |
| 1882† obv 11, rev N | 1500 | 4750 | — | — |
| 1883 obv 12, rev N | 2 | 10 | 75 | 325 |
| 1883 obv11, rev N | 2 | 10 | 75 | 375 |
| 1884 obv 12, rev N | 2 | 6 | 70 | 235 |
| 1885 obv 12, rev N | 2 | 6 | 70 | 235 |
| 1886 obv 12, rev N | 2 | 8 | 75 | 265 |
| 1887 obv 12, rev N | 2 | 7 | 70 | 225 |
| 1888 obv 12, rev N | 2 | 8 | 60 | 200 |
| 1889 obv 12, rev N | 3 | 12 | 85 | 395 |
| 1889 obv 13, rev N | 2 | 6 | 55 | 225 |
| 1890 obv 12, rev N | 2 | 6 | 55 | 225 |
| 1891 obv 12, rev N | 2 | 6 | 55 | 225 |
| 1892 obv 12, rev N | 2 | 6 | 55 | 225 |
| 1893 obv 12, rev N | 2 | 6 | 55 | 225 |
| 1893 obv 12, rev N 3 over 2 | 100 | 325 | 400 | 700 |
| 1894 obv 12, rev N | 2 | 12 | 80 | 285 |

†† *not to be confused with Heaton Mint - H - the mint letter is the first device to disappear on worn specimens*
*Bronze coins graded in this catalogue as BU have full mint lustre*

3955
H Mint mark location

3956
1860 Halfpenny Beaded border

| | F<br>£ | VF<br>£ | EF<br>£ | BU<br>£ |
|---|---|---|---|---|

**3955 Penny.** Similar R. Britannia, H Mint mark below date – (struck by Ralph Heaton
& Sons, Birmingham)

| | | | | |
|---|---|---|---|---|
| 1874 H obv 6, rev G .....5 | 18 | 100 | 325 |
| 1874 H obv 6, rev H .....10 | 25 | 145 | 575 |
| 1874 H obv 6, rev I.....250 | 500 | 750 | — |
| 1874 H obv 7, rev G .....10 | 25 | 120 | 385 |
| 1874 H obv 7, rev H .....5 | 18 | 100 | 325 |
| 1874 H obv 7, rev I.....550 | — | — | — |
| 1875 H obv 8, rev J.....35 | 100 | 975 | 2250 |
| 1876 H obv 8, rev K .....2 | 12 | 90 | 360 |
| 1876 H obv 8, rev J.....8 | 25 | 165 | 500 |
| 1881 H obv 11, rev M.....3 | 12 | 90 | 375 |
| 1881 H obv 9, rev M .....475 | 1250 | 2750 | — |
| 1882 H obv12, rev M.....10 | 20 | 150 | 525 |
| 1882 H obv 12, rev N.....2 | 8 | 70 | 275 |
| 1882/1 H obv 11, rev M.....8 | 20 | 150 | 825 |

**3956 Halfpenny.** Laur. bust l. R. Britannia seated r. date in ex. lighthouse l. ship to r.,
die axis ↑↑

| | | | | |
|---|---|---|---|---|
| 1860 Beaded border.....1 | 5 | 35 | 145 |
| 1860  no tie to wreath .....5 | 12 | 100 | 300 |
| 1860 Toothed border.....2 | 9 | 90 | 225 |
| 1860 Toothed border/Beaded border, mule .....700 | 1400 | 2750 | — |
| 1860 round top light house .....15 | 110 | 400 | — |
| 1860 5 berries in wreath .....3 | 9 | 90 | 350 |
| 1860 — 15 leaves, berries .....1 | 9 | 80 | 225 |
| 1860 — rounded lighthouse .....2 | 9 | 100 | 250 |
| 1860 — Double incuse leaf veins.....3 | 10 | 95 | 225 |
| 1860 — 16 leaves wreath .....8 | 25 | 135 | 425 |
| 1861 5 berries in wreath .....8 | 25 | 120 | 375 |
| 1861 15 leaves in wreath .....5 | 18 | 95 | 325 |
| 1861 — R. no hemline to drapery .....10 | 25 | 120 | 325 |
| 1861 — R. Door on lighthouse.....3 | 10 | 95 | 325 |
| 1861 4 leaves double incuse veins.....1 | 9 | 80 | 225 |
| 1861 16 leaves wreath .....3 | 10 | 90 | 325 |
| 1861 — R. LCW incuse on rock .....10 | 25 | 120 | 375 |
| 1861 — R. no hemline to drapery .....2 | 8 | 90 | 285 |
| 1861 — R. door on lighthouse .....— | 4 | 75 | 225 |
| 1861 HALP error.....300 | 850 | — | — |
| 1861 6 over 8 .....275 | 800 | — | — |
| 1862   .....— | 4 | 45 | 165 |

|  | F | VF | EF | BU |
|---|---|---|---|---|
|  | £ | £ | £ | £ |
| 1862 Die letter to left of lighthouse | | | | |
| A | 300 | 1250 | 2650 | 4000 |
| B | 600 | 2250 | — | — |
| C | 1000 | 2750 | — | — |
| 1863 small 3 | — | 5 | 65 | 235 |
| 1863 large 3 | — | 5 | 65 | 200 |
| 1864 | 1 | 10 | 85 | 250 |
| 1865 | 2 | 12 | 100 | 400 |
| 1865/3 | 45 | 90 | 300 | 1000 |
| 1866 | 1 | 10 | 100 | 375 |
| 1867 | 1 | 10 | 100 | 325 |
| 1868 | — | 8 | 100 | 375 |
| 1869 | 20 | 85 | 400 | 1000 |
| 1870 | 1 | 7 | 80 | 300 |
| 1871 | 20 | 90 | 425 | 900 |
| 1872 | 1 | 7 | 85 | 250 |
| 1873 | 1 | 10 | 90 | 295 |
| 1873 R. hemline to drapery | 1 | 10 | 90 | 300 |
| 1874 | 4 | 20 | 125 | 400 |
| 1874 narrow date | 10 | 50 | 300 | 700 |
| 1874 older features | 5 | 20 | 135 | 400 |
| 1875 | — | 5 | 80 | 250 |
| 1877 | — | 5 | 80 | 250 |
| 1878 | 4 | 20 | 125 | 450 |
| 1878 wide date | 65 | 150 | 400 | 900 |
| 1879 | — | 5 | 65 | 200 |
| 1880 | 1 | 7 | 75 | 200 |
| 1881 | 1 | 7 | 75 | 250 |
| 1883 | — | 7 | 75 | 250 |
| 1883 rose for brooch obv. | 20 | 50 | 150 | 295 |
| 1884 | — | 4 | 55 | 185 |
| 1885 | — | 4 | 55 | 185 |
| 1886 | — | 4 | 55 | 185 |
| 1887 | — | 4 | 50 | 175 |
| 1888 | — | 4 | 75 | 200 |
| 1889 | — | 4 | 75 | 200 |
| 1889/8 | 15 | 45 | 165 | 400 |
| 1890 | — | 4 | 50 | 150 |
| 1891 | — | 4 | 50 | 150 |
| 1892 | 1 | 5 | 75 | 200 |
| 1893 | — | 4 | 70 | 175 |
| 1894 | 1 | 6 | 75 | 200 |

**3957 Halfpenny.** Similar R. Britannia, H Mint mark below date (struck by Ralph Heaton & Sons, Birmingham)

|  | F | VF | EF | BU |
|---|---|---|---|---|
| 1874 H | — | 4 | 75 | 250 |
| 1875 H | — | 5 | 80 | 275 |
| 1876 H | — | 4 | 75 | 250 |
| 1881 H | — | 4 | 75 | 250 |
| 1882 H | — | 4 | 75 | 250 |

*Bronze coins graded in this catalogue as BU have full mint lustre*

3958
1860 Farthing

| | F<br>£ | VF<br>£ | EF<br>£ | BU<br>£ |
|---|---|---|---|---|
| **3958 Farthing.** Laur bust l. ℞. Britannia seated r. date in ex. lighthouse l. ship to r. die axis ↑↑ | | | | |
| 1860 Beaded border | — | 3 | 25 | 85 |
| 1860 Toothed border | | 5 | 20 | 95 |
| 1860 — 5 berries | — | 3 | 30 | 95 |
| 1860 TB/BB mule | 175 | 575 | 1100 | — |
| 1861 5 berries | — | 3 | 40 | 110 |
| 1861 4 berries | — | 3 | 30 | 100 |
| 1862 | 1 | 20 | 90 | 225 |
| 1862 large 8 | 55 | 200 | 425 | — |
| 1863 | 20 | 50 | 300 | 650 |
| 1864 4 no serif | — | 5 | 50 | 165 |
| 1864 4 with serif | — | 7 | 55 | 175 |
| 1865 | — | 3 | 45 | 125 |
| 1865/2 | — | 10 | 50 | 175 |
| 1866 | — | 3 | 40 | 125 |
| 1867 | — | 3 | 45 | 135 |
| 1868 | — | 4 | 45 | 135 |
| 1869 | — | 10 | 55 | 175 |
| 1872 | — | 3 | 45 | 125 |
| 1873 | — | 2 | 30 | 95 |
| 1875 large date | 2 | 10 | 75 | 200 |
| 1875 small date | 10 | 25 | 150 | 450 |
| 1875 —older features | 7 | 20 | 100 | 325 |
| 1877 Proof only £11000 | | | | |
| 1878 | — | 3 | 25 | 100 |
| 1879 large 9 | — | 4 | 40 | 125 |
| 1879 normal 9 | — | 3 | 35 | 110 |
| 1880 | — | 4 | 45 | 135 |
| 1881 | — | 3 | 35 | 120 |
| 1883 | — | 10 | 55 | 150 |
| 1884 | — | 2 | 20 | 75 |
| 1885 | — | 2 | 20 | 75 |
| 1886 | — | 2 | 20 | 75 |
| 1887 | — | 3 | 30 | 110 |
| 1888 | — | 3 | 30 | 100 |
| 1890 | — | 3 | 25 | 90 |
| 1891 | — | 2 | 20 | 90 |
| 1892 | — | 10 | 55 | 165 |
| 1893 | — | 2 | 20 | 90 |
| 1894 | — | 3 | 30 | 100 |
| 1895 | 7 | 25 | 95 | 225 |

*Bronze coins graded in this catalogue as BU have full mint lustre*

|  | F £ | VF £ | EF £ | BU £ |
|---|---|---|---|---|

**3959 Farthing.** Similar R̟. Britannia. H Mint mark below date (struck by Ralph Heaton & Sons, Birmingham)

| | F | VF | EF | BU | | F | VF | EF | BU |
|---|---|---|---|---|---|---|---|---|---|
| 1874 H older features ....3 | 10 | 55 | 150 | | 1876 H large 6..........7 | 30 | 100 | 210 |
| 1874 H, both Gs over sideways G | | | | | 1876 H normal 6 ......3 | 10 | 65 | 150 |
| on obv. ................125 | 350 | 900 | — | | 1881 H................... — | 5 | 25 | 95 |
| 1875 H younger features 80 | 250 | 400 | 850 | | 1882 H................... — | 5 | 25 | 90 |
| 1875 H older features ...... | 2 | 18 | 95 | | | | | |

3960
1868 Third-Farthing

**3960 Third-Farthing** (for use in Malta). Laur. head l. R̟. Crowned date and Value die axis ↑↑

| | F | VF | EF | BU |
|---|---|---|---|---|
| 1866 | — | 4 | 30 | 100 |
| 1868 | — | 4 | 30 | 100 |
| 1876 | — | 5 | 35 | 110 |
| 1878 | — | 4 | 30 | 110 |
| 1881 | — | 5 | 35 | 110 |
| 1884 | — | 4 | 30 | 100 |
| 1885 | — | 4 | 30 | 100 |

**Old Head Issue, 1895-1901, die axis ↑↑**

Proofs exist of most years and are generally extremely rare for all denominations

3961
1897 Penny

**3961 Penny.** Old veiled bust l. R̟. Britannia seated r. date in ex., die axis ↑↑

| | F | VF | EF | BU |
|---|---|---|---|---|
| 1895 | — | 1 | 30 | 125 |
| 1896 | — | 3 | 30 | 100 |
| 1897 | — | 3 | 30 | 100 |
| 1897 O'NE flawed | — | 100 | 385 | 1200 |
| 1898 | — | 7 | 40 | 135 |
| 1899 | — | 3 | 30 | 100 |
| 1900 | — | 5 | 20 | 85 |
| 1901 | — | 1 | 12 | 70 |

| 3961 'Normal Tide' | 3961A 'Low Tide' |
|---|---|
| Horizon is level with folds in robe | Horizon is level with hem line of robe |

|  | F | VF | EF | BU |
|---|---|---|---|---|
|  | £ | £ | £ | £ |

**3961A Penny.** Similar As last but 'Low tide' and 'P' 2mm from trident

| 1895 | ................ | 45 | 200 | 380 | 950 |
|---|---|---|---|---|---|

**3961B Penny.** Similar, higher tide level above two folds of robe

| 1897 | ................ | 20 | 75 | 400 | 1500 |
|---|---|---|---|---|---|

| 3962 | 3964 |
|---|---|
| Old Head Halfpenny | Old Head Farthing |

**3962 Halfpenny.** Old veiled bust l. R. Britannia seated r. date in ex., die axis ↑↑

| 1895 | ................ | — | 3 | 12 | 100 |
|---|---|---|---|---|---|
| 1896 | ................ | — | 2 | 10 | 95 |
| 1897 | ................ | — | 2 | 10 | 95 |
| 1897 Higher tide level | ................ | — | 5 | 15 | 100 |
| 1898 | ................ | — | 3 | 12 | 100 |
| 1899 | ................ | — | 2 | 10 | 95 |
| 1900 | ................ | — | 2 | 10 | 90 |
| 1901 | ................ | — | — | 7 | 70 |

**3963 Farthing.** Old veiled bust l. R. Britannia seated r. date in ex. Bright finish, die axis ↑↑

| 1895 | ................ | — | — | 7 | 50 |
|---|---|---|---|---|---|
| 1896 | ................ | — | 1 | 10 | 55 |
| 1897 | ................ | — | 3 | 12 | 55 |

**3964 Farthing.** Similar Dark finish, die axis ↑↑

| 1897 | ................ | — | — | 7 | 35 |
|---|---|---|---|---|---|
| 1897 Higher tide level | ................ | — | 3 | 12 | 55 |
| 1898 | ................ | — | 1 | 10 | 45 |
| 1899 | ................ | — | 1 | 10 | 35 |
| 1900 | ................ | — | — | 7 | 30 |
| 1901 | ................ | — | — | 4 | 25 |

## PROOF SETS

**PS3** Young head, **1839.** 'Una and the Lion' Five Pounds, and Sovereign to Farthing (15 coins) *FDC* £350000

**PS4** — **1853.** Sovereign to Half-Farthing, including Gothic type Crown (16 coins) *FDC* £120000

**PS5** Jubilee head. Golden Jubilee, **1887.** Five pounds to Threepence (11 coins)*FDC* £45000

**PS6** — — **1887.** Crown to Threepence (7 coins) *FDC* £6000

**PS7** Old head, **1893.** Five Pounds to Threepence (10 coins) *FDC* £48000

**PS8** — — **1893.** Crown to Threepence (6 coins) *FDC* £7500

† *NB Truly 'FDC' proof sets are hardly ever encountered. Component coins showing any surface marks, hairlines or nicks will be worth less than the prices quoted above.*

'Edward the Peacemaker' was born on 9th November 1841, and married Princess Alexandra of Denmark. He indulged himself in every decadent luxury, while his wife tried to ignore his extramarital activities. Edward travelled extensively and was crucial in negotiating alliances with Russia and France. Edward VII died on 6th May 1910.

Five Pound pieces, Two Pound pieces and Crowns were only issued in 1902. A branch of the Royal Mint was opened in Canada at Ottawa and coined Sovereigns of imperial type from 1908.

Unlike the coins in most other proof sets, the proofs issued for the Coronation in 1902 have a matt surface in place of the more usual brilliant finish.

**Designer's initials:**   De S. (G. W. De Saulles 1862-1903)
                               B. P. (Benedetto Pistrucci, d. 1855)
**Engravers and Designers:** WHJ Blakemore, George William De Saulles (1862-1903), Benedetto Pistrucci (1784-1855)

## GOLD

**Die axis: ↑↑**

3966
Matt Proof Five Pounds 1902

|  | F £ | VF £ | EF £ | BU £ |
|---|---|---|---|---|
| **3965 Five Pounds.** Bare head r. R. St. George and dragon, date in ex. |  |  |  |  |
| 1902 ...................................................................1650 | | 1950 | 2500 | 3500 |

**3966 Five Pounds.** Similar Proof. 1902. *Matt surface FDC* £3000
**3966A Five Pounds.** Similar Proof 1902S. S on ground for Sydney Mint, Australia..*Extremely rare*

3967
1902 Two Pounds

**3967 Two Pounds.** Bare head r. R. St George and dragon, date in ex.
1902 .......................................................................750        850        1000        1300
**3968 Two Pounds.** Similar Proof. 1902. *Matt surface FDC* £2000
**3968A Two Pounds.** Similar Proof 1902S. S on ground for Sydney Mint, Australia..*Extremely rare*

*BV= Bullion value only. At the time of going to press the spot price for gold was £1400 per oz.*

3969
1902 Sovereign

|  | F | VF | EF | BU |
|---|---|---|---|---|
|  | £ | £ | £ | £ |

**3969** **Sovereign.** Bare head r. R . St. George and dragon, date in ex. London mint, die axis ↑↑
1902 Matt proof *FDC* £775

| 1902 | — | — | BV | 375 |
|---|---|---|---|---|
| 1903 | — | — | BV | 400 |
| 1904 | — | — | BV | 400 |
| 1905 | — | — | BV | 400 |
| 1906 | — | — | BV | 400 |
| 1907 | — | — | BV | 400 |
| 1908 | — | — | BV | 400 |
| 1909 | — | — | BV | 400 |
| 1910 | | — | BV | 400 |

**3970 Sovereign.** Similar R. C on ground for Ottawa Mint, Canada
1908 C (Satin proof only) *FDC* £12500

| 1909 C | — | 350 | 475 | 800 |
|---|---|---|---|---|
| 1909 C Satin finish specimen *FDC* | | | | *Extremely rare* |
| 1910 C | — | 350 | 450 | 700 |

**3971 Sovereign.** Similar R. St. George M on ground for Melbourne Mint, Australia, die axis ↑↑

| 1902 M | — | — | BV | 400 |
|---|---|---|---|---|
| 1902 M Proof | | | | *Extremely rare* |
| 1903 M | — | — | BV | 425 |
| 1904 M | — | — | BV | 425 |
| 1904 M Proof | | | | *Extremely rare* |
| 1905 M | — | — | BV | 425 |
| 1906 M | — | — | BV | 425 |
| 1907 M | — | — | BV | 425 |
| 1908 M | — | — | BV | 425 |
| 1909 M | — | — | BV | 425 |
| 1910 M | — | — | BV | 425 |
| 1910 M Proof | | | | *Extremely rare* |

**3972 Sovereign.** Similar R. P on ground for Perth Mint, Australia die axis ↑↑

| 1902 P | — | — | BV | 425 |
|---|---|---|---|---|
| 1903 P | — | — | BV | 450 |
| 1904 P | — | — | BV | 450 |
| 1905 P | — | — | BV | 450 |
| 1906 P | — | — | BV | 450 |
| 1907 P | — | — | BV | 450 |
| 1908 P | — | — | BV | 450 |
| 1909 P | — | — | BV | 450 |
| 1910 P | — | — | BV | 425 |

**3973 Sovereign.** Similar R. S on ground for Sydney Mint, Australia die axis ↑↑

| 1902 S | — | — | BV | 400 |
|---|---|---|---|---|
| 1902 S Proof | | | | *Extremely rare* |

*BV= Bullion value only. At the time of going to press the spot price for gold was £1400 per oz.*

| | F | VF | EF | BU |
|---|---|---|---|---|
| | £ | £ | £ | £ |
| 1903 S | — | — | BV | 400 |
| 1904 S | — | — | BV | 400 |
| 1905 S | — | — | BV | 400 |
| 1906 S | — | — | — | 400 |
| 1907 S | — | — | — | 400 |
| 1908 S | — | — | — | 400 |
| 1909 S | — | — | — | 400 |
| 1910 S | — | — | — | 400 |

3974A

1902 Half-Sovereign, no BP in exergue

**3974A Half-Sovereign.** Bare head r. R. St. George. London Mint no BP in exergue, die axis ↑↑
1902 Matt proof *FDC* £400

| | | | | |
|---|---|---|---|---|
| 1902 | — | BV | 185 | 325 |
| 1903 | — | BV | 185 | 325 |
| 1904 | — | BV | 185 | 325 |

**3974B Half-Sovereign.** R. Similar with BP in exergue

| | | | | |
|---|---|---|---|---|
| 1904 | — | BV | 185 | 325 |
| 1905 | — | BV | 185 | 325 |
| 1906 | — | BV | 185 | 325 |
| 1907 | — | BV | 185 | 325 |
| 1908 | — | BV | 185 | 325 |
| 1909 | — | BV | 185 | 325 |
| 1910 | — | BV | 185 | 325 |

**3975 Half-Sovereign.** Similar R. M on ground for Melbourne Mint, Australia, die axis ↑↑

| | | | | |
|---|---|---|---|---|
| 1906 M | BV | 325 | 850 | — |
| 1907 M | BV | 185 | 250 | 750 |
| 1908 M | BV | 185 | 265 | 500 |
| 1909 M | BV | 185 | 275 | 700 |

**3976A Half-Sovereign.** — P on ground for Perth Mint, Australia R. no BP in exergue, die axis ↑↑

| | | | | |
|---|---|---|---|---|
| 1904 P | BV | 275 | 1250 | 5500 |

**3976B Half-Sovereign.** Similar R. P on ground for Perth Mint, Australia R. with BP in exergue, die axis ↑↑

| | | | | |
|---|---|---|---|---|
| 1904 P | | | | *Extremely rare* |
| 1908 P | BV | 250 | 1350 | 4500 |
| 1909 P | BV | 250 | 750 | 2000 |

**3977A Half-Sovereign.** Similar R. S on ground for Sydney Mint, Australia R. No BP in exergue, die axis ↑↑

| | | | | |
|---|---|---|---|---|
| 1902 S | BV | 185 | 250 | 425 |
| 1902 S Proof | | | | *Extremely rare* |
| 1903 S | BV | 185 | 250 | 600 |

**3977B Half-Sovereign.** — S on ground for Sydney Mint, Australia R. with BP in exergue, die axis ↑↑

| | | | | |
|---|---|---|---|---|
| 1906 S | — | BV | 185 | 500 |
| 1908 S | — | BV | 185 | 350 |
| 1910 S | — | BV | 185 | 325 |

*BV= Bullion value only. At the time of going to press the spot price for gold was £1400 per oz.*

# SILVER

3978 - 1902 Crown

|      | F £ | VF £ | EF £ | BU £ |
|------|-----|------|------|------|
| **3978 Crown.** Bare head r. ℞. St. George and dragon date in ex. die axis ↑↑ | | | | |
| 1902 ........................................................................65 | 110 | 200 | 350 |
| 1902 error edge inscription........................................................................*Extremely rare* | | | | |
| **3979 Crown.** Similar Matt proof *FDC* £385 | | | | |

3980 - 1904 Halfcrown                              3981 - Florin

**3980 Halfcrown.** Bare head r. ℞. Crowned Shield in Garter, die axis ↑↑

|      | F | VF | EF | BU |
|------|-----|------|------|------|
| 1902 ........................................................................12 | 30 | 100 | 225 |
| 1902 Matt proof *FDC* £225 | | | | |
| 1903 ........................................................................150 | 485 | 2000 | 4850 |
| 1904 ........................................................................60 | 300 | 950 | 2650 |
| 1905* ........................................................................550 | 1750 | 5250 | 10500 |
| 1906 ........................................................................15 | 60 | 250 | 725 |
| 1907 ........................................................................15 | 55 | 245 | 625 |
| 1908 ........................................................................20 | 55 | 475 | 1100 |
| 1909 ........................................................................15 | 50 | 275 | 750 |
| 1910 ........................................................................15 | 40 | 225 | 600 |

**3981 Florin.** Bare head r. ℞. Britannia standing on ship's bow die axis ↑↑

|      | F | VF | EF | BU |
|------|-----|------|------|------|
| 1902 ........................................................................7 | 20 | 75 | 140 |
| 1902 Matt proof *FDC* £200 | | | | |
| 1903 ........................................................................10 | 30 | 175 | 500 |
| 1904 ........................................................................15 | 45 | 245 | 550 |
| 1905 ........................................................................65 | 250 | 950 | 2000 |
| 1906 ........................................................................10 | 30 | 150 | 475 |
| 1907 ........................................................................10 | 40 | 215 | 525 |
| 1908 ........................................................................15 | 50 | 300 | 650 |
| 1909 ........................................................................15 | 50 | 275 | 525 |
| 1910 ........................................................................10 | 25 | 145 | 300 |

*Beware of 1970's forgeries.*

3982
1902 Shilling

| | F | VF | EF | BU |
|---|---|---|---|---|
| | £ | £ | £ | £ |

**3982 Shilling**. Bare head r. R. Lion passant on crown die axis ↑↑

| | F | VF | EF | BU |
|---|---|---|---|---|
| 1902 | 5 | 12 | 65 | 110 |
| 1902 Matt proof *FDC* £175 | | | | |
| 1903 | 7 | 20 | 175 | 425 |
| 1904 | 7 | 15 | 150 | 425 |
| 1905 | 110 | 350 | 1500 | 3250 |
| 1906 | 5 | 10 | 80 | 225 |
| 1907 | 5 | 10 | 85 | 250 |
| 1908 | 12 | 25 | 200 | 500 |
| 1909 | 12 | 25 | 225 | 600 |
| 1910 | 5 | 10 | 80 | 175 |

3983
1902 Sixpence

**3983 Sixpence**. Bare head r. R. Value in wreath die axis ↑↑

| | F | VF | EF | BU |
|---|---|---|---|---|
| 1902 | 5 | 10 | 80 | 90 |
| 1902 Matt proof *FDC* £135 | | | | |
| 1903 | 4 | 10 | 60 | 150 |
| 1904 | 7 | 25 | 125 | 265 |
| 1905 | 5 | 20 | 90 | 200 |
| 1906 | 4 | 10 | 45 | 100 |
| 1907 | 5 | 10 | 45 | 110 |
| 1908 | 5 | 12 | 60 | 135 |
| 1909 | 4 | 10 | 60 | 135 |
| 1910 | 4 | 7 | 50 | 100 |

**3984 Threepence.** As Maundy but dull finish die axis ↑↑

| | F | VF | EF | BU |
|---|---|---|---|---|
| 1902 | 2 | 5 | 15 | 40 |
| 1902 Matt proof *FDC* £55 | | | | |
| 1903 | 3 | 7 | 30 | 65 |
| 1904 | 4 | 10 | 40 | 115 |
| 1905 | 3 | 7 | 30 | 90 |
| 1906 | 3 | 7 | 50 | 140 |
| 1907 | 3 | 7 | 30 | 65 |
| 1908 | 2 | 5 | 15 | 55 |
| 1909 | 3 | 7 | 30 | 65 |
| 1910 | 2 | 5 | 15 | 55 |

3985
1903 Maundy Set

| | F £ | VF £ | EF £ | BU £ |
|---|---|---|---|---|
| **3985 Maundy Set** (4d., 3d., 2d. and 1d.) Bare head r. die axis ↑↑ | | | | |
| 1902 | — | — | 95 | 150 |
| 1902 Matt proof *FDC* £200 | | | | |
| 1903 | — | — | 95 | 150 |
| 1904 | — | — | 95 | 150 |
| 1905 | — | — | 95 | 150 |
| 1906 | — | — | 95 | 150 |
| 1907 | — | — | 95 | 150 |
| 1908 | — | — | 95 | 150 |
| 1909 | — | — | 150 | 275 |
| 1910 | — | — | 150 | 275 |
| **3986 — Fourpence.** 1902-10 | | *from* | 7 | 30 |
| **3987 — Threepence.** 1902-10 | | *from* | 10 | 30 |
| **3988 — Twopence.** 1902-10 | | *from* | 7 | 30 |
| **3989 — Penny.** 1902-10 | | *from* | 12 | 35 |

*Maundy sets in the original undamaged cases are worth approximately £25 more than the prices quoted. Also see foontnote after 3796.*

# BRONZE

3990 - 1902 Penny

3990 Normal Tide        '3990A 'Low Tide'

|  | VG £ | F £ | VF £ | EF £ | BU £ |
|---|---|---|---|---|---|
| **3990 Penny.** Bare head r. ℞. Britannia seated r. date in ex. die axis ↑↑ | | | | | |
| 1902 | — | — | 1 | 12 | 40 |
| 1903 Normal 3 | — | — | 2 | 25 | 120 |
| 1903 Open 3 | 60 | 150 | 575 | — | — |
| 1904 | — | — | 7 | 35 | 140 |
| 1905 | — | — | 5 | 30 | 130 |
| 1906 | — | — | 4 | 20 | 110 |
| 1907 | — | — | 1 | 25 | 115 |
| 1908 | — | — | 4 | 20 | 120 |
| 1909 | — | — | 5 | 25 | 130 |
| 1910 | — | — | 2 | 15 | 100 |
| **3990A Penny.** Similar ℞. As last but 'Low tide' | | | | | |
| 1902,'2' has wavy base line | — | 7 | 50 | 150 | 300 |

3991 - Halfpenny

|  | VG £ | F £ | VF £ | EF £ | BU £ |
|---|---|---|---|---|---|
| **3991 Halfpenny**. Bare head r. ℞. Britannia seated r. date in ex. die axis ↑↑ | | | | | |
| 1902 | — | — | 1 | 10 | 45 |
| 1903 | — | — | 2 | 15 | 100 |
| 1904 | — | — | 2 | 20 | 125 |
| 1905 | — | — | 2 | 18 | 100 |
| 1906 | — | — | 2 | 18 | 95 |
| 1907 | — | — | 1 | 15 | 90 |
| 1908 | — | — | 1 | 15 | 90 |
| 1909 | — | — | 2 | 18 | 100 |
| 1910 | — | — | 2 | 15 | 90 |

| | F | VF | EF | BU |
|---|---|---|---|---|
| | £ | £ | £ | £ |

**3991A Halfpenny**. Similar R. As last but 'Low tide'
1902 .......................................................................15  85  165  410

3992
Farthing

**3992 Farthing**. Bare head r. R. Britannia seated r. date in ex. Dark finish die axis ↑↑

| | | | | |
|---|---|---|---|---|
| 1902 | — | — | 8 | 20 |
| 1903 | — | 1 | 10 | 25 |
| 1904 | — | 2 | 12 | 25 |
| 1905 | — | 1 | 10 | 25 |
| 1906 | — | 1 | 10 | 25 |
| 1907 | — | 1 | 10 | 25 |
| 1908 | — | 1 | 10 | 25 |
| 1909 | — | 1 | 10 | 25 |
| 1910 | — | 2 | 17 | 30 |

3993
1902 Third-Farthing

**3993 Third-Farthing** (for use in Malta) Bare head r. R. Crowned date and value
die axis ↑↑.
1902 .......................................................................— 7 12 40

*No proofs of the bronze coins were issued in 1902*

**PROOF SETS**
**PS9** Coronation, **1902.** Five Pounds to Maundy Penny, matt surface, (13 coins) *FDC* £6500
**PS10** — **1902.** Sovereign to Maundy Penny, matt surface, (11 coins) *FDC* £2250

† *NB Truly 'FDC' proof sets are hardly ever encountered. Component coins showing any surface
marks, hairlines or nicks will be worth less than the prices quoted above.*

# THE HOUSE OF WINDSOR, 1917-
# GEORGE V, 1910-36

George V, the second son of Edward VII, was born on 3rd June 1865 and married Mary of Teck who bore him five sons and a daughter. He was King through World War I and visited the front on several occassions. He suffered a fall breaking his pelvis on one of these visits, an injury that would pain him for the rest of his life. He watched the Empire divide; Ireland, Canada, Australia, New Zealand and India all went through changes. He died on 20th January 1936 only months after his Silver Jubilee.

Paper money issued by the Treasury during the First World War replaced gold for internal use after 1915 but the branch mints in Australia and South Africa (the main Commonwealth gold producing countries) continued striking Sovereigns until 1930-2. Owing to the steep rise in the price of silver in 1919/20 the issue of standard (.925) silver was discontinued and coins of .500 silver were minted.

In 1912, 1918 and 1919 some Pennies were made under contract by private mints in Birmingham. In 1918, as Half-Sovereigns were no longer being minted, Farthings were again issued with the ordinary bright bronze finish. Crown pieces had not been issued for general circulation but they were struck in small numbers about Christmas time for people to give as presents in the years 1927-36, and in 1935 a special commemorative Crown was issued in celebration of the Silver Jubilee.

As George V died on 20th January, it is likely that all coins dated 1936 were struck during the reign of Edward VIII.

**Engravers and Designers:–** George Kuger Gray (1880-1943), Bertram MacKennal (1863-1931), Benedetto Pistrucci (1784-1855) Percy Metcalfe (1895-1970)

**Designer's initials:**

B. M. (Bertram Mackennal)    P. M. (Percy Metcalfe)
K. G. (G. Kruger Gray)       B. P. (Benedetto Pistrucci; d. 1855)

**Die axis:** ↑↑

## GOLD

**3994 Five Pounds.\*** Bare head l. R. St. George and dragon, date in ex., 1911 (Proof only) £10500
**3995 Two Pounds.\*** Bare head l. R. St. George and dragon, date in ex., 1911 (Proof only) £3250

3996

| | F £ | VF £ | EF £ | BU £ |
|---|---|---|---|---|
| **3996 Sovereign.** Bare head l. R. St. George and dragon. London Mint die axis: ↑↑ | | | | |
| 1911 | — | BV | BV | 400 |
| 1911 Proof *FDC* £1750 | | | | |
| 1911 Matt Proof *FDC of highest rarity* | | | | |
| 1912 | — | BV | BV | 375 |
| 1913 | — | BV | BV | 375 |
| 1914 | — | BV | BV | 375 |
| 1915 | | BV | BV | 375 |
| 1916 | — | BV | 400 | 650 |
| 1917* | — | 5500 | 15000 | — |
| 1925 | — | BV | BV | 350 |

*\*Forgeries exist of these and of most other dates and mints.*

*BV= Bullion value only. At the time of going to press the spot price for gold was £1400 per oz.*

3997 - Canada 'c' Mint mark

| | F | VF | EF | BU |
|---|---|---|---|---|
| | £ | £ | £ | £ |

**3997 Sovereign.** Bare head l. R. St George, C on ground for the Ottawa Mint, Canada die axis: ↑↑

| | | | | |
|---|---|---|---|---|
| 1911 C | — | BV | 365 | 550 |
| 1913 C | — | 450 | 1200 | — |
| 1914 C | — | 400 | 850 | — |
| 1916 C* | — | 7500 | 17500 | — |
| 1917 C | — | BV | BV | 450 |
| 1918 C | — | BV | BV | 450 |
| 1919 C | — | BV | BV | 450 |

**3998 Sovereign.** Similar R. I on ground for Bombay Mint, India

| | | | | |
|---|---|---|---|---|
| 1918 | — | BV | 375 | 550 |

**3999 Sovereign.** Similar R. M on ground for Melbourne Mint, Australia die axis: ↑↑

| | | | | |
|---|---|---|---|---|
| 1911 M | — | — | BV | 395 |
| 1912 M | — | — | BV | 395 |
| 1913 M | — | — | BV | 395 |
| 1914 M | — | — | BV | 395 |
| 1915 M | — | — | BV | 395 |
| 1916 M | — | — | BV | 395 |
| 1917 M | — | — | BV | 395 |
| 1918 M | — | — | BV | 395 |
| 1919 M | — | — | BV | 400 |
| 1920 M | 700 | 1400 | 2300 | 4500 |
| 1921 M | 2750 | 5000 | 7500 | 17000 |
| 1922 M | 1750 | 4000 | 7500 | 13500 |
| 1923 M | — | BV | BV | 400 |
| 1924 M | — | BV | BV | 400 |
| 1925 M | — | — | BV | 395 |
| 1926 M | — | BV | BV | 400 |
| 1928 M | 450 | 900 | 1350 | 2350 |

4000 - 1930 M Sovereign, small head

**4000 Sovereign.** Similar small bare head l. die axis: ↑↑

| | | | | |
|---|---|---|---|---|
| 1929 M | 375 | 750 | 1350 | 2500 |
| 1929 M Proof *FDC* | | | | *Extremely rare* |
| 1930 M | — | BV | 385 | 475 |
| 1931 M | BV | BV | 475 | 600 |

*\* Beware of recent forgeries*

| 4001 | 4003 |
|---|---|
| Perth Mint Sovereign | 1921 Sydney 's' Sovereign |

|  | F | VF | EF | BU |
|---|---|---|---|---|
|  | £ | £ | £ | £ |

**4001 Sovereign.** Similar R. P on ground for Perth Mint, Australia die axis: ↑↑

| 1911 P | — | — | BV | 375 |
|---|---|---|---|---|
| 1912 P | — | — | BV | 375 |
| 1913 P | — | — | BV | 375 |
| 1914 P | — | — | BV | 375 |
| 1915 P | — | — | BV | 375 |
| 1916 P | — | — | BV | 375 |
| 1917 P | — | — | BV | 375 |
| 1918 P | — | — | BV | 375 |
| 1919 P | — | — | BV | 375 |
| 1920 P | — | — | BV | 375 |
| 1921 P | — | — | BV | 375 |
| 1922 P | — | — | BV | 375 |
| 1923 P | — | — | BV | 375 |
| 1924 P | — | BV | BV | 425 |
| 1925 P | BV | BV | 325 | 600 |
| 1926 P | 400 | 675 | 1100 | 2500 |
| 1927 P | BV | BV | 375 | 500 |
| 1928 P | — | BV | BV | 425 |

**4002 Sovereign.** Similar — small bare head l. die axis: ↑↑

| 1929 P | — | BV | BV | 450 |
|---|---|---|---|---|
| 1930 P | — | BV | BV | 450 |
| 1931 P | — | — | BV | 375 |

**4003 Sovereign.** Similar R. S on ground for Sydney Mint, Australia die axis: ↑↑

| 1911 S | — | — | BV | 375 |
|---|---|---|---|---|
| 1912 S | — | — | BV | 375 |
| 1913 S | — | — | BV | 375 |
| 1914 S | — | — | BV | 375 |
| 1915 S | — | — | BV | 375 |
| 1916 S | — | — | BV | 375 |
| 1917 S | — | — | BV | 375 |
| 1918 S | — | — | BV | 375 |
| 1919 S | — | — | BV | 425 |
| †1920 S | | | | Of highest rarity |
| 1921 S | 500 | 800 | 1600 | 2500 |
| 1922 S | 5000 | 9500 | 14000 | 27500 |
| 1923 S | 3500 | 6500 | 12000 | 25000 |
| 1924 S | 400 | 800 | 1450 | 2500 |
| 1925 S | — | — | BV | 400 |
| 1926 S | 6000 | 12500 | 20000 | 31500 |

† *An example of the proof 1920 S sold at a UK auction in May 2012 for £780,000*
*BV= Bullion value only. At the time of going to press the spot price for gold was £1400 per oz.*

| | F | VF | EF | BU |
|---|---|---|---|---|
| | £ | £ | £ | £ |

**4004 Sovereign.** Similar R. SA on ground for Pretoria Mint, South Africa die axis: ↑↑

| 1923 SA | — | 3000 | 10000 | — |
|---|---|---|---|---|
| 1923 SA Proof *FDC* £2750 | | | | |
| 1924 SA | — | 2500 | 5750 | 8500 |
| 1925 SA | — | — | BV | 365 |
| 1926 SA | — | — | BV | 365 |
| 1927 SA | — | — | BV | 365 |
| 1928 SA | — | — | BV | 365 |

**4005 Sovereign.** Similar — small head die axis: ↑↑

| 1929 SA | — | — | BV | 365 |
|---|---|---|---|---|
| 1930 SA | — | — | BV | 365 |
| 1931 SA | — | — | BV | 365 |
| 1932 SA | — | — | BV | 365 |

4006
1914 Half-sovereign

**4006 Half-Sovereign.** Bare head l. R. St. George and dragon date in ex. London Mint die axis: ↑↑

| 1911 | — | BV | BV | 250 |
|---|---|---|---|---|
| 1911 Proof *FDC* £1100 | | | | |
| 1911 Matt Proof *FDC* | | | | *Of highest rarity* |
| 1912 | — | BV | BV | 250 |
| 1913 | — | BV | BV | 250 |
| 1914 | — | BV | BV | 250 |
| 1915 | — | BV | BV | 250 |

**4007 Half-Sovereign.** Similar R. M on ground for Melbourne Mint, Australia die axis: ↑↑

| 1915 M | — | BV | BV | 250 |
|---|---|---|---|---|

**4008 Half-Sovereign.** Similar R. P on ground for Perth Mint, Australia die axis: ↑↑

| 1911 P | — | BV | 175 | 350 |
|---|---|---|---|---|
| 1915 P | — | BV | 175 | 325 |
| 1918 P | 200 | 600 | 2000 | 3750 |

**4009 Half-Sovereign.** Similar R. S on ground for Sydney Mint, Australia die axis: ↑↑

| 1911 S | — | BV | BV | 215 |
|---|---|---|---|---|
| 1912 S | — | BV | BV | 215 |
| 1914 S | — | BV | BV | 215 |
| 1915 S | — | BV | BV | 215 |
| 1916 S | — | BV | BV | 215 |

**4010 Half-Sovereign.** Similar R. SA on ground for Pretoria Mint, South Africa die axis: ↑↑

| 1923 SA Proof *FDC* £1500 | | | | |
|---|---|---|---|---|
| 1925 SA | — | BV | BV | 215 |
| 1926 SA | — | BV | BV | 215 |

*BV= Bullion value only. At the time of going to press the spot price for gold was £1400 per oz.*

# SILVER

**FIRST COINAGE, 1911-19** Sterling silver (.925 fine)

4011
1911 Halfcrown

|  | F | VF | EF | BU |
|---|---|---|---|---|
|  | £ | £ | £ | £ |

**4011 Halfcrown.** Bare head l. R. Crowned shield in Garter die axis: ↑↑

| 1911 | ...................8 | 25 | 85 | 225 |
|---|---|---|---|---|
| 1911 Proof *FDC* £325 | | | | |
| 1912 | ...................8 | 25 | 75 | 275 |
| 1913 | ...................8 | 30 | 85 | 275 |
| 1914 | ...................8 | 12 | 45 | 125 |
| 1915 | ...................8 | 12 | 40 | 100 |
| 1916 | ...................8 | 12 | 40 | 100 |
| 1917 | ...................8 | 15 | 60 | 150 |
| 1918 | ...................8 | 12 | 45 | 125 |
| 1919 | ...................8 | 15 | 55 | 150 |

4012
1912 Florin

**4012 Florin.** Bare head l. R. Crowned Cruciform shields sceptres in angles die axis: ↑↑

| 1911 | ...................6 | 12 | 60 | 165 |
|---|---|---|---|---|
| 1911 Proof *FDC* £225 | | | | |
| 1912 | ...................6 | 15 | 70 | 225 |
| 1913 | ...................8 | 25 | 85 | 250 |
| 1914 | ...................6 | 12 | 50 | 115 |
| 1915 | ...................6 | 20 | 65 | 200 |
| 1916 | ...................6 | 12 | 50 | 115 |
| 1917 | ...................6 | 15 | 55 | 150 |
| 1918 | ...................6 | 12 | 45 | 110 |
| 1919 | ...................6 | 15 | 55 | 150 |

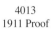

4013
1911 Proof

4014
1911 Sixpence

|  | F | VF | EF | BU |
|---|---|---|---|---|
|  | £ | £ | £ | £ |

**4013 Shilling.** Bare head l. R. Lion passant on crown, within circle die axis: ↑↑

| 1911 | ........3 | 10 | 40 | 85 |
|---|---|---|---|---|
| 1911 Proof *FDC* £150 | | | | |
| 1912 | ........3 | 12 | 45 | 115 |
| 1913 | ........6 | 15 | 75 | 225 |
| 1914 | ........3 | 10 | 40 | 90 |
| 1915 | — | 2 | 30 | 75 |
| 1916 | — | 2 | 30 | 75 |
| 1917 | — | 3 | 40 | 125 |
| 1918 | — | 2 | 35 | 85 |
| 1919 | ........2 | 8 | 45 | 100 |

**4014 Sixpence.** Bare head l. R. Lion passant on crown, within circle die axis: ↑↑

| 1911 | ........1 | 7 | 30 | 60 |
|---|---|---|---|---|
| 1911 Proof *FDC* £115 | | | | |
| 1912 | ........3 | 10 | 40 | 80 |
| 1913 | ........6 | 12 | 45 | 85 |
| 1914 | ........1 | 7 | 30 | 65 |
| 1915 | ........1 | 7 | 30 | 75 |
| 1916 | ........1 | 7 | 30 | 60 |
| 1917 | ........4 | 15 | 55 | 160 |
| 1918 | ........1 | 7 | 30 | 65 |
| 1919 | ........3 | 10 | 35 | 75 |
| 1920 | ........4 | 12 | 45 | 90 |

**4015 Threepence.** As Maundy but dull finish die axis: ↑↑

| 1911 | — | 1 | 5 | 30 |
|---|---|---|---|---|
| 1911 Proof *FDC* £55 | | | | |
| 1912 | — | 1 | 5 | 30 |
| 1913 | — | 1 | 5 | 30 |
| 1914 | — | 1 | 5 | 30 |
| 1915 | — | 1 | 5 | 35 |
| 1916 | — | 1 | 5 | 25 |
| 1917 | — | 1 | 5 | 25 |
| 1918 | — | 1 | 5 | 25 |
| 1919 | — | 1 | 5 | 25 |
| 1920 | — | 2 | 10 | 35 |

4016 - 1915 Maundy Set

| | EF £ | FDC £ |
|---|---|---|
| **4016 Maundy Set** (4d., 3d., 2d. and 1d.) die axis: ↑↑ | | |
| 1911 | 110 | 150 |
| 1911 Proof *FDC* £300 | | |
| 1912 | 110 | 150 |
| 1913 | 110 | 150 |
| 1914 | 110 | 150 |
| 1915 | 110 | 150 |
| 1916 | 110 | 150 |
| 1917 | 110 | 150 |
| 1918 | 110 | 150 |
| 1919 | 110 | 150 |
| 1920 | 135 | 200 |
| **4017 — Fourpence.** 1911-20 *from* | 10 | 30 |
| **4018 — Threepence.** 1911-20 *from* | 12 | 32 |
| **4019 — Twopence.** 1911-20 *from* | 8 | 25 |
| **4020 — Penny.** 1911-20 *from* | 10 | 35 |

*See footnote after 3796*

**SECOND COINAGE, 1920-27** Debased silver (.500 fine). Types as before.

| | F £ | VF £ | EF £ | BU £ |
|---|---|---|---|---|
| **4021 Halfcrown.** Deeply engraved. Bare head l. R. Crowned shield in garter die axis: ↑↑ | | | | |
| 1920 | 3 | 12 | 60 | 185 |
| **4021A** — recut shallow portrait | | | | |
| 1920 | 5 | 15 | 75 | 215 |
| 1921 | 3 | 12 | 60 | 160 |
| 1922 | 3 | 10 | 60 | 160 |
| 1923 | 2 | 6 | 40 | 95 |
| 1924 | 3 | 10 | 60 | 160 |
| 1924 Specimen Finish £4250 | | | | |
| 1925 | 25 | 75 | 375 | 875 |
| 1926 | 3 | 18 | 85 | 195 |
| 1926 No colon after OMN | 15 | 45 | 175 | 395 |
| **4022 Florin.** Deeply engraved. Bare head l. R. Crowned cruciform shields, sceptres in angles die axis: ↑↑ | | | | |
| 1920 | 3 | 12 | 60 | 160 |
| **4022A** — recut shallow portrait | | | | |
| 1920 | 5 | 18 | 75 | 175 |
| 1921 | 2 | 7 | 55 | 120 |
| 1922 | 2 | 6 | 50 | 110 |
| 1922 Proof in gold *FDC* | | | | *Of highest rarity* |
| 1923 | 2 | 6 | 40 | 85 |
| 1924 | 2 | 12 | 65 | 150 |
| 1924 Specimen Finish £3500 | | | | |
| 1925 | 25 | 55 | 200 | 500 |
| 1926 | 2 | 12 | 65 | 150 |

|  | F<br>£ | VF<br>£ | EF<br>£ | BU<br>£ |
|---|---|---|---|---|

**4023 Shilling.** Deeply engraved. Bare head l. R. Lion passant on crown within circle
die axis: ↑↑

| | F | VF | EF | BU |
|---|---|---|---|---|
| 1920 | 3 | 12 | 45 | 100 |
| 1921 nose to S | 12 | 30 | 90 | 225 |

**4023A** — recut shallow portrait

| | F | VF | EF | BU |
|---|---|---|---|---|
| 1920 | 4 | 15 | 65 | 160 |
| 1921 nose to SV | 3 | 15 | 65 | 160 |
| 1922 | 1 | 4 | 45 | 95 |
| 1923 | 1 | 3 | 35 | 90 |
| 1924 | 1 | 4 | 35 | 95 |
| 1924 Specimen Finish £3500 | | | | |
| 1925 | 3 | 12 | 65 | 160 |
| 1926 | 1 | 7 | 35 | 90 |

*Note: 1923 and 1924 Shillings exist struck in nickel and are valued at £2850 each FDC.*

**4024 Sixpence.** Bare head l. R. Lion passant on crown within circle die axis: ↑↑

| | F | VF | EF | BU |
|---|---|---|---|---|
| 1920 | 1 | 5 | 30 | 85 |
| 1921 | 1 | 2 | 25 | 80 |
| 1922 | 1 | 3 | 25 | 80 |
| 1923 | 1 | 4 | 30 | 90 |
| 1924 | 1 | 2 | 20 | 65 |
| 1924 Specimen Finish *FDC* £3000 | | | | |
| 1924 Proof in gold *FDC* £28500 | | | | |
| 1925 | 1 | 2 | 30 | 70 |

4025
George V Sixpence

4026
Threepence

**4025 Sixpence.** Similar new beading and broader rim die axis: ↑↑

| | F | VF | EF | BU |
|---|---|---|---|---|
| 1925 | 1 | 2 | 30 | 60 |
| 1926 | 1 | 4 | 30 | 60 |

**4026 Threepence.** Bare head l. R. Crowned 3 die axis: ↑↑

| | F | VF | EF | BU |
|---|---|---|---|---|
| 1920 | — | 1 | 4 | 28 |
| 1921 | — | 1 | 4 | 28 |
| 1922 | — | 1 | 20 | 90 |
| 1924 Specimen Finish £3000 | | | | |
| 1924 Proof in gold *FDC* £12500 | | | | |
| 1925 | BV | 2 | 22 | 75 |
| 1926 | 1 | 8 | 45 | 150 |

| | EF £ | FDC £ |
|---|---|---|
| **4027 Maundy Set.** (4d., 3d., 2d. and 1d.) die axis: ↑↑ | | |
| 1921 | 100 | 150 |
| 1922 | 100 | 150 |
| 1923 | 100 | 150 |
| 1924 | 100 | 150 |
| 1925 | 100 | 150 |
| 1926 | 100 | 150 |
| 1927 | 100 | 150 |
| **4028** — **Fourpence.** 1921-7 .......................................................*from* | 15 | 35 |
| **4029** — **Threepence.** 1921-7 ...................................................*from* | 12 | 30 |
| **4030** — **Twopence.** 1921-7 ......................................................*from* | 10 | 25 |
| **4031** — **Penny.** 1921-7 ............................................................*from* | 15 | 40 |

<table>
<tr><td>2nd coinage<br>BM more central on tr.</td><td>3rd coinage<br>Modified Effigy, BM to right of tr</td></tr>
</table>

**THIRD COINAGE, 1926-27.** As before but modified effigy, with details of head more clearly defined. The BM on truncation is nearer to the back of the neck and without stops; beading is more pronounced.

| | F £ | VF £ | EF £ | BU £ |
|---|---|---|---|---|
| **4032 Halfcrown.** Modified effigy l. R. Crowned Shield in Garter die axis: ↑↑ | | | | |
| 1926 | 4 | 20 | 75 | 195 |
| 1927 | 3 | 7 | 45 | 110 |
| 1927 Proof in gold *FDC* ...................................................................*Of highest rarity* | | | | |
| **4033 Shilling.** Modified effigy l. R. Lion passant on crown, within circle die axis: ↑↑ | | | | |
| 1926 | 1 | 2 | 30 | 65 |
| 1927 | 1 | 5 | 40 | 75 |
| **4034 Sixpence.** Modified effigy l. R. Lion passant on crown, within circle die axis: ↑↑ | | | | |
| 1926 | — | 3 | 20 | 50 |
| 1927 | 1 | 3 | 25 | 55 |
| **4035 Threepence.** Modified effigy l. R. Crowned 3 die axis: ↑↑ | | | | |
| 1926 | — | 1 | 12 | 55 |

**FOURTH COINAGE, 1927-36**

4036
1927 'Wreath' Crown proof

|  | F | VF | EF | BU |
|---|---|---|---|---|
|  | £ | £ | £ | £ |

**4036 Crown.** Modified Bare head l. R. Crown and date in wreath die axis: ↑↑

† 1927 –15,030 struck Proof only *FDC* £325

   1927 Matt Proof *FDC Extremely rare*

| Year | F | VF | EF | BU |
|---|---|---|---|---|
| 1928* –9034 struck | 80 | 145 | 250 | 425 |
| 1929 –4994 struck | 85 | 175 | 275 | 475 |
| 1930 –4847 struck | 85 | 175 | 285 | 495 |
| 1931 –4056 struck | 90 | 135 | 285 | 575 |
| 1932 –2395 struck | 145 | 285 | 500 | 975 |
| 1933* –7132 struck | 90 | 185 | 300 | 485 |
| 1934 –932 struck | 1100 | 1900 | 2950 | 4500 |
| 1936 –2473 struck | 150 | 300 | 525 | 925 |

4037
1931 Halfcrown

**4037 Halfcrown.** Modified bare head l. R. Shield die axis: ↑↑

†1927 Proof only *FDC* £150

   1927 Matt Proof *FDC of highest rarity*

| Year | F | VF | EF | BU |
|---|---|---|---|---|
| 1928 | 2 | 4 | 18 | 50 |
| 1929 | 2 | 4 | 20 | 55 |
| 1930 | 20 | 95 | 300 | 825 |
| 1931 | 2 | 4 | 25 | 75 |
| 1932 | 3 | 6 | 25 | 85 |
| 1933 | 3 | 4 | 15 | 75 |
| 1934 | 3 | 10 | 75 | 200 |
| 1935 | — | 3 | 15 | 50 |
| 1936 | — | 3 | 12 | 40 |

*†N.B. Proofs of other dates from 1927 also exist, but are extremely rare as they were for V.I.P. issue*
*\* Beware recent counterfeits*

4038
Florin

| | F | VF | EF | BU |
|---|---|---|---|---|
| | £ | £ | £ | £ |

**4038 Florin.** Modified bare head l. R. Cruciform shields, sceptre in each angle die axis: ↑↑

†1927 Proof only *FDC* £150

1927 Matt Proof *FDC*..................................................................................*Extremely rare*

| | | | | |
|---|---|---|---|---|
| 1928 | — | 1 | 14 | 40 |
| 1929 | — | 1 | 18 | 55 |
| 1930 | 3 | 7 | 40 | 95 |
| 1931 | 1 | 4 | 20 | 70 |
| 1932 | 15 | 70 | 400 | 900 |
| 1933 | — | 2 | 15 | 65 |
| 1935 | — | 2 | 12 | 50 |
| 1936 | — | 2 | 10 | 40 |

4039
Shilling

4040
Sixpence

**4039 Shilling.** Modified bare head l. R. Lion standing on crown, no inner circles die axis: ↑↑

| | | | | |
|---|---|---|---|---|
| 1927 | 1 | 3 | 20 | 60 |

†1927 Proof *FDC* £75

1927 Matt Proof *FDC*..................................................................................*Extremely rare*

| | | | | |
|---|---|---|---|---|
| 1928 | — | 2 | 15 | 50 |
| 1929 | — | 2 | 15 | 50 |
| 1930 | 3 | 12 | 50 | 130 |
| 1931 | 1 | 3 | 15 | 55 |
| 1932 | 1 | 3 | 15 | 55 |
| 1933 | — | 2 | 15 | 55 |
| 1934 | 1 | 3 | 20 | 65 |
| 1935 | — | 1 | 15 | 50 |
| 1936 | — | 1 | 10 | 40 |

**4040 Sixpence.** Modified bare head l. R. Three oak sprigs with six acorns die axis: ↑↑

†1927 Proof only *FDC* £85

1927 Matt Proof *FDC*..................................................................................*Extremely rare*

| | | | | |
|---|---|---|---|---|
| 1928 | — | 1 | 8 | 40 |
| 1929 | — | 1 | 8 | 40 |
| 1930 | — | 2 | 12 | 45 |

†*N.B. Proofs of other dates from 1927 also exist, but are extremely rare as they were for V.I.P. issue*

| | F £ | VF £ | EF £ | BU £ |
|---|---|---|---|---|
| **4041 Sixpence.** Similar closer milling die axis: ↑↑ | | | | |
| 1931 | 1 | 3 | 10 | 45 |
| 1932 | 1 | 4 | 18 | 65 |
| 1933 | 1 | 3 | 10 | 45 |
| 1934 | 1 | 3 | 10 | 55 |
| 1935 | — | 1 | 6 | 35 |
| 1936 | — | 1 | 5 | 30 |

4042
Threepence

**4042 Threepence.** Modified Bare head l. R. Three oak sprigs with three acorns die axis: ↑↑

†1927 Proof only *FDC* £150

| | F £ | VF £ | EF £ | BU £ |
|---|---|---|---|---|
| 1927 Matt Proof *FDC* ........................................................................................*Extremely rare* | | | | |
| 1928 | 1 | 3 | 15 | 55 |
| 1930 | 1 | 5 | 20 | 65 |
| 1931 | — | — | 1 | 20 |
| 1932 | — | — | 1 | 20 |
| 1933 | — | — | 1 | 20 |
| 1934 | — | — | 1 | 18 |
| 1935 | — | — | 1 | 20 |
| 1936 | — | — | 1 | 15 |

4043
George V Maundy Set

| | EF £ | FDC £ |
|---|---|---|
| **4043 Maundy Set.** As earlier sets die axis: ↑↑ | | |
| 1928 | 120 | 150 |
| 1929 | 120 | 150 |
| 1930 | 150 | 180 |
| 1931 | 120 | 150 |
| 1932 | 120 | 150 |
| 1933 | 135 | 150 |
| 1934 | 135 | 150 |
| 1935 | 135 | 150 |
| 1936 | 145 | 180 |
| The 1936 Maundy was distributed by King Edward VIII | | |
| **4044 — Fourpence.** 1928-36 .....................................................*from* | 10 | 30 |
| **4045 — Threepence.** 1928-36 ..................................................*from* | 10 | 30 |
| **4046 — Twopence.** 1928-36 .....................................................*from* | 10 | 30 |
| **4047 — Penny.** 1928-36 ...........................................................*from* | 15 | 40 |

*†N.B. Proofs of other dates from 1927 also exist, but are extremely rare as they were for V.I.P. issue*

**Silver Jubilee Commemorative issue,** die axis: ↑↑

4048
1935 'Jubilee' Crown

| | F £ | VF £ | EF £ | BU £ |
|---|---|---|---|---|
| **4048 Crown.** | | | | |
| 1935. R. St. George, incuse lettering on edge – | | | | |
| 714,769 struck | — | 12 | 25 | 40 |
| 1935 — error edge | | | | *Extremely rare* |
| **4049 Crown.** Similar Specimen striking issued in box | — | — | — | 65 |

**4050 Crown.** Similar raised lettering on edge 2,500 struck.
Proof (.925 Æ) *FDC* £850
— error edge inscription Proof *FDC* £5000
— Proof in gold –28 struck £75000

# BRONZE

H Mint mark location – 4052

4052
1912 H Penny

KN Mint mark location
as above – 4053

**4051 Penny.** Bare head l. R. Britannia seated right die axis: ↑↑

| | | | | |
|---|---|---|---|---|
| 1911 | — | 1 | 15 | 60 |
| 1912 | — | 1 | 20 | 70 |
| 1913 | — | 3 | 30 | 95 |
| 1914 | — | 1 | 22 | 75 |
| 1915 | — | 1 | 25 | 80 |
| 1916 | — | 1 | 22 | 75 |
| 1917 | — | 1 | 15 | 65 |
| 1918 | — | 1 | 15 | 65 |
| 1919 | — | 1 | 18 | 65 |
| 1920 | — | 1 | 18 | 70 |
| 1921 | — | 1 | 18 | 65 |
| 1922 | — | 3 | 35 | 135 |
| 1922 Rev. of 1927 | 3500 | 11500 | — | — |
| 1922 Specimen finish | | | | *Extremely rare* |
| 1926 | — | 4 | 40 | 140 |

|  | F £ | VF £ | EF £ | BU £ |
|---|---|---|---|---|

**4052 Penny.** Bare head l. R. Britannia, H (Heaton Mint, Birmingham, Ltd.) to l. of date die axis: ↑↑

| 1912 H | 1 | 15 | 100 | 285 |
| 1918 H | 2 | 30 | 325 | 800 |
| 1919 H | 1 | 25 | 475 | 1150 |

**4053 Penny.** Bare head l. R. Britannia KN (King's Norton Metal Co.) to l. of date die axis: ↑↑

| 1918 KN | 3 | 75 | 450 | 1450 |
| 1918 KN Cupro-nickel | | | *Of the highest rarity* | |
| 1919 KN | 7 | 90 | 850 | 2000 |

**4054 Penny.** Modified effigy l. R. as 4051

| 1926 | 35 | 350 | 1650 | 3500 |

**4054A Penny.** Modified effigy. R. Britannia sl. smaller. Shorter right thumb, date in ex. die axis ↑↑

| 1922 | | | *Of the highest rarity* | |
| 1926 | | | *Of the highest rarity* | |
| 1927 | — | 1 | 12 | 40 |

**4055 Penny.** Small bare head l. R. Britannia Seated r. date in ex. die axis: ↑↑

| 1928 | — | 1 | 12 | 45 |
| 1929 | — | 1 | 12 | 55 |
| 1930 | — | 3 | 20 | 75 |
| 1931 | — | 1 | 18 | 60 |
| 1932 | — | 5 | 35 | 140 |
| 1933 | | | *Extremely rare* | |
| 1934* | — | 3 | 45 | 250 |
| 1935 | — | 1 | 10 | 28 |
| 1936 | — | 1 | 7 | 24 |

4056 - Halfpenny

**4056 Halfpenny.** Bare head l. R. Britannia Seated r. date in ex. die axis: ↑↑

| 1911 | — | 1 | 8 | 45 |
| 1912 | — | 2 | 10 | 50 |
| 1913 | — | 2 | 10 | 50 |
| 1914 | — | 2 | 12 | 55 |
| 1915 | — | 2 | 18 | 60 |
| 1916 | — | 2 | 18 | 60 |
| 1917 | — | 2 | 10 | 50 |
| 1918 | — | 2 | 10 | 50 |
| 1919 | — | 2 | 10 | 50 |
| 1920 | — | 2 | 20 | 60 |
| 1921 | — | 2 | 10 | 50 |
| 1922 | — | 2 | 22 | 90 |
| 1923 | — | 2 | 10 | 50 |
| 1924 | — | 2 | 10 | 50 |
| 1924 Specimen finish | | | *Extremely rare* | |
| 1925 | — | 2 | 10 | 50 |

*Matt proofs also exist of some dates for most denominations and are all extremely rare.*
*\* Most 1934 pennies were mint darkened. Coins with original lustre are rare.*

|  | F<br>£ | VF<br>£ | EF<br>£ | BU<br>£ |
|---|---|---|---|---|

**4057 Halfpenny.** Modified effigy l. R. Britannia Seated r. date in ex. die axis: ↑↑

| | | | | |
|---|---|---|---|---|
| 1925 | — | 3 | 20 | 75 |
| 1926 | — | 2 | 12 | 55 |
| 1927 | — | 2 | 8 | 45 |

4058
Small head

**4058 Halfpenny.** Small bare head l. R. Britannia Seated r. date in ex. die axis: ↑↑

| | | | | |
|---|---|---|---|---|
| 1928 | — | 1 | 7 | 35 |
| 1929 | — | 1 | 7 | 35 |
| 1930 | — | 4 | 10 | 45 |
| 1931 | — | 1 | 7 | 40 |
| 1932 | — | 1 | 7 | 40 |
| 1933 | — | 1 | 7 | 40 |
| 1934 | — | 1 | 10 | 35 |
| 1935 | — | 1 | 7 | 30 |
| 1936 | — | 1 | 5 | 20 |

4059
Farthing

**4059 Farthing.** Bare head l. R. Britannia Seated r. date in ex. Dark finish die axis: ↑↑

| | | | | |
|---|---|---|---|---|
| 1911 | — | — | 4 | 20 |
| 1912 | — | — | 3 | 18 |
| 1913 | — | — | 3 | 18 |
| 1914 | — | — | 3 | 18 |
| 1915 | — | — | 5 | 25 |
| 1916 | — | — | 3 | 18 |
| 1917 | — | — | 3 | 14 |
| 1918 | — | — | 10 | 40 |

**4060 Farthing.** Similar Bright finish, die axis: ↑↑

| | | | | |
|---|---|---|---|---|
| 1918 | — | — | 3 | 18 |
| 1919 | — | — | 3 | 18 |
| 1920 | — | — | 4 | 20 |
| 1921 | — | — | 4 | 20 |
| 1922 | — | — | 4 | 25 |
| 1923 | — | — | 5 | 20 |
| 1924 | — | — | 5 | 20 |
| 1925 | — | — | 4 | 20 |

**4061 Farthing.** Modified effigy l. R. Britannia Seated r. date in ex. die axis: ↑↑

| | | | | |
|---|---|---|---|---|
| 1926 | — | — | 2 | 18 |
| 1927 | — | — | 2 | 18 |
| 1928 | — | — | 2 | 14 |
| 1929 | — | — | 2 | 18 |
| 1930 | — | — | 3 | 20 |
| 1931 | — | — | 2 | 18 |
| 1932 | — | — | 2 | 14 |
| 1933 | — | — | 2 | 18 |
| 1934 | — | — | 2 | 18 |
| 1935 | — | — | 5 | 30 |
| 1936 | — | — | 2 | 14 |

4062
Third-Farthing

| | F | VF | EF | BU |
|---|---|---|---|---|
| | £ | £ | £ | £ |

**4062 Third-Farthing** (for use in Malta). Bare head l. R. Crowned date and Value die axis: ↑↑

| | | | | |
|---|---|---|---|---|
| 1913 | — | 3 | 15 | 40 |

## PROOF SETS

**PS11** Coronation, **1911.** Five pounds to Maundy Penny (12 coins) *FDC* £18500

**PS12** — **1911.** Sovereign to Maundy Penny (10 coins) *FDC* £3750

**PS13** — **1911.** Half crown to Maundy Penny (8 coins) *FDC* £1100

**PS14** New type, **1927.** Wreath type Crown to Threepence (6 coins) *FDC* £675

† *NB Truly 'FDC' proof sets are hardly ever encountered. Component coins showing any surface marks, hairlines or nicks will be worth less than the prices quoted above.*

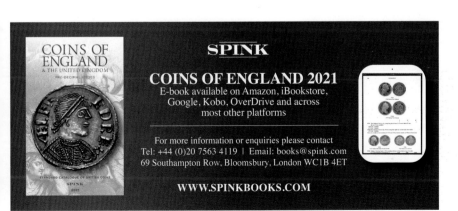

Edward VIII succeeded his father on 20th January 1936 and abdicated 10th December. He was born 23rd June 1894, and was very popular as Prince of Wales. He ruled only for a short time before announcing his intended marriage to the American divorcee Wallis Simpson; a potential religious and political scandal. Edward was not a traditionalist, as evidenced on the proposed coinage, where he insisted against all advice on having his effigy face the same way as his father's, instead of opposite. He abdicated in favour of his brother, and became Edward, Duke of Windsor, marrying Mrs Simpson in France, where they lived in exile. He governed the Bahamas from 1940-45 and died on 28th May 1972.

No coins of Edward VIII were issued for currency within the United Kingdom bearing his name and portrait. The Mint had commenced work on a new coinage prior to the Abdication, and various patterns were made. No Proof Sets were issued for sale and only a small number of sets were struck.

Coins bearing Edward's name, but not his portrait, were issued for the colonial territories of British East Africa, British West Africa, Fiji and New Guinea. The projected U.K. coins were to include a Shilling of essentially `Scottish' type and a nickel brass Threepence with twelve sides which might supplement and possibly supersede the inconveniently small silver Threepence.

**Engravers and Designers**:– George Kruger Gray (1880-1943), Thomas Humphrey Paget (1893-1974), Benedicto Pistucci (1784-1855) Frances Madge Kitchener, Percy Metcalfe (1895-1970), H Wilson Parker (1896-1980)

**Designer's initials:**  H. P. (T. Humphrey Paget)      B.P. (Benedetto Pistrucci, d. 1855)
                   K. G. (G. Kruger Gray)         M. K. (Madge Kitchener)
                   W. P. (H. Wilson Parker)

**Die axis ↑↑**

# GOLD

4063
Edward VIII Proof Five Pounds

**4063 Proof Set**
Gold, Five Pounds, Two Pounds and Sovereign, Silver Crown, Halfcrown, Florin, Scottish Shilling, Sixpence and Threepence, Brass Threepence, Penny, Halfpenny and Farthing, 1937 *FDC*.
*Only one complete set known in private hands..*

**Five Pounds,** Bare head l. R St George and dragon, date in ex ........................................... 650000
**Two Pounds,** Bare head l. R St George and dragon, date in ex ........................................... 300000
**Sovereign**, Bare head l. R. St George and dragon date in ex .................................................. 600000
**Crown**, Bare head l. R. Crowned Shield of arms and supporters........................................... 275000
**Halfcrown**, Bare head l. R. Quartered Standard of arms ...................................................... 135000
**Florin**, Bare head l. R. Crowned rose and emblems ............................................................. 100000
**Shilling**, Bare head l. R. Lion seated facing on crown ........................................................... 85000
**Sixpence**, Bare head l. R. Six interlinked rings.................................................................... 55000
**Threepence**, Bare head l. R. three interlinked rings .............................................................. 42500

4064A

**4064A** Nickel brass. **Threepence**, 1937 Bare head l. R. Thrift plant below ............................. 55000
    Bronze. **Penny**, 1937 ............................................................................................ 100000
    **Halfpenny**, 1937 ................................................................................................. 45000
    **Farthing**, 1937 ..................................................................................................... 40000

*Note: Matt proofs exist of most denominations*

**Pattern**

Edward VIII Brass Threepence

*UNC*
£

**4064B** Nickel brass dodecagonal **Threepence**, 1937. Bare head l. R. Thrift plant of more
    naturalistic style than the modified proof coin. A small number of these coins were
    produced of differing thickness for experimental purposes and a few did get into
    circulation............................................................................................................... 50000

George VI was born on 14th December 1895 and never expected to be King. He suffered ill-health through much of his life and had a stammer. He married Elizabeth Bowes Lyon and together they became very popular especially through the ravages of World War II, when Buckingham Palace was bombed. The war took its toll on George, and ever a heavy smoker he succumbed to lung cancer on 6th February 1952. Elizabeth, known after his death as 'Queen Elizabeth the Queen Mother', lived on to the age of 101 dying on 30th March 2002.

Though they were at first issued concurrently, the twelve-sided nickel-brass Threepence superseded the small silver Threepence in 1942. Those dated 1943-4 were not issued for circulation in the U.K. In addition to the usual English 'lion' Shilling, a Shilling of Scottish type was issued concurrently. This depicts the Scottish lion and crown flanked by the shield of St. Andrew and a thistle. In 1947, as silver was needed to repay the bullion lent by the U.S.A. during the war, silver coins were replaced by coins of the same type and weight made of cupro-nickel. In 1949, after India had attained independence, the title IND:IMP (Indiae Imperator) was dropped from the coinage. Commemorative Crown pieces were issued for the Coronation and the 1951 Festival of Britain.

**Engravers and Designers:**– Frances Madge Kitchener, George Kruger Gray (1880-1943), Percy Metcalfe (1895-1970) Thomas Humphrey Paget (1893-1974), H Wilson Parker (1896-1980), Benedetto Pistrucci (1784-1855)

**Designer's initials:**  K. G. (G. Kruger Gray)     B. P. (Benedetto Pistrucci, d. 1855)
                     H. P. (T. Humphrey Paget)    W. P. (Wilson Parker)

**Die axis** ↑↑

# GOLD

4074
1937 Proof Five Pounds

4076
1937 Proof Sovereign

|  | *FDC* |
|---|---|
|  | £ |
| **4074 Five Pounds.** Bare head l. Ŗ. St. George, 1937. Proof plain edge only (5001 struck) | 7000 |
| **4074-4077** Proof Struck to Matt finish *FDC of highest rarity* | |
| **4075 Two Pounds.** Similar, 1937. Proof plain edge only (5001 struck) | 2750 |
| **4076 Sovereign.** Similar, 1937. Proof plain edge only (5001 struck) | 3500 |
| **4077 Half-Sovereign.** Similar, 1937. Proof plain edge only (5001 struck) | 1000 |

# SILVER

**FIRST COINAGE, 1937-46** Silver, .500 fine, with title IND:IMP

4078 - 1937 Crown

| | VF | EF | BU |
|---|---|---|---|
| | £ | £ | £ |

**4078 Crown.** Coronation commemorative

1937. ℞. Arms and supporters ............................................................. 12 — 30 — 45

**4079 Crown.** Similar 1937 Proof *FDC* £90

Similar 1937 Frosted 'VIP' Proof £1500

4080 - Halfcrown            4081 - 1937 Florin

**4080 Halfcrown.** Bare head l. ℞. Shield die axis: ↑↑

| | | | |
|---|---|---|---|
| 1937 | — | 5 | 25 |
| 1937 Proof *FDC* £40 | | | |
| 1938 | — | 10 | 55 |
| 1939 | — | 5 | 30 |
| 1940 | — | 8 | 35 |
| 1941 | — | 5 | 30 |
| 1942 | — | 5 | 25 |
| 1943 | — | 5 | 30 |
| 1944 | — | 5 | 25 |
| 1945 | — | 5 | 20 |
| 1946 | — | 5 | 20 |

**4081 Florin.** Bare head l. ℞. Crowned rose, etc. die axis: ↑↑

| | | | |
|---|---|---|---|
| 1937 | — | 4 | 25 |
| 1937 Proof *FDC* £35 | | | |
| 1938 | — | 8 | 50 |
| 1939 | — | 4 | 25 |
| 1940 | — | 5 | 30 |
| 1941 | — | 4 | 25 |
| 1942 | — | 4 | 20 |
| 1943 | — | 4 | 25 |
| 1944 | — | 4 | 25 |
| 1945 | — | 4 | 20 |
| 1946 | — | 4 | 20 |

4082
1942 'English' Shilling

4083
1945 'Scottish' Shilling

|  | VF £ | EF £ | BU £ |
|---|---|---|---|
| **4082 Shilling.** 'English' reverse. Bare head l. R. Lion standing on large crown die axis: ↑↑ | | | |
| 1937 | — | 3 | 25 |
| 1937 Proof *FDC* £28 | | | |
| 1938 | — | 8 | 50 |
| 1939 | — | 3 | 25 |
| 1940 | — | 5 | 30 |
| 1941 | — | 3 | 25 |
| 1942 | — | 3 | 25 |
| 1943 | — | 3 | 25 |
| 1944 | — | 3 | 25 |
| 1945 | — | 3 | 18 |
| 1946 | | | |
| **4083 Shilling.** 'Scottish' reverse. Bare head l. R. Lion seated facing on crown die axis: ↑↑ | | | |
| 1937 | — | 3 | 20 |
| 1937 Proof *FDC* £28 | | | |
| 1938 | — | 8 | 45 |
| 1939 | — | 3 | 25 |
| 1940 | — | 5 | 30 |
| 1941 | — | 4 | 30 |
| 1942 | — | 4 | 30 |
| 1943 | — | 3 | 25 |
| 1944 | — | 3 | 25 |
| 1945 | — | 3 | 18 |
| 1946 | — | 3 | 18 |

4084
1945 Sixpence

| **4084 Sixpence.** Bare head l. R. GRI crowned die axis: ↑↑ | | | |
|---|---|---|---|
| 1937 | — | 2 | 15 |
| 1937 Proof *FDC* £25 | | | |
| 1938 | — | 6 | 30 |
| 1939 | — | 2 | 25 |
| 1940 | — | 5 | 30 |
| 1941 | — | 2 | 25 |
| 1942 | — | 2 | 20 |
| 1943 | — | 2 | 20 |
| 1944 | — | 2 | 20 |
| 1945 | — | 2 | 15 |
| 1946 | — | 2 | 15 |

4085
1944 Threepence

| | VF £ | EF £ | BU £ |
|---|---|---|---|
| **4085 Threepence.** Bare head l. R. Shield on rose die axis: ↑↑ | | | |
| 1937 | — | 2 | 15 |
| 1937 Proof *FDC* £20 | | | |
| 1938 | — | 2 | 20 |
| 1939 | — | 6 | 35 |
| 1940 | — | 5 | 30 |
| 1941 | — | 4 | 30 |
| 1942* | 8 | 20 | 45 |
| 1943* | 8 | 25 | 55 |
| 1944* | 15 | 40 | 110 |
| 1945* | | *Extremely rare* | |

*\* issued for Colonial use only*

4086
1937 Maundy Set

| | EF £ | FDC £ |
|---|---|---|
| **4086 Maundy Set.** Silver, .500 fine. Uniform dates die axis: ↑↑ | | |
| 1937 | 90 | 130 |
| 1937 Proof *FDC* £200 | | |
| 1938 | 110 | 140 |
| 1939 | 110 | 140 |
| 1940 | 125 | 150 |
| 1941 | 110 | 140 |
| 1942 | 110 | 140 |
| 1943 | 110 | 140 |
| 1944 | 110 | 140 |
| 1945 | 110 | 140 |
| 1946 | 110 | 140 |
| **4087** — **Fourpence.** 1937-46 *from* | | 20 |
| **4088** — **Threepence.** 1937-46 *from* | | 22 |
| **4089** — **Twopence.** 1937-46 *from* | | 20 |
| **4090** — **Penny.** 1937-46 *from* | | 30 |

|                                         | EF   | FDC  |
|-----------------------------------------|------|------|
|                                         | £    | £    |

**SECOND COINAGE, 1947-48,** Silver, .925 fine, with title IND:IMP (Maundy only)
**4091 Maundy Set** (4d., 3d., 2d. and 1d.). Uniform dates die axis: ↑↑

| 1947 | ..................................................................................... 110 | 140 |
| 1948 | ..................................................................................... 110 | 140 |

**4092 — Fourpence,** 1947-8 ...................................................................................20
**4093 — Threepence,** 1947-8 .................................................................................22
**4094 — Twopence,** 1947-8 ...................................................................................20
**4095 — Penny,** 1947-8.........................................................................................30

**THIRD COINAGE, 1949-52,** Silver, .925 fine, but omitting IND:IMP. (Maundy only)
**4096 Maundy Set** (4d., 3d., 2d. and 1d.). Uniform dates die axis: ↑↑

| 1949 | ..................................................................................... 120 | 150 |
| 1950 | ..................................................................................... 135 | 170 |
| 1951 | ..................................................................................... 135 | 170 |
| 1952 | ..................................................................................... 160 | 220 |

1952 Proof in copper *FDC* £7500

*The 1952 Maundy was distributed by Queen Elizabeth II.*

**4097 — Fourpence,** 1949-52 ..........................................................  *from*  20
**4098 — Threepence,** 1949-52 ........................................................  *from*  22
**4099 — Twopence,** 1949-52 ..........................................................  *from*  20
**4100 — Penny,** 1949-52 ................................................................  *from*  30

*See footnote re Maundy Pennies after 3796.*


## CUPRO-NICKEL

|                                          | VF   | EF   | BU   |
|------------------------------------------|------|------|------|
|                                          | £    | £    | £    |

**SECOND COINAGE, 1947-48,** Types as first (silver) coinage, IND:IMP.
**4101 Halfcrown.** Bare head l. R. Shield die axis: ↑↑

| 1947 | ....................................................................... — | 2 | 15 |
| 1948 | ....................................................................... — | 2 | 12 |

**4102 Florin.** Bare head l. R. Crowned rose die axis: ↑↑

| 1947 | ....................................................................... — | 2 | 15 |
| 1948 | ....................................................................... — | 2 | 15 |

**4103 Shilling.** 'English' reverse. Bare head l. die axis: ↑↑

| 1947 | ....................................................................... — | 2 | 15 |
| 1948 | ....................................................................... — | 2 | 15 |

**4104 Shilling.** 'Scottish' reverse. Bare head l. die axis: ↑↑

| 1947 | 2 | 15 |
| 1948 | ....................................................................... — | 2 | 15 |

**4105 Sixpence.** Bare head l. R. GRI crowned die axis: ↑↑

| 1947 | ....................................................................... — | 2 | 12 |
| 1948 | ....................................................................... — | 2 | 12 |

**THIRD COINAGE, 1949-52,** Types as before but title IND:IMP. omitted

4106
1949 Halfcrown

4110
1952 Sixpence

| | VF £ | EF £ | BU £ |
|---|---|---|---|
| **4106 Halfcrown.** Bare head l. R. Shield die axis: ↑↑ | | | |
| 1949 | — | 3 | 30 |
| 1950 | — | 8 | 45 |
| 1950 Proof *FDC* £45 | | | |
| 1951 | 1 | 8 | 45 |
| 1951 Proof *FDC* £45 | | | |
| 1952 | | | *Unique* |
| 1952 Proof *FDC* £90000 | | | |
| **4107 Florin.** Bare head l. R. Crowned rose die axis: ↑↑ | | | |
| 1949 | — | 5 | 40 |
| 1950 | — | 8 | 40 |
| 1950 Proof *FDC* £45 | | | |
| 1951 | — | 8 | 45 |
| 1951 Proof *FDC* £45 | | | |
| **4108 Shilling.** 'English' reverse. Bare head l. die axis: ↑↑ | | | |
| 1949 | — | 5 | 35 |
| 1950 | — | 8 | 35 |
| 1950 Proof *FDC* £40 | | | |
| 1951 | — | 6 | 35 |
| 1951 Proof *FDC* £35 | | | |
| 1952 Proof *FDC* £47500 | | | |
| **4109 Shilling.** 'Scottish' reverse. Bare head l. die axis: ↑↑ | | | |
| 1949 | — | 5 | 35 |
| 1950 | — | 8 | 35 |
| 1950 Proof *FDC* £40 | | | |
| 1951 | — | 6 | 35 |
| 1951 Proof *FDC* £30 | | | |
| **4110 Sixpence.** Bare head l. R. Crowned cypher die axis: ↑↑ | | | |
| 1949 | — | 1 | 15 |
| 1950 | — | 3 | 20 |
| 1950 Proof *FDC* £30 | | | |
| 1951 | — | 5 | 25 |
| 1951 Proof *FDC* £30 | | | |
| 1951 Matt Proof *FDC* £1500 | | | |
| 1952 | 5 | 45 | 135 |

**Festival of Britain issue** die axis: ↑↑

4111 - Festival of Britain Crown

|  | VF<br>£ | EF<br>£ | BU<br>£ |
|---|---|---|---|
| **4111 Crown.** Bare head l. R. St. George and dragon, date in ex, 1951. *Proof-like.* | | | |
| Two reverse types exist | — | 5 | 15 |
| Similar — 1951 Frosted 'VIP' Proof £1750, narrow edge lettering | | | |
| Similar — 1951 Matt Proof *FDC* £4000 | | | |
| Similar — 1951 Plain edge Proof *FDC* £2000 | | | |

## NICKEL BRASS

**FIRST ISSUE, 1937-48,** with title IND:IMP.

4112 - 1941 Brass Threepence　　　　4113 - Second issue obverse

**4112 Threepence** (dodecagonal). Bare head l. R. Thrift plant die axis: ↑↑

| | | | |
|---|---|---|---|
| 1937 | — | 2 | 15 |
| 1937 Proof *FDC* £22 | | | |
| 1938 | — | 6 | 30 |
| 1939 | — | 10 | 50 |
| 1940 | — | 6 | 30 |
| 1941 | — | 3 | 20 |
| 1942 | — | 2 | 15 |
| 1943 | — | 2 | 15 |
| 1944 | — | 2 | 20 |
| 1945 | — | 5 | 20 |
| 1946 | 30 | 250 | 950 |
| 1948 | — | 10 | 65 |

**SECOND ISSUE, 1949-52,** omitting IND:IMP.

**4113 Threepence.** Bare head l. R. Similar die axis: ↑↑

| | | | |
|---|---|---|---|
| 1949 | 30 | 200 | 750 |
| 1950 | | 25 | 150 |
| 1950 Proof *FDC* £50 | | | |
| 1951 | 3 | 30 | 150 |
| 1951 Proof *FDC* £55 | | | |
| 1951 Matt Proof *FDC* £1250 | | | |
| 1952 | — | 5 | 25 |

# BRONZE

**FIRST ISSUE, 1937-48,** with title IND:IMP.

4114 - 1938 Penny

4115 - 1937 Halfpenny

| | VF £ | EF £ | BU £ |
|---|---|---|---|
| **4114 Penny.** Bare head l. R. Britannia Seated r. date in ex die axis: ↑↑ | | | |
| 1937 | — | 1 | 10 |
| 1937 Proof *FDC* £28 | | | |
| 1938 | — | 3 | 12 |
| 1939 | — | 4 | 20 |
| 1940 | — | 10 | 60 |
| 1940 Double exergue line | — | 4 | 25 |
| 1944* — | — | 6 | 30 |
| 1945* — | — | 5 | 25 |
| 1946* — | — | 2 | 12 |
| 1947 — | — | 1 | 10 |
| 1948 — | — | 1 | 10 |
| 1946 ONE' die flaw | — | 150 | 350 |

*most pennies of these date were darkened at the mint.*

| | VF £ | EF £ | BU £ |
|---|---|---|---|
| **4115 Halfpenny.** Bare head l. R. Ship sailing l. date below die axis: ↑↑ | | | |
| 1937 | — | 1 | 10 |
| 1937 Proof *FDC* £22 | | | |
| 1938 | — | 2 | 15 |
| 1939 | — | 3 | 30 |
| 1940 | — | 3 | 30 |
| 1941 | — | 2 | 12 |
| 1942 | — | 1 | 10 |
| 1943 | — | 1 | 10 |
| 1944 | — | 1 | 10 |
| 1945 | — | 1 | 10 |
| 1946 | — | 3 | 25 |
| 1947 | — | 1 | 12 |
| 1948 | — | 1 | 12 |

4116 - 1943 Farthing

| | VF £ | EF £ | BU £ |
|---|---|---|---|
| **4116 Farthing.** Bare head l. R. Wren l. date above die axis: ↑↑ | | | |
| 1937 | — | 1 | 7 |
| 1937 Proof *FDC* £16 | | | |
| 1938 | — | 2 | 15 |

| | VF £ | EF £ | BU £ |
|---|---|---|---|
| 1939 | — | 1 | 8 |
| 1940 | — | 1 | 8 |
| 1941 | — | 1 | 8 |
| 1942 | — | 1 | 7 |
| 1943 | — | 1 | 7 |
| 1944 | — | 1 | 7 |
| 1945 | — | 1 | 7 |
| 1946 | — | 1 | 7 |
| 1947 | — | 1 | 7 |
| 1948 | — | 1 | 7 |

**SECOND ISSUE, 1949-52**
**4117 Penny.** Bare head l. R. Britannia Seated r. date in ex. die axis: ↑↑

| | | | |
|---|---|---|---|
| 1949 | — | 1 | 10 |
| 1950 | 8 | 20 | 75 |

1950 Proof *FDC* £40

| | | | |
|---|---|---|---|
| 1951 | 12 | 35 | 60 |

1951 Proof *FDC* £55
1952 Proof only *FDC* ...........*Unique*

4118
Second issue Halfpenny

4119
Second issue Farthing

**4118 Halfpenny.** Bare head l. R. Ship Sailing l. date below die axis: ↑↑

| | | | |
|---|---|---|---|
| 1949 | — | 4 | 20 |
| 1950 | — | 3 | 15 |

1950 Proof *FDC* £20

| 1951 | — | 5 | 30 |
|---|---|---|---|

1951 Proof *FDC* £22

| 1952 | — | 1 | 7 |
|---|---|---|---|

**4119 Farthing.** Bare head l. R. Wren l. date above die axis: ↑↑

| 1949 | — | 1 | 8 |
|---|---|---|---|
| 1950 | — | 1 | 7 |

1950 Proof *FDC* £20

| 1951 | — | 2 | 9 |
|---|---|---|---|

1951 Proof *FDC* £22

| 1952 | — | 1 | 7 |
|---|---|---|---|

*The coins dated 1952 were issued during the reign of Elizabeth II.*

**PROOF SETS**
**PS15** Coronation, **1937.** Five pounds to Half-sovereign (4 coins) *FDC* £13500
**PS16** — **1937.** Crown to Farthing, including Maundy Set (15 coins) *FDC* £400
**PS17** Mid-Century, **1950.** Halfcrown to Farthing (9 coins) *FDC* £175
**PS18** Festival of Britain, **1951.** Crown to Farthing (10 coins) *FDC* £235

Elizabeth II was born on 21st April 1926. Our current Monarch has lived a long and glorious reign celebrating her Golden Jubilee in 2002. She married Philip, a distant cousin, in 1947 and has four children, Charles, Anne, Andrew and Edward. Significantly she is the first Monarch to pay taxes and her coinage has been an interesting one with the change to decimal coinage and the numerous bust changes since 1953.

The earliest coins of this reign have the title BRITT:OMN, but in 1954 this was omitted from the Queen's titles owing to the changing status of so many Commonwealth territories. The minting of 'English' and 'Scottish' shillings was continued. A Coronation commemorative crown was issued in 1953, another crown was struck on the occasion of the 1960 British Exhibition in New York and a third was issued in honour of Sir Winston Churchill in 1965. A very small number of proof gold coins were struck in 1953 for the national museum collections, but between 1957 and 1968 gold sovereigns were minted again in quantity for sale in the international bullion market and to counteract the activities of counterfeiters.

Owing to inflation the farthing had now become practically valueless; production of these coins ceased after 1956 and the coins were demonetised at the end of 1960. In 1965 it was decided to change to a decimal system of coinage in the year 1971. As part of the transition to decimal coinage the halfpenny was demonetized in August 1969 and the halfcrown in January 1970. (See also introduction to Decimal Coinage.)

**Designer's initials:**

A. V. (Avril Vaughan, 1937-2006)
B. P. (Benedetto Pistrucci, 1784-1855)
B. R. (Bruce Rushin)
C.D. (Clive Duncan)
C. T. (Cecil Thomas, 1885-1976)
D. C. (David Cornell)
E. F. (Edgar Fuller)
G. L. (Gilbert Ledward, 1888-1960)
I. R. B. (Ian Rank-Broadley)
J. B. (James Butler)
J. C. (Jody Clark)
J. M. (Jeffrey Matthews)
J. M. M. (John Mills)
M. B. (Matthew Bonaccorsi)

M. G. (Mary Gillick, 1881-1965)
M. M. D. (Mary Milner Dickens)
M. N. (Michael Noakes)
M. R. (Michael Rizzello, 1926-2004)
N. S. (Norman Sillman, 1921-2013)
P. N. (Philip Nathan)
R. D. (Ron Dutton)
R. D. M. (Raphael David Maklouf)
R. E. (Robert Elderton)
r. e. (Robert Evans)
R. L. (Robert Lowe)
T. N. (Timothy Noad)
W. G. (William Gardner, 1914-2000)
W. P. (Wilson Parker 1896-1980)

**Other designers whose initials do not appear on the coins:**

Christopher Ironside (1913-1992)
Arnold Machin (1911-1999)
David Wynne (1926-2014)
Professor Richard Guyatt (1914-2007)
Eric Sewell
Oscar Nemon (1906-1985)

Leslie Durbin (1913-2005)
Derek Gorringe
Bernard Sindall (1925-1998)
Tom Phillips
Edwina Ellis
David Gentleman
Matthew Dent

# PRE-DECIMAL ISSUES, 1952-71
## Die axis ↑↑

# GOLD

**FIRST COINAGE,** with title BRITT.OMN, 1953. *Proof only. Originally produced for institutional collecting.*

**4120 Five Pounds.** Young laur. head r. R. St. George 1953..........................................*Of the highest rarity*

**4121 Two Pounds.** Young laur. head r. R. St. George 1953..........................................*Of the highest rarity*

**4122 Sovereign.** Young laur. head r. R. St. George 1953.................................................................£425000

**4123 Half-Sovereign.** Young laur. head r. R. St. George 1953....................................*Of the highest rarity*

**SECOND ISSUE,** BRITT.OMN omitted

4125
1958 Sovereign

|  | EF | BU |
|---|---|---|
|  | £ | £ |
| **4124 Sovereign.** Young laur head r. R̟. St. George, fine graining on edge | | |
| 1957 .................................................................................................BV | | 350 |
| 1957 Proof *FDC* £13500 | | |
| **4125 Sovereign.** Similar, but coarser graining on edge | | |
| 1958 .................................................................................................BV | | 350 |
| 1958 Proof *FDC* £12500 | | |
| 1959 .................................................................................................BV | | 350 |
| 1959 Proof *FDC* £12500 | | |
| 1962 .................................................................................................BV | | 350 |
| 1963 .................................................................................................BV | | 350 |
| 1963 Proof *FDC* £11500 | | |
| 1964 .................................................................................................BV | | 350 |
| 1965 .................................................................................................BV | | 350 |
| 1966 .................................................................................................BV | | 350 |
| 1967 .................................................................................................BV | | 350 |
| 1968 .................................................................................................BV | | 350 |

# SILVER

The Queen's Maundy are now the only coins struck regularly in silver.
The location of the Maundy ceremony is given for each year.

**FIRST ISSUE,** with title BRITT:OMN:

4126
Maundy Set

|  | EF | FDC |
|---|---|---|
|  | £ | £ |
| **4126 Maundy Set** (4d., 3d., 2d. and 1d.), 1953. *St Paul's Cathedral* ......................350 | | 1350 |
| 1953 Proof struck in gold *FDC* ................................................................*Extremely rare* | | |
| 1953 Proof struck in nickel bronze *FDC* ................................................*Extremely rare* | | |
| **4127 — Fourpence.** 1953 ...........................................................................................225 | | |
| **4128 — Threepence.** 1953...........................................................................................200 | | |
| **4129 — Twopence.** 1953..............................................................................................200 | | |
| **4130 — Penny.** 1953 ...................................................................................................325 | | |

*BV= Bullion value only. At the time of going to press the spot price for gold was £1400 per oz.*

|  | EF | FDC |
|---|---|---|
|  | £ | £ |

**SECOND ISSUE,** with BRITT:OMN: omitted

**4131 Maundy Set** (4d., 3d., 2d. and 1d.). Uniform dates

| | EF | FDC |
|---|---|---|
| 1954 *Westminster* | 110 | 165 |
| 1955 *Southwark* | 110 | 165 |
| 1956 *Westminster* | 110 | 165 |
| 1957 *St. Albans* | 110 | 165 |
| 1958 *Westminster* | 110 | 165 |
| 1959 *Windsor* | 110 | 165 |
| 1960 *Westminster* | 110 | 165 |
| 1961 *Rochester* | 110 | 165 |
| 1962 *Westminster* | 110 | 165 |
| 1963 *Chelmsford* | 110 | 165 |
| 1964 Westminster | 110 | 165 |
| 1965 Canterbury | 110 | 165 |
| 1966 Westminster | 110 | 165 |
| 1967 Durham | 110 | 165 |
| 1968 Westminster | 110 | 165 |
| 1969 Selby | 110 | 165 |
| 1970 Westminster | 110 | 165 |

For a continuation of these issues see 'Coins of England, Decimal Issues'.

| | | |
|---|---|---|
| **4132 — Fourpence.** 1954-70 | *from* | 20 |
| **4133 — Threepence.** 1954-70 | *from* | 25 |
| **4134 — Twopence.** 1954-70 | *from* | 20 |
| **4135 — Penny.** 1954-70 | *from* | 35 |

*See footnote after 3796*

## CUPRO-NICKEL

**FIRST ISSUE,** 1953, with title BRITT.OMN.

4136
1953 Coronation Crown

|  | EF | BU | Proof FDC |
|---|---|---|---|
|  | £ | £ | £ |

**4136 Crown.** Queen on horseback. R. Crown in centre of emblematical cross, shield of
Arms in each angle

| 1953 | 3 | 8 | 35 |
|---|---|---|---|

Similar 1953 Frosted 'VIP' proof with more fine detail apparent £1450

4137A                                                4138
1953 Halfcrown - 2nd obverse die              1953 Florin

|  | BU £ | *Proof* FDC £ |
|---|---|---|
| **4137 Halfcrown.** First obverse die, I of DEI points to a space between beads ............ 5 | | 1700 |
| **4137A Halfcrown.** Second obverse die, I of DEI points to a bead, with title BRITT:OMN: Young laur. head r. Ṛ. Arms | | |
| 1953 .................................................................................................................... 5 | | 20 |
| **4138 Florin.** Young laur. head r. Ṛ. Double rose | | |
| 1953 ................................................................................................................... 4 | | 12 |

4139                                              4140
1953 'English' Shilling - 1st obv. die         'Scottish' reverse

| | | |
|---|---|---|
| **4139 Shilling.** 'English' reverse. Young laur. head r. Ṛ. Three lions | | |
| 1953 .................................................................................................................... 2 | | 10 |
| **4140 Shilling.** '— 'Scottish' reverse. Young laur. head r. Ṛ. Lion rampant in shield | | |
| 1953 .................................................................................................................... 2 | | 10 |

4141
1953 Sixpence - 2nd obv. die

| | | |
|---|---|---|
| **4141 Sixpence.** Young laur. head r. Ṛ. Interlaced rose, thistle, shamrock and leek | | |
| 1953 .................................................................................................................... 1 | | 8 |
| **4142** Set of 9 uncirculated cu-ni, ni-br and Æ coins (2/6 to 1/4d.) | | |
| in Royal Mint plastic envelope ................................................................................. 30 | | — |

**SECOND ISSUE,** similar types but omitting BRITT.OMN.

| | |
|---|---|
| 4143 | 4144 |
| 1960 Crown | 1965 Churchill Crown |

| | *BU* | *UNC* |
|---|---|---|
| | £ | £ |
| **4143 Crown,** 1960. Young laur. head r. ℞. As 4136 ................................................5 | | 12 |
| — — Similar, from polished dies (New York Exhibition issue) ...............................10 | | 35 |
| — — 'VIP' *Proof,* frosted design *FDC* £850 | | |
| **4144 Crown,** Churchill commemorative, 1965. As illustration. ℞. Bust of | | |
| Sir Winston Churchill r ....................................................................................................2 | | |
| — — Similar, "Satin-Finish". VIP *Specimen* ...........................................................2000 | | |
| — — —, with 'ON' designer's initials on reverse ....................................................4000 | | |

| | *EF* | *BU* |
|---|---|---|
| | £ | £ |
| **4145 Halfcrown.** Young laur. head r. ℞. As 4137 | | |
| 1954 ................................................................................................................8 | | 50 |
| 1955 ................................................................................................................— | | 12 |
| 1956 ................................................................................................................— | | 18 |
| 1957 ................................................................................................................— | | 8 |
| 1958 ................................................................................................................8 | | 45 |
| 1959 ................................................................................................................8 | | 55 |
| 1960 ................................................................................................................— | | 20 |
| 1961 ................................................................................................................— | | 6 |
| 1961 Polished die ...........................................................................................— | | 25 |
| 1962 ................................................................................................................— | | 6 |
| 1963 ................................................................................................................— | | 6 |
| 1964 ................................................................................................................— | | 8 |
| 1965 ................................................................................................................— | | 5 |
| 1966 ................................................................................................................— | | 3 |
| 1967 ................................................................................................................— | | 3 |
| 1970 Proof *FDC* £14 | | |

4146
1957 Florin

|  | EF | BU |
|---|---|---|
|  | £ | £ |

**4146 Florin.** Young laur. head r. ℞. As 4138

| 1954 | 8 | 55 |
|---|---|---|
| 1955 | — | 12 |
| 1956 | — | 12 |
| 1957 | 8 | 50 |
| 1958 | 10 | 55 |
| 1959 | 10 | 65 |
| 1960 | — | 12 |
| 1961 | — | 12 |
| 1962 | — | 5 |
| 1963 | — | 4 |
| 1964 | — | 4 |
| 1965 | — | 4 |
| 1966 | — | 3 |
| 1967 | — | 3 |

1970 Proof *FDC* £12

**4147 Shilling.** 'English' reverse. Young laur. head r. ℞. As 4139

| 1954 | — | 6 |
|---|---|---|
| 1955 | — | 6 |
| 1956 | — | 12 |
| 1957 | — | 5 |
| 1958 | 8 | 65 |
| 1959 | — | 5 |
| 1960 | — | 8 |
| 1961 | — | 3 |
| 1962 | — | 2 |
| 1963 | — | 2 |
| 1964 | — | 2 |
| 1965 | — | 2 |
| 1966 | — | 2 |

1970 Proof *FDC* £10

**4148 Shilling.** 'Scottish' reverse. Young laur. head r. ℞. As 4140

| 1954 | — | 6 |
|---|---|---|
| 1955 | — | 8 |
| 1956 | — | 12 |
| 1957 | 5 | 35 |
| 1958 | — | 4 |
| 1959 | 10 | 110 |
| 1960 | — | 8 |
| 1961 | — | 20 |
| 1962 | — | 5 |

|      | EF £ | BU £ |
|------|------|------|
| 1963 | — | 2 |
| 1964 | — | 2 |
| 1965 | — | 2 |
| 1966 | — | 2 |

1970 Proof *FDC* £10

**4149 Sixpence.** Young laur. head r. R. As 4141

| | EF £ | BU £ |
|------|------|------|
| 1954 | — | 8 |
| 1955 | — | 4 |
| 1956 | — | 5 |
| 1957 | — | 4 |
| 1958 | — | 10 |
| 1959 | — | 3 |
| 1960 | — | 7 |
| 1961 | — | 6 |
| 1962 | — | 2 |
| 1963 | — | 2 |
| 1964 | — | 2 |
| 1965 | — | 1 |
| 1966 | — | 1 |
| 1967 | — | 1 |

1970 Proof *FDC* £8

# NICKEL BRASS

**FIRST ISSUE,** with title BRITT.OMN.

4152
1953 Brass Threepence - 2nd obv. die Proof

4153
Second issue

**4152 Threepence** (dodecagonal). Young laur. head r. R. Crowned portcullis

| | |
|------|------|
| 1953 | 4 |

— Proof *FDC* £12

**SECOND ISSUE** (omitting BRITT.OMN)
**4153 Threepence** Similar type

| | |
|------|------|
| 1954 | 8 |
| 1955 | 10 |
| 1956 | 10 |
| 1957 | 6 |
| 1958 | 15 |
| 1959 | 6 |
| 1960 | 7 |
| 1961 | 3 |
| 1962 | 2 |
| 1963 | 2 |
| 1964 | 2 |
| 1965 | 2 |
| 1966 | 1 |
| 1967 | 1 |

1970 Proof *FDC* £8

# BRONZE

**FIRST ISSUE,** with title BRITT.OMN.

| 4154 | 4155 | 4156 |
|---|---|---|
| 1953 Penny - 1st obv. die | 1953 Halfpenny<br>2nd obv. die | 1953 Farthing |

| | VF<br>£ | EF<br>£ | BU<br>£ | Proof<br>FDC<br>£ |
|---|---|---|---|---|
| **4154 Penny.** Young laur. head r. ℞. Britannia (only issued with Royal Mint set in plastic envelope) | | | | |
|   1953 Beaded border | 1 | 3 | 10 | 25 |
|   1953 Toothed border *FDC* £3250 | | | | |
| **4155 Halfpenny.** Young laur. head r. ℞. Ship | | | | |
|   1953 | — | — | 3 | 12 |
| **4156 Farthing.** Young laur. head r. ℞. Wren | | | | |
|   1953 | — | — | 2 | 10 |

| | EF<br>£ | BU<br>£ |
|---|---|---|
| **SECOND ISSUE,** omitting BRITT.OMN. | | |
| **4157 Penny.** Young laur. head r. ℞. Britannia (1954-60 *not issued*) | | |
|   1954 *Unique* | | — |
|   1961 | — | 3 |
|   1962 | — | 1 |
|   1963 | — | 1 |
|   1964 | — | 1 |
|   1965 | — | 1 |
|   1966 | — | 1 |
|   1967 | — | 1 |
|   1970 Proof *FDC* £8 | | |
| **4158 Halfpenny.** Young laur. head r. ℞. Ship (1961 *not issued*) | | |
|   1954 | — | 8 |
|   1954 larger border teeth | — | 10 |
|   1955 | — | 6 |
|   1956 | — | 8 |
|   1957 | — | 4 |
|   1957 calm sea | — | 50 |
|   1958 | — | 3 |
|   1959 | — | 2 |
|   1960 | — | 2 |
|   1962 | — | 1 |
|   1963 | — | 1 |
|   1964 | — | 1 |
|   1965 | — | 1 |
|   1966 | — | 1 |
|   1967 | — | 1 |
|   1970 Proof *FDC* £5 | | |

| | EF | BU |
|---|---|---|
| | £ | £ |

**4159 Farthing.** Young laur. head r. R. Wren

| | | |
|---|---|---|
| 1954 | — | 6 |
| 1955 | — | 6 |
| 1956 | 3 | 10 |

## PROOF SETS

**PS19** Coronation, **1953**. Crown to Farthing (10 coins) ..........................................*FDC*   150
**PS20** 'Last Sterling', **1970**. Halfcrown to Halfpenny plus medallion .....................*FDC*   30

# PRE-DECIMAL PROOF SETS

All prices quoted assume coins are in their original case. Issued by the Royal Mint in official case from 1887 onwards, but earlier sets were issued privately by the engraver. All pieces have a superior finish to that of the current coins.

| | | No. of coins | FDC £ |
|---|---|---|---|
| PS1 | **George IV, 1826**. New issue, Five Pounds to Farthing ...............................(11) | | 135000 |
| PS2 | **William IV, 1831**. Coronation, Two Pounds to Farthing .................. ...........(14) | | 100000 |
| PS3 | **Victoria, 1839**. Young head. "Una and the Lion" Five Pounds and Sovereign to Farthing............................................................................ (15) | | 350000 |
| PS4 | — **1853**. Sovereign to Half-Farthing, including Gothic type Crown ......... (16) | | 120000 |
| PS5 | — **1887**. Jubilee bust for Golden Jubilee, Five Pounds to Threepence .......(11) | | 35000 |
| PS6 | — **1887**. Silver Crown to Threepence ......................................... (7) | | 6000 |
| PS7 | — **1893**. Old bust, Five Pounds to Threepence ........................................ (10) | | 48000 |
| PS8 | — **1893**. Silver Crown to Threepence ......................................... (6) | | 7500 |
| PS9 | **Edward VII, 1902**. Coronation, Five Pounds to Maundy Penny. Matt finish to surfaces............................................................................... (13) | | 6500 |
| PS10 | — **1902**. Sovereign to Maundy Penny. Matt finish .....................................(11) | | 2250 |
| PS11 | **George V, 1911**. Coronation, Five Pounds to Maundy Penny....................(12) | | 18500 |
| PS12 | — **1911**. Sovereign to Maundy Penny ......................................................... (10) | | 3750 |
| PS13 | — **1911**. Silver Halfcrown to Maundy Penny............................................... (8) | | 1350 |
| PS14 | — **1927**. New Coinage. Wreath type Crown to Threepence......................... (6) | | 675 |
| PS15 | **George VI, 1937**. Coronation. Five Pounds to Half-Sovereign .................. (4) | | 13500 |
| PS16 | — **1937**. Coronation. Crown to Farthing, including Maundy Set ..............(15) | | 400 |
| PS17 | — **1950**. Mid-Century, Halfcrown to Farthing .......................................... (9) | | 175 |
| PS18 | — **1951**. Festival of Britain, Crown to Farthing....................................... (10) | | 235 |
| PS19 | **Elizabeth II, 1953**. Coronation. Crown to Farthing................................. (10) | | 165 |
| PS20 | — **1970**. "Last Sterling" set. Halfcrown to Halfpenny plus medallion ........ (8) | | 30 |

*Truly flawless FDC sets of the earlier period are commanding prices in excess of catalogue values'*

# APPENDIX I

## A SELECT NUMISMATIC BIBLIOGRAPHY

**Listed below is a selection of general books on British numismatics and other works that the specialist collector will need to consult.**

**General Books:**
BROOKE, G. C. *English Coins*. 3rd ed., 1966.
BULL, M., *English Silver Coinage since 1649* (Spink 2015)
CHALLIS, C. E. (ed.) *A New History of the Royal Mint*. 1992
GRUEBER, H. A. *Handbook of the Coins of Great Britain and Ireland*. Revised 1970
KENYON, R. Ll. *Gold Coins of England*. 1884
NORTH, J. J. *English Hammered Coinage*, Vol. I, c. 650-1272. 1994; Vol. II, 1272-1662. 1991
STEWARTBY, Lord. *English Coins 1180-1551*. 2009
SUTHERLAND, C. H. V. *English Coinage, 600-1900*. 1972

**Specialist Works:**
ABRAMSON, T. *Sceattas, An Illustrated Guide*. 2006
ALLEN, D. *The Origins of Coinage in Britain: A Reappraisal*. Reprint 1978
ALLEN, D. F. *The Coins of the Coritani*. (SCBI no. 3) 1963
ALLEN, D. F. *English Coins in the British Museum: The Cross-and-Crosslets ('Tealby') type of Henry II*. 1951
ALLEN, M. *The Durham Mint*. 2003
ARCHIBALD, M. M. and BLUNT, C. E. *British Museum. Anglo-Saxon Coins. Athelstan to the reform of Edgar*. 924-c.973. 1986
ASKEW, G. *The Coinage of Roman Britain*. (1951) Reprinted 1980.
BESLY, E. M. *Coins and Medals of the English Civil War*. 1990
BIDDLE, M., with HARVEY, Y., *The Winchester Mint* (Oxford 2012)
BLACKBURN, M. A. S. *Anglo-Saxon Monetary History*. 1986
— — *Viking Coinage and Currency in the British Isles*. 2011
BLUNT, C. E. and WHITTON, C. A. *The Coinages of Edward IV and of Henry VI (Restored)*.
BLUNT, C. E., STEWART, B.H.I.H. and LYON, C.S.S. *Coinage in Tenth-Century England. From Edward the Elder to Edgar's Reform*. 1989
BOON, G. C. *Coins of the Anarchy. 1135-54*. 1988
BRAND, J. D. *The English Coinage 1180-1247: Money, Mints and Exchanges* 1994
BROOKE, G. C. *English Coins in the British Museum: The Norman Kings*. 1916
BROWN, I. D., COMBER, C. H. & WILKINSON, W. *The Hammered Silver coins produced at the Tower Mint during the reign of Elizabeth I*. 2006
BROWN, I. D. and DOLLEY, M. *Bibliography of Coin Hoards of Great Britain and Ireland 1500-1967*. 1971
BUCK, I. *Medieval English Groats*. 2000
CARSON, R. A. G. *Mints, Dies and Currency. Essays in Memory of Albert Baldwin*. 1971
CHICK, D. *The Coinage of Offa and his Contemporaries*. 2010
CHURCHILL, R. *Mints and Moneyers during the reign of Henry III*. 2012
CHURCHILL, R. and THOMAS B. *The Brussels Hoard of 1908. The Long Cross Coinage of Henry III*. 2012
CLOKE, H.J. and TOONE, L., *The London Mint of Constantius and Constantine* (Spink 2015)
DAVIES, P. J. *British Silver Coins Since 1816 with Engravers' Patterns and Proofs and Unofficial Pieces*. 1982
DE JERSEY, P. *Coinage in Iron Age Armorica*. 1994
DOLLEY, R. H. M. (ed.). *Anglo-Saxon Coins; studies presented to Sir Frank Stenton*. 1964

EAGLEN, R.J., *The Abbey and Mint of Bury St. Edmunds,* Vol I, to 1279, Vol II, from
1279 (Spink 2006, 2014)

EVERSON, T. *The Galata Guide to The Farthing Tokens of James I & Charles I.* 2007

FREEMAN, M. J. *The Bronze Coinage of Great Britain.* 2006

GRIERSON, P. and BLACKBURN, M. A. S. *Medieval European Coinage, vol. 1, The
Early Middle Ages.* 1986

HOBBS, R. *British Iron Age Coins in the British Museum.* 1996

KEARY, C. and GREUBER, H. *English Coins in the British Museum: Anglo-Saxon
Series.* 1887, reprinted, 1970, 2 volumes.

LAKER, A. J. *The portrait Groats of Henry VIII.* 1978

LAWRENCE, L. A. *The Coinage of Edward III from 1351.*

LINECAR, H. W. A. *The Crown Pieces of Great Britain and the British Commonwealth.* 1962
— — *English Proof and Pattern Crown-Size Pieces.* 1968

MACK, R. P. *The R. P. Mack Collection, Ancient British, Anglo-Saxon and Norman
Coins.* (SCBI no. 20) 1973

MANVILLE, H. E. *Encyclopedia of British Numismatics. Numismatic Guide to British
and Irish Periodicals 1731-1991.* 1993

MANVILLE, H. E. and ROBERTSON, T. J. *An Annotated Bibliography of British
Numismatic Auction Catalogues from 1710 to the Present.* 1986

MARSH, M. A. *The Gold Half Sovereign.* 2nd Edition, revised 2004

MARSH, M. A. *The Gold Sovereign.* 2nd Edition 1999

MASS, J. P. *The J. P. Mass collection of English Short Cross Coins 1180-1247. (SCBI
56).* 2001

MOSSOP H.R., *The Lincoln Mint c.890-1279* (1970)

NAISMITH, R. *The Coinage of Southern England, 796-c.865.* 2011

NORTH, J. J. *Edwardian English Silver Coins 1279-1351. (SCBI 39)* 1989

NORTH J.J., *English Hammered Coinage*, Vol I, c.600-1272, and Vol II, 1272-1662,
third edition (Spink 1994, 1991)

NORTH, J. J. and PRESTON-MORLEY, P. J. *The John G. Brooker Collection: Coins of
Charles I. (SCBI 33)* 1984

PECK, C. W. *English Copper, Tin and Bronze Coins in the British Museum, 1558-1958.* 1970

RAYNER, P.A. *The English Silver Coinage from 1649.* 5th ed. 1992

REECE, R. *Coinage in Roman Britain,* 1987

ROBINSON, Dr. B. *The Royal Maundy.* 1992

RUDD, C. *Ancient British Coins (ABC).* 2009

RUDING, REV. R. *Annals of the Coinage of Great Britain.* 3rd Edition 1840

SEAR, D. R. *Roman Coins and their Values.* 4th Edition (1999) Reprinted 2000

SILLS, J. *Gaulish and Early British Gold Coinage.* 2003

THOMPSON, J. D. A. *Inventory of British Coin Hoards, A.D. 600-1500.* 1956

VAN ARSDELL, R. *Celtic Coinage of Britain.* 1989

VAN ARSDELL, R. D. *The Coinage of the Dobunni.* 1994

WHITTON, C. A. *The Heavy Coinage of Henry VI.*

WILSON, A. and RASMUSSEN, M. *English Patten, Trial and Proof Coin in Gold,
1547-1968.* 2000

WITHERS, P. & B. R. *The Galata Guide to the Pennies of Edward I and II and the
Coins of the mint of Berwick-upon-Tweed.* 2006

WOODHEAD, P. *English Gold Coins 1257-1603. The Herbert Schneider Collection,
vol. 1 (SCBI 47)* 1996

— — English Gold Coins 1603-20th Century. The Herbert Schneider Collection, vol. 2 (SCBI 57) 2002
WREN, C. R. The Short-cross coinage 1180-1247. Henry II to Henry III. An illustrated Guide to Identification. 1992
— — The Voided Long-Cross Coinage 1247-1279. Henry III and Edward I. 1993
— — The English Long-Cross Pennies 1279-1489. Edward I-Henry VII. 1995

For further references to British hammered coinage see *Sylloge of Coins of the British Isles,* a serial publication now comprising 68 volumes cataloguing collections in private hands and institutions. For a full list of the volumes published to date in this series, please contact Spink at the address below.

Other authoritative papers are published in the *Numismatic Chronicle and British Numismatic Journal.* A complete book list is available from Spink & Son Ltd., 69 Southampton Row, Bloomsbury, London WC1B 4ET, Tel: 020 7563 4119. Email: Books@spink.com or by visiting the Spink Books website, www.spinkbooks.com. We carry a wide range of numismatic titles both new and old, including some titles from other publishers. Please feel free to come and browse our showroom if you are in the area.

Further information regarding membership of the British Numismatic Society can be found at www.britnumsoc.org

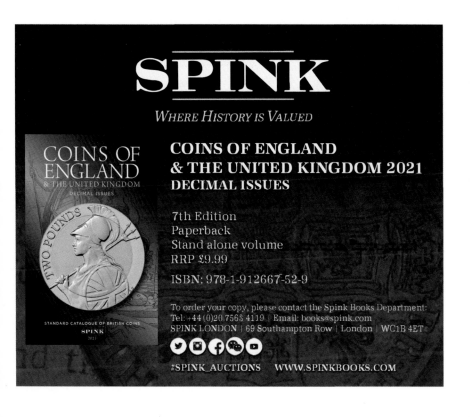

## LATIN OR FOREIGN LEGENDS ON ENGLISH COINS

A DOMINO FACTUM EST ISTUD ET EST MIRABILE IN OCULIS NOSTRIS. (This is the Lord's doing and it is marvellous in our eyes: *Psalm 118.23.*) First used on 'fine' sovereign of Mary.

AMOR POPULI PRAESIDIUM REGIS. (The love of the people is the King's protection.) Reverse legend on angels of Charles I.

ANNO REGNI PRIMO, etc. (In the first year of the reign, etc.) Used around the edge of many of the larger milled denominations.

CHRISTO AUSPICE REGNO. (I reign under the auspice of Christ.) Used extensively in the reign of Charles I.

CIVIUM INDUSTRIA FLORET CIVITAS. (By the industry of its people the State flourishes.) On the 1951 Festival Crown of George VI.

CULTORES SUI DEUS PROTEGIT. (God protects His worshippers.) On gold double crowns and crowns of Charles I.

DECUS ET TUTAMEN. (An ornament and a safeguard: Virgil, *Aenid,* v.262.) This inscription on the edge of all early large milled silver was suggested by Evelyn, he having seen it on the vignette in Cardinal Richelieu's Greek Testament, and of course refers to the device as a means to prevent clipping. This legend also appears on the edge of U.K. and Northern Ireland one pound coins.

DIEU ET MON DROIT. (God and my right.) On halfcrowns of George IV and later monarchs

DIRIGE DEUS GRESSUS MEOS. (May God direct my steps: *Psalm 118.133.*) On the 'Una' Five pounds of Queen Victoria.

DOMINE NE IN FURORE TUO ARGUAS ME. (O Lord, rebuke me not in Thine anger: *Psalm 6, 1.).* First used on the half-florin of Edward III and then on all half-nobles. D*omiNus Deus Omnipotens REX.* (Lord God, Almighty King.) Viking coins.

DUM SPIRO SPERO. (Whilst I live, I hope.) On the coins struck at Pontefract Castle during the Civil War after Charles I had been imprisoned.

EXALTABITUR IN GLORIA. (He shall be exalted in glory: *Psalm 111.9.*) On all quarter-nobles.

EXURGAT DEUS ET DISSIPENTUR INIMICI EIUS. (Let God arise and let His enemies be scattered: *Psalm* 68, 1.) On the Scottish ducat and early English coins of James I (VI) and was chosen by the King himself. Also on Charles I, civil war, and Declaration coins,

FACIAM EOS IN GENTEM UNAM. (I will make them one nation: *Ezekiel, 37, 22.)* On unites and laurels of James I.

FLORENT CONCORDIA REGNA. (Through concord kingdoms flourish.) On gold unite of Charles I and broad of Charles II.

HANC DEUS DEDIT. (God has given this, i.e. the crown .) On siege-pieces of Pontefract struck in the name of Charles II.

HAS NISI PERITURUS MIHI ADIMAT NEMO. (Let no one remove these [letters] from me under penalty of death.) On the edge of crowns and half-crowns of Cromwell.

HENRICUS ROSAS REGNA JACOBUS. (Henry united the roses, James the kingdoms.) On English and Scottish gold coins of James I (VI).

HONI SOIT QUI MAL Y PENSE. (Evil to him who evil thinks.) The Motto of the Order of the Garter, first used on the Hereford (?) halfcrowns of Charles I. It also occurs on the Garter Star in the centre of the reverse of the silver coins of Charles II, but being so small it is usually illegible; it is more prominent on the coinage of George III.

ICH DIEN. (I serve.) Aberystwyth Furnace 2d, and Decimal 2p. The motto of The Prince of Wales.

INIMICOS EJUS INDUAM CONFUSIONE. (As for his enemies I shall clothe them with shame: *Psalm* 132, 18.) On shillings of Edward VI struck at Durham House, Strand.

JESUS AUTEM TRANSIENS PER MEDIUM ILLORUM IBAT. (But Jesus, passing through the midst of them, went His way: *Luke iv. 30.)* The usual reverse legend on English nobles, ryals and hammered sovereigns before James I; also on the very rare Scottish noble of David II of Scotland and the unique Anglo-Gallic noble of Edward the Black Prince.

JUSTITIA THRONUM FIRMAT. (Justice strengthens the throne.) On Charles I halfgroats and pennies and Scottish twenty-penny pieces.

LUCERNA PEDIBUS MEIS VERBUM EST. (Thy word is a lamp unto my feet: *Psalm 119, 105.)* Obverse legend on a rare half-sovereign of Edward VI struck at Durham House, Strand.

MIRABILIA FECIT. (He made marvellously: *Psalm 97.1.*) On the Viking coins of (?) York.

NEMO ME IMPUNE LACESSIT. (No-one provokes me with impunity.) On the 1984 Scottish one pound. Motto of The Order of the Thistle.

NUMMORUM FAMULUS. (The servant of the coinage.) The legend on the edge of the English tin coinage at the end of the seventeenth century.

O CRUX AVE SPES UNICA. (Hail! O Cross, our only hope.) On the reverse of all halfangels.

PAX MISSA PER ORBEM. (Peace sent throughout the world.) The reverse legend of a pattern farthing of Anne.

PAX QUÆRITUR BELLO. (Peace is sought by war.) The reverse legend of the Cromwell broad.

PER CRUCEM TUAM SALVA NOS CHRISTE REDEMPTOR. (By Thy cross, save us, O Christ, our Redeemer.) The normal reverse of English angels.

PLEIDIOL WYF I'M GWLAD. (True am I to my country.) Used on the 1985 Welsh one pound. Taken from the Welsh National Anthem.

POST MORTEM PATRIS PRO FILIO. (After the death of the father for the son.) On siege-pieces struck at Pontefract in 1648 (old style) after the execution of Charles I.

POSUI DEUM ADJUTOREM MEUM. (I have made God my Helper: *comp. Psalm* 54, 4.) Used on many English and Irish silver coins from Edward III until 1603. Altered to POSUIMUS and NOSTRUM on the coins of Philip and Mary.

PROTECTOR LITERIS LITERÆ NUMMIS CORONA ET SALUS. (A protection to the letters [on the face of the coin], the letters [on the edge] are a garland and a safeguard to the coinage.) On the edge of the rare fifty-shilling piece of Cromwell.

QUÆ DEUS CONJUNXIT NEMO SEPARET. (What God hath joined together let no man put asunder: *Matthew 19, 6.)* On the larger silver English and Scottish coins of James I after he succeeded to the English throne.

REDDE CUIQUE QUOD SUUM EST. (Render to each that which is his own.) On a Henry VIII type groat of Edward VI struck by Sir Martin Bowes at Durham House, Strand.

RELIGIO PROTESTANTIVM LEGES ANGLIÆ LIBERTAS PARLIAMENTI. (The religion of the Protestants, the laws of England, the liberty of the Parliament.) This is known as the 'Declaration' and refers to Charles I's declaration to the Privy Council at Wellington, 19 September, 1642; it is found on many of his coins struck at the provincial mints during the Civil War. Usually abbreviated to REL:PROT:LEG: ANG:LIB:PAR:

ROSA SINE SPINA. (A rose without a thorn.) Found on some gold and small coins of Henry VIII and later reigns.

RUTILANS ROSA SINE SPINA. (A dazzling rose without a thorn.) As last but on small gold only.

SCUTUM FIDEI PROTEGET EUM or EAM. (The shield of faith shall protect him, or her.) On much of the gold of Edward VI and Elizabeth.

SIC VOS NON VOBIS (Thus we labour but not for ourselves). 1994 £2 Bank of England.

TALI DICATA SIGNO MENS FLUCTUARI NEQUIT. (Consecrated by such a sign the mind cannot waver: from a hymn by Prudentius written in the fourth century, entitled 'Hymnus ante Somnum'.) Only on the gold 'George noble' of Henry VIII.

TIMOR DOMINI FONS VITÆ. (The fear of the Lord is a fountain of life: *Proverbs, 14, 27.)* On many shillings of Edward VI.

TVAETVR VNITA DEVS. (May God guard these united, i.e. kingdoms.) On many English Scottish and Irish coins of James I.

VERITAS TEMPORIS FILIA. (Truth, the daughter of Time.) On English and Irish coins of Mary Tudor.

**Some Royal Titles:**

REX ANGL*orum*—King of the English.

REX SAXONIORVM OCCIDENTALIVM —King of the West Saxons.

DEI GRA*tia* REX *ANGLiae* ET FRANC*iae DomiNus HYBerniae ET AQVITaniae*—By the Grace of God, King of England and France, Lord of Ireland and Aquitaine.

D*ei GRAtia Magnae Britanniae, FRanciae ET Hiberniae REX Fidei Defensor BRunsviciensis ET Luneburgen-sis Dux, Sacri Romani Imperii Archi-THesaurarius ET ELector*=By the Grace of God, King of Great Britain, France and Ireland, Defender of the Faith, Duke of Brunswick and Luneburg, High Treasurer and Elector of the Holy Roman Empire.

BRITANNIARUM REX —King of the Britains (i.e. Britain and British territories overseas).

BRITT:OMN:REX:FID:DEF:IND:IMP: —King of all the Britains, Defender of the Faith, Emperor of India.

VIVAT REGINA ELIZABETHA — Long live Queen Elizabeth. On the 1996 £5 Queen's 70th birthday £5 crown.

# APPENDIX III

## NUMISMATIC CLUBS AND SOCIETIES

*Coin News, The Searcher* and *Treasure Hunting*, are the major monthly magazines covering numismatics. Many local numismatic societies and clubs in the British Isles are affiliated to the British Association of Numismatic Societies (BANS) which holds an annual Congress and an annual Conference (weekend meetings) with a range of speakers in convivial surroundings. Details and contacts for a club or society near can be found online, www.coinclubs.org.uk or by contacting the Secretary, Bill Pugsley, at the following email address: bill@pugsley.co.uk.

The two principal learned societies are the Royal Numismatic Society (RNS), c/o Department of Coins and Medals, the British Museum, Great Russell Street, Bloomsbury, London WC1B 3DG, and the British Numismatic Society (BNS), c/o The Secretary, Peter Preston-Morley, c/o Dix, Noonan, Webb, 16 Bolton Street, London, W1J 8BQ, email: ppm@dnw.co.uk. Both these societies publish an annual journal. To find out more about membership, meetings and publications, for the RNS go to www.numismatics.org.uk and for the BNS, go to www.britnumsoc.org.uk

## MINTMARKS AND OTHER SYMBOLS ON ENGLISH COINS

A Mintmark *(mm.),* is a term borrowed from Roman and Greek numismatics where it showed the place of mintage; it was generally used on English coins to show where the legend began (a religious age preferred a cross for the purpose). Later, this mark, since the dating of coins was not usual, had a periodic significance, changing from time to time. Hence it was of a secret or 'privy' nature; other privy marks on a coin might be the code-mark of a particular workshop or workman. Thus a privy mark (including the *mintmark)* might show when a coin was made, or who made it. In the use of precious metals this knowledge was necessary to guard against fraud and counterfeiting.

Mintmarks are sometimes termed 'initial marks' as they are normally placed at the commencement of the inscription. Some of the symbols chosen were personal badges of the ruling monarch, such as the rose and sun of York, or the boar's head of Richard III, the dragon of Henry Tudor or the thistle of James I; others are heraldic symbols or may allude to the mint master responsible for the coinage, e.g. the *mm.* bow used on the Durham House coins struck under John Bowes and the WS mark of William Sharrington of Bristol.

A table of mintmarks is given overleaf. Where mintmarks appear in the catalogue they are sometimes referred to only by the reference number, in order to save space, i.e. *mm.* *28* (=mintmark Sun), *mm.28/74 (=mm.* Sun on obverse, *mm.* Coronet on reverse), *mm.* 28/- (=mm. Sun on obverse only).

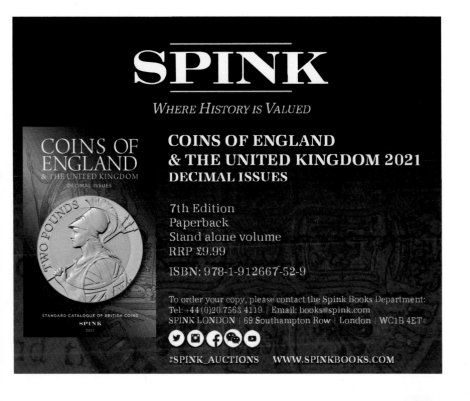

1 Edward III, Cross 1 (Class B+C).
2 Edward III, broken Cross 1 (Class D).
3 Edward III, Cross 2 (Class E)
4 Edward III, Cross 3 (Class G)
5 Cross Potent (Edw. III Treaty)
6 Cross Pattée (Edw. III Post Treaty Rich. III).
7 (a) Plain of Greek Cross. (b) Cross Moline.
8 Cross Patonce.
9 Cross Fleuree.
10 Cross Calvary (Cross on steps).
11 Long Cross Fitchée.
12 Short Cross Fitchée.
13 Restoration Cross (Hen. VI).
14 Latin Cross.
15 Voided Cross (Henry VI).
16 Saltire Cross.
17 Cross and 4 pellets.
18 Pierced Cross.
19 Pierced Cross & pellet.
20 Pierced Cross & central pellet.
21 Cross Crosslet.
22 Curved Star (rayant).
23 Star.
24 Spur Rowel.
25 Mullet.
26 Pierced Mullet.
27 Eglantine.
28 Sun (Edw. IV).
29 Mullet (Henry V).
30 Pansy.
31 Heraldic Cinquefoil (Edw. IV).
32 Heraldic Cinquefoil (James I).
33 Rose (Edw. IV).
34 Rosette (Edw. IV).
35 Rose (Chas. I).
36 Catherine Wheel.
37 Cross in circle.
38 Halved Sun (6 rays) & Rose.
39 Halved Sun (4 rays) & Rose.
40 Lis-upon-Half-Rose.
41 Lis-upon-Sun & Rose.
42 Lis-Rose dimidiated.
43 Lis-issuant-from-Rose.
44 Trefoil.

45 Slipped Trefoil, James I (1).
46 Slipped Trefoil, James I (2).
47 Quatrefoil.
48 Saltire.
49 Pinecone.
50 Leaf (-mascle, Hen. VI).
51 Leaf (-trefoil, Hen. VI).
52 Arrow.
53 Pheon.
54 A.
55 Annulet.
56 Annulet-with-pellet.
57 Anchor.
58 Anchor & B.
59 Flower & B.
60 Bell.
61 Book.
62 Boar's Head (early Richard III).
63 Boar's Head (later Richard III).
64 Boar's Head, Charles I.
65 Acorn (a) Hen. VIII (b) Elizabeth.
66 Bow.
67 Br. (Bristol, Chas. I).
68 Cardinal's Hat.
69 Castle (Henry VIII).
70 Castle with H.
71 Castle (Chas. I).
72 Crescent (a) Henry VIII (b) Elizabeth.
73 Pomegranate. (Mary; Henry VIII's is broader).
74 Coronet.
75 Crown.
76 Crozier (a) Edw. III (b) Hen. VIII.
77 Ermine.
78 Escallop (Hen. VII).
79 Escallop (James I).
80 Eye (in legend Edw. IV).
81 Eye (Parliament).
82 Radiate Eye (Hen. VII).
83 Gerb.
84 Grapes.
85 Greyhound's Head.
86 Hand.
87 Harp.
88 Heart.
89 Helmet.
90 Key.
91 Leopard's Head.

91A Crowned Leopard's Head with collar (Edw. VI).
92 Lion.
93 Lion rampant.
94 Martlet.
95 Mascle.
96 Negro's Head.
97 Ostrich's Head.
98 P in brackets.
99 Pall.
100 Pear.
101 Plume.
102 Plume. Aberystwyth and Bristol.
103 Plume. Oxford.
104 Plume. Shrewsbury.
105 Lis.
106 Lis.
107 Portcullis.
108 Portcullis, Crowned.
109 Sceptre.
110 Sunburst.
111 Swan.
112 R in brackets.
113 Sword.
114 T (Henry VIII).
115 TC monogram.
116 WS monogram.
117 y or Y.
118 Dragon (Henry VII).
119 (a) Triangle (b) Triangle in Circle.
120 Sun (Parliament).
121 Uncertain mark.
122 Grapple.
123 Tun.
124 Woolpack.
125 Thistle.
126 Figure 6 (Edw. VI).
127 Floriated cross.
128 Lozenge.
129 Billet.
130 Plume. Bridgnorth or late declaration
131 Two lions.
132 Clasped book.
133 Cross pommée.
134 Bugle.
135 Crowned T (Tournai, Hen VIII)
136 An incurved pierced cross

*The reign listed after a mintmark indicates that from which the drawing is taken. A similar mm. may have been used in another reign and will be found in the chronological list at the beginning of each reign.*

# ALPHABETICAL INDEX
# OF RULERS AND COIN ISSUES

NOTES

**NOTES**

# NOTES

NOTES